1972

Universities and Colleges of Canada

Association of
Universities and
Colleges of
Canada

151 Slater Street, Ottawa
Ontario, K1P 5N1
Telephone: 613-237-3330

Editor
Claire Franklin

Price $7.50, postage free

1972

Universités et Collèges du Canada

Association des
Universités et
Collèges du
Canada

151, rue Slater, Ottawa
Ontario, K1P 5N1
Téléphone: 613-237-3330

Rédactrice
Claire Franklin

Prix $7.50, franco

PER
L
905
.C44

First issued 1948

Published biannually through 1968

Published annually since 1969

Fifteenth edition, January 1972

Design
Eiko Emori, MFA

Photocomposition
Compkey Ltd., Ottawa

Printer
Bookprint-Rapide Limited, Kingston

ISBN 0-8876-000-0

Publié pour la première fois en 1948

Publié tous les deux ans jusqu'en 1968

Publié chaque année depuis 1969

Quinzième édition, janvier 1972

Présentation
Eiko Emori, MFA

Photocomposition
Compkey Ltd., Ottawa

Imprimeur
Bookprint-Rapide Limited, Kingston

ISBN 0-88876-000-0

New AUCC members / *Nouveaux membres de l'AUCC*

Ordinary membership / *Membre ordinaire*

University of Prince Edward Island, Charlottetown, P.E.I. from provisional to ordinary membership / *membre provisoire est devenue membre ordinaire*

Provisional membership / *Membres provisoires*

Collège Dominicain de philosophie et de théologie, 96, avenue Empress, Ottawa, Ont.

Ryerson Polytechnical Institute, 50 Gould Street, Toronto 2, Ont.

Associate membership / *Membres associés*

Association of Canadian Faculties of Environmental Studies / *Association des facultés canadiennes d'études de conditionnement du milieu.* (Chairman/*Président:* William Perks, dean, faculty of environmental design, University of Calgary, Calgary, Alta.)

Association of Schools of Optometry of Canada / *Association des écoles d'optométrie du Canada.* (Secretary-treasurer/*Secrétaire-trésorier:* E.J. Fisher, director, school of optometry, University of Waterloo, Waterloo, Ont.)

Canadian Association of University Deans, Directors, and Chairmen of Faculties, Schools and Departments of Physical Education / *Association des doyens et des directeurs de facultés, d'écoles et de départements d'éducation physique des universités canadiennes.* (Secretary-treasurer/*Secrétaire-trésorier:* J.T. Powell, director, school of physical education, University of Guelph, Guelph, Ont.)

Council of Deans of Faculties of Management and Business Administration of Canada / *Conseil des doyens des facultés des sciences de la gestion et de l'administration du Canada.* (Secretary-treasurer/*Secrétaire-trésorier:* R. Charbonneau, doyen, Ecole des hautes études commerciales, Université de Montréal, Montréal, Qué.)

Add to the section "Associations and agencies related to higher education" page 547 / Ajouter à la section *"Associations et organismes intéressés à l'enseignement supérieur"* page 574

Council of the Universities of Quebec / *Conseil des universités du Québec, Ministère de l'éducation, 710 est, Grande-Allée, Québec 4 (Qué.)* Président/Chairman: M. Germain Gauthier.

Foreword

Universities and Colleges of Canada provides the university community, counsellors, admissions officers, libraries, Canadian missions abroad, and foreign governments with information on higher education in this country.

The publication first appeared in 1948, and then every second year until 1968. In 1969 the "handbook" became an annual publication. This is the fifteenth edition. Off-prints are available.

The handbook contains separate entries for each member institution of the AUCC; brief notes regarding degree-granting institutions which are not members of the association; a list of Canadian university research institutes; brief notes regarding AUCC associate and honorary members; a list of associations and agencies related to higher education; and a table of programs offered by Canadian universities for degrees, diplomas and certificates.

There are in addition, articles concerning the association itself, higher education in Canada, and admission to Canadian universities and colleges. There is also a bibliography of reference material.

Ottawa
October 1971
M.C.F.

Avant-propos

Universités et Collèges du Canada fournit aux universitaires, aux conseillers en orientation, aux préposés à l'admission, aux bibliothèques, aux missions canadiennes à l'étranger et aux gouvernements étrangers des renseignements sur l'enseignement supérieur au Canada.

Ce répertoire a été publié pour la première fois en 1948 puis tous les deux ans jusqu'en 1968. Depuis 1969, il paraît tous les ans. La présente édition est la quinzième. On peut aussi se procurer des tirés-à-part.

Ce répertoire renferme une mention séparée pour chacune des institutions membres de l'AUCC, de brèves notes concernant les établissements qui confèrent des grades et qui ne sont pas membres de l'association, la liste des instituts de recherche universitaires canadiens, de brèves notes concernant les membres associés et honoraires de l'AUCC, la liste des associations et organismes qui s'intéressent à l'enseignement supérieur et un tableau des programmes d'études offerts par les universités canadiennes et conduisant à l'obtention de grades, de diplômes ou de certificats.

Il y a en outre des articles sur l'association elle-même, sur l'enseignement supérieur au Canada, et sur l'admission aux universités et collèges du Canada. Il y a aussi une bibliographie d'ouvrages de référence.

Ottawa
Octobre 1971
M.C.F

Table of Contents
Table des matières

How to use the handbook

Façon de se servir du répertoire

This handbook is intended for the university community, school counsellors, admissions officers, libraries, Canadian missions abroad and foreign governments. It is intended to supplement — not to replace — the calendars and other publications of the universities.

The material in the handbook is presented in the following order. To begin with, there are three articles:

• The first describes the Association of Universities and Colleges of Canada (AUCC), its objectives, members, board and secretariat, which published this handbook;

• The second outlines briefly the structure of post-secondary education in Canada;

• The third is an article on admission to Canadian universities and colleges.

The next, and most extensive section of the handbook presents in comparable form descriptions of the 64 member institutions along with the two degree-granting institutions which are not members of the association.

This basic information includes a general description of the institution, its location, size, programs of study, annual expenses, financial assistance, extension programs, publications, academic year, grading system, research institutes, administrative and academic officers, and where to write for further information.

In addition each university description contains information about admission to graduate studies. (For details concerning admission to undergraduate study, please consult the companion volume to the handbook, *Perspective: requirements for admission to Canadian colleges and universities,* available from the Service for Admission to College and University (SACU), 151 Slater St., Ottawa, Ont., K1P 5N1 ($1.50 prepaid).)

These statements were prepared by the institutions in the summer and fall of 1971. Because some changes in the

Le présent répertoire est publié à l'intention des universitaires, des conseillers en orientation, des préposés à l'admission, des bibliothèques, des missions canadiennes à l'étranger et des gouvernements étrangers. Il vise à fournir un supplément, non à remplacer, les annuaires et les autres publications des universités.

Voici l'ordre suivi. D'abord, il y a trois articles:

• Le premier décrit l'Association des Universités et Collèges du Canada (AUCC) et ses objectifs; il énumère aussi ses institutions membres, les membres du Conseil et du secrétariat qui ont publié le présent répertoire;

• Le deuxième article donne un bref aperçu de la structure de l'enseignement post-secondaire au Canada;

• Le troisième article porte sur l'admission aux universités et collèges du Canada.

La section suivante et la plus volumineuse du répertoire décrit dans un ordre semblable les 64 institutions membres ainsi que les deux institutions qui confèrent des grades et qui ne sont pas membres de l'Association.

On y trouve les renseignements généraux suivants: description générale de l'établissement d'enseignement, locaux et services, importance, programmes d'études, dépenses annuelles, programmes d'aide financière et d'éducation permanente, publications, année universitaire, système de mentions, instituts de recherches, personnel administratif et enseignants supérieurs et noms des endroits où s'adresser pour obtenir de plus amples renseignements.

La description de chaque université contient en outre des renseignements sur l'admission aux études post-grade. Pour de plus amples détails sur l'admission aux études pré-grade, veuillez consulter le volume qui apporte un supplément au répertoire, *Perspective: conditions d'admission aux collèges et universités du Canada,* qu'on peut se procurer du Service

information and college practices are inevitable during the period the handbook is in use, the student is encouraged to write directly to the institutions in which he is interested for detailed information. A brief section on statistics follows the university entries and consists of five tables: 1) full-time student enrolment; 2) part-time student enrolment; 3) full-time foreign student enrolment; 4) earned degrees conferred; 5) full-time university teaching staff. This information was provided by Statistics Canada and the reader should consult the following publications for further information:

• Survey of higher education; part I: fall enrolment in universities and colleges. Catalogue No. 81-204. (1.50 prepaid)

• Survey of higher education; part II: degrees, staff and summary. Catalogue No. 81-211. (.75 prepaid)

• Salaries and qualifications of teachers in universities and colleges. Catalogue No. 81-203. (.75 prepaid)

Degrees, diplomas, certificates awarded by degree-granting institutions. Catalogue No. 81-112. (.75 prepaid)

All of these publications are prepared by Statistics Canada and may be ordered from Information Canada Bookstore, Ottawa, Ont., K1P 5H7.

The next section of the handbook contains brief articles about the associate members and honorary associates of the AUCC. The first are national inter-university academic and administrative groups; the latter are four national research bodies.

Each university entry includes information about its own research institutes and centres. In addition, this information for all universities has been gathered to form another section of the handbook. We hope that this national listing will help the individual researcher to see where work is being done in his field across the country. For details about any one institute the reader should refer to the appropriate university entry.

The list of associations and agencies related to higher education are listed alphabetically in English and in French. Included for each is the full name of the association, the mailing address of its secretariat, the names and titles of the persons who act as president and secretary along with their addresses (since many of

d'admission au collège et à l'université (SACU), 151, rue Slater, Ottawa, Ontario, K1P 5N1 ($1.50 port payé).

Ces renseignements nous ont été fournis par les institutions membres à l'été et à l'automne de 1971. Vu que des changements sont inévitables durant la période d'utilisation du répertoire, on invite l'étudiant à écrire directement à la maison d'enseignement qui l'intéresse pour obtenir des renseignements détaillés.

Une brève section sur les statistiques suit les mentions des universités et comprend cinq tableaux: 1) inscriptions des étudiants à plein temps; 2) inscriptions des étudiants à temps partiel; 3) inscriptions des étudiants étrangers à plein temps; 4) grades conférés; 5) personnel enseignant à plein temps. Statistique Canada a fourni ces renseignements et le lecteur devrait consulter les publications suivantes pour obtenir de plus amples renseignements:

• Relevé de l'enseignement supérieur; partie I: inscriptions d'automne aux universités et collèges. Catalogue no. 81-204. ($1.50 port payé.)

• Relevé de l'enseignement supérieur; partie II: grades, personnel et résumé. Catalogue no. 81-211 (.75 port payé.)

• Traitement et qualifications des professeurs des universités et collèges. Catalogue no. 81-203 (.75 port payé.)

Grades diplômes, certificats décernés par les universités et collèges. Catalogue no 81-211 (.75 port payé.)

Toutes ces publications sont préparées par Statistique Canada et doivent être commandées à la Librairie d'Information Canada, Ottawa, Ontario, K1P 5H7.

La section suivante du répertoire contient de brefs articles sur les membres associés et les associés honoraires de l'AUCC. Les premiers sont des groupes nationaux interuniversitaires éducatifs et administratifs; les derniers comprennent quatre organismes de recherches nationaux.

La mention de chaque université comprend des renseignements sur les instituts et centres de recherches. En outre, ces renseignements pour toutes les universités ont été groupés dans une autre section du répertoire. Nous espérons que cette liste nationale aidera le chercheur individuel à savoir où s'effectue le travail dans son domaine au pays. Pour obtenir des détails sur un institut particulier, le lecteur doit

these associations do not have permanent secretariats).

Two indices to this list have been provided to help the reader who may not know the official title of the association: 1) an index of acronyms and initialisms — all associations which use these have been cross-referenced in this index, e.g., CAGS — see Canadian Association of Graduate Schools; 2) an index of key words or subjects — e.g., graduate schools — see Canadian Association of Graduate Schools.

Abbreviations of degrees, diplomas and certificates used throughout the handbook have been compiled in an alphabetical listing which forms the next section of the handbook.

Where there are more than one institution with the same name, the location of each is indicated (e.g., Saint Paul — Ottawa; St. Paul's — Winnipeg). Where an institution does not grant its own degrees, the granting institution is indicated within brackets (e.g, Saint Paul — Ottawa (Ottawa); St. Paul's — Winnipeg (Manitoba).

The glossary contains explanations of terms which are used commonly in Canadian higher education.

A brief bibliography of reference material on Canadian higher education follows.

The final section of the handbook is an alphabetical listing of the programs of study available at Canadian universities and colleges. Included with each entry in this list are the names of the institutions offering the program along with an indication of the level(s) at which it is offered (e.g., philosophy — Alberta 6,3,1, which indicates to the reader that philosophy is available at The University of Alberta at the bachelor (6), master (3) and doctoral (1) levels).

Theoretically the prospective student must make a choice between more than 60 universities and colleges in Canada. He must reduce this number to a few colleges which appear to be most appropriate for him, and then to study these in detail to select the one or more to which he will apply for admission. To do this, he needs information about the colleges. The handbook is one source of this information.

We suggest that the student consult the last section of the handbook first. Once he

consulter la mention de l'université appropriée.

Les associations et agences qui s'intéressent à l'enseignement supérieur sont énumérées en anglais et en français par ordre alphabétique. On y trouve le nom au complet de l'association, l'adresse postale de son secrétariat, les noms et titres des personnes qui font fonction de président et de secrétaire ainsi que leurs adresses (vu qu'un grand nombre de ces associations n'ont pas de secrétariat permanent).

Deux index sont ajoutés à cette liste afin d'aider le lecteur qui ne connaît pas le titre officiel de l'association: 1) un index des sigles — toutes les associations qui s'en servent sont énumérées dans cet index, p. ex., ACEES, cf. Association canadienne des écoles d'études supérieures. 2) un index des mots clés ou des sujets, p. ex., écoles d'études supérieures, cf. Association canadienne des écoles d'études supérieures.

On a dressé la liste alphabétique des abréviations des grades, des diplômes et des certificats dont on fait mention dans le répertoire; cette liste forme la section suivante du répertoire.

Quand plus d'un établissement d'enseignement porte le même nom, l'endroit de chacun d'eux est indiqué (p. ex., Saint-Paul — Ottawa; St. Paul's — Winnipeg). Quand un établissement d'enseignement ne confère pas ses propres grades, l'institution qui confère les grades est indiquée entre parenthèses (p. ex., Saint-Paul — Ottawa (Ottawa); St. Paul's — Winnipeg (Manitoba).

Le glossaire explique les termes utilisés couramment dans l'enseignement supérieur au Canada.

Suit une brève bibliographie d'ouvrages de référence sur l'enseignement supérieur au Canada.

La dernière section du répertoire consiste en une liste alphabétique des programmes d'études offerts dans les universités et collèges du Canada. Chaque mention de cette liste comprend les noms des institutions qui offrent le programme ainsi que le(s) niveau(x) de ce programme (p. ex., philosophie — Alberta 6,3,1, qui indique aux lecteurs que l'Université de l'Alberta offre des programmes d'études en philosophie aux niveaux du baccalauréat (6), de la maîtrise (3) et du doctorat (1).

has isolated the programs which interest him and knows the universities and colleges which offer those programs, he should then turn to the entries for those institutions. He should also consult *Perspective* mentioned above.

Faculty and administrative staff will find the information on research institutes and the lists of administrators, deans, and department chairmen at other institutions useful.

School counsellors, who seldom have calendars from all of the institutions in Canada will find the individual university entries and the lists of programs helpful. However, they should be aware that the information is in capsule form and the final details should be obtained from the university or college. School counsellors should also refer to *Perspective* (see above).

The handbook which is in its fifteenth year, has always been placed in Canadian university and college libraries, is found in many schools and public libraries and is carried by many college libraries in the United States and abroad.

The Department of External Affairs of the Canadian government provides copies of the handbook for its offices abroad. These are used to counsel students and professors planning to study or teach in Canadian universities. In addition, educational associations and universities abroad carry the handbook and the Association of Commonwealth Universities uses some of the material in the AUCC handbook when preparing its *Commonwealth Universities Yearbook*.

En théorie, l'étudiant éventuel doit faire un choix entre plus de 60 universités et collèges au Canada. Il peut ensuite réduire ce nombre à quelques collèges ou universités qui lui semblent les plus appropriés et ensuite les étudier en détail afin de choisir celui ou ceux à qui il veut présenter une demande d'admission. A cette fin, il a besoin de renseignements sur les universités et les collèges et le répertoire constitue une de ces sources de renseignements.

Nous conseillons à l'étudiant de consulter d'abord la dernière section du répertoire. Une fois qu'il a relevé les programmes d'études qui l'entéressent et qu'il connaît les universités et les collèges qui les offrent, il devrait ensuite lire les mentions de ces maisons d'enseignement. Il devrait aussi consulter le livre *Perspective* mentionné plus haut.

Les membres du personnel enseignant et administratif trouveront utiles les renseignements sur les instituts de recherches et les listes des administrateurs, des doyens et des directeurs de département.

Les mentions de chaque université et les listes des programmes d'études seront utiles aux conseillers en orientation qui ont parfois les annuaires de toutes les maisons d'enseignement du Canada. Toutefois, ils ne doivent pas oublier que ces renseignements sont résumés et qu'ils pourront obtenir de plus amples renseignements des universités ou des collèges. Les conseillers en orientation devraient aussi consulter *Perspective* (cf. plus haut).

La présente édition du répertoire est la quinzième; on peut le consulter dans les bibliothèques des universités et collèges du Canada, dans un grande nombre de bibliothèques municipales et d'écoles ainsi que dans un grand nombre de bibliothèques de collèges américains et d'établissements d'enseignement de l'étranger.

Le ministère des Affaires extérieures envoie des exemplaires du répertoire à ses missions canadiennes à l'étranger afin de conseiller les étudiants et les professeurs qui songent à étudier ou à enseigner dans les universités canadiennes. En outre, des associations éducatives et des universités de l'étranger utilisent le répertoire ainsi que l'Association of Commonwealth Universities qui s'en sert pour préparer son ouvrage *Commonwealth Universities Yearbook*.

Association of Universities
and Colleges of Canada

Association des Universités
et Collèges du Canada

The Association of Universities and Colleges of Canada is a voluntary association of 64 universities and colleges, including virtually all Canada's degree-granting institutions. It is supported solely by membership fees and exists to promote the development of higher education in Canada.

The association's activities fall into three major categories:

It encourages, and provides a forum for the discussion of the national and international aspects of higher education, and offers a focal point for voluntary co-ordination of action;

It provides members with services, through its secretariat, which they would find difficult, or too costly, to provide for themselves;

It provides information on Canadian universities to member institutions, to governments and to the general public.

The association dates back to 1911, when a number of universities agreed to meet annually to discuss issues and problems of national concern. In 1957 a secretariat was established to carry out special research projects and to handle the administrative load. The present name of the association was approved in 1965 by an act of parliament.

Membership is by institution only and is either ordinary or provisional. New members are admitted at the annual meeting of the association held each fall.

Associate membership is open to national inter-university groups with academic or administrative concerns, for example, The Canadian Association of Graduate Schools (see p. 507). The Canada Council, and National Research Council, The Medical Research Council and the Defence Research
Board are honorary associates of the AUCC
(see p. 527).

The officers of the AUCC are the president, vice-president, immediate past-president and the executive director, all of whom serve *ex-officio* on the 22-member board of directors. The president and the vice-president hold office for one year. Members of the board are elected for three-year terms, on a rotating basis, by voting delegates at the annual meeting.

The secretariat, located in Ottawa, provides services in English and French. Its chief components are:

L'Association des Universités et Collèges du Canada est un organisme à participation volontaire groupant 64 universités et collèges et comprenant presque tous les établissements qui confèrent des grades au Canada. Il est maintenu seulement grâce aux cotisations que lui versent ses membres et vise à promouvoir le progrès de l'enseignement supérieur au Canada.

Les activités de l'association entrent dans trois catégories principales:

Encourager la discussion des aspects nationaux et internationaux de l'enseignement supérieur et constituer le foyer de la coordination volontaire des travaux.

Par son secrétariat, mettre à la disposition de ses membres des services qu'ils pourraient difficilement se procurer eux-mêmes ou à un prix aussi minime.

Fournir des renseignements sur les universités du Canada à ses institutions membres aux gouvernements et au public en général.

L'idée de cette association remonte à 1911, date à laquelle un certain nombre d'universités ont accepté de se réunir chaque année afin de discuter de questions et problèmes d'intérêt national. En 1957, le secrétariat a été formé pour effectuer les projets spéciaux de recherches et accomplir les tâches administratives. Un acte du Parlement a approuvé le nom actuel de l'association en 1965.

L'AUCC ne compte que des établissements d'enseignement parmi ses membres ordinaires ou provisoires. Les nouveaux membres sont admis à l'occasion de l'assemblée annuelle de l'association, qui se tient chaque automne.

On admet comme membres associés des groupes interuniversitaires et nationaux intéressés à l'enseignement ou à l'administration, par exemple, l'Association canadienne des écoles d'études supérieures; voir mention spéciale. Le Conseil des arts du Canada, le Conseil national de recherches du Canada, le Conseil des recherches médicales et le Conseil de recherches pour la défense sont des membres associés honoraires de l'AUCC; voir mention spéciale.

Les directeurs de l'AUCC comprennent le président, le vice-président, le président sortant et le directeur administratif, tous membres d'office du conseil d'administration qui se compose de 22 membres. Le président et le vice-président sont nommés pour un an. Une partie des membres du conseil est élue

1. An executive director, responsible to the board of directors for the management of AUCC affairs.

2. An associate director, who also directs the international programs division. This division's activities include:

● Programs of cultural exchange. The division has academic responsibility for the administration of the Commonwealth Scholarships and Fellowships committee. It also works with the Commission mixte France-Canada in matters of equivalence of degrees and academic exchanges.

● Programs of technical assistance. The division co-operates with professors seeking employment abroad and with foreign agencies or institutions looking for personnel. The division arranges for visits of representatives of other countries or universities to Canada.

● Latin-American co-operation. The division has worked to increase contacts with Latin-American university associations and certain universities. It has prepared a directory of Latin-American scholars and has supported the creation of the Canadian Association of Latin-American Scholars.

● Research and information. The division operates a service for the interpretation of academic documents — but for institutions not for individuals. The division acts as consultant on such studies as that on Resources of Canadian Universities for International Co-operation.

● International contacts. The director keeps in touch with national and international associations of universities and frequently represents the AUCC at international university conferences.

3. An associate director responsible for the domestic programs division. This division handles membership matters, including the admission of new members, and works with several standing committees of the AUCC, such as those on the financing of higher education and the AUCC Constitution and By-laws committee. A particular example of the work of the Committee on Financing of Higher Education is the brief on university financing which was presented to governments in 1970. The division is concerned with employment of students, development of faculty retirement systems, and also provides secretariat services for committees such as the Joint Committee on Health Sciences Education, and the

chaque année pour trois ans, à l'assemblée annuelle, par les délégués qui ont droit de vote.

Le secrétariat, situé à Ottawa, fournit des services bilingues. Il comprend principalement:

1. Un directeur administratif responsable au conseil d'administration de la gestion des affaires du l'AUCC.

2. Un directeur adjoint qui dirige la division des programmes internationaux dont les activités portent sur:

● Les programmes d'échange culturel. Cette division a la responsabilité d'administrer, en ce qui a trait aux études, le Comité des bourses d'études et de recherches du Commonwealth. Elle collabore aussi avec la Commission mixte France-Canada en matière d'équivalence des diplômes et d'échanges universitaires.

● Les programmes d'aide technique. Cette division collabore avec les professeurs qui désirent être embauchés à l'étranger et avec les organismes ou les institutions de l'étranger qui recrutent du personnel. Elle organise des visites de représentants d'autres pays ou de diverses universités du Canada.

● La collaboration avec l'Amérique latine. La division travaille à accroître les contacts avec les associations universitaires de l'Amérique latine ainsi qu'avec certaines universités. Elle a préparé un répertoire des spécialistes canadiens des études latino-américaines.

● Les recherches et l'information. Cette division fournit un service d'interprétation des documents scolaires, mais seulement à l'intention des établissements d'enseignement. Elle joue le rôle d'expert-conseil de certaines études comme celle sur les ressources des universités canadiennes pour la coopération internationale.

● Relations internationales. Le directeur maintient les liens avec des associations nationales et internationales d'universités et représente fréquemment l'AUCC aux conférences universitaires internationales.

3. Un directeur adjoint responsable de la division des programmes nationaux. Cette division s'occupe des questions relatives aux membres y compris l'admission des nouveaux membres et elle travaille en collaboration avec plusieurs comités permanents de l'AUCC

Continuing Committee on Manpower Needs and Education in the Field of Social Welfare.

The division is responsible for liaison with member institutions, associate members, government departments, voluntary societies and other associations. An example of liaison between agencies of the federal government and universities was the negotiations with the Department of Energy, Mines and Resources on the research needs of universities in connection with the inland waters research project at Burlington, Ontario. The division was responsible for Operation Retrieval and still acts as a consultant to the Department of Manpower and Immigration.

The division is also responsible for some of the conferences held throughout the year. For example it participated in the planning of a Conference on Social Services Manpower, held in February 1971, and the Second National Health Manpower Conference, held in October 1971. The division is also involved in following up the recommendations of such conferences.

4.   A research division, which includes the library.

The research division is responsible for: initiating and conducting "in-house" research; supervising "extra-mural" research that is commissioned; and for liaison with individual institutions and national, regional and provincial bodies which carry out research in higher education.

"In-house" research includes work on the financing, the economics, the administration and the sociology of higher education.

Commissioned research studies in progress or recently completed include:

● A study of the rationalization of university research (report due in the fall of 1972);

● A study on student housing (report published 1970);

● A study on accessibility to higher education (report published 1970);

● A study of university costs, made as a joint project with the Canadian Association of University Teachers and the Canadian Association of University Business Officers (report published by AUCC 1970).

comme le Comité pour le financement de l'enseignement supérieur et le Comité de l'AUCC pour la constitution et les statuts administratifs. Le mémoire sur le financement des universités, présenté aux gouvernements en 1970, est un exemple du travail du Comité pour le financement de l'enseignement supérieur. Cette division s'occupe des emplois d'été pour les étudiants, de l'élaboration des régimes de retraite pour les professeurs et fournit aussi les services de secrétariat pour des comités comme le Comité mixte pour l'éducation dans les sciences de la santé et le Comité permanent pour les besoins de personnel et d'éducation dans le domaine du bien-être social.

Cette division est responsable de maintenir les relations avec les institutions membres, les membres associés, les ministères gouvernementaux, les sociétés à participation volontaire et d'autres associations. Les négociations avec le ministère de l'Energie, des Mines et des Ressources sur les besoins des universités relativement au projet de recherches sur les eaux intérieures, à Burlington (Ontario) ont constitué un exemple de liaison entre les agences du gouvernement fédéral et les universités. Cette division a été responsable de l'Opération Rappel et joue encore le rôle d'expert-conseil du ministère de la Main-d'oeuvre et de l'Immigration.

Cette division est aussi responsable de certaines des conférences qui se tiennent au cours de l'année. Par exemple, elle a participé à la planification de la conférence sur le personnel des services sociaux, tenue au mois de février 1971 et à la deuxième conférence nationale sur le personnel sanitaire, tenue au mois d'octobre 1971. Elle s'occupe aussi de donner suite aux recommandations de ces conférences.

4.   Le service des recherches qui comprend la bibliothèque.

Le service des recherches est chargé de proposer et poursuivre les recherches qui se font à l'intérieur du secrétariat, surveiller les recherches commandées qui sont effectuées à l'extérieur du secrétariat et maintenir les liens entre les institutions et les organismes nationaux, régionaux et provinciaux qui poursuivent des recherches sur l'enseignement supérieur.

A l'intérieur du secrétariat, des recherches sont effectuées sur le financement, l'économique, l'administration et la sociologie de l'enseignement supérieur.

The division and library staff play a key role in answering information queries from member institutions and from individuals. The library has a collection of more than 5,000 books and reports, plus some 7,000 pamphlets, and subscribes to more than 150 periodicals. Material includes: Canadian and foreign university publications; government documents; and UNESCO publications. The library is open to anyone interested in higher education.

The library also prepares a quarterly select bibliography on higher education.

5. An information division, reponsible for providing information to all members of the university community, to governments, the news media and the public.

The section prepares several AUCC publications including: *University Affairs,* published 10 times a year; *Canadian Universities and Colleges,* published annually; a *Guide to Foundations;* and an annual report on university fund-raising campaigns. All issues of *University Affairs* list academic and administrative vacancies in Canadian universities.

Canadian Universities and Colleges is a résumé of all Canadian university calendars, plus a list of degree courses and articles on other aspects of higher education.

Under the aegis of the domestic programs division, the director visited all member institutions in 1970-71, encouraging them to make use of AUCC services.

6. An awards division, which advises on and administers private and public scholarship and fellowship programs. For example, a company wishing to offer 10 graduate fellowships a year to Canadian students may ask the AUCC to select winners (through means of an academic board) and make the fellowship payments.

The division now administers 63 individual programs — 31 at the undergraduate level and 32 for graduate, post-doctoral or other forms of advanced study. Some 450 new awards are involved each year.

Under agreement with the Canadian International Development Agency, the AUCC is responsible for the "housekeeping" details of the Commonwealth Scholarship and Fellowship Plan, in addition to the academic aspects. There are some 300 Commonwealth scholars in Canada in a given academic year.

Les recherches commandées qui se poursuivent présentement ou ont été terminées récemment, comprennent:

● L'étude de la rationalisation de la recherche universitaire (le rapport doit paraître à l'automne de 1972).

● L'étude sur le logement des étudiants (rapport publié en 1970).

● L'étude sur l'accessibilité à l'enseignement supérieur (rapport publié en 1970).

● L'étude sur les coûts des programmes universitaires, projet conjoint de L'Association canadienne du personnel administratif universitaire et l'Association canadienne des professeurs d'université (rapport publié par l'AUCC en 1970).

Le service des recherches et le personnel de la bibliothèque jouent un rôle important en répondant aux demandes de renseignements qui proviennent des institutions membres et des individus. La bibliothèque compte plus de 5,000 livres et rapports, environ 7,000 brochures et est abonnée à plus de 150 périodiques. Elle comprend des publications des universités canadiennes et étrangères, des documents gouvernementaux et des publications de l'UNESCO. La bibliothèque est ouverte à tous ceux qui désirent consulter des ouvrages sur l'enseignement supérieur.

La bibliothèque prépare aussi tous les trois mois une bibliographie choisie sur l'enseignement supérieur.

5. Le service d'information est chargé de fournir des renseignements à tous les universitaires, aux gouvernements, aux organes d'information et au public en général.

Ce service prépare également plusieurs publications de l'AUCC, dont *Affaires Universitaires* qui paraît dix fois par année, *Universités et Collèges du Canada* qui paraît chaque année, le *Répertoire des Fondations* et le rapport annuel sur les campagnes de souscription des universités. Chaque numéro d'*Affaires Universitaires* énumère les postes vacants dans le personnel enseignant et administratif des universités du Canada.

Universités et Collèges du Canada résume les annuaires des universités du Canada et contient en outre la liste des cours conduisant à un grade ainsi que des articles sur d'autres aspects de l'enseignement supérieur.

The division also handles some 15,000 general letters of enquiry a year on student awards.

7.   A new learning media division, established in 1970. This division will act as a centre for information on all forms of new learning media and computer-assisted learning. It is also responsible for liaison with government and university agencies and groups concerned with new learning media.

8.   The Canadian Council on Animal Care, which has published guidelines for the care of experimental animals. The council works to improve the standard of care in Canadian university laboratories through assessment panels and by providing advisory services to universities and research institutes.

9.   The Association of Canadian Medical Colleges, an associate member of AUCC, represents in association with the AUCC secretariat, the continuum of medical education — undergraduate, graduate and continuing.

For complete information, see page 493.

Sous l'égide de la division des programmes nationaux, le directeur du service d'information a visité toutes les institutions membres en 1970-1971 afin de les encourager à recourir aux services qu'offre l'AUCC.

6.   Le service des bourses est chargé d'administrer les programmes privés et publics de bourses d'études et de fournir des renseignements à leur sujet. Par exemple, une compagnie qui désire offrir dix bourses d'études supérieures par année à des étudiants canadiens peut demander à l'AUCC de choisir les boursiers (par l'entremise d'un jury universitaire) et d'effectuer le paiement des bourses.

Ce service administre présentement 63 programmes dont 31 au niveau pré-grade et 32 au niveau post-grade, post-doctoral ou à l'intention d'étudiants qui poursuivent d'autres sortes d'études supérieures. Ces programmes comprennent environ 450 bourses offertes chaque année.

En vertu du contrat conclu avec l'Agence canadienne de développement international, l'AUCC est responsable des détails administratifs courants du programme des bourses d'études et de recherches du Commonwealth en plus de continuer à administrer ce programme en ce qui a trait aux études. Il y a environ 300 boursiers du Commonwealth au Canada chaque année.

Ce service répond également chaque année à environ 15,000 lettres demandant des renseignements généraux sur les bourses offertes aux étudiants.

7.   La division des nouveaux moyens didactiques a été établie en 1970. Elle joue le rôle d'un centre d'information sur tous les nouveaux moyens didactiques et l'enseignement programmé. Elle est aussi chargée de maintenir des relations avec le gouvernement et les groupes et organismes universitaires qui s'intéressent aux nouveaux moyens didactiques.

8.   Le Conseil canadien de protection des animaux a publié des directives sur les soins à prodiguer aux animaux de laboratoire et il travaille à améliorer les normes de protection dans les laboratoires des universités du Canada en surveillant et en conseillant les universités et les instituts de recherches.

9.   L'Association des facultés de médecine du Canada, membre associé de l'AUCC, représente, de concert avec le secrétariat de l'AUCC, les niveaux successifs de

l'enseignement médical: études médicales universitaires, études de spécialisation et de perfectionnement.

Pour des renseignements complets, voir page 493.

Member institutions/Institutions membres

Acadia University

Alberta, The University of

Bishop's University

Brandon University

Brescia College

British Columbia, The University of

Brock University

Calgary, The University of

Carleton University

Dalhousie University

Guelph, University of

Huron College

Jean-de-Brébeuf, Collège

King's College, University of (Halifax)

King's College (London)

Lakehead University

Laurentian University of Sudbury/
Laurentienne de Sudbury, Université

Laval, Université

Lethbridge, The University of

Loyola College

Manitoba, The University of

Marianopolis College

McGill University

McMaster University

Memorial University of Newfoundland

Moncton, Université de

Montréal, Université de

Mount Allison University

Mount Saint Vincent University

New Brunswick, University of

Notre Dame University of Nelson*

Nova Scotia Agricultural College

Nova Scotia College of Art and Design*

Nova Scotia Technical College

Ontario Institute for Studies in Education

Ottawa, University of/Ottawa, Université d'

Prince Edward Island, University of

Québec, Université du*

Queen's University at Kingston

Royal Military College of Canada

St. Francis Xavier University

St. Jerome's College

St. John's College

Saint Mary's University

St. Michael's College

Saint Paul University/Saint-Paul, Université
(Ottawa)

St. Paul's College (Winnipeg)

St. Thomas More College

Saskatchewan (Regina Campus), University
of

Saskatchewan, University of (Saskatoon)

Sherbrooke, Université de

Simon Fraser University

Sir George Williams University

Toronto, University of

Trent University

Trinity College, University of

Victoria, University of (B.C.)

*Provisional member, AUCC/Membre
provisoire de l'AUCC

Victoria University (Toronto)

Waterloo, University of

Waterloo Lutheran University

Western Ontario, The University of

Windsor, University of

Winnipeg, The University of

York University

Associate members/Membres associés

Association of Canadian Faculties of
Dentistry
Association des facultés dentaires du Canada

Association of Canadian Medical Colleges
Association des facultés de médecine du
Canada

Association of Canadian University
Information Bureaus
Association des bureaux de l'information des
universités du Canada

Association of Deans of Pharmacy of
Canada
Association canadienne des doyens de
pharmacie

Association of Faculties of Veterinary
Medicine in Canada
Association des facultés de médecine
vétérinaire du Canada, L'

Association of Registrars of the Universities
of Canada
Association des registraires d'université du
Canada, L'

Canadian Association for Education in the
Social Services
Association canadienne d'éducation pour les
services sociaux

Canadian Association of College and
University Libraries
Association canadienne des bibliothèques de
collège et d'université

Canadian Association of Deans and Directors
of University Faculties of Education
Association canadienne des doyens et
directeurs de faculté de pédagogie

Canadian Association of Departments of
Extension and Summer Schools
Association des services d'éducation des
adultes et écoles d'été des universités du
Canada

Canadian Association of Graduate Schools
Association canadienne des écoles d'études
supérieures

Canadian Association of Library Schools
Association canadienne des écoles de
bibliothécaires

Canadian Association of University
Development Officers
Association des dirigeants du service de
développement des universités canadiennes

Canadian Association of University Schools
of Nursing
Association canadienne des écoles
universitaires de nursing

Canadian Intercollegiate Athletic Union
Union sportive interuniversitaire canadienne

Canadian University Service Overseas
Service universitaire canadien outre-mer

Committee of Canadian Law Deans
Comité des doyens de droit du Canada

Council of Associations of University Student
Personnel Services
Conseil des associations des services
universitaires aux étudiants

National Committee of Deans of
Engineering and Applied Science
Comité national des doyens de génie et
sciences appliquées

Service for Admission to College and
University
Service d'admission au collège et à l'université

Honorary associates/Associés honoraires

Canada Council, The
Conseil des arts du Canada, Le

Defence Research Board
Conseil de recherches pour la défense

Medical Research Council
Conseil de recherches médicales

National Research Council of Canada
Conseil national de recherches du Canada

Secretariat/Secrétariat

Executive director/Directeur administratif
Colin Mackay, SM, CQ, BA, LLB, DCL,
DèsL, LLD

Secretary, board of directors/Secrétaire,
conseil d'administration
Wayne Primeau, BA

Associate director; director, international
programs; secretary, Canadian
Commonwealth scholarship and fellowship
committee/Directeur adjoint; directeur,
programmes internationaux; secrétaire,
comité canadien des bourses du
Commonwealth
Mgr Jacques Garneau, cs, BA, LPh, DTh,
LLD

Director, domestic programs/Directeur,
programmes nationaux
W.J. Waines, MA, LLD

Assistant director (domestic programs)/
Directrice adjointe (programmes nationaux)
Denise Michaud, BScNEd

Director of research/Directeur des
recherches
Lucien Michaud, sj, LPh, LTh, MA, EdD

Research officer/Agent aux recherches
J.F. Houwing, LLM

Librarian/Bibliothécaire
Richard Greene, BA, BLS

Information officer/Agent d'information
Rosemary Cavan, BA

Director of awards; assistant secretary,
Canadian Commonwealth scholarship and
fellowship committee/Directeur du service
des bourses; secrétaire adjoint, comité
canadien des bourses du Commonwealth
Guy d'Auray, BSc

Director of new learning media/Directeur
des nouveaux moyens didactiques
William Young, BA, MA

Finance officer/Conseiller financier
F.H. Badgley, BA(Bus), CA

Office manager/Directrice du bureau
Joan Rondeau

Post-secondary education in Canada

by Edward F. Sheffield, professor of
higher education, University of Toronto;
revised by L.F. Michaud, director of
research, Association of Universities and
Colleges of Canada, July 1, 1971

Enseignement post-secondaire au Canada

article rédigé par Edward Sheffield,
professeur de l'enseignement supérieur à
l'Université de Toronto et revisé par L.F.
Michaud, directeur du service de recherche
à l'Association des Universités et Collèges
du Canada, le 1er juillet 1971

Although the universities are the principal institutions of post-secondary education in Canada, there are others that provide education and training for persons who have completed the work of the high school. Chief among these are the government-operated colleges for the training of elementary-school teachers, hospital schools of nursing, and a growing number of community colleges—most of which are public institutions. There are still others, though of less significance in terms of the numbers of students served: a college for the training of chiropractors—operated by the profession; Church-run schools for the training of priests, ministers, pastors and other Church workers; colleges of art — most of them private; the ubiquitous but disappearing business school or college, for the training of office workers — usually a private business enterprise; and a variety of trade schools, also profit-making enterprises.

Until recently, there was a good deal of confusion between the words "college" and "university" when applied to institutions of post-secondary education and it was difficult to distinguish between them. With the rise of the community colleges, however, there is a trend toward the use of the word university to describe degree-granting institutions and to use the word college to designate part of a university, or institutions of post-secondary education offering courses below degree level.

Universities

The universities of Canada, numbering roughly 60, exhibit variety on almost every score. The largest, composed of many faculties and professional schools, enrol more than 10,000 full-time students. There are 10 in this class. At the other extreme are small colleges of liberal arts, with fewer than 1,000 students.

In most universities the language of instruction is English. In others it is French, e.g. l'Université Laval and l'Université de Moncton. There are a few in which both English and French are languages of instruction. Notable among these are the University of Ottawa and Laurentian University of Sudbury.

Historically, a high proportion of the universities of Canada were begun by the Churches and there are some still under Church auspices. Examples of Church-related institutions are: Mount St. Vincent University in Halifax, Nova Scotia and Waterloo Lutheran University in Waterloo, Ontario. A

Les principaux établissements d'enseignement post-secondaire au Canada sont sans doute les universités, mais il en existe d'autres qui dispensent l'enseignement et la formation aux personnes qui ont terminé leurs études secondaires. Au premier rang viennent les collèges d'Etat pour la formation des instituteurs du niveau primaire, les écoles de nursing des hôpitaux et un nombre croissant de collèges d'enseignement post-secondaire (fréquemment désignés sous le nom de "community colleges" au Canada anglais), dont la plupart relèvent des pouvoirs publics. Il reste enfin d'autres établissements, moins importants du point de vue des effectifs étudiants: le collège de formation des chiropraticiens, dirigé par la profession elle-même, les écoles ecclésiastiques pour la formation des prêtres, des ministres, des pasteurs et des autres personnes qui se consacrent au service de l'Eglise; des collèges d'art, institutions privées pour la plupart; les omniprésents collèges commerciaux (dont le nombre tend cependant à diminuer), qui forment des employés de bureau et dont la grande majorité sont des entreprises privées; enfin des écoles de métiers de tous genres, elles aussi, entreprises à but lucratif.

Jusqu'à ces derniers temps, les termes "collège" et "université" appliqués aux institutions d'enseignement post-secondaire portaient beaucoup à confusion et il était difficile de distinguer entre les deux. Toutefois, avec la venue des collèges d'enseignement post-secondaire, on tend de plus en plus à réserver le mot "université" aux établissements conférant des grades, et à employer le mot "collège" pour désigner soit une partie de l'université, soit un établissement d'enseignement post-secondaire, mais ne conférant pas un premier diplôme.

Universités

Les universités du Canada, au nombre d'environ 60, varient à presque tous les points de vue. Les plus grandes, qui comprennent de nombreuses facultés et des écoles d'enseignement professionnel comptent plus de 10,000 étudiants à plein temps. Il y en a sept dans cette catégorie. A l'autre extrême se trouvent les petits collèges où l'on enseigne les arts libéraux et qui comptent moins de 1,000 étudiants.

Dans la plupart des universités, l'enseignement se donne en anglais. Dans d'autres, il se donne en français: c'est le cas de l'Université Laval et de l'Université de

good many of the universities which began under Church control have become secular institutions, particularly during the present century. Among these are Queen's University at Kingston, Ontario; Brandon University at Brandon, Manitoba; the University of Windsor and the University of Montreal. Another large number, particularly in western Canada, were established by the provinces and are commonly referred to as "provincial universities", a term equivalent to the "state universities" of the United States. Examples are The University of British Columbia, the University of Saskatchewan, the University of Toronto and the University of New Brunswick. The third common type, as far as control is concerned, is represented by institutions which were created by neither Church nor state but rather by interested groups of citizens. Outstanding examples of these are McGill University in Montreal, Dalhousie University in Halifax, and Carleton University in Ottawa.

In 1970-71 there were almost 317,000 full-time students in the universities of Canada, about 6% of them from countries outside of Canada and about 10% of them pursuing graduate studies. A statistical table at the end of this article provides a historical review of the growth of higher education in Canada. A projection prepared for the Economic Council of Canada in 1969 suggests that there may be as many as 560,000 full-time students in the universities by 1975 and 750,000 by 1980. The enrolment of part-time students seeking university degrees equals about one-third of the enrolment of full-time students and is increasing even more rapidly than full-time enrolment.

Teachers' colleges

For many years teachers for the elementary schools were prepared in what were called normal schools. The program of training usually took one year following completion of secondary school. In first one province and then another the universities were encouraged to add responsibility for the training of elementary-school teachers to their traditional responsibility for the training of secondary-school teachers. Thus, by 1969-70, elementary-school teachers were being trained in university in the provinces of British Columbia, Alberta, Saskatchewan, Manitoba, Prince Edward Island and Newfoundland. There was participation by the universities in the training of elementary-school teachers in Nova Scotia, New

Moncton. Dans quelques-unes enfin, il se donne en français et en anglais; parmi celles-là on remarque l'Université d'Ottawa et l'Université Laurentienne de Sudbury.

Si l'on remonte à leurs origines, nombre d'universités canadiennes ont été fondées par des groupements religieux, desquels plusieurs relèvent encore. Comme exemples d'institutions confessionnelles, on peut nommer l'Université Mount St. Vincent à Halifax (Nouvelle-Ecosse) et l'Université Waterloo Lutheran à Waterloo (Ontario). Bon nombre des universités qui relevaient à l'origine d'autorités ecclésiastiques sont devenues laïques, surtout au cours du présent siècle. Parmi celles-ci, il y a l'Université Queen's à Kingston (Ontario), l'Université de Brandon (Manitoba), l'Université de Windsor et l'Université de Montréal. D'autres, particulièrement nombreuses dans l'Ouest canadien, ont été fondées par les provinces et sont souvent appelées "universités provinciales" de la même façon qu'on parle des "universités d'Etat" aux Etats-Unis. L'Université de la Colombie-Britannique, celles de la Saskatchewan, de Toronto et du Nouveau-Brunswick en sont des exemples. Il faut enfin ranger dans une troisième catégorie celles dont la création n'est due ni à une église, ni à l'Etat, mais à un groupe de citoyens intéressés. Parmi celles-ci, les plus connues sont l'Université McGill de Montréal, l'Université Dalhousie d'Halifax et l'Université Carleton d'Ottawa.

En 1970-1971 il y avait environ 317,000 étudiants à temps complet dans les universités du Canada, dont environ 6 p. 100 venaient de l'étranger et environ 10 p. 100 faisaient des études post-grade. Le tableau statistique à la fin du présent article fournit l'historique de l'expansion de l'enseignement supérieur au Canada. D'après des prévisions établies pour le compte de Conseil économique du Canada en 1969, le nombre d'étudiants à temps complet dans nos universités pourrait être de 560,000 en 1975 et de 750,000 en 1980. Le nombre d'étudiants à temps partiel préparant des diplômes universitaires est d'environ le tiers des effectifs étudiants à temps complet et augmente même plus rapidement que le nombre d'étudiants à plein temps.

Collèges de formation pédagogique

Pendant de nombreuses années la formation des instituteurs du niveau primaire se donnait dans les écoles normales. D'ordinaire, on exigeait des futurs maîtres une année d'études

Brunswick, Ontario, and Quebec, but there were still government operated teachers' colleges independent of the universities in those provinces. In 1968 the normal schools of Quebec ceased to accept new students and the universities began to take over this task. In 1969 the first two of 13 teachers' colleges in Ontario were absorbed by universities as part of a plan by which all should be similarly taken over within a few years.

In 1970-71, it is estimated that the total enrolment of the teachers' colleges for the preparation of elementary-school teachers will be approximately 12,000. As these colleges are absorbed by the universities, the enrolment in separately identified teachers' colleges will be reduced.

Schools of nursing

In 1970-71 there were some 27,000 students enroled in hospital schools of nursing preparing for diplomas as registered nurses. Normally this is a three-year program of combined study and apprenticeship, although there are current experiments with two-year programs which emphasize study more than training on the job.

The trend is toward the training of nurses in educational institutions rather than in service institutions (hospitals). Increasingly, initial professional training leading to registration is being provided in regional schools of nursing or (in a few cases) in community colleges. Most universities now offer courses leading to the degree of bachelor of science in nursing. It is possible for a student to take this as an undergraduate, although it is also possible in some institutions for nurses who have been trained in hospitals to take additional work in the university for a year or more to qualify for a university degree.

Community colleges

The most dramatic of the recent developments in the field of post-secondary education in Canada has been the creation of provincial systems of community colleges.

In British Columbia, there is a system of two-year colleges providing both 'university' courses (from which one may transfer to a university for completion of first-degree work) and so-called 'terminal' courses,

après l'école secondaire. D'abord dans une province, puis dans une autre, on a encouragé les universités, auxquelles avait toujours incombé la formation des maîtres du niveau secondaire, à assumer aussi la formation des instituteurs de l'enseignement primaire, si bien qu'en 1969-70 la formation des enseignants du niveau primaire relevait des universités dans les provinces suivantes: Colombie-Britannique, Alberta, Saskatchewan, Manitoba, Ile du Prince-Edouard et Terre-Neuve. Dans quatre autres provinces, soit la Nouvelle-Ecosse, le Nouveau-Brunswick, l'Ontario et le Québec, les universités participent à la formation des maîtres du niveau primaire, mais il existe encore des collèges de formation pédagogique indépendants des universités. En 1968, les écoles normales du Québec ont cessé d'accepter de nouveaux étudiants et les universités ont commencé à prendre en main cette tâche. En 1969, les deux premiers des 13 collèges de formation des maîtres de l'Ontario ont été absorbés par des universités dans le cadre du projet selon lequel tous ces collèges devraient connaître le même sort d'ici quelques années.

On estimait, en 1970-1971, à environ 12,000 le nombre des étudiants dans les écoles normales chargées de la formation des enseignants du niveau primaire. A mesure que ces écoles normales seront absorbées par les universités, leur effectif étudiant diminuera.

Ecoles de nursing

En 1970-1971 le nombre des élèves qui préparaient le diplôme d'infirmière licenciée dans les écoles attachées aux hôpitaux était d'environ 27,000. Ces écoles offrent en général un programme de trois ans qui comporte études et travaux pratiques, mais quelques-unes font actuellement l'essai de programmes de deux ans où l'accent est mis sur les études plutôt que sur la pratique.

Il y a tendance à confier la formation des infirmières aux établissements d'enseignement plutôt qu'aux hôpitaux. De plus en plus la formation professionnelle initiale conduisant à la licence se donne dans des écoles régionales de nursing ou, parfois, dans des collèges d'enseignement post-secondaire. La plupart des universités offrent aujourd'hui des cours conduisant au baccalauréat en sciences infirmières. Ce programme d'études est accessible aux élèves non diplômés, mais certaines universités acceptent aussi des infirmières formées dans

essentially vocational in nature. In Alberta, there are colleges which have the same two features but emphasize the first of them. In Ontario, a network of twenty colleges of applied arts and technology came into being in 1967 and now have campuses in a total of 40 centres. These, for the present at least, have only the second of the two features characteristic of the British Columbia and Alberta institutions: they do not offer university-parallel courses. In the province of Quebec, the first of a system of more than thirty *collèges d'enseignement général et professionnel* (CEGEP) with two-year university preparatory courses (referred to above) and three-year courses preparing students for the labour force were opened in 1967. A new college of applied arts and technology (its first) was established in Prince Edward Island in 1969. Full-time enrolment in the post-secondary courses of community colleges and related institutions was 106,000 in 1969-70.

One institute of technology which is not a community college in the sense just referred to, is the Ryerson Polytechnical Institute in Toronto. It began as a two-year institute of technology but has become a large, complex institution. A new charter granted in 1971 has given it the range and level of a university.

Agencies for coordination and cooperation

(See separate section entitled Associations and agencies related to higher education.)

One result of the increase in numbers of students and of institutions of post-secondary education has been vastly increased governmental expenditure in this field. This has led to the creation of new agencies, chiefly within the provinces, to deal with the development and financing of universities and, in some cases, of community colleges.

Although they differ from one another in name and function, there are governmental agencies for the coordination of higher education (usually university education only, but in some cases other post-secondary education too) in British Columbia, Alberta, Manitoba, Ontario, Quebec, New Brunswick, Prince Edward Island, and Nova Scotia. Relations between government and university are direct in Saskatchewan and Newfoundland; in each of those provinces there is but one university. An Interprovincial Committee on University Rationalization

les hôpitaux à des cours supplémentaires durant un an ou davantage afin d'obtenir ainsi un diplôme universitaire.

Collèges d'enseignement post-secondaire

La création, par les provinces, de systèmes de collèges d'enseignement post-secondaire est l'une des innovations récentes les plus révolutionnaires.

En Colombie-Britannique, des collèges offrent un programme d'études de deux ans fournissant à la fois un enseignement "universitaire" (qui peut conduire à l'université pour l'obtention du premier grade) et l'enseignement censément appelé "terminal", de nature essentiellement professionnelle. En Alberta, il y a des collèges qui ont les mêmes caractéristiques, mais qui mettent l'accent sur la première d'entre elles. En Ontario, un réseau de vingt collèges des arts appliqués et de technologie a vu le jour en 1967 et a maintenant des campus dans quarante centres. Ces collèges, du moins pour le moment, ont seulement la deuxième des deux caractéristiques des collèges de la Colombie-Britannique et de l'Alberta: ils n'offrent pas de cours parallèles à ceux offerts dans les universités. Dans la province de Québec, on a établi en 1967 les premiers d'une trentaine de collèges d'enseignement général et professionnel (CEGEP) qui offrent un programme d'études de deux ans préparatoire à l'université (dont on a fait mention ci-dessus) et un programme d'études de trois ans préparant les étudiants au marché du travail. On a établi, en 1969, à l'Ile du Prince-Edouard, le premier collège des arts appliqués et de technologie de cette province. Le nombre des inscriptions à plein temps dans les collèges post-secondaires et les institutions connexes étaient de 106,000 en 1969-1970.

Un institut de technologie qui n'est pas un collège communautaire dans le sens qu'on a mentionné précédemment, le Ryerson Polytechnical Institute de Toronto, a commencé par offrir l'enseignement technique de deux ans, mais est devenu une vaste institution complexe. La nouvelle charte qui lui a été accordée en 1971 lui donne le statut d'une université.

operates for the three prairie provinces. At the federal level, there is an agency established in 1966 which is now called the Education Support Branch of the Department of the Secretary of State.

The universities too have forms of association — national, regional and provincial. Canada-wide organizations include the Association of Universities and Colleges of Canada and the Canadian Association of University Teachers. The national student organization, the Canadian Union of Students, disbanded in 1969. The universities of the provinces of Nova Scotia, New Brunswick and Prince Edward Island belong to an Association of Atlantic Universities (also a member is the University of the West Indies). There is a committee of presidents of universities in New Brunswick, a Conférence des recteurs et des principaux des universités du Québec, a Council of Ontario Universities, and an informal organization of the presidents of the universities of the western provinces. One of the chief tasks of each of these organizations of universities or of their presidents is to provide a medium for communication and sometimes negotiation with the government agencies outlined above. Another, increasingly important task, is to facilitate co-operation among the universities themselves.

Organismes de coordination et de coopération

(Cf. section distincte intitulée Associations et organismes intéressés à l'enseignement supérieur.)

L'augmentation du nombre d'étudiants et d'institutions au niveau post-secondaire s'est traduite par une augmentation considérable des dépenses gouvernementales à ce chapitre, ce qui a entraîné la création de nouveaux organismes, surtout provinciaux afin d'assurer le développement et le financement des universités et, dans certains cas, des collèges d'enseignement post-secondaire.

Bien qu'ils diffèrent les uns des autres par le nom et la fonction, il y a des organismes gouvernementaux qui s'occupent de la coordination de l'enseignement supérieur c.-à-d. d'ordinaire l'enseignement universitaire seulement, mais parfois aussi d'autres genres d'enseignement post-secondaire) en Colombie-Britannique, en Alberta, au Manitoba, en Ontario, au Québec, au Nouveau-Brunswick, dans l'Ile du Prince-Edouard et en Nouvelle-Ecosse. En Saskatchewan et à Terre-Neuve, provinces qui ne possèdent chacune qu'une université, le gouvernement traite directement avec l'université. Pour les trois provinces des prairies, il existe un comité interprovincial unique pour la rationalisation universitaire.

Au niveau fédéral, un organisme créé en 1966 porte aujourd'hui le nom de Direction de l'aide à l'éducation du Secrétariat d'Etat.

Les universités se sont aussi groupées en associations aux niveaux national, régional et provincial. Les organismes d'envergure nationale comptent l'Association des Universités et Collèges du Canada et l'Association canadienne des professeurs d'université. L'organisation nationale des étudiants, l'Union canadienne des étudiants, a été dissoute en 1969. Les universités de la Nouvelle-Ecosse, du Nouveau-Brunswick et de l'Ile du Prince-Edouard font partie de l'Association des universités de l'Atlantique (dont fait partie également l'Université des Antilles). Il existe enfin un comité des présidents d'université au Nouveau-Brunswick, une conférence des recteurs et des principaux des universités du Québec, un conseil des universités de l'Ontario et une association, sans caractère officiel, groupant les présidents des universités des provinces de l'Ouest. L'une des tâches principales de

chacune de ces associations d'universités ou
de présidents, est de fournir un moyen de
communiquer et parfois de négocier avec les
organismes gouvernementaux mentionnés ci-
dessus. Elles ont, en outre, une fonction, de
plus en plus importante, celle de faciliter la
collaboration entre les universités elles-
mêmes.

Statistics on universities and colleges

Statistiques des universités et collèges

See also separate section on individual university statistics

Voir aussi la section séparée sur les statistiques des universités particulières

Full-time enrolment in winter session	Inscriptions à plein temps, session d'hiver	1951–52	1961–62	1969–70	1970–71
Students enrolled for university-level degrees, diplomas or certificates:	Etudiants inscrits en vue de l'obtention d'un grade, diplôme ou certificat de niveau universitaire:				
Undergraduates	Sous-diplômés	59,849	121,547	263,013	277,061*
Graduates	Diplômés	3,650	7,347	30,231	33,174
Students enrolled for non university-level diplomas or certificates	Etudiants inscrits en vue de l'obtention d'un diplôme ou certificat de niveau non universitaire	..	..	1,439	1,292*
Students not preparing university awarded degrees, diplomas or certificates	Etudiants qui ne préparent pas un grade, diplôme ou certificat accordé par l'université	†	†	5,206	5,429
Total	Total	63,499**	128,894**	299,889	316,956

.. Figures not available.

* Figures subject to minor changes.

† Included in undergraduates enrolled for university-level degrees, diplomas or certificates.

** Excludes students enrolled for non university-level diplomas or certificates.

.. Chiffres indisponibles.

* Chiffres sujets à des changements mineurs.

† Inclus avec les sous-diplômés inscrits en vue de l'obtention d'un grade, diplôme ou certificat de niveau universitaire.

** Exclut les étudiants inscrits en vue de l'obtention d'un diplôme ou certificat de niveau non universitaire.

Part-time enrolment in winter session	Inscriptions à temps partiel, session d'hiver	1951–52	1961–62	1969–70	1970–71
Students enrolled for university-level degrees, diplomas or certificates:	Etudiants inscrits en vue de l'obtention d'un grade, diplôme ou certificat de niveau universitaire:				
Undergraduates	Sous-diplômés	3,466	..	85,791	99,274
Graduates	Diplômés	667	..	13,719	14,336
Students enrolled for non university-level diplomas or certificates	Etudiants inscrits en vue de l'obtention d'un diplôme ou certificat de niveau non universitaire	*	..	84	4,265
Students not preparing university awarded degrees, diplomas or certificates	Etudiants qui ne préparent pas un grade, diplôme ou certificat accordé par l'université	*	..	25,672	41,035
Total	Total	4,133	..	125,266	158,910

* Included in undergraduates enrolled for university-level degrees, diplomas or certificates.

* Inclus avec les sous-diplômés inscrits en vue de l'obtention d'un grade, diplôme ou certificat de niveau universitaire.

Full-time foreign students	Etudiants étrangers à plein temps	1951–52	1961–62	1969–70	1970–71
Undergraduates (by place of residence)	Sous-diplômés (par lieu de domicile)	..	..	..	11,608
Graduates (by citizenship)	Diplômés (par citoyenneté)	..	..	..	10,771
Total	Total	3,012	7,900	19,921	22,379*

* There were also 7,778 unclassified students which may or may not be foreign.	* Il y avait aussi 7,778 étudiants non classifiés qui pouvaient être ou ne pas être étrangers.

Degrees awarded	Grades accordés	1951–52	1961–62	1969–70	1970–71
Undergraduate certificates	Certificats de niveau pré-grade	..	..	2,282	..
Undergraduate diplomas	Diplômes de niveau pré-grade	..	..	2,847	..
Bachelor's and first professional degrees	Baccalauréats et premiers grades professionnels	14,123	23,102	60,453	..
Graduate diplomas	Diplômes du niveau post-grade	..	..	1,007	..
Master's degrees	Maîtrises	1,443	2,813	8,461	..
Doctor's degrees (earned)	Doctorats (acquis)	234	321	1,375	..
Total	Total	15,800*	26,236*	76,425	..

* Excludes undergraduate and graduate certificates and diplomas.	* Exclut les certificats et diplômes des niveaux pré-grade et post-grade.

Teaching staff	Personnel enseignant	1951–52	1961–62	1969–70	1970–71
Full-time teaching and research staff	Professeurs et personnel de recherche à plein temps	6,207	10,540	21,840	24,460
Median salary of teachers at 19 universities	Traitement médian des professeurs de 19 universités	$4,797	$8,646	$13,839	$14,887

Expenditures (millions of $)	Dépenses (en millions de $)	1951–52	1961–62	1969–70	1970–71
Operating expenditures (including assisted research)	Dépenses d'exploitation (y compris les recherches subventionnées)	56	211	1,084	1,247*
Capital expenditures	Dépenses en capital	..	85	356	375*
Total	Total	..	296	1,440	1,622*

* Estimated.

Principal sources: Statistics Canada Catalogues Nos. 81–203, 81–204, 81–211 and 81–212, and information provided by the Education Division, Statistics Canada.

* Chiffres estimatifs.

Sources principales: Statistique Canada Catalogues Nos 81–203, 81–204, 81–211 et 81–212 et renseignements fournis par la Division de l'éducation de Statistique Canada.

Admission to university in Canada

based on articles by Dr. Léopold Lamontagne, executive director, Service for Admission to College and University and Msgr. Jacques Garneau, associate director (international programs), Association of Universities and Colleges of Canada

Admission aux universités canadiennes

d'après les articles de M. Léopold Lamontagne, directeur général, Service d'admission au collège et à l'université et de Mgr Jacques Garneau, directeur adjoint (programmes internationaux), Association des Universités et Collèges du Canada

Introduction

Education in Canada is a provincial responsibility, and in this regard the 10 provinces are considered as independent. Each province has its own curriculum and awards its own certificates of completion of secondary school studies; Canadian universities have individual admission requirements based on certificates awarded in the province, but all treat certificates of other provinces as approximately equivalent. They differentiate only between the two secondary graduation certificates: one generally referred to as "junior matriculation" (corresponding to grade 11 in the provinces of Quebec, Nova Scotia, Newfoundland, Alberta, Manitoba and Saskatchewan, and to grade 12 in the other provinces); the other involving an additional year of study, referred to as "senior matriculation" (corresponding to grade 12 in the provinces of Quebec, Newfoundland, Nova Scotia, Manitoba, Alberta, Saskatchewan, and to grade 13 in the other provinces).

1   Admission to first degree

In practice, for admission to courses leading to a first degree, over 60% of universities, mainly in Ontario and the western provinces, admit only at the senior matriculation level, and require specified grades in appropriate subjects, as well as a specified overall average; all other universities also admit at junior matriculation level, requiring specified grades in appropriate subjects, and a specified overall average.

Generally, a student with a minimum overall average of at least 60% with no subject below 50% should gain admission to university, though not always to the course or institution of his first choice. It should also be noted that admission to certain faculties, such as law, medicine, dentistry, nursing, education and divinity, sometimes requires the completion of a bachelor's degree, or at least two years' study beyond senior matriculation.

In June 1972 a central admissions clearing house will be opened for Ontario students applying to Ontario universities. A common application form will be used, and students will list three universities of their choice. When an applicant has been accepted by one university, the clearing house will advise the other two. If a student cannot be accepted by

Introduction

L'enseignement au Canada relève de la compétence provinciale et, à cet égard, chacune des dix provinces est considérée comme étant indépendante. Chaque province a ses propres programmes et décerne ses propres certificats d'études secondaires. Chaque université canadienne établit ses propres conditions d'admission selon les certificats que la province accorde, mais toutes considèrent les certificats des autres provinces comme approximativement équivalents. Elles établissent une différence seulement entre les deux certificats conférés au niveau secondaire: l'un est généralement désigné sous le nom d'immatriculation junior (il correspond à la 11e année dans les provinces de Québec, de la Nouvelle-Ecosse, de Terre-Neuve, de l'Alberta, du Manitoba et de la Saskatchewan, et à la 12e année dans les autres provinces) et l'autre, qui est décerné après une année d'études supplémentaires est connu sous le nom d'immatriculation senior (il correspond à la 12e année dans les provinces de Québec, de Terre-Neuve, de la Nouvelle-Ecosse, du Manitoba, de l'Alberta et de la Saskatchewan, et à la 13e année dans les autres provinces).

1   Admission aux études du premier cycle

Dans la pratique, plus de 60 p. cent des universités, surtout en Ontario et dans les provinces de l'Ouest, admettent les élèves qu'après l'immatriculation senior et exigent certains pourcentages prévus dans des matières déterminées. Certains établissements (Toronto par exemple) exigent une moyenne générale définie. Les autres universités admettent les détenteurs du diplôme d'immatriculation junior, mais elles exigent des moyennes définies dans les matières déterminées. D'ordinaire, l'élève qui détient un certificat indiquant une note d'au moins 50 p. cent dans chaque matière et une moyenne générale d'au moins 60 p. cent est admissible même si ce n'est pas toujours dans le cours ou l'établissement qu'il préfère. Il faut également signaler que pour être admis à certaines facultés, telles que les facultés de droit, de médecine, d'art dentaire, de nursing, de pédagogie et de théologie, il faut parfois posséder un baccalauréat ès arts ou avoir fait au moins deux ans d'études après l'immatriculation senior.

one of his three selections, he will be informed of openings at other institutions.

The French-language universities of Quebec require students to submit evidence of facility in the French language and a certificate of completion of college studies "diplôme d'études collégiales" in most cases. In September 1967 there were 12 institutions called the "collèges d'enseignement général et professionnel" established in different regions of the province. There are now some 35 of them. The CEGEP acts as a bridge between secondary and university levels offering a two-year course to which students are admitted after their secondary studies (usually following grade 12). Admission to Quebec universities for both French- and English-language candidates is enacted upon completion of this two-year college program.

2 Admission to studies leading to the master's degree

Admission to a master's degree program requires either a general or honors bachelor's degree with at least second-class standing (65-70%) and in some cases, with first-class standing in one or two courses in which the candidate is specializing.

The student must demonstrate fluency in the language of instruction of the institution, and usually competence in one or more other languages, as determined by the department.

The master's degree will require at least one year's study following the honors bachelor's degree and two years following the general or pass bachelor's degree. In most cases, the master's degree must be completed within three to six years from the initial date of admission into the program.

Candidates admitted into the program with an honors degree are required to register in up to five courses of which two may ordinarily be replaced by a thesis. Courses are taken at the graduate level though some may also be permitted at the honors undergraduate level. Courses must be approved by the department which will also determine the division of studies between research and courses.

Studies generally comprise seminars, reading courses, and a course in bibliography and research methods. Courses already taken at the graduate level may, in some cases, be counted toward the master's program if they

A partir du mois de juin 1972, les élèves Ontariens devront s'adresser à un centre des admissions. Ils utiliseront une formule d'admission commune sur laquelle ils indiqueront trois choix. Lorsqu'ils seront acceptés dans une université, le centre en préviendra les deux autres. Il signalera les possibilités qui existent ailleurs aux élèves qui ne seront acceptés par aucune des trois universités choisies.

Les universités de langue française au Québec exigent que les élèves justifient d'une bonne connaissance du français et présentent un diplôme d'études collégiales. On compte environ 35 "collèges d'enseignement général et professionnel" dans diverses régions de la province en plus d'un certain nombre de collèges indépendants. Ces établissements permettent de passer du niveau secondaire au niveau universitaire en offrant un cours de deux ans aux élèves qui ont terminé leurs études secondaires (en général la 12e année). Les candidats de langue anglaise et de langue française sont donc admis aux universités du Québec après avoir terminé ce cours postsecondaire de deux ans.

2 Admission aux études de maîtrise (2e cycle)

Pour être admis à la maîtrise, un étudiant doit normalement avoir obtenu un baccalauréat avec spécialisation et avoir conservé une moyenne d'au moins 70 p. cent au cours de ses dernière et avant-dernière années d'études et, en certains cas, 80 p. cent dans un ou plusieurs des cours faisant partie de la discipline de sa spécialisation.

Tout candidat doit faire valoir son aptitude à suivre les cours dans la langue d'enseignement de l'université où il veut poursuivre ses études (le français où l'anglais). Pour les candidats possédant un baccalauréat avec spécialisation, la durée des études préparatoires à la maîtrise est d'au moins une année complète à l'université. Les candidats ne justifiant que d'un baccalauréat général doivent consacrer au moins deux ans à la préparation d'une maîtrise.

En règle générale, la préparation d'une maîtrise ne doit pas excéder de six ans la date d'admission à ce grade. Le programme des études et le projet de thèse sont déterminés, pour chaque candidat, en consultation avec le directeur du département où doit être préparée sa maîtrise. Ils doivent être approuvés par le directeur de l'école des

have not already counted as credit toward the baccalaureate degree.

A thesis is ordinarily required, though it may, in a very few cases, be replaced by a research paper or dissertation. The thesis must display original scholarship expressed in satisfactory literary form consistent with the discipline studied.

If the thesis is not completed in a period of three to six years, the candidate is required to withdraw.

An average of 66-70% is required in all courses taken at the master's level though in some cases a mark as low as 60% may be accepted in one course. Frequently, general and comprehensive written and oral examinations are required at the discretion of the faculty or department. An oral examination on the content of the thesis is also usually required.

In some cases a supplemental examination may be permitted in no more than one or two courses for which less than 60% was originally obtained. In other cases no supplemental examination is permitted.

3   Admission to studies leading to the doctoral degree

Graduates holding the master's degree with high second-class standing (70-80%) or the bachelor's honors degree with first-class or high second-class standing may be admitted to a program of doctoral studies.

Candidates having successfully completed the first year of the master's program may also be admitted.

Candidates must demonstrate the ability to carry out research of high quality leading to an advance in knowledge in their field of study, and must exhibit a comprehensive mastery of their subject. Some university departments require candidates to sit for graduate record examinations and to submit the results with their application. Candidates must be fluent in the language of instruction (English or French) and competent in one or more other languages, as determined by the department.

Candidates admitted into a doctoral degree program holding the master's degree must spend at least two full years in residence,

gradués ou par un comité inter-disciplinaire nommé par lui. Les études en vue de la maîtrise (en un an) comportent une scolarité d'environ cinq cours dont deux peuvent être remplacés par une thèse. En plus des cours magistraux, la scolarité de maîtrise comporte la participation aux colloques, des lectures obligatoires, l'établissement d'une bibliographie et l'initiation aux méthodes de recherche. L'assiduité aux cours est une condition d'admission aux examens.

La présentation d'une thèse est habituellement requise pour l'obtention d'une maîtrise. Exceptionnellement cette thèse peut être remplacée par un exposé des recherches effectuées ou par une dissertation. Une thèse doit manifester une certaine originalité de pensée, être écrite en style convenable et compatible avec le sujet traité.

Un examen est requis pour chacun des cours suivis et le candidat doit y conserver une moyenne de 66 à 70 p. cent. Exceptionnellement une note aussi basse que 60 p. cent peut être acceptée, mais seulement pour un des examens. Fréquemment, un examen compréhensif écrit et oral est requis, à la discrétion du département ou de la faculté concernée. La thèse doit être lue par deux examinateurs au moins.

3   Admission aux études préparatoires au doctorat (3e cycle)

Pour être admis au doctorat, un candidat doit normalement avoir obtenu sa maîtrise avec grande distinction (70 à 80 p. cent). Exceptionnellement, certains des meilleurs candidats à la maîtrise peuvent être autorisés à passer directement au doctorat sans avoir à présenter une thèse de maîtrise. L'admission des candidats se fait toujours après examen de leur dossier universitaire. En plus de cet examen, certains départements exigent qu'un candidat leur soumette les résultats d'un test spécial d'aptitude aux études supérieures dans le domaine particulier de sa spécialisation.

Tout candidat doit pouvoir s'exprimer couramment en français ou en anglais, selon la langue d'enseignement de l'université de son choix.

La durée des études pour les candidats justifiant d'une maîtrise et admis de plein droit à un programme de doctorat est d'au moins deux années complètes à l'université. Les candidats admis conditionnellement doivent s'attendre à ce que l'on exige d'eux

while those with an honors bachelor's degree must spend at least three years in residence.

Candidates are required to register for each year the degree is being pursued and are expected to complete full requirements for the degree within five to seven years from the initial date of admission into the degree program.

Candidates are required to outline their proposed course and research program in consultation with the head of the department in which they are specializing and writing their thesis, and with the director of research to whom they have been assigned. The program must have the approval of the dean of the faculty of graduate studies and, in many universities, of a committee of three members set up to supervise the candidate's progress. The department and faculty share the responsibility for arranging examinations and adjudicating the thesis.

The number of courses for the doctoral degree is not usually specified for candidates admitted with the master's degree, although they are required generally to choose both a major field and one or two minor fields in related disciplines. A program of studies usually consists of seminars, formal courses at the graduate level, assigned reading, field work or consultations. Frequently, candidates who have not fulfilled the language requirements for the degree are required to attend language reading courses.

The doctoral thesis must constitute a significant contribution to knowledge, embody the results of original investigation and analysis, and be of such value as to merit publication.

The subject of the thesis must be approved by the faculty of graduate studies within at least one year of the date of registration for the degree, and the thesis itself must be submitted within five to seven years from the date of admission. The thesis is generally submitted to three examiners, of whom one is an "outside-examiner".

In some cases, if the thesis is found unacceptable, a candidate is permitted to rewrite or revise it, and resubmit it within a period of six to twelve months. Candidates are not normally permitted, however, to submit the thesis more than twice.

Candidates must obtain at least 66-70% in each examination and 75-80% in their subjects of major specialization.

une scolarité plus longue. Un candidat a de cinq à sept ans pour terminer la préparation de son doctorat.

C'est au candidat lui-même qu'il appartient ordinairement, en consultation avec le directeur du département où il se spécialisera, de proposer le programme de ses études et son projet de recherche. La proposition du candidat doit être approuvée par le directeur de l'école des gradués et par un comité spécial de trois membres chargé de suivre les progrès du candidat et de l'aider dans la planification de son travail et la préparation de sa thèse. La connaissance d'une ou parfois de deux langues étrangères est aussi requise pour l'obtention du doctorat.

Même si un candidat au doctorat n'est pas astreint à un programme d'études déterminé d'avance, il doit néanmoins suivre un certain nombre de cours principaux et de cours secondaires. A ces cours s'ajoutent la participation aux colloques, des lectures prescrites, le travail sur place ou en laboratoire, ainsi que des rencontres périodiques avec son directeur de thèse et, au besoin, avec d'autres professeurs. Tout candidat au doctorat dont la connaissance des langues étrangères requises est insuffisante doit suivre des cours de perfectionnement.

Une des deux ou trois années de la scolarité, mais jamais la dernière, peut se faire dans un autre établissement que l'université qui décerne le doctorat.

La préparation et la soutenance d'une thèse sont absolument requises pour l'obtention du doctorat. Cette thèse doit représenter une contribution réelle au savoir, être le résultat de recherches originales et d'analyses personnelles et être présentée dans un style qui la rende digne d'être publiée. Le sujet de la thèse doit être approuvé par l'école des gradués dans l'année qui suit la première inscription d'un candidat au doctorat. La thèse elle-même doit être soumise dans une période variant entre cinq et sept ans, selon les universités, après la première inscription du candidat. La thèse d'un candidat au doctorat est habituellement soumise à trois examinateurs, dont un n'est pas de l'université fréquentée. En cas du refus de sa thèse, le candidat a entre six mois et un an pour la reviser et présenter un texte corrigé. Une thèse de doctorat ne peut être normalement soumise plus de deux fois.

Un candidat au doctorat doit conserver entre 66 et 70 p. cent à chacun de ses examens, et dans son sujet majeur de spécialisation, il doit conserver entre 75 et 80 p. cent. Au milieu de

Comprehensive oral and/or written examinations, called candidacy or preliminary examinations, are generally held mid- or partway through, or at the end of the second year of the doctoral program when the thesis is well under way, in order to test the candidate's mastery of his major and minor fields of study and to determine his eligibility to continue in the program with full doctoral status. Further course examinations may be held at the time of submitting the thesis.

As candidates are urged to complete their language requirements by the end of the penultimate year of their residence, they are generally required to sit for either one examination in two foreign languages, if two languages are required, or two examinations held at an interval of several months, in one foreign language, if only one language is required.

Upon acceptance of the thesis, a final oral examination is held to test the candidate's defence of his thesis.

4   Early admission

In general, universities do not accept students before the last year's final examinations have been written. However, there are an increasing number of exceptions to this rule, particulary in Ontario, where many institutions accept a candidate's early application on the basis of his high school record, a confidential report from the principal, and the results of some aptitude and achievement tests.

Especially in those provinces where the grade 13 departmental examinations are no longer given, such tests are becoming common criteria for admission.

5   Tests as an admission requirement

Most of the 45 Canadian universities either require or recommend that candidates take the Canadian Scholastic Aptitude Test (Test d'aptitude générale aux études postsecondaires) and the Canadian English-Language Achievement Test (Test de français langue maternelle) prepared by the Service for Admission to College and University, (151 Slater Street, Ottawa), an interprovincial and interuniversity organization, with the co-operation of the Ontario Institute for Studies

sa scolarité, ou au plus tard avant de présenter sa thèse, il doit subir un examen compréhensif écrit et oral, appelé examen de candidature ou préliminaire, pour permettre d'apprécier sa maîtrise des matières inscrites à son programme d'études et d'autoriser la poursuite de son travail pré-doctoral. Au cours de l'avant-dernière année de scolarité, un candidat doit subir avec succès un examen sur deux langues étrangères ou deux examens, passés à quelques mois d'intervalle, sur une langue étrangère, selon qu'on exige d'en connaître une ou deux. Une fois sa thèse présentée et acceptée par le jury de ses examinateurs, le candidat doit en faire la soutenance devant eux.

4   Admission anticipée

En général, les universités n'admettent pas de candidats avant qu'ils aient subi les examens finals de leur dernière année. Cependant on s'en tient de moins en moins à cette règle, particulièrement en Ontario et au Manitoba où de nombreuses institutions acceptent les demandes anticipées de candidats en se fondant sur leur dossier scolaire au niveau secondaire, sur le rapport confidentiel du directeur, et sur les résultats des tests d'aptitudes et de connaissances. Dans les provinces où les examens du ministère de l'Education ont disparu, ces tests deviennent l'un des critères d'admission couramment utilisés.

5   Les tests d'admission

La plupart des 45 universités canadiennes exigent ou recommandent que tous les candidats passent le Test d'aptitude générale aux études postsecondaires (Canadian Scholastic Aptitude Test) et le Test de français langue maternelle (Canadian English-Language Achievement Test) préparés par le Service d'admission au collège et à l'université (151, rue Slater, Ottawa), organisme interprovincial et interuniversitaire, avec la collaboration de l'Ontario Institute for Studies in Education (Toronto) et le Service de mesure et d'évaluation (Québec).

Ces tests seront offerts au moins deux fois au cours de l'année 1971-1972. La principale séance d'examens aura lieu le 1er décembre 1971 dans les écoles secondaires, le 15 avril 1972, dans quelques collèges et universités.

in Education, Toronto, and the Service for Measurement and Evaluation (SEMEV), Quebec City.

These tests will be administered twice in the school year 1971-72. The main general administration will be held on December 1, 1971, in high schools, and the second administration will be on April 15, 1972, in approximately 50 selected centres across Canada, mainly universities. It is not intended that the tests be used as the sole criterion for admitting students to university, and institutions continue to require the certificate of completion of secondary school studies, school record, and principal's recommendation.

6   Student aid

Financial assistance, in the form of scholarships, bursaries, fellowships, grants-in-aid, assistantships, and loans, is available to some but not to the majority of students. Awarding bodies include the government of Canada through various departments and agencies, provincial governments, the universities, business and industrial corporations, voluntary associations, and professional societies.

Details are to be found in the calendars of the universities, in *Requirements for admission to Canadian colleges and universities,* SACU, 151 Slater St., Ottawa, Ont., K1P 5N1, Canada, in *Awards for Graduate Study and Research*, and in the publication *National Student Aid Information Service* of the Canadian Scholarship Trust Foundation. (See separate section entitled "Associations and agencies related to higher education".)

7   Admission of foreign students

A growing number of foreign students attend Canadian universities. They are usually required to show facility in English or French by passing SACU tests, or one of the English-language proficiency tests administered by CEEB or the universities of Cambridge and Michigan. Candidates from the United States are required to pass the College Board Scholastic Aptitude and Achievement tests. Graduation from an American high school is usually the equivalent of Canadian junior matriculation, while the freshman year at college is equivalent to senior matriculation.

6   Aide aux étudiants

Certains étudiants peuvent obtenir de l'aide financière sous forme de bourses d'études, de bourses d'entretien, de bourses de perfectionnement, de subventions, d'assistants et de prêts. Les organismes qui accordent une telle aide comprennent le gouvernement du Canada, par l'intermédiaire de divers ministères et agences, les gouvernements provinciaux, les universités, les sociétés commerciales et industrielles, les associations bénévoles et professionnelles.

On trouvera des détails dans les annuaires des universités, dans *Conditions d'admission dans les collèges et universités du Canada,* SACU, 151, rue Slater, Ottawa (Ont.) K1P 5N1, Canada, dans *Bourses d'études supérieures et de recherches,* dans *Service de renseignements, aide nationale aux étudiants,* de la Canadian Scholarship Trust Foundation. (Voir section intitulée "Associations et organismes intéressés à l'enseignement supérieur".)

7   Admission des étudiants étrangers

Un nombre croissant d'étudiants étrangers viennent au Canada. On leur demande d'ordinaire de justifier leur connaissance de l'anglais ou du français au moyen des tests de SACU. Dans bien des cas, on exige que les candidats venant des Etats-Unis passent le "Scholastic Aptitude Test" du College Board. Le certificat d'un "high school" des Etats-Unis est généralement considéré comme l'équivalent de l'immatriculation junior, et la première année universitaire équivaut à l'immatriculation senior.

Tous ceux qui désirent venir au Canada afin de poursuivre leurs études devraient se renseigner et prendre les mesures nécessaires plusieurs mois et, de préférence, une année avant la date où ils désirent commencer leurs études. Ils ne devraient pas quitter leur pays avant que leur demande d'admission à une université ait été officiellement acceptée. Ils ne doivent pas compter être en mesure de gagner assez d'argent pour acquitter leurs dépenses au cours de leurs études.

Outre les directeurs et les organismes des universités mêmes, les principales associations nationales se consacrant à l'accueil, l'orientation et le bien-être des étudiants étrangers sont le Bureau canadien de l'éducation internationale et l'Entr'aide

Students who hope to enter Canada to study should make their initial inquiries and arrangements several months, preferably a full year, before the date they wish to begin study. They should not leave for Canada until they have official acceptance of their application for admission to a university. They should not count on being able to earn their expenses during the course of their studies.

In addition to the officers and organizations in the universities themselves, there are several national associations devoted to the reception, orientation, and welfare of students from abroad. The main ones are World University Service of Canada and the Canadian Bureau for International Education. (See separate section entitled "Associations and agencies related to higher education".)

"Notes for foreign students who wish to attend a Canadian university" is available from SACU, Information Division (151 Slater St., Ottawa, Ont., K1P 5N1).

Details of awards available to foreign postgraduate students can be found in *Study Abroad (Etudes à l'étranger; Estudios en el Extranjero)*, a Unesco publication. This directory is available in most university libraries, or from the Unesco sales agent in the student's own country.

universitaire mondiale du Canada. (Voir section intitulée "Associations et organismes intéressés à l'enseignement supérieur".)

On peut obtenir les "Renseignements destinés aux étudiants étrangers" au Service d'information, SACU, 151, rue Slater, Ottawa (Ont.), K1P 5N1.

On trouvera des renseignements détaillés sur les bourses offertes aux étudiants du niveau supérieur dans *Etudes à l'étranger (Study Abroad; Estudios en el Extranjero)*, publication de l'UNESCO. On peut la consulter dans la plupart des bibliothèques d'université ou se la procurer auprès du représentant de l'UNESCO dans son propre pays.

Member institutions of
the Association of
Universities and
Colleges of Canada
including those institutions
which are federated with
or affiliated to member
institutions

Institutions membres de
l'Association des
Universités et Collèges
du Canada, y compris
ceux qui sont fédérées
ou affiliées aux membres

Acadia University*

Wolfville, Nova Scotia

Telephone: 902-542-2201
Direct general correspondence to the registrar

Total full-time student enrolment 2,350; see also separate section *Statistics on Canadian universities and colleges*

Executive and administrative officers

President and vice-chancellor
J.M.R. Beveridge, BSc, PhD, MD, DSc, LLD, FCIC, FRSC

Vice-president (academic)
E.C. Smith, BSc, AM, PhD

Vice-president (administration)
F.J. Elderkin, LLB

Vice-president (development)
N. Moore

Registrar
D.J. Green, BA, MA

Dean of student affairs and provost
E.S. Hansen, BSc, PhD

Dean of women
K. Grant (Mrs), BA, MA

Director of summer school, extension, and student assistance
R.H. MacNeill, MSc, FGAC

Director of alumni affairs and information services
W. Parker, BA

University librarian
H.W. Ganong, BA, BLS

Constituent college

Acadia Divinity College.
Principal: A.J. Langley, BTh, MA, BD, DD. Associate dean: M.R. Cherry, BA, BD, ThD, DD. Registrar: D.J. Green, BA, MA. Courses offered lead to the degrees of BTh, BD, and MTh.

Background

The roots from which the university grew were Horton Academy, set up by the Baptists of Nova Scotia in 1828 as a literary and theological seminary, and Queen's College, founded on the same campus in 1838. In 1841 the name Acadia College was adopted and in 1891 the Nova Scotia legislature approved changing the name to Acadia University. Another special bill was passed in 1966 reapportioning the powers of appointing governors. Although the founders of Acadia were Baptist, denominational tests have never been permitted. The design of the founders and the governing bodies has been to provide qualified students with a liberal education.

Authority in purely academic matters is assigned to a senate, comprised of approximately 40 members of whom six are governors, six - of whom two are students - are appointed by the senate from the population at large, and the remaining members are from the faculty, either by election or by virtue of the position they occupy.

Facilities and services

Acadia University is located in the Annapolis Valley town of Wolfville, Nova Scotia, a beautiful residential town of 3,000 people. The university is situated on a high terraced slope that faces the broad diked meadows of the historic Evangeline country, and the tidal waters of the Minas Basin, the body of water

*Ordinary member, AUCC.

in the north-eastern part of the Bay of Fundy.

There are 10 academic buildings, a central library with several departmental branches (over 180,000 volumes), an administration building, a students' union building, a well-equipped gymnasium with extensive other sports facilities, 11 student residences accommodating over 1,600 students, two dining halls, a faculty club, and a chapel.

The affiliated Acadia Divinity College is located on the university campus. Harvey Denton hall, the newest building on campus, contains a 400-seat lecture and concert hall, and houses the school of music.

Calendars and brochures

General calendar, admissions calendar, awards calendar, divinity college calendar, graduate studies calendar, extension calendar, summer school calendar.

Courses and degrees

Arts
(Faculty of arts)

Bachelor of arts (BA).
Four years beyond junior matriculation or three years beyond senior matriculation with major specialization in biology, chemistry, computer science, economics, English, French, geology, German, history, Latin, mathematics, music, philosophy, physics, political science, psychology, religious studies, sociology, and Spanish.

Bachelor of arts (Honors) [BA (Hons)].
Four years beyond either junior or senior matriculation with major specialization in economics, English, French, German, history, philosophy, political science, psychology and sociology.

Master of arts (MA).
At least one year beyond BA. Offered in classics, economics, English, French, history, mathematics, political science, and psychology.

Business administration
(School of business administration)

Bachelor of business administration (BBA).
Four years from junior matriculation or three years from senior matriculation. The program is designed to provide a foundation in liberal arts in the preparatory year and the study of business organization and management principles in the last three years.

Education
(School of education)

Bachelor of education (BEd).
Persons who have received the degree of bachelor of arts, science, engineering, or commerce from an approved university, may apply for admission to a one-year program of studies leading to the degree of bachelor of education from Acadia University and the teaching certificate, class 5, from the Nova Scotia Department of Education.

Junior and senior diplomas in education.
A diploma in education is awarded to students who complete two or three years of study at Acadia, and who complete an additional year of study in the school of education. A junior diploma in education requires 10 university courses together with a year of education; the Nova Scotia Department of Education will award a teacher's certificate class 3 on successful completion of this program. A senior diploma in education requires 15 university courses and a year of education; a teacher's certificate class 4 will be awarded by the Nova Scotia Department of Education on successful completion of this program.

Master of education (MEd).
At least one year from bachelor of education degree, or equivalent, with at least two years' successful teaching experience. Four programs are offered: (a) general program designed for teachers who wish to increase their knowledge in the field of education and in their special teaching field; (b) educational administration; (c) guidance and counselling; (d) special education with emphasis on learning difficulties and exceptional children.

Engineering, see science, applied

Home economics
(School of home economics)

Bachelor of science (home economics)
[BSc(HE)].
Four years from junior matriculation or three
years from senior matriculation with either a
general major or a foods and nutrition major.

Music
(School of music)

Bachelor of music (BMus).
Four years from junior matriculation
including grade VIII in applied music. Major
in composition or piano, organ, voice, violin,
viola, and brass instruments.

Bachelor of arts (major in music) [BA(Mus).].
Four years from junior matriculation or three
years from senior matriculation with grade
VI in applied music. Major in composition or
piano, organ, voice, violin, viola, and brass
instruments.

Bachelor of music education (BMusEd).
Four years from junior matriculation or three
years from senior matriculation with grade
VI in applied music. The program is designed
to prepare persons to teach music in the
public schools and consequently includes
courses from the school of education and the
faculty of arts.

Science
(Faculty of science)

Bachelor of science (BSc).
Four years beyond junior matriculation or
three years beyond senior matriculation with
major specialization in biology, chemistry,
computer science, geology, mathematics,
physics, or psychology.

Bachelor of science (honors) [BSc(Hons)].
Four years beyond either junior or senior
matriculation with major specialization in
biology, chemistry, geology, mathematics,
physics or psychology.

Master of science (MSc).
At least one year beyond BSc. Offered in
biology, chemistry, geology, mathematics,
and psychology.

Science, applied
(Ivan Curry school of engineering)

Certificate of applied science (CertAppSci).
Three-year engineering program beyond
junior matriculation giving a broad
foundation in the areas of pure science and
the specialized applied science courses
necessary for the final two years of
engineering degree programs offered by the
various engineering schools in chemical, civil,
electrical, geological, industrial, mechanical,
or mining engineering.

Bachelor of science and *certificate in applied*
science.
A four-year program of study beyond junior
matriculation or a three-year program beyond
senior matriculation, allowing for a bachelor
of science degree with major in chemistry,
mathematics or physics combined with the
certificate in applied science.

Secretarial science
(School of secretarial science)

Bachelor of secretarial administration (BSA).
Four years beyond junior matriculation or
three years beyond senior matriculation.
Program of studies includes arts, business
administration, and secretarial science courses
and is designed for those who will seek
responsible positions in business.

Diploma in secretarial science.
Students who wish to obtain a knowledge of
the theory of business and skill in office and
secretarial techniques, may combine courses
in secretarial science with a program of
studies leading to either a bachelor of arts,
bachelor of commerce, or bachelor of science
degree.

Theology
(Courses given by the Acadia Divinity
College)

Bachelor of divinity (BD).
Three years from BA or equivalent bachelor's
degree.

Bachelor of theology (BTh).
A four-year course from junior matriculation
of mixed arts and theology.

Master of theology (MTh).
At least one year from BD, in clinical pastoral
education.

Extension programs

For university credit:

Undergraduate courses offered during the
winter session at various centres in arts,
business administration, education, and
science. Certain courses in arts, business
administration, education, and theology are
also offered by correspondence. For
information contact the director of the
department of extension.

Undergraduate courses are offered in arts,
business administration, education, physical
education and recreation, and science, and
graduate courses are offered in education, at a
summer session. For information contact the
director of summer school.

Admission requirements

For a general statement regarding admission
to university study, see article *Admission to
university in Canada.*

For information regarding admission to
undergraduate study, consult *Requirements
for admission to Canadian colleges and
universities* available from Service for
Admission to College and University, 151
Slater St., Ottawa, Ont., K1P 5N1, $1.50
prepaid.

School of education.
Applicants must have received an
undergraduate degree with specialization
relevant to high school or primary school
needs with satisfactory academic standing
and a demonstrated aptitude for this field of
study.

Graduate studies.
Applicants must have received an
undergraduate degree, honors or equivalent,
from an approved university with a major in
a relevant field of study and at least a B
average in the major and minor courses of the
last two years of study. Departments may
require additional criteria.

Academic year

Winter session: early September to late April.

Summer session: early July to mid-August.

Grading system

Excellent: A+ — 94%-100%; A — 87%-93%;
A- — 80%-86%. Good: B+ — 77%-79%; B —
73%-76%; B- — 70%-72%. Fair: C+ — 67%-
69%; C — 63%-66%; C- — 60%-62%. Pass:
D+ — 57%-59%; D — 53%-56%; D- — 50-
52%.

Fees and costs

Tuition fees per academic year.
Undergraduate full-time: applied science,
arts, business administration, education,
home economics, music, science and
secretarial science $565; undergraduate part-
time, except music, less than three courses
$125 per course; divinity $400; graduate
$350 first year and $50 each subsequent year.

Miscellaneous compulsory fees per year:
undergraduate, $55; graduate, BD, and BEd,
$45.

Residence rates, board and room, $915
double and $990 single.

Financial awards and assistance

Acadia University offers a number of
undergraduate scholarships ranging from an
entrance scholarship of $300 to a university
scholarship of $6,000 ($1,500 annually for
four years). Scholarships are awarded on the
basis of high school grades, departmental
examinations, class standing, SACU scores,
principals' recommendations, and overall
student ability.

Bursaries are available to students who have
been accepted by the university and who
show a need for additional financial support
which is not available from other sources.

Graduate fellowships, scholarships, and
assistantships are available from the
university through the head of the
department.

Deans and directors of faculties and schools

Arts
A.H. MacLean, CD, CM, BA, MA, PhD

Business administration
D.L. Misener, BComm, BEd, MS

Education
W.R. MacDonald, BA, BEd, MA, AIE, EdD

Home economics
V.A. Campbell, BSc, MSc, PhD

Music
J. Kalejs

Science
E.C. Smith, BSc, AM, PhD

Science, applied
F.C. Turner, BE, MEng

Secretarial science
J.E. March, BA, MA

Theology
M.R. Cherry, BA, BD, ThD

Department heads

Art
I. James, MFA

Biology
G.M. Curry, BA, MS, PhD

Chemistry
E.P. Linton, BSc, MSc, PhD

Classics
W.G. Fletcher, BA, MA, PhD

Computer science
D.A. Bonyun, BA, MA

Economics
J. Winter, BA, MA

English
C. Tracy, BA, PhD

French
K. Rayski-Kietlicz, MPhil, DLitt

Geology
G.R. Stevens, AB, MA, PhD

German
G.S. Waseem, MA

History
A.H. MacLean, CD, CM, BA, MA, PhD

Mathematics
K.D.C. Haley, BA, MS, PhD

Philosophy
H. Lewis, BA, MA, PhD

Physical education and recreation
G.C. Chapman, BS, MSEd

Physics
R.H. Magarvey, BSc, MSc

Political science
D.G.L. Fraser, CD, BA, MA

Psychology
W.H.D. Vernon, BA, MA, AM, PhD

Religious studies
J.R.C. Perkin

Sociology
F.J. Schrag, BA, BD, PhD

Spanish
J.A. Valverde, BA, MA

The University of Alberta*

Edmonton 7, Alberta

Telephone: 403-432-3111
Direct general correspondence to the registrar

Total full-time student enrolment 18,742; see also separate section *Statistics on Canadian universities and colleges*

Executive and administrative officers

Chancellor
L.A. Desrochers, BA, LLB, QC

President and vice-chancellor
M. Wyman, BSc, PhD, FRSC

Vice-president (academic)
H. Kreisel, MA, PhD

Vice-president (planning and development)
W.D. Neal, BSc, BA, MEd, PhD

Vice-president (finance and administration)
D.G. Tyndall, BCom, MA, PhD

Registrar
A.D. Cairns, BA

Provost and executive assistant to the president
A.A. Ryan, MA

Director of extension
D.D. Campbell, BComm, MA

Director, summer session and evening credit program
S.C.T. Clarke, MA, EdD

Director, student counselling
A.J.B. Hough, MA, LTh

Librarian
B.B. Peel, MA, BLS

Dean of men
Major R.C.W. Hooper, DipRMC, PSC

Dean of women
Isabel Munro, BA

Administrator of student awards
R.B. Wishart, BCom

Constituent college

Collège universitaire Saint-Jean,
8406-91 Street, Edmonton, Alberta.
Rector: Rev. F.J. McMahon, omi, BA, MTh.
Co-educational. Founded 1961 and affiliated with the university in 1963. The college offers a bilingual program towards the BA, BEd, and BSc degrees.

Background

The University of Alberta was inaugurated by an act of the legislative assembly of that province in 1906, and instruction began in 1908. The first degrees were awarded in 1911.

From 1946 to 1964, the university also offered programs of study at Calgary. However, in 1964, the University of Alberta at Calgary became autonomous in academic matters and in 1966 was constituted a separate provincial university known as The University of Calgary.

The University of Alberta is a co-educational, non-denominational publicly supported institution. It is governed by a board of governors, a senate and a general faculties council. The former co-ordinating council of the universities at Calgary and Edmonton has been replaced by a "universities co-ordinating council" with provision for the inclusion of representatives not only from The University of Alberta, The University of Calgary, and The University of Lethbridge, but also from any other provincial universities that may be established. In addition a "universities commission" has been created, primarily to study the financial needs of the provincial universities and to advise the government

*Ordinary member, AUCC.

with regard to the granting of financial assistance for university purposes.

Facilities and services

The campus is located in the city of Edmonton (population 468,750), the provincial capital, on the south bank of the North Saskatchewan River on a site of 154 acres. The university farm, extending to 724 acres, is some two miles to the south.

There are 28 teaching buildings, two swimming pools, a year-round ice rink, four libraries (over 1,200,000 volumes), two administration buildings, a students' union building, a printing services building, sports and food services facilities, four student residences accommodating 1,080 men and 1,070 women, a faculty club, two car parks, and married students housing for 299 couples.

Affiliated residential colleges with buildings on the campus are St. Stephen's and St. Joseph's. Integrated with the university is the Collège universitaire Saint-Jean.

Adjoining the campus are The University Hospital, the Research Council of Alberta, the Aberhard Memorial Tuberculosis Sanatorium, the Northern Alberta Jubilee Auditorium and the W.W. Cross Cancer Institute.

Calendars and brochures

The university calendar is available in separate sections and the prospective student should ask for the calendar entitled "University regulations and information for students" and the calendar for the faculty or school which he wishes to enter. These may be obtained from the office of the registrar.

"Information for prospective students" may be obtained from the student counselling services.

"Information for foreign students" is available from the foreign student adviser.

Courses and degrees

Agriculture
(Faculty of agriculture)

Bachelor of science in agriculture (BSc).
Four years from senior matriculation or from a diploma (with additional high school credits) at a provincial school of agriculture. Specialization offered in agricultural economics and rural sociology, agricultural mechanization, agricultural engineering, animal and poultry science, entomology, field crops and plant breeding, crop ecology and weed science, forest resources management with options in forest management and forest biology, horticulture, plant pathology, plant physiology and biochemistry, food chemistry, food processing and food microbiology, soil genesis and classification, soil physics, soil chemistry, soil microbiology, soil fertility, soil conservation.

(Faculty of graduate studies and research)

Master of science (MSc).
At least one year from a bachelor's degree in agriculture. Offered in all the fields listed above.

Doctor of philosophy (PhD).
At least two years from MSc, or three years from BSc. Offered in the fields listed for the BSc with the exception of agricultural mechanization and agricultural engineering.

Arts
(Faculty of arts)

Bachelor of arts (BA).
(a) General course, three years from senior matriculation. (b) Special course, four years from senior matriculation. (c) Honors course, four years from senior matriculation, available in single or combined programs. Available in ancient history, anthropology, classical archeology, classics, comparative literature, drama, economics, English, French, French-Canadian language and literature, geography, German, history, history of art, Italian, linguistics (general, Germanic, romance or Slavic), mathematics, philosophy, political science, psychology, romance languages, Slavic languages, sociology, Soviet and east European studies, Spanish and Spanish-American studies, and combinations of these.

General and special BA programs require some concentration in two subjects in addition to those listed above and music, Polish, religious studies, Russian, Scandinavian languages and Ukrainian are available for this purpose.

(Faculty of graduate studies and research)

Master of arts (MA).
At least two years from ordinary BA or at least one year from honors BA. Offered in anthropology, archeology, classics, comparative literature, drama, economics, English, French, geography, German, Greek, history, ancient history, Latin, linguistics, philosophy, political science, psychology, romance languages, Slavic languages, sociology.

Doctor of philosophy (PhD).
At least two years from MA, or three years from honors BA. Offered in anthropology, classics, comparative literature, economics, English, French, geography, German, history, philosophy, political science, psychology, romance languages, Slavic languages, sociology, Spanish.

Commerce
(Faculty of business administration and commerce)

Bachelor of commerce (BCom).
Ordinary course, four years from senior matriculation. Specialization possible in accounting, data processing, economics, finance, industrial relations, marketing, management science, organizational theory and behavior.

(Faculty of graduate studies and research)

Master of business administration (MBA).
One year from four-year BCom. Two years from an undergraduate degree.

Community development
(Faculty of graduate studies and research)

Master of arts (MA).
A program administered by an interdepartmental committee responsible to the faculty of graduate studies. At least one year, including a four-month field internship, for students with adequate background in required subjects; otherwise an initial qualifying year required.

Dentistry
(School of dental hygiene)

Diploma in dental hygiene.
Two years from senior matriculation.

(Faculty of dentistry)

Doctor of dental surgery (DDS).
Four years from two years of science beyond senior matriculation.

(Faculty of graduate studies and research)

Master of science (MSc).
At least one year from an undergraduate degree.

Education
(Faculty of education)

Bachelor of education (BEd).
Four years from senior matriculation, or two years for students with a bachelor's degree. Specialization offered in elementary school teaching, industrial arts, secondary school teaching, and vocational education.

Graduate diploma in education.
One year following an approved program which resulted in a university degree and a professional teaching certificate.

(Faculty of graduate studies and research)

Master of education (MEd).
At least one year from bachelor's degree in education. Offered in adolescent psychology, child psychology, clinical psychology, curriculum and teaching in secondary education, educational administration, educational foundations, educational psychology, elementary education, exceptional children, guidance, history of education, industrial arts, mental hygiene, philosophy of education, school psychology, testing and measurement, vocational education.

Doctor of education (EdD).
At least two years from MEd degree. (Prerequisites: several years of successful teaching, reading knowledge of an appropriate modern language.)

Doctor of philosophy (PhD).
At least two years from MEd degree. Offered in the fields provided for the master's degree except industrial arts and vocational education.

Engineering
(Faculty of engineering)

Bachelor of science in engineering (BSc).
Four years from senior matriculation.
Specialization offered in chemical, civil,
electrical, mechanical, metallurgical, and
mining engineering.

(Faculty of graduate studies and research)

Graduate programs are offered in all fields of
engineering listed for BSc, and also in
petroleum engineering.

Master of engineering (MEng).
At least 9 months from bachelor's degree in
engineering.

Master of science (MSc).
At least one year from bachelor's degree in
engineering.

Doctor of philosophy (PhD).
At least two years from the master's degree in
engineering, or three years from the
bachelor's degree in engineering.

Fine arts
(Faculty of arts)

Bachelor of fine arts (BFA).
Four years from senior matriculation.
Applicants must present a portfolio for art
and design or pass an audition for drama.
Available in arts and design or in drama with
specialization in acting or design.

(Faculty of graduate studies and research)

Master of fine arts (MFA).
One year from four-year BFA. Offered in
drama, design or directing.

Food science
(Faculty of agriculture, school of household
economics and faculty of science)

*Bachelor of science in food science
[BSc(FdSc)].*
A four-year program administered by an
inter-disciplinary committee of the faculties
of agriculture and science and the school of
household economics.

Household economics
(School of household economics)

Bachelor of science [BSc(HEc)].
Four years from senior matriculation. Three
programs available: food and nutrition,
clothing and textiles, or family studies.

(Faculty of graduate studies and research)

Master of science (MSc).
Usually two years from BSc in household
economics. Offered in nutrition and foods,
clothing and textiles, and family studies.

Law
(Faculty of law)

Bachelor of laws (LLB).
Three years from either the BA or some other
degree, or the completion of two or three
years of a program leading to a BA degree.

(Faculty of graduate studies and research)

Master of laws (LLM).
At least one year from LLB degree.

Library science
(School of library science)

Bachelor of library science (BLS).
One year from BA or other acceptable degree.

Medicine
(Faculty of medicine)

*Bachelor of science in medical laboratory
science (BSc).*
Four years from senior matriculation.

Bachelor of science in medicine (BSc).
Normally, one year in a branch of medical
science after completion of two of the four
undergraduate years of study in the MD
course.

Doctor of medicine (MD).
Four years after two years of science beyond
senior matriculation.

(Faculty of graduate studies and research)

Master of science (MSc).
At least one year from an undergraduate
degree. Available in anatomy, bacteriology,
biochemistry, experimental medicine,
ophthalmology, paediatrics, pathology,
pharmacology, physiology, radiology, and
experimental surgery.

Master of health services administration.
(MHSA).
A two-year program from an undergraduate
degree.

Doctor of philosophy (PhD).
At least two years from the master's degree,
or at least three years from honors BSc or
from MD degree. Available in anatomy,
biochemistry, pharmacology, physiology and
surgery.

Music
(Faculty of arts)

Bachelor of music (BMus).
Four years from senior matriculation.
Applicants must pass an audition test.
Available in theory and composition, applied
music (keyboard, orchestral or voice), and
music history and literature.

(Faculty of graduate studies and research)

Master of music (MMus).
One year from four-year BMus. Offered in
applied music, composition, music history and
literature, and music theory.

Nursing
(School of nursing)

Bachelor of science in nursing (BSc).
Four years from senior matriculation.

*Bachelor of science in nursing for registered
nurses (BSc).*
Two years plus summer school after
graduation from an approved RN diploma
program in nursing.

Certificate in advanced practical obstetrics.
Five months for qualified registered nurses.

Pharmacy
(Faculty of pharmacy and pharmaceutical
science)

Bachelor of science in pharmacy (BSc).
Four years from senior matriculation.
Provision for specialization in community
pharmacy, hospital pharmacy, and
pharmaceutical sciences.

Hospital residency.
One year from four-year BSc in pharmacy.
Emphasis of program on organized training
in hospital pharmacy.

(Faculty of graduate studies and research)

Master of science (MSc).
At least one year from four-year BSc in
pharmacy. Available in various fields,
including pharmaceutical chemistry,
biopharmacy, pharmaceutics, natural product
chemistry, bionucleonics and/or
radiopharmacy.

Master of hospital pharmacy (MHP).
At least two years after four-year BSc in
pharmacy; includes a residency.

Doctor of philosophy (PhD).
At least two years from four-year BSc in
pharmacy. Available in the fields provided
for the MSc, except radiopharmacy.

Physical education
(Faculty of physical education)

Bachelor of physical education (BPE).
Four years from senior matriculation.

Bachelor of arts in recreation administration.
Four years from senior matriculation.

(Faculty of graduate studies and research)

*Master of arts (MA) or master of science
(MSc).*
At least one year from four-year BPE degree.

Doctor of philosophy (PhD).
Three years from four-year BPE degree or
two years from MA or MSc in physical
education.

Rehabilitation medicine
(School of rehabilitation medicine)

*Diploma in physical therapy, diploma in
occupational therapy.*
Three years from senior matriculation.

Bachelor of occupational therapy (BOT).
Four years from senior matriculation.

Bachelor of physical therapy (BPT).
Four years from senior matriculation.

Bachelor of science in speech pathology and audiology (BSc).
Four years from senior matriculation.

Diploma in teaching occupational therapy.
Two-year program open to graduates in occupational therapy with minimum of two years of experience following graduation.

Science, applied, see engineering

Science, pure
(Faculty of science)

Bachelor of science (BSc).
(a) General program, three years from senior matriculation. (b) Professional program, four years from senior matriculation. Available in biochemistry, chemistry, computing science, entomology, geology, mathematics, microbiology, physics and psychology. (c) Honors program, four years from senior matriculation. Available in biochemistry, botany, chemistry, computer science, entomology, genetics, geography, geology, geophysics, linguistics, mathematics, applied mathematics, microbiology, pharmacology, physics, applied physics, physiology, psychology, statistics, zoology, and combinations of these. (d) Students who intend to proceed to MD or DDS degrees may follow a prescribed program in two pre-professional years to qualify for the BSc at the end of a further two years in the faculties of medicine or dentistry.

(Faculty of graduate studies and research)

Master of science (MSc).
At least two years from general BSc, or one year from honors BSc. Available in botany, chemistry, computing science, genetics, geography, geology, linguistics, mathematics, meteorology, microbiology, physics, mathematical physics, psychology, statistics, zoology.

Doctor of philosphy (PhD).
At least two years from MSc or three years from honors BSc. Available in botany, chemistry, computing science, genetics, geography, geology, linguistics, mathematics, microbiology, physics, mathematical physics, psychology, statistics, zoology.

Theology

Degree and continuing education programs in theology offered by St. Stephen's College, Edmonton, an affiliated college.

Combined courses

Combined courses in science and either medicine or dentistry enable a student to obtain two degrees in less time than if the two courses were taken separately.

Extension programs

For university credit:

Evening credit program.
Undergraduate classes offered during the winter session at various centres primarily in arts and science, commerce and education.

Summer session.
Courses are offered for undergraduates proceeding to a degree and for teachers who may wish to improve their professional qualifications by working towards graduate degrees and diplomas in education. Subjects offered are chiefly in arts, science, and education; also a limited number in household economics and physical education.

For no university credit:

The department of extension offers some 350 non-credit courses, classes and seminars in liberal studies; business, technical and professional studies; community resources development; public affairs; fine arts; human relations; and public administration. Of the 13,150 students registered in these programs over 2,850 are enroled in programs leading to a university certificate.

The department maintains a library of 72,900 volumes which is used both to supplement the course work and to provide reading opportunities to citizens in outlying areas.

The educational media division offers the use of a large library of films, slides, filmstrips, records, videotapes, cassette tapes; offers instruction in education through the use of these media; and undertakes the development of independent study programs which make use of all media including books and audio-visual materials.

Admission requirements

For a general statement regarding admission to university study, see article *Admission to university in Canada.*

For information regarding admission to undergraduate study, consult *Requirements for admission to Canadian colleges and universities* available from Service for Admission to College and University, 151 Slater St., Ottawa, Ont., K1P 5N1, $1.50 prepaid.

For admission to dentistry or medicine students must have completed a minimum of two years with appropriate selection of subjects in arts and science beyond senior matriculation.

Admission requirement for law is normally a BA degree.

For admission to graduate studies a student must have obtained a first degree with specified grades in appropriate studies.

Academic year

Winter session: early September to end of April.

Summer session: early July to mid-August.

Intersession (for graduate students): early May to early September.

Grading system

Nine-point grading system as follows: 9, 8, (excellent); 7, 6 (good); 5, 4 (pass); 3 (conditional); 2, 1 (fail). For students proceeding toward an undergraduate degree the passing grade is normally 4; in courses taken toward a graduate degree the passing grade is 6.

Fees and costs

Tuition fees per year; full-time: (a) undergraduate — agriculture, arts, commerce, dental hygiene, education, household economics, law, library science, nursing, pharmacy, physical education, rehabilitation medicine, and science, $400; engineering, $500; dentistry, medicine, $600; (b) graduate, $500.

Miscellaneous compulsory fees per year: undergraduate — $38.50, graduate — varies, $30 or $43 (depending on student union privileges).

Residence rates, board and room, $95 a month.

Financial awards and assistance

The university has a program of scholarships and bursaries at each of the three levels: matriculation, undergraduate, and graduate studies. Application dates are July 15, June 15, and February 1, respectively. Many of the matriculation awards are restricted to students from Alberta high schools, and most of the undergraduate awards are based on academic work done at this university. Most of the graduate studies awards are open to graduates of any university but who are Canadian citizens or landed immigrants at the date of application.

Many graduate studies departments also offer assistantships.

Students who are Canadian citizens or landed immigrants and who have been in Alberta for one year may apply for financial assistance in the form of loans on a basis of financial need.

For information on awards and financial assistance, write to the administrator of student awards.

For information on assistantships write to the faculty of graduate studies or the particular department concerned.

Research institutes

The Boreal Institute for Northern Studies.
The principal function of the institute is to promote and support scientific research in the circumpolar regions. This aspect of activities includes the financial support of short-term field research which is awarded annually to individual scholars. Longer term and more comprehensive research programs are also operated under the aegis of the institute.
The institute maintains a library which also serves as an information centre on existing material concerning the North.
Inquiries regarding the work of the institute should be addressed to the director and those for information from the reference service to the librarian.

Cancer Research Institute.
Established in co-operation with the Canadian Cancer Society and the university. The institute is one of four such units located by the National Cancer Institute in Canadian medical schools.
Several post-doctoral research fellowships are available each year.

Institute of Law Research and Reform.
The institute was established to promote law reform, particularly at the provincial level, and to encourage legal research in co-operation with the faculty of law.

Centre for the Study of Mental Retardation.
The centre is a multi-disciplinary research institute sponsored by the university and the Canadian Association for the Mentally Retarded.
Its purposes are to: (a) develop a centre staffed by research scientists probing problems of intellectual subnormality; (b) encourage faculty and graduate students to carry out investigations; (c) secure financial and other support for approved research projects; (d) publish and disseminate the findings of such research.
The centre provides assistance for scientists conducting studies on mental retardation and the treatment and education of mentally retarded children.

Nuclear Research Centre.
The centre conducts studies to determine the fundamental properties of the nucleus of atoms. The central facility for research is a six million volt Van de Graaff accelerator. In addition the present staff is directly involved in the construction of a 500 million electron volt cyclotron at Vancouver. The centre offers

research fellowships to physicists for research in nuclear physics.

Surgical-Medical Research Institute.
The institute offers facilities for members of the clinical faculty in the field of experimental medicine. Facilities are available for research fellows in clinical departments to conduct projects under the supervision and direction of the faculty. The institute offers a one-trimester post-graduate course in experimental surgery.

Institute of Theoretical Physics.
The institute was established to promote research in theoretical physics. The research interest ranges over astrophysics, statistical physics, physical acoustics, general relativity, etc. The permanent membership is comprised of the university staff actively engaged in research in theoretical physics.
There are currently about a dozen post-doctoral fellows carrying out research under the sponsorship of the institute, which offers in addition, special visiting fellowships to physicists of distinction.

Centre for Advanced Study in Theoretical Psychology.
The centre offers a program of education and research to enrich, clarify and deepen the theoretical foundations of psychological science. An important feature of the centre's activities is the distinguished visiting scholars program wherein world-wide leaders in theoretical-philosophical psychology are invited to visit the centre for an extended period for the mutual exchange of ideas.

Affiliated colleges

St. Joseph's College, Edmonton, Alberta.
Rector: Rev. J.B. Courtney, CSB, MA. Roman Catholic (Basilian Fathers). Co-educational. Established 1926 as an affiliate of the university with the right to offer undergraduate courses in philosophy and history. The college offers courses in philosophy and Christian theology. Residence for men only.

St. Stephen's College, Edmonton, Alberta.
Principal: Rev. G.M. Tuttle, BA, BD, ThD, DD. Dean: Rev. D.J.C. Elson, MA, DD. United Church. Co-educational. Established 1927 through the union of Robertson College (1910) and Alberta College South. Affiliated with the university since 1909. Offers certain courses for credit towards degrees at the

university as well as conferring degrees in theology and providing courses in continuing education for ministry. Two buildings: academic and residential.

Affiliated under the regulations relating to community colleges:

Camrose Lutheran College, Camrose, Alberta. Dean: R.J. Ostrem, MA, PhD. Lutheran. Co-educational. Established 1959 and affiliated to the university as a junior college. Two years of instruction after senior matriculation.

Canadian Union College, Lacombe, Alberta. President: P.G. Miller, MEd. The application from Canadian Union College, Lacombe, Alberta, has been tentatively approved for one year of affiliation subject to securing satisfactory academic staff.

Concordia Lutheran College, Edmonton, Alberta. President: R.A. Frantz, BA, BD. Lutheran. Co-educational. Established 1921 and affiliated to the university in 1968. One year of instruction after senior matriculation.

Grande Prairie College, Grande Prairie, Alberta. President: H.M. Anderson, BEd, BA, PhD. Non-denominational. Co-educational. Established 1966 and affiliated to the university as a junior college. One year of instruction after senior matriculation.

Red Deer College, Red Deer, Alberta. President: Mervyn Eastman, BEd, BA, MEd, MBA, DBA. Non-denominational. Co-educational. Established 1964 and affiliated to the university as a junior college. Two years of instruction after senior matriculation. (Only arts, science, physical education, and education programs offered in second year.)

Also affiliated to the university are the following non-university institutions: The University Hospital (Edmonton), the Glenrose Provincial General Hospital (Edmonton), the Research Council of Alberta, the Provincial Laboratory of Public Health, and the Western Board of Music.

Deans of faculties

Agriculture
F.V. MacHardy, BSc, MSc, PhD

Arts
D.E. Smith, MA, PhD

Business administration and commerce
E.J. Chambers, BCom, BA, MA, PhD

Dentistry
J. McCutcheon, BA, MSc, DDS

Education
H.T. Coutts, MA, PhD

Engineering
G. Ford, BSc, MSc, PhD

Graduate studies
J.R. McGregor, BSc, BEd, MEd, PhD

Law
G.H.L. Fridman, BA, BCL, MA

Medicine
W.C. MacKenzie, BSc, MD, CM, MS, LLD, FACS, FRCS(C), FRCS(E)

Pharmacy and pharmaceutical sciences
M.J. Huston, MSc, PhD, FCIC

Physical education
M.L. Van Vliet, MS, EdD

Science
D.M. Ross, MA, PhD, ScD

Collège universitaire Saint-Jean
F.J. McMahon, BA, MTh

Directors of schools

Dental hygiene
M.B. MacLean, BSc, BSc

Household economics
Elizabeth Empey, BSc, PhD

Library science
Mary Henderson (acting), BLS, MA

Nursing
S.M. Stinson (acting), BSc, MN, EdD

Rehabilitation medicine
J.B. Redford, BA, MD, MS

Department chairmen

Anthropology
H.T. Lewis, BA, MA, PhD

Art
R.A. Davey, BA

Botany
W.N. Stewart, BA, MS, PhD

Chemical and petroleum engineering
F.D. Otto (acting), BSc, MSc, PhD

Chemistry
H.E. Gunning, BA, MA, PhD, DSC

Civil engineering
S.R. Sinclair, BSc, MSc

Classics
R.J. Buck, BA, MA, PhD

Comparative literature
M.V. Dimic, Dip

Computing science
J.P. Penny (acting), BSc, MSc, PhD

Drama
G.B. Peacock, BEd, MFA

Economics
T.L. Powrie, BSA, MA

Educational administration
G.L. Mowat, BSc, MA, EdD

Educational foundations
R.S. Patterson, MEd, PhD

Educational psychology
B.R. Corman, BA, MA, PhD

Electrical engineering
G.B. Walker, MA, PhD

Elementary education
M. Horowitz, BA, MEd, EdD

English
R.G. Baldwin, BA, MA, PhD

Genetics
R.C. von Borstel, BA, MSc, PhD

Geography
P.J. Smith, BA, MA, Dip, PhD

Geology
R. J. St. Lambert

Germanic languages
G. Marahrens, PhD

History
B.L. Evans, BA, PhD

Industrial and vocational education
J.E. Gallagher, BEd, MEd

Linguistics
C.I.J.M. Stuart, BA, MA

Mathematics
S.G. Ghurye, BSc, MSc, PhD

Mechanical engineering
J.S. Kennedy (acting), BSc, MSc, PhD

Microbiology
D.W.S. Westlake, BSc, MSc, PhD

Mining and metallurgy
E.O. Lilge, BSc, MSc

Music
R.A. Stangeland, BMus, MMus, DMA

Philosophy
P.A. Schouls, BA, MA, PhD

Physics
J.T. Sample, BA, MA, PhD

Political science
G.R. Davy, BA, MA, PhD

Psychology
T.M. Nelson, BA, MA, PhD

Religious studies
P.J. Cahill, LittB, MA, STD

Romance languages
C.H. Moore, BA, DU

Secondary education
G.L. Berry, BA, MA, BEd, EdD

Slavic languages
G.H. Schaarschmidt, MA

Sociology
J. Forster, MA, PhD

Zoology
W.A. Fuller, BA, MA, PhD

Bishop's University*

Lennoxville, Quebec

Telephone: 819-569-9551
Direct general correspondence to the registrar

Total full-time student enrolment 1,159; see also separate section *Statistics on Canadian universities and colleges*

Executive and administrative officers

Chancellor
J.H. Price, SM, OBE, MC, DCL

Principal
D.M. Healy, MA, PhD

Registrar
Captain J.P.T. Dawson, CD, RCN (retd)

Librarian
L.M. Allison, BA, BLS

Alumni secretary
R. Paul, BA, MA (on leave of absence 1971-)
T. Belford (acting), BA

Director of athletics
B. Coulter

Background

Bishop's University was founded in 1843 by the Right Reverend G.J. Mountain, third bishop of Quebec, as a liberal arts college. In 1853 it was constituted a university with the power to grant degrees. Teaching began in 1845 and the first degrees were awarded in 1855.

The university remained under the control of the Church of England until 1947; it is now controlled by a corporation with jurisdiction over business affairs. There is a senate which governs the academic work of the university subject to the jurisdiction of the corporation.

Facilities and services

The university is located in the St. Francis Valley (population of Lennoxville approximates 4,000) on a site of 310 acres. There is residential accommodation for 326 men and 234 women. In addition to the usual academic buildings, library (over 85,000 volumes), chapel, gymnasium, students centre, book store, artificial ice arena, theatre, etc., homes for some of the faculty are provided on the campus.

Calendars and brochures

Calendar; summer school brochure; brochure for certificate in industrial management.

Courses and degrees

Arts
(Faculty of arts)

Bachelor of arts (BA).
(a) Pass course, two collegial years, and three university years from junior matriculation. Areas of emphasis: classics, economics, English, French, geography, Greek, history, Latin, mathematics, philosophy, political science, psychology, sociology, theology, and combinations of these. (b) Honors course, two collegial years and three university years from junior matriculation, available in classics, economics, English, French, geography, history, Latin, mathematics, modern languages, philosophy, political science, psychology, sociology, theology, and combinations of these.

Master of arts (MA).
At least one year from an honors bachelor's degree or two years from a pass bachelor's degree. Available in English, history, and theology.

---

*Ordinary member, AUCC.

Business administration
(Faculty of arts)

*Bachelor of arts in business administration
[BA(Business Administration)].*
Four years from junior matriculation.

Commerce, see business administration above

Education
(Graduate school of education)

Class I certificate.
Post-graduate year after completion of arts or science degree.

Master of arts (MA).
At least one year from an honors bachelor's degree or two years from a pass bachelor's degree.

Master of education (MEd).
Two years from a bachelor's degree plus two years of teaching experience. May be taken entirely at summer sessions.

Science, pure
(Faculty of science)

Bachelor of science (BSc).
Pass and honors courses, two collegial years and three university years from junior matriculation. Areas of emphasis: biology, chemistry, mathematics, physics, and combinations of these.

Master of science (MSc).
At least one year from an honors bachelor's degree or two years from a pass bachelor's degree. Available in biology and chemistry.

Theology
(Faculty of theology)

Licentiate in sacred theology (LST).
One year, if taken following BA in theology at Bishop's University, otherwise, two years from the BA degree.

Bachelor of sacred theology (STB).
Three years from BA degree.

Master of arts (MA).
At least one year from an honors bachelor's degree or two years from a pass bachelor's degree.

Bachelor of divinity (BD).
Awarded on recommendation of board of examiners of general synod of Church of England in Canada.

Doctor of divinity (DD).
Awarded on recommendation of board of examiners of general synod of Church of England in Canada.

Extension programs

For university credit:

Summer school.
For the benefit of teachers, the university conducts a summer session during which graduate courses with credit towards the degree of MEd are offered. The session is of six weeks' duration. Four summer sessions are usually necessary to meet the course requirements for the MEd degree.

Admission requirements

For a general statement regarding admission to university study, see article *Admission to university in Canada.*

For information regarding admission to undergraduate study, consult *Requirements for admission to Canadian colleges and universities* available from Service for Admission to College and University, 151 Slater St., Ottawa, Ont., K1P 5N1, $1.50 prepaid.

For admission to courses leading to a first degree in divinity and education: a bachelor's degree. Early admission will be made in April or June based on the results of the College Entrance Examination Board tests and the principal's confidential reports.

For admission to graduate study a student must have obtained a degree with specified grades in appropriate subjects.

Academic year

Winter session: mid-September to mid-May.

Summer session: early July to mid-August.

Grading system

Standing is graded as follows — first-class: 80% and over; second-class: 65-79%; third-class: 50-64%; failure: below 50%.

Fees and costs

Tuition fees per year: full-time undergraduate and graduate, arts, $630; divinity, $550; education, $520; science, $695; theology, $500; graduate, 1st year $400, 2nd year $225; part-time (per subject), $130. Summer school fees: tuition (per course), $45; three courses, $125; room and board, $35 per week; degree fee MEd, $25. Residence rates, board and room: single, $990; double, $865.

Financial awards and assistance

Bishop's offers 62 entrance scholarships, ranging in value from $300 to $4,000, available by competition to high school graduates with honors standing. A student loan fund is administered by the university. Except in special circumstances grants from this fund are not awarded to first-year students. These loans are interest-free until six months after leaving the university. Loans are also offered by the department of education of the government of Quebec. A small number of bursaries are awarded to deserving applicants.

Dean of faculty

Dean of the faculty
J.A. Philip, BA, DLitt

Divisional chairmen

Business administration
R.S. Jain, BSc, MBA, PhD

Graduate studies and research
Rev. S. Fellicoe, MA, BD, DD, DCL

Humanities
J. Gray, MA, MA, PhD, FRSA

Natural sciences
J.W. McCubbin, MSc, PhD, MCIC

Social sciences
E.A. Prince, BA, MA, PhD

Brandon University*

Brandon, Manitoba

Telephone: 204-727-5401
Direct general correspondence to the registrar

Total full-time student enrolment 1,150; see also separate section *Statistics on Canadian universities and colleges*

Executive and administrative officers

Chancellor
Stanley Knowles, BA, BD, MP

President and vice-chancellor
A.L. Dulmage, BA, MA, PhD

Registrar (acting)
A.R. Balchen, BA, MEd

Director, summer school and extension
H.S. Perdue, MA, PhD, FGAC

Dean, student affairs
R.B. McFarlane, BA

Librarian
Eileen McFadden, BA, BLS

Alumni secretary
E. Brownridge (Mrs), BA

Background

Brandon University is the outgrowth of Brandon College, which was originally organized in 1899 by the Baptist Union of Western Canada. In 1938 it became non-denominational and was reorganized as Brandon College Incorporated. Teaching at the college began in September 1899. From 1899 to 1910 the college was affiliated to The University of Manitoba; from 1911 to 1938 it was affiliated to McMaster University. From 1938 to 1967 the college was affiliated to The University of Manitoba which granted degrees to students of the college.

The authority for the organization of Brandon University is The Universities Establishment Act of the legislative assembly of the province of Manitoba of 1966, and an order-in-council under the act passed in January 1967. It is non-denominational and co-educational. The order-in-council provides for a board of governors and a senate. The board of governors is responsible for the business management, and the senate is responsible for academic policy.

Facilities and services

Brandon University is situated in the western section of the city of Brandon (population, 1970 estimate 35,000) with a site of approximately 18 acres. The original building now houses administrative and faculty offices. There is a science building with a temporary extension. The first stage of new buildings constructed since 1960, includes a library (100,000 volume capacity) and arts building, a 300-seat lecture theatre, a music building, an education building, ladies' residence for 150, men's residence for 150, a co-educational residence tower for 280 students, a dining-hall to accommodate 500 people, a physical education building serving all faculties, and the Western Manitoba Centennial Auditorium.

The J.R. Brodie science centre is to be completed in the fall of 1971.

Student services include an accident insurance plan, guidance and counselling, medical consultation, a housing registry, employment service, athletic and recreational facilities.

---

*Ordinary member, AUCC.

Calendars and brochures

General calendar which includes all faculties.
Summer school and intersession calendar.
Evening session calendar. Faculty calendars
and brochures.

Courses and degrees

Arts

Bachelor of arts (BA).
General course, three years from senior
matriculation.

Education

Bachelor of teaching.
A three-year course for high school
graduates.

Certificate of education.
First of two years of work towards BEd
degree in full-time course. Open to holders of
BA, BSc, or other bachelor's degree, or to a
person within one year of completion of such
a degree. Successful candidates are awarded
a certificate of the Department of Education.

Bachelor of education.
The second year of work is offered in
extension courses on a part-time basis.
Holders of a bachelor's degree may obtain
the BEd.

Music

Bachelor of music (BMus).
With specialization in music education or
performance, four years from senior
matriculation.

Science

Bachelor of science (BSc).
General course, three years from senior
matriculation.

Wildlife biology certificate.
One year beyond BSc graduation with a
zoology major.

Extension programs

For university credit:

Evening and Saturday classes.
Undergraduate classes in arts, science, and
education. Write to director of evening
session for complete details.

Summer school.
Courses offered in arts, science and education
for undergraduates proceeding to a degree
and for teachers who may wish to improve
their professional qualifications. Write to
director of summer school for complete
details.

For no university credit:

*Diploma and certificate courses not requiring
matriculation.*
Certificates in music under the program of
the Western Board of Music, and of the
Toronto Conservatory of Music.

General interest courses.
Music, oral French, etc.

The IMPACTE program — *Indian Metis
Project for Careers Through Teacher
Education* — is designed for Indian and
Metis students. It aims to produce fully
qualified-certified teachers through the
faculty of education to teach Indian and
Metis children.

Indian and Eskimo summer school program.
This program, five summers in length, is
designed to meet the emergency need for
native teachers.

Admission requirements

For a general statement regarding admission
to university study, see article *Admission to
university in Canada.*

For information regarding admission to
undergraduate study, consult *Requirements
for admission to Canadian colleges and
universities* available from Service for
Admission to College and University, 151
Slater St., Ottawa, Ont., K1P 5N1, $1.50
prepaid.

Academic year

Winter session: first-term registration — mid-September; second-term registration — January.

Intersession: May and June.

Summer session: early July to mid-August.

Grading system

A plus, A, A minus, (superior); B plus, B, B minus (good); C plus, C (average); D (barely passing); F (failure); I (incomplete).

Fees and costs

Full-time tuition fees per year: arts, science, music and education, $425. Part-time: $85 per subject. Auditor's fee, $42.50.

Miscellaneous fees per year: student organization, $44. Degree fee, $15. Graduand's fee, $10.

Residence rates, board and room, per week: $21.50-$25.00.

Financial awards and assistance

Scholarships and bursaries are available for entering students. For complete details write the registrar, Brandon University.

Deans of faculties

Arts
R.F.B. King, MA, PhD

Education
R.R. Pippert, BA, MS, PhD

Science
D.R. Moir, MSc, PhD

Director of school

Music
Lorne Watson, MA, LTCM

Department heads

Botany
D.R. Moir, MSc, PhD

Chemistry
W. Rodewald, MSc, PhD

Economics
G.F. MacDowell, BA, MA

English
R.F. King, MA, PhD

Geography
J.L. Tyman, MA

Geology
H.S. Perdue, MA, PhD, FGAC

History
W.N. Hargreaves-Mawdsley, BA, MA, DPhil, FSA

Mathematics
E.A. Birkinshaw, BSc

Music
L. Watson, BA, LTCM

Philosophy
K.R. Hanly, MA, PhD

Physics
W.G. Wong, BSc, MA

Political science
M.V. Naidu, MA, LLB, LLM, PhD

Psychology
E.J. Tyler, MSc, PhD

Religion
R.W. Brockway, BA, BD, PhD

Zoology
J.A. McLeod, BSc, PhD

Brescia College*

(Affiliated with The University of Western Ontario)
London 72, Ontario

Telephone: 519-432-8353
Direct general correspondence to the registrar

Total full-time student enrolment 275; see also separate section *Statistics on Canadian universities and colleges*

Executive and administrative officers

Dean
Sister Arleene Walker, BA, MA

Registrar
E.M. Arnold (Mrs)

Librarian
Sister Pierina Caverzan, BA, MALS

Dean of students
Sister Mary Patrick, BA

Alumni adviser
Sister Margaret Hanley, MA

Background

Brescia College was established and affiliated with The University of Western Ontario in 1919 as a women's college under Roman Catholic auspices, though open to students of all faiths.

It is an undergraduate arts college, offering in co-operation with the university's faculties of arts and social sciences all the general and some of the honors arts programs of the university.

It operates the department of home economics for the university (the latter offering the science courses prescribed in the program of home economics) from which students graduate with a BA. All Brescia College graduates receive the BA degree granted by The University of Western Ontario.

Facilities and services

The main residence building, which also accommodates some of the home economics laboratories, was opened in 1925, with a wing added in 1949. There are facilities for approximately 400 students, with residence facilities for 174. The Mother St. James memorial building, opened in 1963, provides administration offices, classrooms, laboratories, and auditorium. One wing of this building is the Bishop Michael Francis Fallon memorial library. The campus adjoins that of The University of Western Ontario.

The population of London is approximately 216,000.

Courses and degrees

Bachelor of arts (BA).
a) General program in arts and social sciences, three years from senior matriculation. b) General program with home economics options, three years from senior matriculation. c) Honors programs, four years from senior matriculation, available in English, French, history, philosophy, or any combination containing one of these. d) The college offers a preliminary program which is the equivalent of Ontario grade XIII.

Admission requirements

For a general statement regarding admission to university study, see article *Admission to university in Canada.*

---

*Ordinary member, AUCC.

For information regarding admission to undergraduate study, consult *Requirements for admission to Canadian colleges and universities* available from Service for Admission to College and University, 151 Slater St., Ottawa, Ont., K1P 5N1, $1.50 prepaid.

Admission requirements are the same as for The University of Western Ontario.

Academic year

Winter session: early September to mid-May.

Grading system

Same as for The University of Western Ontario.

Fees and costs

Tuition and incidental fees per year: $542.50.
Preliminary year: $592.50.
Residence rates: $1,050 for winter session.

Department heads

Classical studies
Sister Mary Turner, PhD

English
Sister Corona Sharp, PhD

German
Sister Mary Teresa, BA

Home economics
Rhoda Penney (Miss), MS

Philosophy
Sister St. Michael Guinan, PhD

Psychology
Sister Dolores Kuntz, PhD

Sociology
Sister Arleene Walker, BA, MA

The University of British Columbia*

Vancouver 8, British Columbia

Telephone: 604-228-2844
Direct general correspondence to the registrar

Total full-time student enrolment 20,157; see also separate section *Statistics on Canadian universities and colleges*

Executive and administrative officers

Chancellor
A.M. McGavin, CD

President and dean of inter-faculty and student affairs
W.H. Gage, CC, MA, LLD

Deputy president
William Armstrong, BASc, PEng, MCIM

Deputy president and bursar
William White, CGA

Registrar
J.E.A. Parnall, BEd, MA

Director, academic planning
R.M. Clark, BA, BCom, AM, PhD

Director, alumni
J.K. Stathers, MA

Director, athletics
R.J. Phillips

Director of the botanical garden
R.L. Taylor, MSc, PhD

Director, centre for continuing education
G.R. Selman, MA

Director, ceremonies
M.F. McGregor, MA, PhD, FRSC

Director, computing centre
J.M. Kennedy, MA, PhD

Director, data processing
J.W. Poole

Director, health service and health service hospital
A.M. Johnson, MD, FRCP(C)

Director, information services
T.A. Myers

Director, international house
D.W. Roxburgh, BPE

Director, residences
Leslie Rohringer, BArch

Director, student services
A.F. Shirran, MA

Director, summer session
W.H. Auld, BA, EdM

Director, systems services
R.A. Jahelka, BCom

Dean of women
Helen McCrae (Mrs), BA, MSW

Executive director, publications
A.N. Blicq

Librarian
B. Stuart-Stubbs, BA, BLS

Background

A university for the province of British Columbia was first advocated in 1877; in 1890 an act of the legislature established The University of British Columbia. However, this endeavour failed when the first meeting of the senate lacked a quorum.

* Ordinary member, AUCC.

In 1899, Vancouver High School was affiliated to McGill University and in 1906, the McGill University College was formed to offer an expanded academic program. In 1908, the act of 1890 was repealed and a new act established and incorporated the new University of British Columbia. In 1915, the university took over the classes of the McGill University College; the first degrees were awarded in 1916.

The university is provincial, non-denominational and co-educational. It is governed by a board of governors, a senate, a convocation and a faculty council.

Facilities and services

The campus, consisting of 1,000 acres, is situated on the peninsula of Point Grey bounded on three sides by the Gulf of Georgia.

There are more than 62 buildings in which lectures are held, including some converted army huts used for teaching, library (2,000,000 volumes), administration building, gymnasium, auditorium; permanent student residences and temporary buildings housing a limited number of suites for married couples; faculty club and social centre; student union building, International house, Panhellenic house; graduate student centre. Also located on the campus are the provincial research council building, the federal fisheries, forestry, and agricultural sciences building and the following buildings: The Anglican Theological College of British Columbia, Union College of British Columbia – United Church (the two are now combined to form the Vancouver School of Theology), St. Mark's College (Roman Catholic), St. Andrew's Hall (Presbyterian), and Carey Hall (Baptist).

Student services include health services, counselling service, housing registry, employment service, as well as several cafeterias.

Campus organizations serving students from abroad are: International house, World University Service of Canada (WUSC), Friendly Relations with Overseas Students (FROS).

The population of greater Vancouver approximates 787,000.

Calendars and brochures

Calendars and brochures are available at the office of the registrar.

Composite calendar of academic year.
Summer session calendar.
Independent study correspondence courses.
Extension credit courses.

Courses and degrees

Agriculture
(Faculty of agricultural sciences)

Bachelor of science in agriculture [BSc(Agr)].
Four years from secondary school graduation. Specialization offered in agricultural economics, agricultural engineering, agricultural microbiology, agronomy, animal genetics, animal nutrition, animal physiology, dairy science, entomology, food science, horticulture, plant genetics, plant nutrition, plant protection, poultry genetics, poultry nutrition, poultry physiology, poultry processing, soil science.

(Faculty of graduate studies)

Master of science (MSc).
At least one year from a bachelor's degree in agriculture. Specialization offered in agricultural economics, agricultural extension, agricultural mechanics, animal science, dairying, food science, genetics (animal, plant and poultry sciences), plant science, poultry science, soil science.

Doctor of philosophy (PhD).
At least two years from master's degree in agriculture. Available in agricultural microbiology (dairying, soil science), genetics (animal, plant and poultry sciences), animal and poultry sciences, plant science, soil science.

Architecture
(School of architecture, faculty of applied science)

Bachelor of architecture (BArch).
Three years from a bachelor's degree in arts, science, or engineering.

(Faculty of graduate studies)

Master of architecture (MArch).
At least one year from BArch. Theory of
design, housing, and structures.

See also community and regional planning.

Arts
(Faculty of arts)

Bachelor of arts (BA).
(a) Major course, four years from secondary
school graduation. (b) Single honors, the
same, but course load heavier. (c) Combined
honors, the same but specialization in two
subjects. (d) Double honors, an additional
year. Areas of emphasis: anthropology, Asian
studies, Chinese, classical studies, creative
writing, economics, English, fine arts, French,
geography, German, Greek, history, Italian,
Japanese, Latin, linguistics, mathematics,
music, philosophy, Polish, political science,
psychology, religious studies, romance
studies, Russian, Slavonic studies, sociology,
Spanish, theatre.

(Faculty of graduate studies)

Master of arts (MA).
At least one year from an approved
bachelor's degree. Specialization offered in
anthropology, Asian studies, classics,
comparative literature, creative writing,
economics, education, English, fine arts,
French, geography, German, Greek, history,
Italian, Latin, linguistics, mathematics,
philosophy, political science, psychology,
religious studies, romance studies, Slavonic
studies, sociology, Spanish, theatre.

Doctor of philosophy (PhD).
At least two years from master's degree.
Available in anthropology, Chinese, classics,
economics, English, French, geography,
German, Greek, history, Japanese, Latin,
philosophy, political science, psychology,
romance studies, Slavonic literature,
sociology, Spanish.

Business, see commerce and business
administration below

Commerce and business administration
(Faculty of commerce and business
administration)

Bachelor of commerce (BCom).
(a) Ordinary course, four years from first year
arts. (b) Combined law and commerce:
BCom degree granted after three years of
commerce and two years of law. Options:
accounting and management information
systems, commerce and economics, commerce
and teaching, finance, industrial
administration, marketing, organizational
behavior and industrial relations,
transportation and utilities, urban land
economics.

A program of study for university graduates
leading to a degree of licentiate in accounting
is offered. (Two years.)

(Faculty of graduate studies)

Master of business administration (MBA).
At least one year from a BCom degree; two
years from other degrees.

Doctor of philosophy (PhD).
At least two years from master's degree.
Fields of specialization: accounting, finance,
management science, marketing,
organizational behavior.

Community and regional planning
(Faculty of graduate studies)

Either *master of arts (MA)* or *master of
science (MSc).*
Two years from a bachelor's degree in
agriculture, architecture, arts, commerce,
engineering, forestry, law, science, or social
work.

Doctor of philosophy (PhD).
At least two years from master's degree.

Dentistry
(Faculty of dentistry)

Diploma in dental hygiene (DipDentHyg).
Two years from first year science.

Doctor of dental medicine (DMD).
Four years from the third year of arts or
science.

Education
(Faculty of education)

Bachelor of education (BEd).
(a) Elementary field, four years from secondary school graduation. (b) Secondary field, five years from secondary school graduation. Specialization offered in high school teaching fields.

(Faculty of graduate studies)

Master of arts (MA in education).
One year from bachelor's degree followed by teacher training and teaching experience. Specialization in education courses.

Master of education (MEd).
At least one year from BEd or bachelor's degree and teacher training, no thesis required.

Doctor of education (EdD).
At least two years from master's degree.

Engineering
(Faculty of applied science)

Bachelor of applied science (BASc).
Four years from first year science. Specialization offered in agricultural, chemical, civil, electrical, geological, mechanical, metallurgical, and mineral engineering and engineering physics.

(Faculty of graduate studies)

Master of applied science (MASc).
One year from a bachelor's degree in engineering. Specialization offered in agricultural, chemical, civil, electrical, forest, geological, geophysical, mechanical, metallurgical, and mineral engineering, and engineering physics.

Master of engineering (MEng).
One year from a bachelor's degree in engineering. A non-thesis program with specialization offered in agricultural, chemical, civil, electrical, mechanical, metallurgical and mineral engineering.

Doctor of philosophy (PhD).
At least two years from master's degree in engineering. Specialization offered in chemical, civil, electrical, mechanical, geological, geophysical, and mineral engineering, metallurgy, and engineering physics.

Forestry
(Faculty of forestry)

Bachelor of science in forestry (BSF).
Four years from first year science. Specialization offered in forest business administration, forest entomology, forest management, forest pathology, forest products and wood technology, logging, silvics, and wildlife management.

(Faculty of graduate studies)

Master of science (MSc).
One year from BSc, BASc, BSA or BSF.

Master of forestry (MF).
One year from BSF, or BASc in forest engineering.

Master of applied science (MASc).
One year from BASc in forest engineering.

Doctor of philosophy (PhD).
At least two years from master's degree, in co-operation with the departments of botany and zoology.

Home economics
(School of home economics, faculty of arts)

Bachelor of home economics (BHE).
Four years from secondary school graduation major in foods and nutrition or general.

Master of science in human nutrition.
One year from appropriate bachelor's degree.

Law
(Faculty of law)

Bachelor of laws (LLB).
Three years beyond penultimate year in four-year bachelor of arts course.

(Faculty of graduate studies)

Master of laws (LLM).
At least one year from bachelor's degree in law.

Librarianship
(School of librarianship, faculty of arts)

Master of library science (MLS).
Two years from an acceptable bachelor's degree.

Medicine
(Faculty of medicine)

Doctor of medicine (MD).
Four years from the third year of arts or science beyond secondary school graduation.

(Faculty of graduate studies)

Master of science (MSc).
At least one year from an MD or honors BSc degree. Specialization offered in anatomy (human), audiology and speech sciences, biochemistry, neurology, pathology, pharmacology, physiology, psychiatry, surgery.

Doctor of philosophy (PhD).
At least two years from master's degree. Available in anatomy, biochemistry, pathology, pharmacology, physiology.

Music
(Faculty of arts)

Bachelor of music (BMus).
Four years from secondary school graduation.

Master of music (MMus).
At least one year from bachelor of music degree or equivalent.

Nursing
(School of nursing, faculty of applied science)

Diploma in community health nursing.
One year from secondary school graduation and RN training.

Bachelor of science in nursing (BSN).
Four years from first year arts or science, or three years following qualification as RN.

Master of science in nursing (MSN).
Two years from BSN.

Pharmacy
(Faculty of pharmaceutical sciences)

Bachelor of science in pharmacy [BSc(Pharm)].
Four years from first year arts or science. Specialization in drug distribution, hospital pharmacy, product development.

(Faculty of graduate studies)

Master of science in pharmacy (MSc).
One year from BSc(Pharm) or other acceptable bachelor's degree.

Doctor of philosophy (PhD).
At least two years from master's degree.

Physical education
(School of physical education, faculty of education)

Bachelor of physical education (BPE).
Four years from secondary school graduation.

Bachelor of recreation education (BRE).
Four years from secondary school graduation.

(Faculty of graduate studies)

Master of physical education (MPE).
At least one year from BPE.

Rehabilitation medicine
(School of rehabilitation medicine, faculty of medicine)

Bachelor of science in rehabilitation (BSR).
Four years from secondary school graduation. Occupational therapy and physiotherapy.

Science, applied, see engineering

Science, pure
(Faculty of science)

Bachelor of science (BSc).
(a) General course, four years from secondary school graduation. (b) Single major course, four years from secondary school graduation. (c) Single and combined honors, four years from secondary school graduation. Areas of emphasis: astronomy, biochemistry, biology, botany, chemistry, computer science, geology, geophysics, mathematics, microbiology, physical geography, physics, physiology, zoology.

(Faculty of graduate studies)

Master of science (MSc).
At least one year from an approved
bachelor's degree, not necessarily a BSc.
Specialization offered in astronomy,
biochemistry, biology, botany, chemistry,
fisheries, food sciences, genetics, geology,
geophysics, mathematics, metallurgy,
microbiology, neurology, oceanography,
pharmacology, physics, physiology, zoology.

Doctor of philosophy (PhD).
At least two years from master's degree.
Available in agricultural microbiology,
astronomy, biochemistry, botany, chemistry,
fisheries, genetics, geology, geophysics,
mathematics, metallurgy, microbiology,
oceanography, pharmacology, physics,
physiology, zoology.

Social work
(School of social work, faculty of arts)

Master of social work (MSW).
Two years from an acceptable bachelor's
degree.

Theology

Courses offered at affiliated colleges.

Extension programs

For university credit:

Correspondence courses.
Twenty arts courses and two education
courses are offered.

Evening classes.
Chiefly undergraduate arts and education
courses.

Summer school.
Graduate courses in education,
undergraduate courses in arts, education,
commerce, home economics, nursing, physical
education, and science.

For diploma or certificate credit:

Diploma courses in: adult education;
criminology; early childhood education;
engineering administration; social work
registration; and vocational instructors'
certificate program.

For no university credit:

Continuing professional education. Short
courses, conferences, seminars in most
professional fields. Liberal education, public
affairs, community programs, creative arts,
public and agency leadership. Various
formats.

Admission requirements

For a general statement regarding admission
to university study, see article *Admission to
university in Canada.*

For information regarding admission to
undergraduate study, consult *Requirements
for admission to Canadian colleges and
universities* available from Service for
Admission to College and University, 151
Slater St., Ottawa, Ont., K1P 5N1, $1.50
prepaid.

For admission to courses leading to a first
degree in applied science, commerce, forestry,
nursing and pharmacy, first year arts or
science of college or university with adequate
standing.

For admission to a first degree in dentistry,
law and medicine, three years beyond
secondary school graduation.

For admission to a first degree in architecture,
social work and librarianship, a bachelor's
degree.

For admission to graduate studies, an honors
bachelor's or a first professional degree.

Academic year

Winter session: early September to late April.

Summer session: early July to mid-August.

Grading system

Standing is graded in each subject as: class 1, 80-100%; class 2, 65-79%; pass, 50-64% (60-64% in medicine); failed, below 50% (in medicine, dentistry, graduate studies below 60%).

Fees and costs

Tuition fees per year: full-time for first degree — agriculture, $472; applied science, $554; architecture, $551; arts, $457; home economics, $459; social work (1st year), $503; commerce and business administration (1st year), education, physical education, science, $457; pharmacy (1st year), $462; commerce and business administration (other years), dental hygiene, $535; law, $538; pharmacy (other years), $540; dentistry, $693; librarianship, $503; medicine (first and second years), $675, (third and fourth years), $661; music, $573; forestry, $539; nursing, $412; rehabilitation medicine (1st year), $463, (other years), $415; social work (2nd year), $457; industrial arts emergency day, program, $39; graduate studies, master's, and doctoral (1st year), $455, each subsequent year, $426; part-time, $30 per unit; summer session per 3-unit course, $100.

Residence rates, board and room, during the winter session: in camp dormitories, $617 (double room), $660 (single room); in permanent residences, $774 (double room), $810 (single room).

Research institutes

Institute of Animal Resource Ecology
aims to identify principles of theoretical ecology, applied ecology and population genetics and to relate them to specific ecological systems — freshwater and marine communities, mammal, bird, fish and insect populations and human systems. Director: C.S. Holling, MSc, PhD.

Institute of Applied Mathematics and Statistics
is to co-ordinate advanced teaching in statistics and applied mathematics and to promote the growth of interdisciplinary research activities in these fields. Acting director: B.N. Moyls, MA, PhD.

Institute of Asian and Slavonic Research
is concerned mainly with the promotion and direction of post-graduate research in these fields, with emphasis on interdisciplinary studies in the social sciences, including modern history. Director: B.M. Morrison, MA, PhD.

Arctic and Alpine Research
involves biology, geography, geology and glaciology in both Alpine and Arctic environments. Current areas of special interest to the committee are the Mackenzie River Basin, N.W.T., and the Keremeos region of B.C.

Institute of Astronomy and Space Science
has been formed to co-ordinate research and graduate studies in astronomy and space science carried out in several departments of The University of British Columbia. Acting director: M.H.L. Pryce, MA, PhD, FRS.

Institute of Industrial Relations
includes the study of manpower analysis, collective bargaining studies, the study of human relations issues as well as economic and social analyses of these areas. The program is interdisciplinary in character. Director: N.A. Hall, BComm, MBA, DBA.

Institute of International Relations
encourages interdisciplinary research and study in the relations between states, their organizations and laws, and the social, political, and cultural conditions affecting those relations, organizations, and laws. Director: M.W. Zacker, MA, PhD.

Institute of Oceanography
represents the co-operative effort of the departments of botany, chemistry, geology, geography, mathematics, physics and zoology to train graduate students in one or more of these branches in the principles and techniques of oceanographic research. Director: G.L. Pickard, MBE, MA, DPhil, FRSC.

Affiliated institutions

The Vancouver School of Theology,
Vancouver, British Columbia. Principal: W.S. Taylor, MA, PhD, DD. Continues the work of the former Anglican Theological College of British Columbia and the former Union College of British Columbia. Provides theological education for laymen, future clergy and for graduates in theology.

Carey Hall, Vancouver, British Columbia.
Dean of residence: Lt. Col. J.W. Duncan,
MBE, CD, BA, BTh. Baptist. For men only.
Student residence accommodation.

St. Andrew's Hall, Vancouver, British
Columbia.
Dean of residence: Rev. J.A. Ross, MS, BD,
PhD. Presbyterian. For men only. Student
residence accommodation.

St. Mark's College, Vancouver, British
Columbia.
Principal: Rev. R.W. Finn, CSB, MA, LMS.
Roman Catholic. For men only. Incorporated
1965. Student residence accommodation.

Deans of faculties

Agricultural sciences
M. Shaw, MSc, PhD, FLS, FRSC

Applied science
W.D. Finn, BE, MSc, PhD, MAmSocCE,
MASEE

Arts
Douglas T. Kenny, MA, PhD

Commerce and business administration
P.H. White, MSc, FRICS

Dentistry
S.W. Leung, BSc, DDS, PhD

Education
N.V. Scarfe, MA

Forestry
J.A.F. Gardner, MA, PhD, FCIC

Graduate studies
I. McTaggart-Cowan, BA, PhD, FRSC

Law
A.J. McClean, LLB, PhD

Medicine
J.F. McCreary, MD, FRCP(C)

Pharmaceutical sciences
B.E. Riedel, MSc, PhD

Science
R.F. Scagel (acting), MA, PhD, FRSC, FLS

Directors of schools

Architecture
H. Elder, MBE, FRIBA, MRAIC, FIIAL

Community and regional planning
H.P. Oberlander, BArch, MCP, PhD
V.S. Pendakur (acting to December 31,
1971), BE, MSc, MSCE, PhD

Home economics
M. Lee, MA, PhD
Winnifred Bracher (acting to June 30, 1972),
BSc(HEc), AM

Librarianship
R. Stokes, MA, FLA

Nursing
Muriel Uprichard, MA, PhD

Physical education
R.F. Osborne, BA, BEd

Rehabilitation medicine
B.M. Fahrni, MD, FRCP(C), FACP

Social work
G.M. Hougham, MA, PhD

Department heads

Agricultural economics
G.R. Winter, BSc, MS, PhD

Agricultural engineering and agricultural
mechanics
W.D. Powrie, MA, PhD

Animal science
W.D. Kitts, MSA, PhD

Anthropology and sociology
C.S. Belshaw, MA, PhD, FRSC

Asian studies
E.G. Pulleyblank, BA, MA, PhD

Botany
R.F. Scagel, MA, PhD, FRSC, FLS

Chemical engineering
F.E. Murray, BSc, PhD, PEng, MTappi,
MTechSectCPPA

Chemistry
C.A. McDowell, MSc, DSc, FRIC, FCIC,
FRSC

Civil engineering
S.L. Lipson, BASc, MS, MEIC

Classics
M.F. McGregor, MA, PhD, FRSC

Computer science
J.E.L. Peck, MSc, PhD

Creative writing
R. Harlow, DFC, BA, MFA

Economics
A.M. Moore, BA, AM

Electrical engineering
A.D. Moore, MSc, PhD, PEng,
SenMemIEEE

English
R.M. Jordan, MA, PhD

Fine arts
G. Knox, MA, PhD

Food science
W.D. Powrie, MA, PhD

French
L.L. Bongie, BA, DUParis

Geography
J.D. Chapman, MA, PhD

Geology
J.W. Murray (acting), BSc, MA, PhD

Geophysics
R.D. Russell, MA, PhD

German
M.S. Batts, BA, DrPhil
M. Boulby (acting to June 30, 1971), MA,
PhD

Hispanic and Italian studies
H.V. Livermore, MA

History
Margaret Ormsby, MA, PhD, LLD, FRSC

Linguistics
B. Saint-Jacques (executive secretary), LèsL,
MA, MSc, DUParis

Mathematics
R.D. James, MA, PhD, FRSC

Mechanical engineering
J.P. Duncan, BE, ME, DSc, PEng, ChE,
FIMechE, FIProdE, AInstP

Metallurgy
E. Teghtsoonian, BASc, MA, PhD

Microbiology
J.J.R. Campbell, BSA, PhD, FRSC

Mineral engineering
J.B. Evans, BME, BSc, PEng, MAIMM

Music
D.M. McCorkle, BMus, AM, PhD

Philosophy
P. Remnant, MA, PhD

Physics
G.M. Volkoff, MBE, MA, PhD, DSc, FRSC

Plant science
V.C. Runeckles, BSc, PhD, DipImpColl

Political science
W.D. Young, BA, MA, PhD

Poultry science
W.D. Kitts, MSA, PhD

Psychology
E. Signori (acting), MA, PhD

Religious studies
W. Nicholls, MA

Slavonic studies
B. Czaykowski (acting to June 30, 1972), BA,
MA

Soil science
C.A. Rowles, MSc, PhD

Theatre
J. Brockington, BA, DFA

Zoology
W.S. Hoar (acting), BA, MA, PhD, DSc,
FRSC

Brock University*

Merrittville Highway, St. Catharines, Ontario

Telephone: 416-684-7201
Direct general correspondence to the registrar

Total full-time student enrolment 2,163; see also separate section *Statistics on Canadian universities and colleges*

Executive and administrative officers

Chancellor
Charles Sankey, BASc, MSc, PhD, FCIC, FAAAS, FRSA, PEng

President and vice-chancellor
James Gibson (on leave 1971-72), BA, MA, BLitt, DPhil, LLD

Provost and acting president
Alan Earp, BA, MA, MLitt, LLD

Dean of students
Arnold Lowenberger, BEd, MS, PhD

Registrar
Albert Tunis, BA, CPRS(Acc)

University librarian
James Hogan, BA, DiplLibr

Chief administrative officer
Robert Nairn, BA

Director of finance
Terrence Varcoe, MBA, CA

Assistant registrar (records)
Ainsley Towe, BA

Assistant registrar (admissions)
John Bird, BA

Director of athletics and recreational activities
Arnold Lowenberger, BEd, MS, PhD

*Ordinary member, AUCC.

Director of the computer centre
F.R. Skilton, FBCS

Director of continuing education
Josephine Meeker, BA, MA

Director of information and development
To be appointed

Secretary, board of governors
Edward Mitchelson, BSA

Director of personnel services
R.F. Anderson, BCom

Director of planning
C.P. Ind, ARIBA, MRAIC, DipArch

Director of administrative services
D.M. Edwards

Staff director, physical plant
Ray Woodfield, BSc(EE), PEng

Administrative officer (book store)
Valentina Bubovich (Miss), BA

Counselling service
David Jordan, BA, MA, PhD

Constituent college

College of Education, Brock University, Merrittville Highway, St. Catharines, Ont. Dean: Sidney Irvine, BA, MEd, PhD. Associate dean: Reginald Moase, BA, MEd. Registrar: Albert Tunis, BA, CPRS(Acc). The College of Education was founded in June of 1965. It became a college of Brock University on July 1, 1971. The college is co-educational and offers a professional training program of 8 months' duration. The minimum level of entry is second year university. Application can be made through the housing office for residence applications.

Background

The university is young. The first class entered its doors in September 1964. The official opening had been preceded by seven years of vigorous action on the part of numerous citizen groups seeking a university within the Niagara peninsula. Their efforts were successful when the Brock University Act was passed by the Ontario legislature in March 1964, and subsequently revised in June 1971.

The university is named after Sir Isaac Brock, killed in action at Queenston Heights on the Niagara River during the war of 1812.

The university is controlled by a board of trustees with jurisdiction over financial aspects and by the senate which is responsible for the academic policy.

The university is co-educational. The population of St. Catharines approximates 106,000.

Facilities and services

The university has two campuses: a small one, the Glenridge campus, housing the science laboratories, and a large 600-acre De Cew campus, where a 14-storey building, the Brock Tower, contains a library of 158,000 volumes, classrooms, cafeteria and administration. The "Thistle" complex, with theatres, lecture rooms and bookstore, surrounds the Brock Tower. Residence facilities of ten houses accommodating 400 (125 women, 280 men) students were completed in 1970.

Up-to-date research equipment is available in the various science departments; for detailed information write the appropriate departmental chairman.

Student services include health service, counselling centre, housing registry, student affairs office, job placement service, cafeteria, and many athletic and social clubs.

Campus organization serving students from abroad is World University Service of Canada.

Calendars and brochures

Calendars, departmental brochures, admissions bulletin, and the Brock University international students' association handbook are obtainable from the registrar's office.

Courses and degrees

Arts
(Faculty of arts and science)

Bachelor of arts (BA).
Available in classics, economics, English and drama, French, geography, geological sciences, German, history, Italian, philosophy, politics, psychology, Russian, sociology, and Spanish. (a) General course, three years from senior matriculation. (b) Honors course, four years from senior matriculation.

Master of arts (MA).
Anticipated in geography, philosophy, and politics.

Education
(College of Education)

Certificate in education.
One-year certificate course. Candidates who are eligible for admission to the second year arts and sciences at Brock University are qualified for admission to the college.

Science, pure
(Faculty of arts and science)

Bachelor of science (BSc).
Available in biological sciences, chemistry, geological sciences, mathematics, and physics. (a) General course, three years from senior matriculation. (b) Honors course, four years from senior matriculation.

Master of science (MSc).
Available in biological sciences, chemistry, geological sciences, and physics.

Special programs

Interdisciplinary programs.
The university is establishing a special interest in administration and urban and Asian studies. Senate, therefore, has approved three interdisciplinary programs at Brock — Asian studies, urban studies, and administration.

These programs involve contributions from several disciplines to provide a broader focus in these fields than could otherwise be possible by trying to select appropriate courses from just one or two departments.

Extra-departmental programs.
These are elective courses for credit towards a degree. At present it is not possible to major in these disciplines or areas: computer science; linguistics; music; special summer school program for grade 12 students.

This is an experimental program for Ontario grade l2 students of the highest calibre. The purpose is to identify those students who, in the judgment of their high school teachers and members of the Brock faculty, are ready for university entrance from grade 12.

A limited number of these students, recommended for admission by their principal or guidance officers, will participate in a summer school program consisting of lectures, labs, small group discussions with faculty members, and the preparation of seminar papers, reports and essays. Upon completion of the program, students judged likely to succeed in year I will be eligible for admission to Brock University in September.

For further details about the program, principals and guidance officers are invited to write to the registrar's office.

Extension programs (continuing education division)

For university credit:

Evening session.
Undergraduate courses in arts and science.

Summer session.
Courses offered in arts and science for undergraduates proceeding to a degree, and for teachers who may wish to improve their professional qualifications.

For no university credit:

Adult education services.
Systematic courses in the humanities on a non-credit basis.

Admission requirements

For a general statement regarding admission to university study, see article *Admission to university in Canada.*

For information regarding admission to undergraduate study, consult *Requirements for admission to Canadian colleges and universities* available from Service for Admission to College and University, 151 Slater St., Ottawa, Ont., K1P 5N1, $1.50 prepaid.

Academic year

Winter session: mid-September to early May.

Summer evening session (for extension work): May — mid-July.

Summer day session (for extension work): early July to mid-August.

Grading system

A — first-class honors: 80% and over; B — second-class honors: 70-79%; C — satisfactory: 60-69%; D — pass: 50-59%; lowest passing grade: 50%; F — below 50%; FN — failed, no supplemental.

Fees and costs

Tuition fee per year $515. Student activity fee: $46. Fees for part-time studies: $110 per course.

Residence fees are as follows: single room with 2 meals a day, 5 days per week, $875; single room with 2 meals a day, 7 days per week, $975; double room with 2 meals a day, 5 days per week, $825; double room with 2 meals a day, 7 days per week, $925.

Students are required to take one of the above food options. "Two meals" refers to lunch and supper.

Financial awards and assistance

The university awards both entrance and in-course scholarships to students of academic excellence. All students applying for admission to full-time studies will be considered for an award.

In-course awards will be available to students entering the second, third, and fourth year.

Departmental prizes are awarded for excellence in a particular area of study. No application is required.

All students who can show evidence of financial need are expected to apply for assistance under the Ontario students awards program. Application forms are obtainable from secondary schools and the student awards officer at Brock University.

Bursaries are usually awarded late in the academic year to students who have satisfactory standing and can show that without some financial assistance they are unable to complete the academic year.

Deans of faculties

Arts and science
Colin Plint, MA, PhD

Education, College of
Sidney Irvine, MA, MEd, PhD

Department heads

Administration
Maurice Perkins, BA, MSc, PhD

Biological sciences
Arthur Houston, BSc, MA, PhD

Chemistry
Martin Gibson, MA, DPhil

Classics
William Boggess, AB, PhD

Economics
Maurice Perkins, BA, MSc, PhD

English and drama
Marion Smith, MA, PhD

Geography
John McClellan, BA, MS

Geological sciences
Jaan Terasmae, FilKand, PhD

Germanic and Slavic studies
Claude Owen, MA, PhD

History
Craig Hanyan, BA, MA, PhD

Mathematics
John Reed, BSc, MSc

Music
Ronald Tremain, BMus, DMus

Philosophy
Zygmut Adamczewski, BA, AM, PhD

Physics
Geoffrey Kidson, MSc, PhD

Politics
W.D.K. Kernaghan, BA, MA, PhD

Psychology
John Lavery, BA, PhD

Romance studies
René Bismuth, LèsL, DèsL

Sociology
Nicholas Yarmoshuk, BEng, MBA, PhD

Urban studies institute
Robert Hoover

The University of Calgary*

Calgary 44, Alberta

Telephone: 403-284-5110
Direct general correspondence to the registrar

Total full-time student enrolment 9,256; see also separate section *Statistics on Canadian universities and colleges*

Executive and administrative officers

Chancellor
W.A. Friley, BS

President and vice-chancellor
A.W.R. Carrothers, BA, LLB, LLM, SJD

Vice-president, academic
J.B. Cragg, BSc, MSc, DSc, DThPT

Vice-president, business and finance
H.W. Bliss, FCA

Vice-president, capital resources
F.A. Campbell, BSc, MA, PhD

Registrar and academic secretary
W.F.M. Stewart, MA, PhD

Director, institutional research
B.S. Sheehan, BE, SM, PhD, PEng

Director, information services
D.H. Norrie, BE, BSc, PhD

Chief librarian
T.M. Walker, MA, PhD

Administrative assistant to the president
M.G. McGinley, BA, MBA, CA

Academic assistant to the president
T.E. Flanagan, BA, MA, PhD

Chief student affairs officer
C.W.H. Linton, BA

Head, data centre
To be appointed

Director, communications media
L.A. Robertson, MBE, BEd, MFA

Controller
J.A. Hamilton, BComm, CA

Director, physical planning
H.R. Hayes, BSc, PEng, MEIC

Manager, administrative systems
E.F. Nowakowsky, CA

Supervisor, auxiliary services
J.G. Roberts, CA

Director, office of fund development
P.R. Judge, BA, LTh, BD

Personnel officer
D.R. Franklin, BA

Superintendent, buildings and grounds
I.W. Duncan, BSc, PEng, MEIC

Public relations and information officer
Dorothy R. Patterson

Director, student health services
D.L. McNeil, MD, FRCP(C), FACP

Director, student counselling
M.B. Manley, BS, PhD

Background

The University of Calgary began in 1945 as a branch of the faculty of education of The University of Alberta. By 1960, when it moved to its present campus, The University of Alberta at Calgary offered a full program for the degrees of bachelor of arts and bachelor of science, the first two years of education and the first year of engineering and commerce. In 1963 a faculty of arts and science, a faculty of education, a division of the faculty of engineering, and a department of the school of physical education were set up at Calgary with their own heads.

*Ordinary member, AUCC.

In 1964, The University of Alberta at Calgary gained autonomy in academic matters and in that same year, a faculty of graduate studies was established. A school of social welfare was established in 1967. A school of physical education, the faculty of business, and the faculty of fine arts were also established in 1967. A faculty of medicine was established in 1967 and accepted its first students in 1970. The faculty of environmental design accepted its first students in 1971.

In 1966, The University of Calgary was established as a non-denominational, co-educational and provincial university; it is governed by a board of governors, a senate, and a general faculties council. General co-ordination of the provincial universities is effected through The Alberta Universities Commission and the Universities Co-ordinating Council.

Facilities and services

The University of Calgary campus consists of 314 acres, adjacent to a large reserve of land for higher education, located in the northwest section of the city of Calgary (population approximates 400,000).

Construction on the campus was started in 1958 with two buildings. Since that time the following buildings have been erected: physical education building, opened in 1962; university library, opened in 1963; stage I of the engineering complex, completed in 1964; two residence halls (one for men and one for women) each accommodating 420 students, with adjacent 1,100-seat dining centre; Calgary hall, first stage of a fine arts complex, both opened in 1965. Structures completed in 1966 were a music wing and a 500-seat university theatre, the second stages of both the science complex and engineering complex. A central heating and cooling plant, an environmental sciences centre at Kananaskis on the Trans-Canada highway west of Calgary, MacEwan hall — a 2-storey student centre, and stage III of the engineering complex were completed in 1967. A 14-storey education complex, and stage IV of the engineering complex were completed in 1968. In 1969, five floors of the social science building and the mathematics and computing centre were completed.

In 1970 the upper floors of the social science building, science theatres, and married student housing facilities were completed.

Presently under construction are additions to the physical education building, and university library as well as a health sciences centre and biological sciences centre building.

The university library building, opened in 1963, contains over 350,000 volumes in addition to large and rapidly developing collections of government publications, microfilms, maps, etc. and is currently increasing its bookstock at the rate of 50,000 volumes a year. Approximately 7,000 periodicals are currently received by subscription.

The university theatre, while designed primarily for academic purposes, also provides excellent facilities for drama, music, exhibitions, films, and lectures. Other community facilities for the arts are also in close proximity to the campus, i.e., the Southern Alberta jubilee auditorium and the Allied arts centre.

Student services on the campus include a health service, counselling, student awards offices; a dining centre, students' union and employment services.

The Banff School of Fine Arts, held in trust by The University of Calgary, is located on the slopes of Tunnel Mountain above the town of Banff. It has one large, and a number of smaller, instructional buildings, as well as residences and a theatre arts centre which embraces a fully equipped 1,000-seat theatre, a 300-seat practice theatre, stagecraft workshop, costume department, and a teaching wing with studios, classrooms, and practice facilities.

The school provides an ideal setting and excellent facilities for training in the arts and all types of seminars, meetings, and conferences. It is the headquarters of the Banff School of Advanced Management, and also conducts a number of annual short courses in specialized fields of management training.

The dean of women serves as advisor to international students. General information about Calgary and the university, assistance in finding suitable accommodation, and reception arrangements are among the services provided. International students in all other respects use the same services as are provided for Canadian students, i.e., student counselling, student health services, student

awards and financial aid, dean of men and dean of women.

The International students' association works closely with the advisor to plan social, cultural, and recreational activities throughout the year. Faculty members serve on various committees with international students such as the World University Service committee and the Canadian University Service Overseas committee. International faculty members join students in the celebration of various national days throughout the year.

Calendars and brochures

The university publishes four calendars annually: the general calendar, which includes all faculty programs and course offerings; the calendar of the faculty of graduate studies; and the evening credit program and summer session calendars which serve a special function. Individual calendars are also published by the faculty of medicine and school of nursing.

Courses and degrees

Arts
(Faculty of arts and science)

Bachelor of arts (BA).
General and honors course, four years from senior matriculation. Principal and/or second subjects of study: anthropology, archaeology, classics, economics, English, French, geography, German, Greek, history, Latin, Latin-American studies (second subject of study only), linguistics, mathematics, philosophy, political science, psychology, Russian, sociology, Spanish, and urban studies (second subject of study only).

(Faculty of graduate studies)

Master of arts (MA).
At least two years full-time from ordinary BA. Available in the departments of archaeology, economics, English, geography, Germanic and Slavic studies (German), history, linguistics, philosophy, political science, resources—the environment and planning, romance studies (French), sociology, and anthropology.

Doctor of philosophy (PhD).
At least two years full-time from MA with two years' residence required. Available in archaeology, economics, geography, philosophy, and political science.

Commerce
(Faculty of business)

Bachelor of commerce (BComm).
Four years from senior matriculation. Specialization offered in accounting, finance, management, and marketing.

Education
(Faculty of education)

Bachelor of education (BEd).
Four years from senior matriculation or two years from approved degree in arts or science. Specialization available in elementary school teaching, secondary school teaching.

Diploma in education.
One year from approved degree and a professional or permanent professional teaching certificate. Specialization in curriculum and instruction, educational administration, and educational foundations.

(Faculty of graduate studies)

Master of education (MEd).
At least 12 months full-time from bachelor's degree in education or equivalent. Specialization in curriculum and instruction, educational administration, educational foundations, and educational psychology.

Doctor of philosophy (PhD).
At least two years full-time from master's degree with two years' residence required. Available only in educational psychology.

Engineering
(Faculty of engineering)

Bachelor of science in engineering (BSc).
Four years from senior matriculation. Specialization available in chemical, civil, electrical, and mechanical engineering.

Diploma in engineering.
Four full courses after approved degree or equivalent. Specialization in designated areas.

(Faculty of graduate studies)

Master of science (MSc).
At least one year full-time from bachelor's degree in engineering. Specialization available in chemical, civil, electrical, and mechanical engineering.

Master of engineering (MEng).
Minimum one year from bachelor's degree and practical professional experience; by course of instruction, examination, and thesis in area of engineering design or analysis. Full-time residence requirements waived.

Doctor of philosophy (PhD).
At least two years full-time from the master's degree in engineering. Available in chemical, civil, electrical, and mechanical engineering.

Environmental design
(Faculty of environmental design)

The faculty of environmental design will offer a graduate program in three major areas of interdisciplinary study: architecture, urbanism, and environmental sciences in relation to man. The degree program will be operational in September 1972. In general, applicants will be required to present a recognized baccalaureate degree with a major discipline acquired in arts, sciences, fine arts, or engineering.

Fine arts
(Faculty of fine arts)

Bachelor of fine arts (BFA).
Four years from senior matriculation available in art and drama.

Medicine
(Faculty of medicine)

Doctor of medicine (MD).
Three years' general medical studies, two further years of graduate training in one of: the specialty of family practice, one of the other specialties, or training in preparation for a career as a medical scientist leading to an MSc and subsequently to a PhD. The normal entrance requirement will be three years of study in an acceptable undergraduate degree program majoring in biochemistry, microbiology, physics, psychology, or zoology. Limited enrolment.

Music
(Faculty of fine arts)

Bachelor of music (BMus).
Four years from senior matriculation. Candidates must have completed grade VIII practical and grades IV and V theoretical examinations of the Western Board of Music or present equivalent standing. Specialization available in applied music, music history and literature, school music, and theory and composition.

Nursing
(School of nursing)

Bachelor of nursing (BN).
Four years from senior matriculation. Limited enrolment.

Physical education
(School of physical education)

Bachelor of physical education (BPE).
Three years from senior matriculation. Honors course, four years from senior matriculation.

Science, pure
(Faculty of arts and science)

Bachelor of science (BSc).
General (and honors) course, four years from senior matriculation. Available in archaeology, biochemistry, botany, chemistry, computing science, geography, geology, geophysics, mathematics, microbiology, physics, psychology (experimental), statistics, and zoology.

In addition to the above programs, by special arrangement with other universities, students may be permitted to take the following programs at The University of Calgary: the first year only of courses leading to degrees in agriculture, household economics, and pharmacy. Students wishing to enter architecture, dentistry, law, medicine, or veterinary medicine at certain other universities, may also complete the pre-professional requirements by special arrangement.

(Faculty of graduate studies)

Master of science (MSc).
At least two years full-time from general BSc.
Available in departments of biology,
chemistry, geography, geology, mathematics,
physics, psychology, and resources—the
environment and planning.

Doctor of philosophy (PhD).
At least two years full-time from MSc.
Available in biology, chemistry, geography,
geology, mathematics, physics, and
psychology.

Social work
(School of social welfare)

Bachelor of social work (BSW).
Four years from senior matriculation.
Limited enrolment.

(Faculty of graduate studies)

Master of social work (MSW).
At least two years full-time by course of
instruction, examination, practicum and thesis
in an area of social welfare. Applicants will
be required to present an undergraduate
degree with second-class standing or better
with emphasis on social and behavioral
sciences.

Special programs

Environmental sciences centre at Kananaskis;
Cosmic ray laboratory (atop Sulphur
Mountain) at Banff; foreign studies program;
resources, the environment and planning.

Extension programs

For university credit:

Evening credit program.
Undergraduate classes and some at the
graduate level are offered during the winter
session in arts and science, business,
education, engineering, fine arts, nursing, and
social welfare.

Summer session.
Courses are offered for undergraduates
proceeding to a degree and for teachers who
may wish to improve their professional
qualifications — chiefly subjects in arts,

science, and education; also a few in physical
education.

Banff School of Fine Arts.
A limited number of courses in art, drama,
French, and music are offered for credit
towards a degree or diploma at the
university.

For non-university credit:

Preparatory courses.
A small number of courses at matriculation
level are available for students who have not
been able to complete matriculation because
of the lack of certain subjects in the high
schools which they attended.

Adult education services.
Non-credit evening classes are conducted
through the department of extension in a
wide variety of subjects. Non-credit courses
at the Banff School of Fine Arts summer
session in: ballet, creative writing, figure
skating, geology, handicrafts, modern
languages, music, musical theatre, painting,
photography, theatre arts. The Banff School
of Advanced Management offers
management development programs.

Admission requirements

For a general statement regarding admission
to university study, see article *Admission to
university in Canada.*

For information regarding admission to
undergraduate study, consult *Requirements
for admission to Canadian colleges and
universities* available from Service for
Admission to College and University, 151
Slater St., Ottawa, Ont., K1P 5N1, $1.50
prepaid.

For admission to graduate study (including
environmental design and social work), a
student must have obtained a recognized and
acceptable first degree with specified grades
in appropriate subjects.

For entrance to the faculty of medicine, a
student is normally required to present three
years of study in an acceptable undergraduate
degree program majoring in biochemistry,
microbiology, physics, psychology, or
zoology.

Academic year

The academic year is 12 months in duration: July 1 to June 30.

Winter session: early September to late April.

Summer session: early July to mid-August.

Grading system

Since the beginning of the 1967 academic year, the university has been using a five-letter grading system; A, B, C, D, and F. In 1970, the letter grades A+ and B+ were added.

For students proceeding toward an undergraduate degree, the clear passing grade for each course is a C unless otherwise specified; in courses taken towards a graduate degree, the passing grade is a B.

In the determination of the grade point average (GPA) the grades are based on: A+ (outstanding) — 4; A (excellent) — 4; B+ (very good) — 3; B (good) — 3; C (satisfactory) — 2; D (minimal pass) — 1; and F (fail) — 0; and courses will be weighted on a basis of full, half, or quarter courses.

Fees and costs

Tuition fees per year: full-time for (a) all programs offered in undergraduate faculties except engineering and medicine, $400; part-time (per subject), $135 per full course or $67.50 per half course; (b) full-time engineering, $500; part-time (per subject), $170 per full course or $85 per half course; (c) full-time medicine, $800; part-time (per subject), $200 per full course or $100 per half course; (d) for master's degree (one-year program), $500; (two-year program), $1,000; (e) for doctor's degree (two-year program), $1,500. Part-time (per subject), $170 per full course or $85 per half course.

Compulsory general fees per year: undergraduate, $44.50; graduate, $16; medicine, $35.50.

Residence rates, board and room, $90-$100 a month.

Financial awards and assistance

Awards and financial assistance are available to matriculated and undergraduate students, provided they are 21 years of age and have been residents of the province of Alberta for 12 consecutive months; or if under the age of 21, provided their family resides in the province of Alberta.

Further information together with applications may be obtained from the student awards office at The University of Calgary. Completed applications must be received no later than June 15, for undergraduate awards and August 1, for matriculation awards. Awards and financial assistance are also available to graduate students. Inquiries should be directed to the graduate awards service, faculty of graduate studies, The University of Calgary.

Research institutes

Environmental Sciences Centre (Kananaskis). The university centre for advanced teaching and research on the properties of the environment and the interactions which occur between living things and their environment. Closely associated with the work of the university's committee on resources, the environment and planning.

Petroleum Recovery Research Institute.

Institute of Transportation Studies.

See also special programs.

Affiliated colleges

The colleges named below were affiliated to the university in 1966 under the terms of the university transfer programs. The admission regulations, course requirements and the examinations are those set down by the university. None of these colleges has the right to confer degrees. Courses directly transferable to The University of Calgary are those which carry the same number as courses offered on the Calgary campus. Other programs are also offered by the following colleges. Advance credit is awarded on an individual basis.

Medicine Hat College, 101-5th St. S.W.,
Medicine Hat, Alberta.
(Telephone 527-2277.) Dean: N.O.
Matthews, BSc, BT, MEd. Registrar: B.A.
Perrin, BSc, DipEd. Co-educational. Non-
denominational. Established 1965. Two years
of instruction after senior matriculation.

Mount Royal College, 8th Ave. and 11th St.
S.W., Calgary, Alberta.
(Telephone 266-4611.) President: W.B.
Pentz, BA, MA, EdD. Registrar: C.B. Brewer,
BSc. Co-educational. Residence
accommodation available for out-of-town
students. Original college established 1910.
Affiliated to The University of Alberta as a
junior college since 1931. One year of
instruction after senior matriculation. In
September 1966, Mount Royal College
became a public college. The old United
Church association was transferred to the
George W. Kerby College.

Constituent teaching organization

Banff School of Fine Arts, Banff, Alberta.
Director: D.S.R. Leighton, BA, MBA, DBA.
Associate director (programs and promotion):
J.C.K. Madsen, BComm. Associate director
(operations): D.F. Becker, BA, BSc. Associate
director (management studies): A.H.
Anderson, BASc, MBA. Established in 1933
as a school in the arts related to the theatre.
Co-educational and non-denominational.
Provides residence and dining
accommodation, meeting and seminar
arrangements. The summer session courses
are offered for university credit, Banff School
certificates, or simply for recreation and
pleasure.

Deans of faculties

Arts and science
R.W. Wright, BComm, DipBusAd, MA, PhD

Business
J.M.A. Robinson, BSc, MBA, PhD

Education
J. MacDonald, MA, DipEd, BEd, PhD

Engineering
R.A. Ritter, BE, MSc, PhD

Environmental design
W.T. Perks, BEng, MCD

Fine arts
A.R. Johnston, BMus, MMus, PhD

Graduate studies
J.B. Hyne, BSc, PhD, FCIC

Medicine
W.A. Cochrane, MD, FRCP(C), FACP.
FAAP

Directors of centres and schools

Banff School of Fine Arts
D.S.R. Leighton, BA, MBA, DBA

Continuing education
F. Terentiuk, BSc, MA, PhD

Environmental sciences centre
J.B. Cragg, BSc, MSc, DSc, DThPT

Nursing
Shirley Good, RN, BSN, MEd, EdD

Physical education
L. Goodwin, BA, BEd, MEd, PhD

Social welfare
F.H. Tyler, BComm, BSW, MSW, EdD

Department heads

Anaesthesia
F.L. Parney, BSc, MD, FFARCS, FRCP(C)

Archaeology
P.L. Shinnie, FSA, BA, MA

Art
E.M. Dodd, BA, DipT, MA

Biology
D. Parkinson, BSc, PhD

Chemistry
D.A. Armstrong, BSc, PhD, FCIC

Classics
B. Baldwin, BA, PhD

Community health sciences
J.H. Read, BSc, MD, DPH, CRCP(C)

Continuing medical education
J.L. Dawson, MD, FRCP(C), FACP

Diagnostic radiology
H.E. Duggan, MD, LMCC

Drama
V.E. Mitchell, BA, AM, LGSM

Economics
H.K. Betz, BA, MA, PhD

Education administration
F.D. Oliva, BEd, MEd, EdD

Educational foundations
R.F. Lawson, BA, MA, PhD

Educational psychology
J.G. Woodsworth, BA, BEd, EdD

Education curriculum and instruction
S.A. Lindstedt, BSc, MEd, PhD

Engineering, chemical
E.L. Tollefson (acting), PEng, BA, MA, PhD, FCIC

Engineering, civil
H.A.R. de Paiva, BSc, MS, PhD

Engineering, electrical
F.N. Trofimenkoff, BE, MSc, PhD, DIC

Engineering, mechanical
To be appointed

English
A.G.R. Petti, BA, MA, DLit

Family practice
T.C. Saunders, MD, CM

Geography
M.R.C. Coulson, BA, MA, PhD

Geology
P.S. Simony, BSc, MSc, PhD, DIC

Germanic and Slavic studies
R.S. Struc, Absolutorium, MA, PhD

History
J.B. Owen, MA, BSc, DPhil, FRHists

Linguistics
H.Z. Izzo, AB, AM, BS, PhD

Mathematics
H.K. Farahat, BSc, PhD

Medical biochemistry
R.B. Church, BSc, MSc, PhD, DipTransplant

Medical biophysics
S. Rowlands, BSc, PhD, FIP, MRCS, LRCP

Medical educational planning and assessment
L.A. Fisher, BSc, BEd, MEd, PhD

Medical physiology
K.E. Cooper, MB, BS, BSc, MSc, MA, DSc

Medical vivarium
To be appointed

Medicine
L.E. McLeod, BSc, MSc, MD, FRCP(C), FACP

Morphological science
A.D. Dickson, MB, BCH, BAO, MD, MA

Music
W.K. Cole, BA, MA, EdD

Obstetrics and gynaecology
H. Brody, BSc, MD, FRCS(C), DABOG

Paediatrics
G.H. Holman, BSc, MD

Pathology
R. Lannigan, MB, CHB, MD, PhD, FCPath

Pharmacology and therapeutics
K.L. MacCannell, BSc, MD, PhD, FRCP(C), LMCC

Philosophy
C.B. Martin, BA

Physics
H.R. Krouse, BSc, PhD

Political science
F. MacKinnon, BA, MA, PhD, LLD, SM

Psychiatry
K.I. Pearce, MB, BS, MD, MRCS, LRCP, LMCC, LRCP(C), CRCPS(C)

Psychology
W.R.N. Blair, CD, BA, MA, PhD

Romance studies
R.M. Chadbourne, BA, MA, PhD

Sociology/anthropology
D.L. Mills, BA, MA, PhD

Surgery
N.T. McPhedran, MD, FRCS(C), FACS

Visual education
V.T. Mason, MB, CHB, DRCOG, CRCPS

Carleton University*

Ottawa, Ontario, K1S 5B6

Telephone: 613-231-4321
Direct general correspondence to the registrar

Total full-time student enrolment 8,270; see also separate section *Statistics on Canadian universities and colleges*

Executive and administrative officers

Chancellor
Lester Pearson, PC, CC, OBE, BA, MA, LLD, DCL, FRAIC

President and vice-chancellor
Davidson Dunton, CC, LLD, DSc

Registrar
James Jackson, DFC, BA, MFA

Bursar
A.B. Larose, BCom, CA

Information officer
Judy Patterson (Mrs), BJ

Associate registrar — admissions
J.L. Sevigny, BA, BPE

Awards officer
Jean Loates (Mrs), BA

Development officer
M.D. Roberts

Director of alumni affairs
Brian Curley

Director of athletics
Keith N. Harris, BA, BPHE

Director of counselling and health services
Norman Fenn, BS, MEd

Director of planning
G.R. Love, MA, PhD

Director of student housing and food services
R.A. Brown, BA

High school liaison officer
D.J. Geddie, BA

Placement officer
Irene Davern (Mrs)

Librarian
Geoffrey Briggs, BA, MA, DipLib, DipArch

Overseas student advisor
J. Coates, MA

Provost of residences
A.M. Beattie, AM, PhD

Registrar (St. Patrick's Campus)
J.B. Zachary, OMI, MSc

Background

Carleton College was established in 1942 by the Ottawa Association for the Advancement of Learning. The association was incorporated in 1943 and operated Carleton College; the first degrees in journalism and public administration were awarded in 1946. In 1952, the Carleton College Act changed the corporate name to Carleton College and endowed it with the power to grant degrees. In 1957 the name was changed to Carleton University and the institution moved to the new Rideau River campus.

In July 1967, Carleton University acquired the St. Patrick's College property from the English Oblates of eastern Canada, and members of the college became staff members of the university. At the same time, Carleton established a new division of its faculty of arts to be referred to as the St. Patrick's College division. Members of the staff of the school of social welfare located at St. Patrick's College also became staff members of the university, to serve in the new school of social work which was established by Carleton University, and which is located at the St. Patrick's College campus.

The university is co-educational and non-sectarian. It is governed by a board of governors, a senate, and four faculty boards.

*Ordinary member, AUCC.

The population of Ottawa approximates 536,000.

Facilities and services

The main campus is situated in Ottawa south between the Rideau River and the Rideau Canal, on a 130-acre site. A smaller, St. Patrick's College campus, is located two miles down the Rideau Canal towards the centre of the city. The main campus has ten teaching and research buildings, an administration building, a library (600,000 volumes), four residences which accommodate 1,317 students and a gymnasium. A university centre houses a variety of recreational and extra-curricular facilities.

The St. Patrick's College campus has two teaching and research buildings in addition to a library (53,891 volumes), and a graduate school of social work library (12,000 volumes), and two residences which accommodate 72 students.

The campus organization, World University Service of Canada, a foreign students' advisor, and administrative officers provide services for foreign students. The community offers international house on Somerset Street as an international meeting place.

Calendars and brochures

The following publications are produced by Carleton University and are available upon request from the registrar's office: Carleton University undergraduate calendar (Rideau River and St. Patrick's College); graduate studies calendar; school of social work calendar; summer school calendar; handbook for students entering first year, (faculty of arts); school of architecture brochure; school of journalism brochure; Soviet and east European studies brochure; campus on the move – a booklet introducing the campus, the facilities, and the courses; guidance counsellors handbook (Ontario only); extension division brochure; part-time studies guide; faculty of arts brochure; faculty of engineering brochure; St. Partick's College brochure; art history brochure; residence brochure; off-campus housing brochure; and general admissions brochure.

Courses and degrees

Architecture
(School of architecture, faculty of engineering)

Bachelor of architecture (BArch). Pass course, six years from junior matriculation, five years from senior matriculation.

Arts
(Faculty of arts)

Note: Carleton University recently abolished all compulsory first-year courses in favour of a "free choice" system. Incoming students will be able to choose any five courses from a list of courses designated open to first-year students.

Bachelor of arts (BA).
(a) Pass course, four years from junior matriculation, three years from senior matriculation. Major programs are offered in the following areas: anthropology, art history, biology, classics, economics, English, French, geography, German, history, Italian, law, linguistics, mathematics, music, philosophy, political science, psychology, religion, Russian, sociology, and Spanish. (b) Honors course, four years from senior matriculation (three years in special cases). Honors programs are offered in the following areas: anthropology, classics, economics, English, French, geography, German, history, mathematics, philosophy, political science, psychology, public administration, religion, Russian, sociology, Soviet and east European studies, and Spanish.

(Faculty of graduate studies)

Master of arts (MA).
Normally two years' full-time study from the pass BA, or normally one year from the honors BA; available in Canadian studies, classics, comparative literature, economics, English, French, geography, German, history, international affairs, philosophy, political science, psychology, public administration, sociology, Soviet and east European studies, and Spanish.

Doctor of philosophy (PhD).
At least two years' full-time study from the MA; available in biology, chemistry, economics, engineering, geology, mathematics, physics, political science, psychology, and sociology.

Business, see commerce below

Commerce
(School of commerce, faculty of arts)

Bachelor of commerce (BCom honors).
Five years from junior matriculation; four years from senior matriculation. The course is designed to provide a broad foundation in academic disciplines bearing on business and economic affairs in general and to permit a measure of concentration in one of the following fields: economics, accounting and finance, quantitative methods, and labor and industrial relations.

Engineering
(Faculty of engineering)

Bachelor of engineering (BEng).
Five years from junior matriculation, four years from senior matriculation. The first three years of the program are devoted to the foundations of engineering: chemistry, mathematics, physics, and the engineering sciences. In the fourth year three options are offered: civil, electrical, and mechanical engineering.

(Faculty of graduate studies)

Master of engineering (MEng).
Normally two years from a bachelor's degree in engineering; available in aeronautical, civil, electrical, materials, and mechanical engineering.

Doctor of philosophy in engineering (PhD).
At least two years' full-time study from the MEng; available in aeronautical, civil, electrical, materials, and mechanical engineering.

Journalism
(School of journalism, faculty of arts)

Bachelor of journalism (BJ honors).
Two programs are available: (a) five years from junior matriculation, four years senior matriculation; (b) one year after completion of a first degree.

Public administration
(School of public administration, faculty of arts)

Certificate in public service studies (CPSS).
Junior matriculation is required for admission. Applicants without their junior matriculation will be considered on their merits and the completion of certain subjects at Carleton University may be required before admission. Length of term: six courses to be completed in full-time or part-time study.

Bachelor of arts with honors in public administration (BA).
Five years from junior matriculation, four years from senior matriculation.

(Faculty of graduate studies)

Graduate diploma in public administration (DPA).
One year from a bachelor's degree from a recognized college or university in the required pattern.

Master of arts in public administration (MA).
One year or more from either a bachelor's degree and the graduate diploma in public administration; or a bachelor's degree with either honors or an additional year of graduate work.

Science, pure
(Faculty of science)

Bachelor of science (BSc).
(a) Pass course, four years from junior matriculation, three years from senior matriculation. Areas of emphasis: biology, chemistry, geology, mathematics, and physics. (b) Honors course, four years from senior matriculation (three years in special cases), available in biochemistry, biology, chemistry, geology, mathematics, physics, psychology, combined programs in biology and geology; geology and physics; mathematics and physics. (c) General science degree, three years from senior matriculation. A total of 15 courses required. Eight or more courses must be from the faculty of science and the remaining from outside the faculty

of science, that is, humanities, social science, and engineering.

(Faculty of graduate studies)

Master of science (MSc).
Normally two years from a pass BSc, or one year from an honors BSc. Available in biology, chemistry, geology, mathematics, and physics.

Doctor of philosophy (PhD).
At least two years of full-time study after the MSc; available in biology, chemistry, geology, mathematics, and physics.

Social work
(School of social work)

Master of social work (MSW).
At least two years from a bachelor's degree.

Special programs

School of public administration; School of international affairs; Institute of Canadian studies; School of social work; School of journalism; Soviet and east European studies.

Interdisciplinary courses are offered in computing science, engineering humanities, and science.

St. Patrick's College offers a unified liberal arts program which is designed to foster and develop the intellectual life of the participant by means of an integrated approach to the study of selected themes of continuing concern to man.

Extension programs

For university credit:

Evening courses.
Undergraduate classes in arts, science, and commerce. The following degrees, certificates, or diplomas may be taken entirely by evening study — BA, CPSS, DPA, and with special permission MA in public administration. Studies for the BSc, BCom, and BJ may be begun in evening classes, but candidates must expect to take a substantial part of their degree work in the day division.

Summer session.
The summer session at Carleton University is designed for students proceeding to a degree by part-time study, for students taking courses towards professional and vocational qualifications, and for full-time students needing courses additional to their regular program. Virtually all disciplines are represented in the summer session, day and evening classes.

For no university credit:

The division of extension offers a wide variety of non-credit evening courses in liberal arts; communication arts; business and professional development; and languages.

The division also sponsors an extensive series of public lectures on a wide range of topics, concerts, drams, films, and other cultural events of interest to the general adult community.

Admission requirements

For a general statement regarding admission to university study, see article *Admission to university in Canada.*

For information regarding admission to undergraduate study, consult *Requirements for admission to Canadian colleges and universities* available from Service for Admission to College and University, 151 Slater St., Ottawa, Ont., K1P 5N1, $1.50 prepaid.

Professional schools

Architecture (first-year):
the Ontario secondary school honor graduation diploma with a minimum 60% average and including two credits in mathematics and one credit in physics.

Commerce (first-year):
the Ontario secondary school honor graduation diploma with a minimum 65% average, including two credits in mathematics and one credit in either English or a language other than English.

Engineering (qualifying university year):
a minimum 70% average in six subjects at the Ontario grade 12 level, five-year program as

follows: (a) mathematics; (b) science (physics and chemistry); (c) three subjects from the following list: English, French, geography, German, Greek, history, Italian, Latin, Russian, Spanish; (d) one other recognized subject. *Note:* it is recommended that qualifying year applicants present aptitude test scores.

Engineering (first-year):
the Ontario secondary school honor graduation diploma with a minimum 60% average and including two credits in mathematics and one credit in each of chemistry and physics.

Journalism (first-year):
the Ontario secondary school honor graduation diploma with a minimum 65% average and including one credit in a language other than English (French is recommended).

Note: the only graduate professional degree offered is in engineering.

Graduate studies

For admission to a master's program, an honors bachelor's degree (or the equivalent) with at least second-class standing is required. Applicant must also be recommended by the department in which he plans to undertake his studies.

For admission to a doctoral program, a master's degree is ordinarily required with at least high second-class standing from a recognized university.

Academic year

Winter session: mid-September to early May.

Summer session: evening division — last week of May to mid-August.

Day division — first week of July to mid-August.

Grading system

Standing is graded as follows for all faculties — A: 80-100%; B: 70-79%; C: 60-69%; D: 50-59%.

Fees and costs

All-inclusive fees comprise: tuition, students' association, athletics and health fees and where applicable, laboratory, graduation, and summer survey fees. Full-time, (a) for first degree — arts and science, $541.50; engineering and architecture, $601.50; (b) for graduate studies — $541.50 to $546.50. Part-time (per subject), $101.

Room and board residence per session, $950 to $1,025.

Financial awards and assistance

Carleton University offers approximately 100 entrance scholarships, the average value being $400. These scholarships are open to all qualifying and first-year applicants to the university.

Bursary assistance is available to students not qualifying for government assistance.

Deans of faculties

Arts, director, division II
R.A. Wendt, MA

Art, associate dean, division I
Treavor Tolley, BA

Engineering
Donald George, BEng, MS, ScD

Graduate studies
J. Ruptash, BSc, MASc, PhD

Science
H.H.J. Nesbitt, BA, MA, PhD, DSc, FLS, FRES, FZS

St. Patrick's College
D.W. Sida, BSc, MSc, PhD

Directors of schools

Architecture
Douglas Shadbolt, BArch, FRAIC

Canadian studies, Institute of
Pauline Jewett, MA, PhD

Commerce
T.N. Brewis, MCom, PhD

International affairs
H.E. English, BA, PhD

Journalism
T.J. Scanlon, BJ, DPA, MA

Public administration
To be appointed

Social work
S. Govenlock, LTh, MSW

Soviet and east European studies
B.R. Bociurkiw, MA, PhD

Department chairmen

Accounting
G. Paquet, MA

Art
M.-L. Funke, BA

Biology
J.M. Neelin, BSc, PhD

Chemistry
J.M. Holmes, BSc, MA, PhD, FCIC

Classics
A.T. Hodge, MA, PhD

Economics
G. Paquet, MA

English
B.W. Jones, BA, AM, PhD

French
H.P. Clive, BA, PhD

Geography
D.M. Anderson, BSA, MSc

Geology
W.M. Tupper, MSc, PhD

German
B.F. Mogridge, BA,
MA, Dipdud'EBruges

History
H.B. Neatby, BA, MA, PhD

Italian
R.L. Jackson, BA, MA, PhD

Law
D. Fraser, LLB

Linguistics
I.W.V. Pringle, MA

Mathematics
V. Dlab, RNDr, CSc, PhD, DSc

Music
J. Churchill, BMus, FRCO, GRSM, LRAM,
ARCM

Philosophy
R.S. Talmage, MA

Physics
R.L. Clarke, BSc, PhD

Political science
K.Z. Paltiel, BA, MA, PhD

Psychology
T.J. Ryan, MA, PhD

Religion
C.G. Williams, BA, BD, MA

Russian
V.I. Grebenschikov, MA, PhD

Sociology
D.R. Whyte, BSc, MSc, PhD

Spanish
R.L. Jackson, BA, MA, PhD

Dalhousie University*

Halifax, Nova Scotia

Telephone: 902-424-2211
Direct general correspondence to the registrar

Total full-time student enrolment 5,545; see
also separate section *Statistics on Canadian
universities and colleges*

Executive and administrative officers

Chancellor
Lady Beaverbrook

President and vice-chancellor
H.D. Hicks, CC, QC, BSc, BCL, MA, DEd,
LLD, DCL

Vice-president (health sciences)
C.B. Stewart, CD, BSc, MD, CM, DrPH,
FAPHA, FRCP(C)

Vice-president (academic)
W.A. MacKay, BA, LLM

Vice-president (administration)
D.H. McNeill, BSc, RIA

Registrar and director, student services
H.J. Uhlman, MA, MEd, AIE, PhD

Associate registrar (acting registrar 1970-71)
P.G. Griffiths, BSc

Dean of men
T.W. Sommerville, BCom, LLB, LLM

Dean of women
Christine Irvine, CA, BCom

Director, university health services
W.B. Kingston, BA, MD

Director, student counselling centre
H.D. Beach, BA, PhD

Director of admissions
To be appointed

Director, awards and secretary to the Killam
trust
G.G. Steedman, BA

Director, communications services
L.G. Vagianos, BA, MS, MA

Director of athletics
K.D. Gowie, BA, MA

Director, computer centre
E.J. Payne (Mrs), BSc

Director, summer school and extension
F.T. Parker, BA, MA, LLD

University engineer
A.F. Chisholm, BEng, MEIC

Director, planning and development
J.G. Sykes, BA, BArch

Director, alumni affairs
B.G. Irwin, CD, BCom

Director, information and public relations
Derek Mann, CPRSAcc

University librarian
Dorothy Cooke (Mrs), BA, BLS

Background

Dalhousie University was founded in 1818 by
the ninth Earl of Dalhousie, who was then
lieutenant-governor of Nova Scotia.
However, except for a few years between
1838 and 1845, Dalhousie did not function as
a university until 1863. The first degree of
bachelor of arts was awarded in 1866.

Dalhousie University is a non-
denominational, co-educational institution.

Facilities and services

Located on 62 acres in a residential area of
the south-west end of Halifax, with a
metropolitan population of 205,000, it has
over 10 teaching and research units; a

*Ordinary member, AUCC.

gymnasium and skating rink, a student union building, a residence for women (Shirreff hall) and a residence for men (Howe hall) are located on campus. Each residence can accommodate about 400 students. Also on campus is a 113-unit married student residence which contains a pre-school child care centre, and in addition there are a number of houses which are available for students. Included in off-campus accommodation is Fenwick towers which accommodates approximately 812 students.

Student services under the dean of student services: a chaplaincy unit, a health service, a counselling centre, a student financial aid office and dining rooms. In addition an employment service and a bookstore are operated. Student council, newspaper, and other student organizations have accommodation in the student union building.

Laboratories are well equipped for a wide variety of research in the pure, applied and medical sciences. Other research being carried on includes: Family medical centre, Atlantic research centre for mental retardation, Centre for foreign studies, Dalhousie legal aid, Advanced management centre.

Major buildings: arts and administration building, Killam memorial library, student union building, life sciences centre, arts centre, chemistry building, Sir James Dunn science building, Weldon law building, Sir Charles Tupper medical building.

The Sir James Dunn science building houses the laboratories for the departments of engineering, geology and physics, while the chemistry building contains the research areas for the department of chemistry.

Medical science facilities are located in the Sir Charles Tupper medical complex. This complex houses the departments of anatomy, biochemistry, microbiology, pathology, physiology and pharmacology. The animal care centre and the audio-visual department are located in the Tupper building.

The faculty of health professions is also located in the Tupper complex. This faculty has the responsibility for the schools of nursing, physiotherapy, physical education as well as the college of pharmacy.

In close association with these are a number of affiliated institutions and teaching hospitals for medical training.

The Maritime school of social work of Dalhousie University is situated also on the Studley campus having been integrated into the university in 1969.

The dentistry building contains the laboratories and teaching clinics for instruction in those subjects of a purely dental nature.

The Dalhousie computer centre is equipped with a CDC 6400 series computer. Other computers installed on the campus include an XDS sigma 5 computer (biophysics) and two decline-8 computers (biology and psychology) which are used for laboratory experimentation.

There is an arts centre for the performing and visual arts with auditorium, ancillary areas for music activities, a drama theatre with supporting workshops and teaching quarters and an art gallery.

The Institute of Public Affairs carries out activity in four main areas: regional studies; support for industrial development through research, management services, labour education and labour-management bureau, conferences and training programs, residential and in-service courses; educational and research support for community organizations and citizens.

The university library system accommodates the needs expressed in the undergraduate teaching programs, and specialized professional schools. Its component units are: law library (62,000 volumes); health sciences library (82,000); Killam library (over 300,000).

The International Students Association provides a common meeting ground for overseas students attending Dalhousie; promotes a feeling of fellowship among overseas and Canadian students, thus furthering the education of all concerned. The association aids overseas students in solving particular problems which they encounter while attending Dalhousie, and hosts a welcome reception for new students, a Christmas program, films, folk nights, dances, and an international soirée. Other campus organizations serving foreign students are: African students society; Dal-Chinese students society; Dal-West Indian society; Indisa.

Included in the religious organizations are: Encounter, Dalhousie Christian fellowship, Hillel society (Jewish), Newman club (Catholic), Movement for Christian action.

There are many clubs and societies in which the students may participate; some examples are: Dalhousie chorale, concert band, Dawson geology club, Dalhousie liberal association, Cameron house film society, Dalhousie commerce society, Law society, Pre-med society, Canadian University Service Overseas (recruits qualified Canadians to work in their fields of specialty for two years in a developing country), Art gallery committee, and Dal-King's reading club.

Calendars and brochures

Calendars: faculty of arts and science; faculty of graduate studies; faculty of health professions; faculty of law; faculty of medicine; faculty of dentistry.

Departmental brochures: dental hygiene; school of nursing; physical education; public administration; business administration; chemistry; economics; history; philosophy; political science; physiology and biophysics; psychology; theatre; Institute of Public Affairs undergraduate admissions; information and admissions.

Awards: financial aid for first-year students booklet; scholarships, prizes and financial aid booklet.

Other: Dalhousie review (quarterly); Alumni news (quarterly); MeDal (annually); University news (fortnightly tabloid).

Courses and degrees

Arts
(Faculty of arts and science)

Bachelor of arts (BA).
(a) Ordinary course, three years from senior matriculation. (b) Honors courses, four years from senior matriculation. Available in classics, economics, English language and literature, French, German, history, mathematics, modern languages, music, philosophy, political science, psychology, sociology and anthropology, Spanish and theatre.

Bachelor of music education (BMusEd).
A four-year program following senior matriculation.

(Faculty of graduate studies)

Master of arts (MA).
At least two years from ordinary BA. The holder of a BA degree with honors or of an ordinary degree with very high standing may complete the requirements in one year, provided that full time is devoted to the course. Available in classics, economics, education, English, German, history, mathematics, modern languages, philosophy, political science, psychology, and sociology and anthropology.

Diploma in clinical psychology (DipClinPsychol).
Twelve consecutive months' internship from MA in psychology.

Doctor of philosophy (PhD).
At least two years from MA. Available in economics, English, history, mathematics, political science and psychology.

Business, see commerce below

Commerce
(Faculty of arts and science)

Bachelor of commerce (BCom).
(a) Ordinary course, three years from senior matriculation. (b) Honors course, four years from senior matriculation.

(Faculty of graduate studies)

Master of business administration (MBA).
Two-year program following bachelor's degree.

Combined *MBA/LLB.*
Four-year program following bachelor's degree.

Dentistry
(Faculty of dentistry)

Diploma in dental hygiene.
Two-year diploma course beyond senior matriculation.

Doctor of dental surgery (DDS).
Four years from three years of arts or science beyond junior matriculation or from two years beyond senior matriculation.

Education
(Faculty of arts and science)

Bachelor of education (BEd).
Four years beyond senior matriculation for undergraduate degree and BEd or five years for honors degree.

Sequential course.
One year from BA in arts, science or commerce.

(Faculty of graduate studies)

Master of arts in education [MA(Ed)].
One year from BEd with at least second-class standing, or degree of MA or MSc with professional teachers' certificate, class 11, of the province of Nova Scotia, or equivalent.

Engineering
(Faculty of arts and science)

Diploma in engineering (EngDip).
First three years of engineering course from senior matriculation. Arrangements have been made with other Canadian universities to permit holders of this diploma to attain their engineering degree in two additional years. After two years (beyond senior matriculation), students may enter the architecture course at Nova Scotia Technical College.

Bachelor of science in engineering physics [BSc(EnginPhys)].
Four years from senior matriculation.

Law
(Faculty of law)

Bachelor of laws (LLB).
Three years from arts, science or commerce degree or from three years leading to such degree beyond junior matriculation, or from two years beyond senior matriculation.

(Faculty of graduate studies)

Master of laws (LLM).
At least one year from LLB.

Combined *MBA/LLB.*
Four-year program following bachelor's degree.

Library service
(Faculty of graduate studies)

Master of library service (MLS).
Four-term course to be taken on a: a) two-year schedule; b) one-year (12 months) schedule; c) part-time schedule (to be completed in five years). The one-year schedule is limited to applicants with an honors undergraduate degree, or equivalent, and previous library work experience. The course includes academic course electives, optional thesis, required library work experience in addition to professional courses.

Medicine
(Faculty of medicine)

Doctor of medicine (MD).
Four years of university and one year of internship, following three years in arts or science beyond junior matriculation or two years beyond senior matriculation.

Also in affiliation with the associated hospitals, postgraduate training in clinical specialties; in association with the faculties of arts and science, health professions and graduate studies, instruction leading to diplomas, bachelor's (honors) and master's degrees and the PhD degree in all or most of subjects of anatomy, biochemistry, microbiology, pathology, pharmacology, and physiology and biophysics.

Nursing
(School of nursing, faculty of health professions)

Bachelor of nursing (BN).
Four calendar years from senior matriculation, or three years from graduation from a recognized school of nursing.

Diploma courses.
Entrance requirements — one year after graduation from a recognized school of nursing and a satisfactory period of professional experience.

One-year diploma in (a) public health nursing, or (b) nursing service administration.

Two-year diploma in outpost nursing. One academic year at Dalhousie and one year supervised internship in northern Canada.

Pharmacy
(College of pharmacy, faculty of health professions)

Bachelor of science in pharmacy
[BSc(Pharm)].
Four years from senior matriculation.

(Faculty of graduate studies)

Master of science (MSc).
Normally two years from BSc in pharmacy.
Twelve months of resident study and
research is a minimum requirement.

Physical education
(Faculty of health professions)

Bachelor of physical education (BPE).
Four years from senior matriculation.

(Faculty of graduate studies)

Master of physical education (MPE).
One academic year plus thesis from
bachelor's level.

Physiotherapy
(Faculty of health professions)

Diploma in physiotherapy.
Two years after senior matriculation.

Political science
(Faculty of arts and science)

Certificate in public administration (CPA).
One academic year. May be taken on a part-
time basis.

(Faculty of graduate studies)

Master of public administration and *graduate
diploma in public administration (MPA* and
DPA).
A two-year program leading to a degree of
master of public administration, and a one-
year program leading to a graduate diploma
in public administration are also available
through the department of political science.
The latter, and the final year of the former,
may be taken on a part-time basis. A separate
brochure is available on these programs, and
further information on them may be
obtained from the co-ordinator of the

programs in public administration,
department of political science.

Centre for Foreign Policy Studies
The purpose of the centre is to promote
advanced teaching and research on foreign
policy-making processes. The centre's focus is
comparative and its work is interdisciplinary,
although its operations and staff are located
in the department of political science, and
students specializing in foreign policy studies
pursue BA, MA, and PhD degrees under the
department's supervision. The centre offers a
number of graduate and research fellowships
each year. For further information write: the
director, Centre for Foreign Policy Studies,
Dalhousie University.

Science, applied, see engineering

Science, pure
(Faculty of arts and science)

Bachelor of science (BSc).
(a) Ordinary course, three years from senior
matriculation. (b) Honors courses, four years
from senior matriculation. Available in
biochemistry, biology, chemistry, geology,
mathematics, and physics.

(Faculty of graduate studies)

Master of science (MSc).
At least two years from ordinary BSc. The
holder of a BSc degree with honors or of an
ordinary degree with very high standing, may
complete the requirements in one year
provided that full time is devoted to the
course. Available in anatomy, microbiology,
biochemistry, biology, chemistry, geology,
oceanography, oral surgery, pathology*,
pharmacology, physics, physiology and
biophysics.

Doctor of philosophy (PhD).
At least three years from honors bachelor's
degree, or two years from master's degree.
Available in biochemistry, biology,
biophysics, chemistry, economics, English,
geology, history, mathematics, microbiology,
oceanography, pharmacology, physics, and
physiology.

*Master of laboratory science (MLabSc).
Offered by the department of pathology. At
least two years from ordinary BA or BSc.
Candidate must have some background in
chemistry and the biological sciences. Holders
of a bachelor's degree with honors may

complete the requirements in one year, provided that full time is devoted to the course.

Social work
(Faculty of graduate studies)

Master of social work (MSW).
At least two years from bachelor's degree.

Special programs

Experimental classes.
A number of classes not listed in the university calendar may be given in either semester, if there is sufficient demand. Such courses are called experimental and have equivalent value with regular classes given.

Transition year program.
The TYP program, initiated in September 1970, provides an opportunity for students who do not have the usual educational qualifications for university to spend a year of concentrated training at Dalhousie. The program is designed to develop skills necessary for entrance to regular degree courses and admits young black and Indian Nova Scotians between the ages of 17 and 24. Only members of the province's black and Indian communities will be considered for admission.

Extension programs

For university credit:

Classes offered in arts and science and commerce.

Evening classes.
Late afternoon and evening.

Summer session.
Six weeks in May and June and six weeks in July and August. Up to five credits may be earned, one per summer session.

For no university credit:

Evening classes.
Late afternoon and evening courses with or without examinations and certificates; evening courses in public affairs.

Extension program.
Includes lecture series offered through the Institute of Public Affairs as well as through the extension department.

Computer courses.
A series of lectures and workshops on computer programming offered through the computer centre.

Admission requirements

For a general statement regarding admission to university study, see article *Admission to university in Canada.*

For information regarding admission to undergraduate study, consult *Requirements for admission to Canadian colleges and universities* available from Service for Admission to College and University, 151 Slater St., Ottawa, Ont., K1P 5N1, $1.50 prepaid.

For admission to LLB, DDS or MD, a student must have completed three years in arts or science beyond junior matriculation.

For admission to a course in the faculty of graduate studies: for MA or MSc, a bachelor's degree, second-class standing or the equivalent, is required to reach the minimal requirements; for LLM, the degree of LLB with high standing from Dalhousie or another approved university; for PhD, a bachelor's degree with honors or the equivalent, or a master's degree.

Academic year

Winter session: early September to end of April.

Summer session: six weeks in May and June; six weeks in July and August.

Grading system

Faculty of *arts and science* — letter grade, no numeric equivalent.

Faculty of *dentistry* — distinction, 80-100%; pass, 55-79%; pass mark, 55%; average of 60% required on all subjects of the year.

Faculty of *graduate studies* — pass mark, 65%; thesis grading, A, B, C, D, or failed.

Faculty of *health professions* — nursing and physical education, numeric grade, pass mark, 50%; physiotherapy, pass mark, 55% with overall average of 60%; pharmacy, division A, 80-100%; division B, 65-79%; division C, 56-64%; division D, 50-55%; pass mark 50%.

Faculty of *law* — A+ — 80%; A — 77-79%; A- — 74-76%; B+ — 71-73%; B — 68-70%; B- — 65-67%; C — 60-64%; D — 55-59%; E — 50-54%; F — below 50%; overall average of 55%, pass mark 50%.

Faculty of *medicine* — distinction, 80-100%; pass, 55-79%; pass mark, 55%; average of 60% required on all subjects of the year.

Fees and costs

Approximate tuition fees per year: full-time (a) for first degree - arts, commerce, pre-law, science, nursing, pre-medical, pre-dental, education, engineering, pharmacy, physiotherapy, $720; law, $674; medicine, $815 (1st, 2nd, 3rd and 4th years) and $520 (5th year); dentistry, $835; dental hygiene, $720; (b) for master of arts or science or laws, $725 for first year; (c) for doctor's degree, $725 for each required year of residence. Above fees inclusive (library, athletics, societies, etc.).

Part-time, one or two classes, per class, $145.

Residence rates, board and room, $980 — $1,055.

Financial awards and assistance

Dalhousie offers the following student financial support:

1) Entrance scholarships — awarded to graduating high school students on the basis of academic performance.
2) Bursaries — awarded to full-time students who demonstrate financial need.
3) Undergraduate scholarships — awarded to undergraduates at Dalhousie on the basis of academic performance.
4) Post-graduate scholarships and fellowships — awarded to new and continuing post-graduate students on the basis of academic performance.
5) Prizes and medals — awarded to eligible students during an undergraduate career or at graduation.

The awards office co-ordinates all student financial support programs and offers financial and budgetary counselling.

Research institutes

The Clinical Research Centre
which is connected by a link to the Tupper medical building tower, houses the research laboratories for the departments of medicine, obstetrics, paediatrics and preventive medicine.

The Atlantic Research Centre for Mental Retardation
is situated in the link area between the Clinical Research Centre and the Tupper building.

The George A. Burbidge pharmacy building
is equipped with modern research and teaching laboratories to accommodate programs in pharmaceutical research.

Facilities are available for research in microbiology and pathology in the *Pathology Institute* of the Nova Scotia Department of Health. Excellent equipment for advanced research has been established at this centre.

The Institute of Oceanography
is housed in the life sciences centre and includes a running seawater facility which contains controlled environmental rooms and large tanks and flumes suitable for experimental work in marine geology and biology. Opportunities for ocean-going research are provided by federal

oceanographic ships, particularly those of the Bedford Institute.

The institute provides a curriculum leading to the MSc and PhD in oceanography. Properly prepared undergraduates are admitted to these courses by special permission. The institute, in co-operation with the departments of biology, chemistry, geology, and physics, works in close association with other organizations in the area which have marine interests. These include the Bedford Institute, Nova Scotia Technical College, the Nova Scotia Research Foundation, the Atlantic Regional Laboratory of the National Research Council, and the Defense Research Establishment Atlantic. Together they form a powerful inter-institutional group for study of oceanographic and fisheries problems in the Canadian Maritimes.

There are extensive laboratories in the *psychology* section of the life sciences complex designed for research with humans, small mammals, birds, fish, and primates. Among the specialized facilities are a nursery school for the study of child behavior, and a seawater tank for the study of marine mammals. A mobile laboratory is available for off-campus study of nursery, elementary, and secondary school students. The department has access to well-equipped psychological laboratories located at the Nova Scotia, Camp Hill, and Lane Memorial hospitals.

Associated universities

University of King's College, Halifax, Nova Scotia.
In 1923 the University of King's College moved from Windsor, Nova Scotia, to Halifax and became associated with Dalhousie. Under the terms of this association, King's holds in abeyance its power of granting degrees, except in divinity. In arts and science, the two staffs are combined.
See separate entry.

Mount Saint Vincent University, Rockingham, Nova Scotia.
In 1969 a five-year agreement was signed to permit improvement in fields of education mutual to the two institutions.
See separate entry.

Nova Scotia Technical College, Halifax, Nova Scotia.
In 1969 a five-year agreement was signed to permit closer relationship in the fields of architecture and engineering.
See separate entry.

Dalhousie accepts for credit purposes recognized courses offered at these institutions.

Deans of faculties

Arts and science
G.R. MacLean, BA, MA, PhD

Dentistry
J.D. McLean, DDS, FICD, FACD

Graduate studies
G.F.O. Langstroth, BSc, MSc, PhD

Health professions
R.M. MacDonald, BSA, MB, ChB, FRCP(C)

Law
R.T. Donald, MBE, QC, BA, LLB, FCIS

Medicine (pro tem)
L.B. Macpherson, MBE, BSc, PhD

Directors of schools, institutes, and colleges

Dental hygiene, school of
Kate MacDonald, CertDHyg, BS

Library service, school of
J.C. Harrison, FLA, MLS

Nursing, school of
E.A.E. MacLennan, AM, RN, FAPHA

Oceanography, institute of
G.A. Riley, BS, MS, PhD, DSc

Pharmacy, college of
J.G. Duff, BSP, MSc, PhD

Physical education, school of
A.J. Coles, MEd, EdD

Physiotherapy, school of
A.H. Shears, MD, CM

Public affairs, institute of
Guy Henson, BA

Social work, Maritime school of
L.T. Hancock, BA, MA, BSW, MA

Department chairmen

Anaesthesia
C.C. Stoddard, MD, CM, FACA, FICA,
CRCP(C)

Anatomy
R.L. deC.H. Saunders, MD, ChB, FRSEd,
FRSSAf

Biochemistry
C.W. Helleiner, BA, PhD

Biology
K.E. von Maltzahn, MS, PhD

Chemistry
D.E. Ryan, BSc, MA, PhD, DIC, DSc

Classics
R.D. Crouse, MA, MTh, PhD

Commerce
J.D. Misick, BA, MBA

Continuing medical education, division of
L.C. Steeves, MD, CM, FRCP(C), FACP,
LLD

Economics
N.H. Morse, MA, PhD

Education
S.W. Semple, BA, MEd, EdD

Engineering and engineering physics
K.F. Marginson, BEng, MEng, MEIC, PEng

English
M.G. Parks, MA, PhD

Family medicine, division of
D.C. Brown, BSc, MD

Geology
M.J. Keen, MA, PhD

German
D.H. Steffen, PhD

History
P. Burroughs, BA, PhD, FRHistF

Mathematics
A.J. Tingley, MA, PhD

Medicine
R.C. Dickson, OBE, MD, FRCP(C), FACP

Microbiology
C.E. van Rooyen, MD, ChB, DSc, MRCP,
FRCP(C), FRS(C)

Music
R.D. Byham, BM, MM

Neurosurgery
W.D. Stevenson, MD, FRCS(C), MS

Obstetrics and gynaecology
W.R.C. Tupper, BSc, MD, CM, FACS, FICS

Ophthalmology
D.M. MacRae, BSc, MD, CM, FACCP

Oral diagnosis and oral surgery
R.H. Bingham, DDS, FICD

Otolaryngology
J.S. Hammerling, BSc, MD, FACS

Paediatric and community dentistry
B.P. Kearney, MBE, CD, DDS, FICD

Paediatrics
R.B. Goldbloom, MD, CM, FRCP(C)

Pathology
D.T. Janigan, BSc, MD, CM

Pharmacology
J.G. Aldous, MA, PhD

Philosophy
R.P. Pucetti, BA, Ddel'Univ

Physics
R.H. March, BSc, MSc, PhD

Physiology and biophysics
J.C. Szerb, MD

Political science
J.H. Aitchison, BA, BEd, BSc, PhD

Preventive medicine
P.C. Gordon, BSc, MD, CM

Psychiatry
R.O. Jones, BSc, MD, CM, FAPA, FRCP(C),
DEng

Psychology
C.J. Brimer, BCom, MA, PhD

Radiology
J.S. Manchester, MD, CM

Restorative dentistry
H.J. MacConnachie, DDS

Romance languages
B.H. Rasmussen, BA

Russian
I. Coffin (Mrs), LicèsL

Sociology and anthropology
D.H. Clairmont, BA, MA, PhD

Surgery
G.W. Bethune, BSc, MD, CM, FRCS(C)

Theatre
A.R. Andrews, MA

Urology
C.L. Gosse, BSc, MD, CM, FACS, FICS

University of Guelph*

Guelph, Ontario

Telephone: 519-824-4120
Direct general correspondence to the registrar

Total full-time student enrolment 6,217; see also separate section *Statistics on Canadian universities and colleges*

Executive and administrative officers

Chancellor
The Honorable Mr. Justice E.M. Hall, LLB, DCL, DMed

President and vice-chancellor
W.C. Winegard, BASc, MASc, PhD

Vice-president, academic
J.P. Smith, BA, MA, PhD

Vice-president, administration
W.W. Bean, BA

Registrar
A.G. Holmes (acting), BSA

Associate registrar (admissions)
W.R. Heath, BSA

Associate registrar (records)
A.G. Holmes, BSA

Assistant registrar (awards)
C.A. Frank, BComm, MBA, CA

Provost
R.P. Gilmor, BA, MA

Chief librarian
Margaret Beckman, BA, MLS

Director of alumni and development
J.D. Babcock, BSA

Director of diploma course
W.S. Young, BSA, MS, PhD

Director of information
D.L. Waterston, BSc(Agr)

Background

The University of Guelph was created by an act of the Ontario legislature in 1964. Prior to this, the Ontario Veterinary College, the Ontario Agricultural College, and Macdonald Institute operated under the federated colleges of the Ontario Department of Agriculture and were affiliated to the University of Toronto from 1888.

The Ontario Veterinary College was established under private charter in 1862. The Ontario Agricultural College was established by the province of Ontario in 1874. Macdonald Institute was established in 1903 as a division of home economics at the Ontario Agricultural College. Wellington College was established in 1964 for the teaching of arts and science at the university.

In 1970 a major academic administrative reorganization was approved by senate which restructured the colleges and schools to deal with the rapid growth and development of the university. The university now consists of seven colleges and four schools, i.e. college of arts, college of biological science, college of social science, college of physical science, college of family and consumer studies, Ontario Agricultural College, Ontario Veterinary College, and schools of hotel and food administration, landscape architecture, engineering, and physical education.

The University of Guelph is non-denominational and co-educational; it is administered by a board of governors and a senate.

Facilities and services

The university is situated on College Heights within the city limits with some 800 acres comprising the campus. In addition to some 25 teaching and research buildings, there is a main library (350,000 volumes), a physical

*Ordinary member, AUCC.

education building, eight dining halls, seven residences for women accommodating 1,650, and seven residences for men accommodating 1,650, and a coffee shop.

Student services include accident and health insurance, counselling and employment services.

Calendars and brochures

The university publishes separate graduate and undergraduate calendars each year. In addition there are undergraduate admission circulars and booklets describing the various degree programs.

Courses and degrees

Agricultural science
(Ontario Agricultural College)

Bachelor of science in agriculture [BSc(Agr)].
Eight semesters from senior matriculation. Specialization offered in agricultural biology, agricultural economics and business, animal science, environmental horticulture, plant science, and resources.

(Faculty of graduate studies)

Master of science (MSc).
Minimum of two semesters from honors bachelor's degree, or equivalent. Specialization offered in agricultural economics, agrometeorology, animal science, apiculture, botany (including plant pathology and plant physiology), crop science, food science, extension education, genetics, horticulture, hydrology, microbiology, nutrition, plant physiology, poultry science, resources development, soil science, and zoology (including entomology, fisheries, marine biology, and wildlife biology).

Doctor of philosophy (PhD).
Minimum of five or seven semesters from recognized master's or honors bachelor's degree, respectively. Specialization offered in agrometeorology, animal science, apiculture, botany (including plant pathology and plant physiology), crop science, genetics, horticulture, hydrology, microbiology, nutrition, plant physiology, poultry science, soil science, zoology (including entomology, fisheries, marine biology, and wildlife biology).

Arts
(College of arts, college of social science)

Bachelor of arts (BA).
(a) General program, six semesters from senior matriculation. (b) Honors program, eight semesters from senior matriculation. Available in art, Asian studies, drama, economics, English, French, geography, German, history, Italian, Latin, mathematics, philosophy, political studies, psychology, sociology-anthropology, and Spanish.

(Faculty of graduate studies)

Master of arts (MA).
Minimum of two semesters from honors bachelor's degree, or equivalent. Specialization offered in economics, English language and literature, geography, history, international programs, philosophy, political studies, psychology, resources development, Scottish studies, and sociology-anthropology.

Doctor of philosophy (PhD).
Minimum of five or seven semesters from recognized master's or honors bachelor's degree, respectively. Specialization offered in history and Scottish studies.

Engineering
(School of engineering)

Bachelor of science in engineering [BSc(Eng)].
Eight semesters from senior matriculation. Specialization offered in environmental design, mechanical design for agriculture, and water resources design.

(Faculty of graduate studies)

Master of science (MSc).
Minimum of two semesters from bachelor's degree, or equivalent. Specialization offered in electrification, environmental control, hydrology, machinery, materials handling, power, processing, resources development, and structures.

Doctor of philosophy (PhD).
Minimum of five or seven semesters from master's or bachelor's degree respectively. Specialization offered in hydrology, fluid and thermodynamic processes and design.

Family and consumer studies
(College of family and consumer studies)

Bachelor of household science (BHSc).

Eight semesters from senior matriculation. Specialization offered in applied human nutrition, consumer studies, early childhood education, family studies, and textiles.

(Faculty of graduate studies)

Master of science (MSc).
Minimum of two semesters from honors bachelor's degree, or equivalent. Specialization offered in applied human nutrition, clothing, family studies, food administration, foods, and textile science.

Doctor of philosophy (PhD).
Minimum of five or seven semesters from recognized master's or honors bachelor's degree, respectively. Specialization offered in food administration, foods, nutrition, and textile science.

Hotel and food administration
(School of hotel and food administration)

Bachelor of commerce (BComm).
Eight semesters from senior matriculation.

Landscape architecture
(School of landscape architecture)

Bachelor of landscape architecture (BLA).
Eight semesters from senior matriculation.

(Faculty of graduate studies)

Master of science (MSc).
Minimum of two semesters from bachelor's degree, or equivalent.

Physical education
(School of physical education)

Bachelor of science in physical education [BSc(PE)].
Eight semesters from senior matriculation.

Science
(College of physical science, Ontario Agricultural College)

Bachelor of science (BSc).
(a) General science, six semesters from senior matriculation. (b) Honors program, eight semesters from senior matriculation.

Specialization offered in biology, botany, chemistry, computing science, genetics, fisheries and wildlife, food science, marine biology, mathematics, microbiology, physics, science, and zoology.

(Faculty of graduate studies)

Master of science (MSc).
Minimum of two semesters from honors bachelor's degree, or equivalent. Specialization offered in chemistry (including analytical, biochemical, inorganic, organic, and physical), mathematics and statistics, and physics.

Doctor of philosophy (PhD).
Minimum of five or seven semesters from recognized master's or honors bachelor's degree, respectively. Specialization offered in chemistry (including biochemical, inorganic, organic, and physical), and physics.

Veterinary medicine
(Ontario Veterinary College)

Doctor of veterinary medicine *(DVM).*
Professional course, eight semesters.

(Faculty of graduate studies)

Intern/residency program (graduate diploma).
Three semesters (one calendar year) from DVM degree or equivalent. Specialization in clinical studies and in pathology.

Master of science (MSc).
Minimum of two semesters from honors bachelor's or other first degree, or equivalent. Specialization offered in biomedical sciences (including anatomy, histology, pharmacology, and physiology), clinical studies (including medicine, radiology, reproduction, and surgery), immunology, pathology (including parasitology), and veterinary microbiology.

Doctor of philosophy (PhD).
Minimum of five or seven semesters from recognized master's or honors bachelor's or other first degree, respectively. Specialization offered in biological immunology, biomedical sciences (including cell biology, cytogenetics, developmental biology, endocrinology, neuroanatomy, oncology, pharmacology, physiology, radiobiology, and toxicology), pathology (including parasitology), and veterinary microbiology.

Special programs

Programs in arts and science are offered on a continuous year-round teaching program of three semesters. In addition agricultural science and family and consumer studies have a modified form of trimester. Students in arts and science commence university work in September, January, and April each year. Ontario grade 13 students may enter in April without completing grade 13.

Extension programs

The office of continuing education through the various colleges offers lecture series, seminars, and courses in arts, social sciences, agriculture, and languages as non-credit courses throughout the three semesters for the general public.

Professional development courses are also offered in agriculture and veterinary science.

A three-year correspondence program leading to the Ontario diploma in horticulture is available with specialization in park management, nursery management, or landscape contracting.

Admission requirements

For a general statement regarding admission to university study, see article *Admission to university in Canada.*

For information regarding admission to undergraduate study, consult *Requirements for admission to Canadian colleges and universities* available from Service for Admission to College and University, 151 Slater St., Ottawa, Ont., K1P 5N1, $1.50 prepaid.

For admission to veterinary medicine, four semesters of university work in science from the senior matriculation level is required.

For admission to graduate study, a student must have obtained a first degree with second-class honors from an institution recognized by the senate of the University of Guelph and on a university program acceptable to the faculty of graduate studies.

Academic year

Academic year commences with the spring semester.

Spring semester: early May until early August.

Fall semester: early September until end of December.

Winter semester: early January until late April.

Grading system

First degree programs: first-class honors — 75-100%; second-class honors — 66-74%; pass — 60-65%. Standing in individual courses is graded as follows: first-class honors — 75-100%; second-class honors — 66-74%; pass—50-65%. Graduate studies: A — 75-100%; B — 66-74%; C — 60-65%.

Fees and costs

Tuition fees per semester: full-time (a) for first degree — family and consumer studies, agriculture, veterinary medicine — $237.50 per semester; arts — $245 per semester; hotel and food administration — $242.50; physical education, science — $250 per semester; engineering — $272.50 per semester; landscape architecture — $302.50 per semester; (b) for graduate studies — $485 per annum. Tuition fees for part-time undergraduate — $60 per course. Tuition for part-time graduate — $140 per annum. Other university fees — $24 per semester.

Room and board — $545 per semester.

Financial awards and assistance

Numerous scholarships and bursaries are available for Ontario students entering the various undergraduate programs.

Scholarships, fellowships, and department assistantships are available for graduate studies.

Research institutes

Centre for Educational Disabilities.
The centre is an inter-disciplinary
organization which gives psychologists,
sociologists, physiologists, and representatives
of other disciplines an opportunity to work in
partnership and share facilities on work in
the causes and remediation of educational
failure at all levels.

Centre for International Programs, The.
This centre has an interdepartmental role in
supporting and co-ordinating the university's
expanding interest and activities in
international affairs, both on campus and
overseas.

Centre for Resources Development, The.
The various departments in the university
concerned with renewable, non-renewable
and human resources co-operate under the
aegis of the centre in a graduate program,
with an inter-disciplinary approach to the
philosophy and problems of resources
development.

Institute of Computing Science.
This institute was created to co-ordinate the
data processing activities of the university. In
addition to providing computer facilities the
institute provides and promotes technical
assistance in computing systems and
programming.

Deans of colleges and faculty

Arts
M.H.M. MacKinnon, BA, MA, PhD

Family and consumer studies
Janet Wardlaw, BA, MS, PhD

Graduate studies
H.S. Armstrong, MA, PhD, DSc

Ontario Agricultural College
N.R. Richards, BSA, MS, DSc

Ontario Veterinary College
D.G. Howell, BSc, PhD

Research
W.E. Tossell, BSA, MSA, PhD

Science, biological
K. Ronald, BSc, MSc, PhD, DipRadBiol

Science, physical
E.B. MacNaughton, BA, MA, PhD

Science, social
J.W. Skinner, BA, MA, PhD

Directors of schools

Athletics
W.F. Mitchell, BSA

Computing science, Institute of
K. Okashimo, BA, MA, PhD

Continuing education
C.E. McNinch (acting), BSA

Educational disabilities, Centre for
D.H. Stott, MA, PhD

Engineering
H.D. Ayers, BE, MS

Hotel and food administration
G.D. Bedell, BA, MA

International programs, Centre for
H.R. Binns, BSc, MA

Landscape architecture
V. Chanasyk, BSc(Agr), BS(LA), MLA

Physical education
J.T. Powell, MS, PhD

Resources development, Centre for
N. Pearson, BA

Department heads

Agricultural economics
T.K. Warley, BSc, MSc

Animal and poultry science
W.D. Morrison, BSA, MS, PhD

Biomedical sciences
H.G. Downie, DVM, MVSc, MS, PhD

Botany
To be appointed

Chemistry
A.K. Colter, BSc, PhD

Clinical studies
C.A.V. Barker (acting), DVM, MSc, DVSc

Consumer studies
R.E. Vosburgh, BS, MBA, DBA

Crop science
E.E. Gamble, BSA, MSA, PhD

Economics
J. Vanderkamp, BEcSc, MBA, PhD

English language and literature
A.M. Ross, BA, MA

Environmental biology
F.L. McEwen, BSc, MSc, PhD

Extension education
H.W. Caldwell, BSA, MSc(Ed), PhD

Family studies
Kathryn Kopf, BSc(HEc), MA, PhD

Fine art
E. Cameron, BA

Food science
J.M. deMan, ChemEng, PhD

Geography
F.A. Dahms, BA, MA, PhD

History
Margaret Evans, BA, MA, PhD

Horticultural science
D.P. Ormrod, BSA, PhD

Land resource science
D.R. Elrick, BSA, MS, PhD

Languages
R.A. Barrell, BA, BSc, MA

Mathematics and statistics
T.D. Newton, BA, MA, PhD

Microbiology
D.C. Jordan, BSA, MSA, PhD

Nutrition
S.J. Slinger, BSA, MSA, PhD

Pathology
R.G. Thomson, DVM, MVSc, PhD

Philosophy
D. Odegard, BA, MA, PhD

Physics
P.A. Egelstaff, BSc, PhD

Political studies
J.F. Melby, AB, MA, PhD

Psychology
H.M.B. Hurwitz, BA, BA, PhD

Sociology and anthropology
To be appointed

Veterinary microbiology and immunology
D.A. Barnum, DVM, DVSc, DVPH

Zoology
To be appointed

Huron College*

(Affiliated to The University of Western Ontario)
London, Ontario

Telephone: 519-438-7224
Direct general correspondence to the registrar

Total full-time student enrolment 543; see also separate section *Statistics on Canadian universities and colleges*

Executive and administrative officers

Chairman of the corporation
Rt. Rev. C.J. Queen, BA, LTh, DD

Chairman of the executive board
R.W. Mitchell, QC

Principal
The Ven. J.G. Morden, BA, LTh, BD, STM, DTh, DD

Registrar
J. Catharine Ridley (Miss)

Comptroller
L.G. Barnes, BA

Librarian
Rev. J.L. Henderson, BA, BD, DD

Background

Huron College was founded in 1863 and became an affiliated college of The University of Western Ontario in 1923.

The faculty of arts at Huron College is fully integrated with the university's faculty of arts and science. All courses offered, together with the instructors offering them, are approved by the university senate. Arts students at Huron College write the same examinations as those set in the university, and the faculty of arts participates in the setting and marking of these examinations. The bachelor of arts degree granted to Huron College students is that of The University of Western Ontario.

In 1956 the college became an associate member of the American Association of Theological Schools. In 1958 the college received its new charter under the Ontario provincial government to grant its own degrees in theology.

Facilities and services

In 1933, the college council purchased land directly opposite the university property. The new building on this site was opened in November 1951. Facilities are provided for 550 students in arts and theology, of whom 200 men and 100 women live in residence. The new residence for women opened in September 1963. The Silcox Memorial library (81,000 volumes) was opened in December 1958, and the student activity centre opened in October 1962.

Calendars and brochures

General annual calendar; brochure.

Courses and degrees

Arts

Bachelor of arts (BA).
(a) General course, three years from senior matriculation. (b) Honors courses, four years from senior matriculation. Available in English and French, English and German, English and history, English and Latin, English and philosophy, English and Russian, English language and literature, French language and literature, history, history and philosophy, philosophy, philosophy and psychology.

Theology

Master of divinity (MDiv).
Three years beyond a bachelor's degree from a recognized university.

Bachelor of ministry (BMin).
Three years beyond a bachelor's degree from a recognized university (or in the case of the special student, after he has completed five arts subjects and has obtained a pass in all subjects of the three-year theological course including the Bible and comprehensive examinations).

Admission requirements

For a general statement regarding admission to university study, see article *Admission to university in Canada.*

For information regarding admission to undergraduate study, consult *Requirements for admission to Canadian colleges and universities* available from Service for Admission to College and University, 151 Slater St., Ottawa, Ont., K1P 5N1, $1.50 prepaid.

Academic year

Winter session: mid-September to mid-May.

Grading system

The same as The University of Western Ontario; see separate entry.

Fees and costs

Tuition fees per year: full-time students — arts, $540; theology, $450.

Residence rates: arts, $1,075; theology, $1,075.

Financial awards and assistance

Entrance scholarships available as outlined in general calendar.

Deans of faculties

Arts
F.W. Burd, BA, MA

Theology
G.H. Parke-Taylor, BA, MA, LTh, BD, DD

Department chairmen

English
E.D. McVey, BA, MA, PhD

French
G.A. Black, BA, MA

History
J.L. Henderson, BA, BD, DD

Philosophy
Reese Miller, BA, BPhil, MA

Psychology
Moira Samsom, BA, BA, BLS, PhD

Religious studies
J.G. Morden, BA, LTh, BD, DD, STM, DTh

Collège Jean-de-Brébeuf*

(affilié à l'Université de Montréal)
3200, Côte Sainte-Catherine, Montréal 250
(Québec)

Téléphone: 514-342-1320
Prière d'adresser la correspondance d'ordre
général au directeur des études

Total des inscriptions des étudiants à plein
temps 184; voir aussi la section distincte,
intitulée *Statistiques sur les universités et
collèges du Canada*

Dirigeants

Recteur
R.P. Georges Legault, SJ, LPh, LTh

Directeur des études, cours collégial
R.P. Edouard Trudeau, SJ, MA, LTh, DEd

Trésorier
R.P. Jacques De Carufel, SJ, LPh, LTh, MA

Directeur des étudiants, cours collégial
R.P. Bernard Morin, SJ, LPh, MEd

Directeur des étudiants, cours secondaire
Jean Pennober, BA, BPéd

Directeur des relations extérieures et de
l'Association des anciens
R.P. Lucien Thibodeau, SJ, LTh

Historique

Le Collège Jean-de-Brébeuf est un collège
dirigé par les Pères de la Compagnie de Jésus.
Il a été incorporé par un acte de la province
de Québec, sanctionné le 22 février 1929.

Le collège signait, le 12 mars 1929, une
entente avec l'Université de Montréal qui lui
confère un statut universitaire spécial. Ce
statut privilégié, la loi concernant la charte de
l'Université de Montréal (14 Georges VI,
chapitre 142, sanctionnée le 29 mars 1950) le
reconnaissait dans les termes suivants: 'Dans
le statut d'affiliation qui pourra être arrêté
entre l'université et les collèges tenus par le
RR.PP. Jésuites, l'université tiendra compte
du privilège qui leur a été, jusqu'en 1920,
reconnu par l'Université Laval, en
conformité, quant à la nature du privilège,
des prescriptions de la constitution
Jamdudum du 2 février 1889." (Ch. 142,
art. 6.)

Dans la nouvelle charte de l'Université de
Montréal (Bill 97, sanctionné le 12 août 1967,
15-16 Elisabeth II, chapitre 129, article 42):
'Les droits et privilèges des collèges des Pères
Jésuites à Montréal, reconnus par l'article 6 de
la loi 14 Georges VI, chapitre 142, sont
maintenus à l'égard des étudiants inscrits
dans ces collèges avant le dernier jour de
juillet 1972". Le Collège Jean-de-Brébeuf
institue lui-même ses programmes et ses
examens et désigne ses propres candidats au
grade de bachelier ès arts. Sur présentation
d'un certificat signé des autorités du collège,
l'Université de Montréal confère le diplôme
de bachelier.

Le Collège Jean-de-Brébeuf est un collège
privé reconnu d'intérêt public par le ministère
de l'Education de la province de Québec.

Installations et services

Situé sur le flanc nord-ouest de la montagne,
à proximité de l'Université de Montréal, le
campus du Collège Jean-de-Brébeuf
comprend actuellement: le bâtiment central
(1928), le pavillon Lalemant (1957), la
bibliothèque (80,000 volumes), l'auditorium,
la résidence des étudiants (215 places), la
station géophysique et un gymnase.

*Membre ordinaire de l'AUCC.

Cours et grades

Arts

Le collège offre le cours collégial conduisant au diplôme d'études collégiales. Ce programme est reconnu par le ministère de l'Education, qui confère le diplôme d'études collégiales. Ce programme prépare à toutes les facultés universitaires.

Cours pré-immatriculation

Cours secondaire de cinq années, avec choix d'options.

Programmes spéciaux

Un centre de recherches en géophysique et une section de radio-météorologie. La station de séismologie et de météorologie fait partie du réseau international des stations géophysiques.

Conditions d'admission

Un certificat de fin d'études secondaires, soit en secondaire V, soit en llème classique ou scientifique. On demande aux étudiants de llème année (secondaire IV) entre 70% et 75% de moyenne générale.

Année universitaire

Du 30 août au 13 mai.

Système de mentions

La note de succès dans chaque matière est de 60%. La promotion se fait par matière. Pour le diplôme d'études collégiales, les mentions sont accordées suivant le barème de la Direction générale de l'enseignement collégial du ministère de l'Education.

Droits d'inscription

Les frais de scolarité sont déterminés conformément à la loi des institutions privées. Comme le collège est reconnu 'd'intérêt public", les frais de scolarité s'élèvent à environ 30% du coût moyen de la scolarité dans le secteur public, soit à environ $400.

Directeurs

Etudes, cours collégial
R.P. Edouard Trudeau, SJ, MA, LTh, DEd

Etudes, cours secondaire
R.P. Guy Demers, SJ, LPh, MEd

University of King's College*

(Associated with Dalhousie University)†
Halifax, Nova Scotia

Telephone: 902-423-7497
Direct general correspondence to the registrar

Total full-time student enrolment 285; see also separate section *Statistics on Canadian universities and colleges*

Executive and administrative officers

Visitor and chairman of the board of governors
Rt. Rev. W.W. Davis, Bishop of Nova Scotia

President
J.G. Morgan, BA, MA, DPhil

Vice-president
Harry Granter, BA, AM

Registrar
G.S. Clark (Mrs)

Bursar
J.A. Conrod (Miss)

Librarian
J.E. Lane (Mrs), BA

Dean of residence
David Jones, BA

Dean of women
E.G. Jones (Mrs), RN

*Ordinary member, AUCC.

†Holds in abeyance its degree-granting powers in arts and science during the term of association with Dalhousie University.

Executive secretary, alumni association
J. Desrosiers (Mrs)

Director, public relations
Glen Hancock, BA, DipJourn

Director, Speech arts
S.A. Kryszek (Mrs), LGSM

Background

The University of King's College was established in 1789 by an act of the provincial legislature and established at Windsor, Nova Scotia. Teaching began that year and the first degrees were probably awarded in 1802 or 1803.

Following a fire in 1920, the university was re-established in Halifax in 1923 by means of private subscriptions and with the financial aid of the Carnegie Corporation of New York, which endowed the teaching of liberal arts. The university became associated with Dalhousie University and, under the terms of this association, holds in abeyance its power to grant degrees, except in divinity and other faculties not forming a part of Dalhousie. In arts and science the two staffs are combined. King's also retains complete control over present endowments, administration of residences and all internal matters.

King's is an Anglican, co-educational institution. It operates under a board of governors which appoints an executive council. Both the dioceses of Nova Scotia and of Fredericton contribute grants to the university.

The University of King's College is one of the founding partners of the Atlantic School of Theology, an inter-denominational institution established in Halifax in July 1971, for ministerial and theological studies. Students enroled in the faculty of divinity of King's College receive the majority of their classes and instruction from the staff of the Atlantic School of Theology.

Facilities and services

The University of King's College is situated on five acres of land on the north-west corner of the Dalhousie University campus in Halifax (population, metro area 122,000). The principal building houses the offices of

administration, classrooms, and the library (50,000 volumes). There is residence accommodation for 125 men and 100 women, the president's lodge, a dining hall, a chapel, a large recreation hall, a gymnasium and a swimming pool.

Student services include a health service, guidance and counselling, and a housing registry (by special agreement with Dalhousie).

Calendars and brochures

Publications: calendar and brochures available from the registrar.

Courses and degrees

Arts

Bachelor of arts (BA).
Offered through Dalhousie University (see separate entry.)

Divinity
(School of divinity)

Testamur.
Three years.

Licentiate in theology (LTh).
Three years after BA, four years without BA.

Associate in theology (ATh).
On recommendation of board of examiners of general synod of Anglican Church of Canada.

Bachelor of sacred letters (BSLitt).
Three years after BA or BSc.

Bachelor of sacred theology (BST).
Three years after BA, BSc, or BComm.

Bachelor of divinity (BD).
Three years after BA on recommendation of board of examiners of general synod of Anglican Church of Canada.

Associate of King's College (Nova Scotia) [AKC(NS)].
Equivalent to two years' postgraduate study after LTh or STh.

Master of sacred theology (MST).
Two years after bachelor's degree.

Science, pure

Bachelor of science (BSc).
Offered through Dalhousie University (see separate entry).

Extension programs

For no university credit:

The department of extension offers periodic courses for the general public in general theology, a public relations course and a course in speech arts.

Admission requirements

For a general statement regarding admission to university study, see article *Admission to university in Canada.*

For information regarding admission to undergraduate study, consult *Requirements for admission to Canadian colleges and universities* available from Service for Admission to College and University, 151 Slater St., Ottawa, Ont., K1P 5N1, $1.50 prepaid.

For admission to courses leading to a first degree in divinity, a bachelor's degree is required.

Academic year

Winter session: mid-September to early May.

Grading system

Division 1 — grade A, 3 points; division II — grade B, 2 points; division III — grade C, 1 point; grade D, no points.

Fees and costs

Tuition fees in arts and science (approximate) per year: full-time, $685. Part-time - per class, $150. Divinity — per year, $350. Part-time — per class, $75.

Residence accommodation (room and board), $950-$1,075 per year.

Incidental expenses, approximately $100.

Financial awards and assistance

A wide range of scholarships, bursaries, and prizes are offered. For information on scholarships write to the registrar.

Research institute

Institute of Pastoral Training.
The objective of the institute is to bring pastors and theological students face to face with human misery as it exists both in and out of institutions, through courses in clinical pastoral education in both general and mental hospitals, reformatories and juvenile courts, homes for the aged, alcoholism treatment centres, and other social agencies. Other goals of the institute include the production of teaching materials, the promotion of workshops, and the establishment of a first-class library and reference centre at the institute's office. All inquiries concerning courses offered should be addressed directly to the secretary of the institute, the Reverend Howard Taylor, University of King's College, Halifax.

Deans of faculties

Arts and science
In this faculty the staff of both Dalhousie University and King's College are combined.

Divinity
Rev. J.B. Hibbitts, MA, BSLitt, STM, DPhil

King's College*

(Affiliated with The University of Western Ontario)
London, Ontario

Telephone: 519-433-3491
Direct general correspondence to the registrar

Total full-time student enrolment 751; see also separate section *Statistics on Canadian universities and colleges*

Executive and administrative officers

Honorary chairman of the board of directors
Most Rev. G.E. Carter, DD, PhD, DHL, LLD

Chairman, board of directors
Wm. Chizmar, LLD

Principal and dean of arts
A.F. McKee, MA, MSc(Ec), DUP

Registrar
J.H. Campbell, BA, BEd, MA

Background

King's College is a co-educational undergraduate college of liberal arts and social sciences sponsored by the Roman Catholic diocese of London and open to students of all beliefs. The present name of the college dates from 1966.

The College of Christ the King, an arts college for non-clerical students, was established in 1955 and its graduates received their degrees from The University of Western Ontario through an existing St. Peter's Seminary College of Arts affiliation. In 1966 the affiliation agreement with the university was transferred to King's College.

All faculty appointed to and courses given by the college are approved by the university senate and the degrees conferred on all students are that of The University of Western Ontario. The principal is an ex officio member of the senate. The college is under the governance of a board of directors, and faculty committees along with the dean of the college supply academic guidance.

Facilities and services

King's College is situated on Epworth Avenue at Waterloo Street, directly opposite the faculty of music of the university, and two blocks from the main entrance to the university. An inter-lecture bus service operates between the college and the main campus. This permits a valuable integration of courses given in various parts of the university.

The principal building houses faculty, student, and administration offices, classrooms, a chapel, a cafeteria, lounges, and the women's residence. Three separate buildings provide residence accommodation for 200 men. The college library houses some 30,000 volumes. As members of The University of Western Ontario community, King's students have full privileges at Western's libraries. The theology department of St. Peter's Seminary, located within short walking distance, provides further course and library facilities available with some restrictions to King's College students. Students at King's College also share the services offered students of The University of Western Ontario: athletic facilities, teams clubs, employment services, voluntary military training, and many others.

The population of London approximates 208,000.

Calendars and brochures

The college publishes a calendar as its supplement to the main calendar of The University of Western Ontario.

*Ordinary member, AUCC.

Courses and degrees

Arts

Bachelor of arts (BA).
(a) General program, three years from senior matriculation, in liberal arts and social sciences and a two-year pre-business program. (b) Honors program, four years from senior matriculation, in comparative literature, English and French, English and German, English and history, English and Latin, English and philosophy, English and Russian, English language and literature, French language and literature, French and Latin, history, history and German, history and philosophy, modern languages and literatures, philosophy, philosophy and German, philosophy and mathematics, philosophy and psychology, philosophy and sociology.

Bachelor of social welfare (BSW).
Four-year program beyond senior matriculation. This is a first professional degree for persons interested in a career in social work or in the broader field of social welfare.

Special programs

The college from time to time offers special programs supplementary to a large number offered by The University of Western Ontario.

Extension programs

Same as for The University of Western Ontario.

Admission requirements

For a general statement regarding admission to university study, see article *Admission to university in Canada.*

For information regarding admission to undergraduate study, consult *Requirements for admission to Canadian colleges and universities* available from Service for Admission to College and University, 151

Slater St., Ottawa, Ont., K1P 5N1, $1.50 prepaid.

Same as for The University of Western Ontario.

For admission to the BSW program, it is necessary to have a minimum overall average of 70% in the first year at university together with an acceptable departmental interview.

Academic year

Winter session: mid-September to mid-May.

Grading system

Same as that of The University of Western Ontario.

Fees and costs

Same as for The University of Western Ontario. Full-time tuition fees per year: $570.50; part-time (per course): $105.

Residence rates (room and board) winter session: $1,050.

Financial awards and assistance

King's College offers a limited number of entrance scholarships ($150 – $500). The student should make enquiries upon academic application.

Dean of faculty

Arts
A.F. McKee, MA, MSc(Ec), DUP

Department heads

Consult the listings for The University of Western Ontario.

Lakehead University*

Thunder Bay, Ontario

Telephone: 807-345-2121
Direct general correspondence to the
secretary of the university

Total full-time student enrolment 2,931; see
also separate section *Statistics on Canadian
universities and colleges*

Executive and administrative officers

Chancellor
The Hon. Mr. J.B. Laskin, MA, LLB, LLM,
LLD, DCL, FRSC

Chairman of the board of governors
J.M. Fleming, BScEng

President and vice-chancellor
W.G. Tamblyn, BASc, MCom, LLD

Vice-president
W.D.R. Eldon, BA, AM, PhD

Secretary of the university
Donald E. Ayre, BA

Registrar
W.J. McDonnell, BA, MA

Librarian
E.J. Belton, MA, FLA

Dean of students
J.W. Kerr, BA, STM, MSEd

Comptroller
Grant Thompson, CA

Chief of academic services
H.J. Parker, BA, BD

Director, information services
R.D. Penfold, BA

*Ordinary member, AUCC.

Background

Lakehead University evolved from Lakehead
Technical Institute established in 1946 by
order-in-council of the province of Ontario.
Classes began in 1948 in temporary rented
quarters in downtown Port Arthur. In the
same year first-year university courses were
added to the curriculum. Lakehead College of
Arts, Science and Technology was established
by an act of the Ontario legislature assented
to in 1956, and proclaimed in 1957. The
government and control of Lakehead
Technical Institute were transferred to the
board of governors of the Lakehead College.

The present university site, donated by the
city of Port Arthur, was occupied in 1957.
Second-year arts courses were added in 1960-
61, and in 1962 the original Lakehead
College of Arts, Science and Technology Act
was amended to give the college "university
powers" to establish faculties, etc., and to
confer university degrees in arts and science.
The first degrees in arts and science were
granted on May 6, 1965.

The Lakehead University Act, 1965, was
given the royal assent by the lieutenant-
governor of Ontario on June 22, 1965, and
came into force on July 1, 1965. The
Lakehead College of Arts, Science and
Technology, thereafter known as Lakehead
University, was continued under this new
charter.

Under the terms of the Lakehead University
Act, the university is governed by a board of
governors, which has jurisdiction over
business affairs of the university, and the
senate, which is responsible for academic
policy. The board of governors consists of 30
members, including the president, three
members named by the lieutenant-governor-
in-council, and two members appointed by
the board. Senate consists of the vice-
chancellor and president of the university, the
academic vice-president, if any, the librarian,
and the registrar; deans of all faculties; heads
or chairmen of teaching departments; and
such other members of teaching staff elected
or appointed in such a manner as the senate
may determine. The president is chairman of
the senate.

Facilities and services

Lakehead University is situated in the heart of Thunder Bay (population, 108,048). On May 7, 1969, an order-in-council of the province of Ontario amalgamated the cities of Port Arthur and Fort William and the townships of McIntyre and Neebing to form the city of Thunder Bay. Thunder Bay is located in northwestern Ontario at the head of Lake Superior, on the Great Lakes, about 438 miles east of Winnipeg, Manitoba.

The original college site comprised some 80 acres of land lying between the cities of Port Arthur and Fort William, and was donated by the city of Port Arthur. In 1962 an additional 105 acres of adjoining land were purchased and in 1965, 110 acres of land were purchased in anticipation of future expansion.

The advisory committee conducted a building fund campaign from which the sum of $175,000 was raised, from local industries and individuals.

The first college building, constructed by the Department of Public Works of the province of Ontario, was formally opened on October 2, 1957. A new library wing was added in March 1960, and in the fall of 1969, two extensions providing additional lecture rooms and laboratory space were opened.

A men's residence, including recreational and dining facilities for 52 students and a resident staff member, was opened in September 1962. In 1966, 32 additional double bedrooms were added to the residence. A section of the new structure was made available as a residence for women. A new $2,750,000 residence village comprising 10 new buildings and providing residence for 480 male students and 106 female students has been completed.

The village is situated on the banks of the McIntyre River within easy walking distance of all university buildings and athletic facilities.

On February 15, 1964, the university centre was officially opened. It has a 380-seat theatre-auditorium, as well as lecture and seminar rooms, club rooms, and a cafeteria. Also in 1964, an additional wing was added to the original building and in 1965, a new library building was erected. An additional three floors were added to the new library building in September 1967. In March 1968,

an athletic centre gymnasium was constructed on the other side of the McIntyre River opposite the main university buildings. September 1969 saw the official opening of the Centennial building which houses the science and technology laboratories, classrooms, and faculty offices. An administrative wing and an addition to the university centre building which includes a new cafeteria and dining hall were also completed in that year.

A man-made lake is in the centre of the campus; its creation was planned with the regional conservation authorities as an important flood control project for the McIntyre River which runs through the campus.

Construction currently underway on the campus includes: a new academic building, which will provide additional faculty offices and much needed classroom space; an addition to the athletic centre will encompass an olympic-size swimming pool, three squash courts, a general purpose training room, a wrestling room, two classrooms, shower rooms, and additional office space. The academic building and the addition to the athletic centre are slated for completion in September 1972; an addition to the education building will house a library on the second floor, with offices and classrooms below; the power house complex is being enlarged so as to better supply the needs of a rapidly growing university.

Calendars and brochures

Lakehead University calendar.
Lakehead University review.

Courses and degrees

Arts
(Faculty of arts)

Bachelor of arts (BA).
(a) General course, three years from honor high school graduation (or senior matriculation). Major subjects: anthropology, economics, English, French, geography, German, history, Italian, Latin, mathematics, philosophy, political science, psychology, Russian, sociology, and Spanish. (b) Honors course, four years from honor high school

graduation (or senior matriculation).
Available in anthropology, economics,
English, English and French, French,
geography, history, mathematics, philosophy,
political science, psychology, sociology, and
Spanish.

Master of arts (MA).
A minimum of one year from an honors
bachelor's degree. Available in economics,
English, history, mathematics, and
psychology.

Education

*Interim elementary school teacher's certificate
standard 2.*
Two years.

*Degree program for elementary school and
secondary school teachers (BABEd, BScBEd).*
Four years.

*Degree program for holder of approved
degrees.*
One year.

Science, pure
(Faculty of science)

Bachelor of science (BSc).
(a) General course, three years from honor
high school graduation (or senior
matriculation). Major subjects: biology,
general sciences, geology, mathematics,
natural sciences, and physics. (b) Honors
course, four years from honor high school
graduation (or senior matriculation).
Available in biology, chemistry, geology,
mathematics, mathematical physics, and
physics.

Master of science (MSc).
A minimum of one year from an honors
bachelor's degree. Available in chemistry,
mathematics, and physics.

University schools:.

Business administration
(School of business administration)

Bachelor of commerce (BCom).
Four years from honor high school
graduation (or senior matriculation).

*Diploma in business administration
(DipBusAdmin).*
Three years.

*Diploma in business administration (computer
systems option).*
Three years.

Graduate diploma in business administration.
One year after first degree.

Engineering
(School of engineering)

Bachelor of applied science (BASc).
Four years from honor high school
graduation (or senior matriculation).

*Diploma in engineering technology
(DipEngTechnol).*
Three years: chemical engineering
technology, civil engineering technology,
electronic engineering technology, mechanical
engineering technology.

Forestry
(School of forestry)

Bachelor of science in forestry (BScF).
First two years only offered at present.

Diploma in forest technology (DipForTechnol).
Two years.

Certificate in environmental forest technology.
One year after forest diploma.

Certificate in logging technology.
One year after forest diploma.

Library technology
(School of library technology)

*Diploma in library technology
(DipLibTechnol).*
Two years.

Nursing
(School of nursing)

Bachelor of science in nursing (BScN).
Three years (post-basic); 4 years (basic).

Physical and health education
(School of physical and health education)

Bachelor of physical and health education (BPHE).
Four years from honor high school graduation (or senior matriculation). First three years presently offered.

Special programs

Canadian studies; environmental planning; graduate diploma in economic development; humanistic studies; industrial relations; international studies; liberal science; Taiga studies; theatre arts.

Extension programs

For university credit:

Off-campus courses.
Undergraduate courses in arts for students proceeding to a degree and for teachers who may wish to improve their professional qualifications. Courses are presently being offered at Atikokan, Dryden, Fort Frances, Geraldton, Kenora, Manitouage, Marathon, Nipigon/Red Rock, Red Lake, Sioux Lookout, and Terrace Bay.

Evening session.
Undergraduate courses in arts and science.

Summer session.
Courses offered in arts and science for undergraduates proceeding to a degree and for teachers who may wish to improve their professional qualifications by working towards degrees and diplomas in education. Also, a limited number of courses in physical education.

For no university credit:

Adult education services:
systematic courses in the humanities and other areas of proper concern to a university on a non-credit basis.

Special short courses:
professional refresher or maintenance courses.

Admission requirements

For a general statement regarding admission to university study, see article *Admission to university in Canada.*

For information regarding admission to undergraduate study, consult *Requirements for admission to Canadian colleges and universities* available from Service for Admission to College and University, 151 Slater St., Ottawa, Ont., K1P 5N1, $1.50 prepaid.

For admission to graduate study a student must have attained a first degree with at least second-class standing in appropriate subjects.

Academic year

Winter session: mid-September to early May.

Summer session: early July to mid-August.

Grading system

First-class: 75% and over; second-class: 66 to 74%; third-class: 60 to 65%; pass: 50 to 59%; lowest passing grade in all programs: 50%. In honors programs an overall average of 60% must be maintained, with a 66% in honor subject or subjects.

Fees and costs

Tuition fees per year (1971-72): full-time (a) for first degree — arts, commerce, education, graduate diploma in business administration, nursing, $515; science, forestry, $525; applied science, $570; (b) for master's degree — arts, science, $485; (c) university schools, $250; part-time (per subject on pro rata basis), $115 and up. Miscellaneous fees; Alma Mater Society and athletic fee $50.

Residence rates, board and room, per university year: men, single room, $1,035, double room, $985; women, single room, $1,035, double room $985.

Financial awards and assistance

The principal awards in the various categories are listed below.

Entrance scholarships: Lakehead University entrance scholarships; C.J. Sanders scholarship.

Undergraduate scholarships: Allied Chemical Canada, Ltd. scholarship; J.P. Bickell Foundation scholarship; Great Lakes Paper Company forestry scholarship; Great West Timber scholarship; Dr. Crawford C. McCullough memorial scholarship.

Entrance bursaries and awards: Imperial Oil higher education awards; IBM-Thomas J. Watson memorial bursaries; Inco bursary; Lions Club bursary; Joseph Marien memorial bursaries; Marion E. Tomlinson memorial bursary.

Undergraduate bursaries and awards: Atkinson Charitable Foundation bursaries; A.T.A. Trucking Industry Education Foundation Inc. bursaries; IBM-Thomas J. Watson memorial bursaries; International Pipe Line Company bursaries; Ontario Department of Health bursaries for public health nursing; Thunder Bay Medical Association bursary.

In addition to the Lakehead University graduate fellowships, a number of other fellowships are available and are listed in the Lakehead University calendar.

Deans of faculties

Arts
Tim Ryan, BA, BComm, MA, FREcons, FCIS

Education
James Angus, BA, BEd, MEd, PhD

Science
Robert Ross, BSc, PhD, FRIC

University schools
Harold Braun, CD, BA, LLD

Directors of schools

Business administration
Michael Zablocki, BA, MBA, CA

Engineering
Henry North, BSc, DCAe

Forestry
Kenneth Hearnden, BScF

Library science
To be appointed

Nursing
Jane Holliday, BSPHN, MA, EdD

Physical and health education
James Widdop, DPE, BSc, MA, PhD

Summer session and extension
K.L. Morrison, MA

Department heads

Biology
Douglas Lindsay, BSc, MSc

Chemistry
Stanley Walker, DSc, MA, DPhil, FRIC

Economics
Koilpillai Charles, MA, PhD

English
George Merrill, AB, PhD

Geography
Brian Phillips, BSc, PhD

Geology
Edward Mercy, PhD, DIC

History
Elizabeth Arthur, BA, MA, PhD

Languages
Leo Zawadowski, MA, PhD

Mathematics
Clement Kent, MS, PhD

Philosophy
William Morris, BA, PhD

Physics
Vireshwar Paranjape, MSc, PhD

Political science
Geoffrey Engholm, BSc, PhD

Psychology
William Melnyk, MADipClinPsychol, PhD

Sociology and anthropology
To be appointed

Laurentian University of Sudbury*

Université Laurentienne de Sudbury*

Ramsey Lake Road, Sudbury, Ontario

Chemin du Lac Ramsey, Sudbury (Ont.)

Telephone 705-675-1151
Direct general correspondence to the registrar

Total full-time student enrolment 2,108; see also separate section *Statistics on Canadian universities and colleges*

Téléphone: 705-675-1151
Prière d'adresser la correspondance d'ordre général au secrétaire général

Total des inscriptions des étudiants à plein temps 2,108; voir aussi la section distincte, intitulée "*Statistiques sur les universités et collèges du Canada*"

Executive and administrative officers

Dirigeants

President
R.J.A. Cloutier (acting), PhD

Vice-president (administration)
F.J. Turner (pro tem), BCom, MA

Vice-president (academic) and vice-president (student affairs)
H. Albert (pro tem 1971-72), DPh

Registrar
John Clarke, BA

Chief librarian
Rev. Paul-Emile Filion, SJ, MSinLS, DUL
B. MacNeil (pro tem), BSc, MLS

Director, extension division
Gérard Lafrenière, BA, LPh

Public relations officer
Bernard Lalande, BA

Comptroller
Carl Numi, BComm, CA

Business officer
H. Lemire, BPh, MA

Recteur
Roland Cloutier (intérimaire), PhD

Vice-recteur des affaires administratives
F.J. Turner (pro tem), BCom, MA

Vice-recteur (enseignement) et vice-recteur des affaires étudiantes
H. Albert (pro tem 1971-72), DPh

Secrétaire général
John Clarke, BA

Conservateur de la bibliothèque
Rév. Paul-Emile Filion, SJ, MSinLS, DUL
B. MacNeil (intérimaire), BSc, MLS

Directeur de la division de l'extension de l'enseignement
Gérard Lafrenière, BA, LPh

Directeur des relations publiques
Bernard Lalande, BA

Contrôleur
Carl Numi, BCom, CA

*Ordinary member, AUCC.

*Membre ordinaire de l'AUCC

Director, physical plant and planning
J.R. Harrison, PEng

Director, computer services
B. Byce, BSc, MMath

Admissions officer
Shirley Vincent, BA

Student awards officer
Linda Ronald, BA

Assistant registrar, statistics
Mirko Mehes, BA

Publications officer
Jean Baxter (Mrs), BA

Assistant registrar, records
S. Greenberg, BA

Admissions counsellor
B. Silverman, BCom, MEd

Secondary school liaison officer
R. Patry, BA

Director of counselling services
J. Dardick, BSc, MA

Student affairs co-ordinator
G.C. Dumas, BA

Assistant director of extension
J.G. Maitlant, BSc

Assistant to the director of extension
F. Thibodeau

Préposée aux admissions
Shirley Vincent, BA

Préposée à l'aide financière
Linda Ronald, BA

Secrétaire général adjoint, statistiques
Mirko Mehes, BA

Responsable des publications
Jean Baxter (Mme), BA

Secrétaire général adjoint, dossiers
S. Greenberg, BA

Directeur des services
H. Lemire, BPh, MA

Directeur des installations et de la
planification
J.R. Harrison, IngP

Directeur des services de l'ordinateur
B. Byce, BSc, MMath

Conseiller des admissions
B. Silverman, BCom, MEd

Chargé des rapports avec les écoles
secondaires
R. Patry, BA

Directeurs des services de consultation
J. Dardick, BSc, MA

Coordonnateur des affaires étudiantes
G.C. Dumas, BA

Directeur adjoint de l'éducation permanente
J.G. Maitland, BSc

Assistant du directeur de l'éducation
permanente
F. Thibodeau

Constituent college

University College, Ramsey Lake Road.
Acting principal, dean of students and
registrar: J.M. Porter, MEd. Co-educational.
Non-denominational. Bilingual. Founded
1960. Constituent college within the
university faculty of arts and science. Offers
courses at the undergraduate level, beyond
senior matriculation. Has residential
accommodation.

Background

Laurentian University was established by an
act of the Ontario legislature in 1960 as a
non-denominational, bilingual and co-
educational institution. Teaching began in

Collège constituant

University College, Chemin du Lac Ramsey.
Principal intérimaire, doyen des étudiants et
secrétaire général: J.M. Porter, MEd.
Institution mixte, non confessionnelle, et
bilingue, fondée en 1960. Collège constituant
de la faculté universitaire des arts et des
sciences. Il offre des cours au niveau d'études
pré-grade à partir de l'immatriculation senior.
Résidences.

1960 and the first degrees were conferred in 1961.

The provincial act provided for the federation of denominational universities or colleges with Laurentian University. In 1960, the University of Sudbury (Roman Catholic), founded in 1913, and Huntington University (United church), incorporated in 1960, federated with Laurentian. Thorneloe University (Anglican) joined the federation in 1963.

By the acts of federation, the degree-granting powers of the federated universities are held in abeyance except in theology. Under the federating agreements each of these church-related universities provides a college in the faculty of arts and science of Laurentian University. At present, the federated colleges limit their instruction to philosophy and religious studies; philosophy is also offered within the joint university department of philosophy. All students receive their degrees from Laurentian University.

The university is administered by two senior bodies: the board of governors and the senate. The board of governors consists of 24 voting members (6 appointed by the government of Ontario, 6 by the University of Sudbury, 6 by the United Church of Canada, and 6 by the synod of the Anglican diocese of Algoma) and 7 non-voting members (2 appointed by faculty, 2 by senate, 2 by the student general association and 1 by the extension student general association). Senate is composed of university academic members, ex officio, and representatives of the faculty, the federated colleges and University College, 8 students (4 elected, 2 appointed by the student general association and 2 from the board of governors).

Facilities and services

The university is located within the limits of the city of Sudbury (population 90,000; district, 167,000), on a 700-acre campus, only a ten-minute drive from downtown Sudbury. The land rises in an arc of hills overlooking three lakes.

The first two phases of Laurentian University's master plan have been completed. They include the H.J. Fraser science building with classrooms,

Historique

L'Université Laurentienne de Sudbury a été établie par acte de l'assemblée législative de l'Ontario en 1960, à titre d'institution non confessionnelle, bilingue et mixte. Elle a commencé son enseignement en 1960 et a conféré ses premiers grades en 1961.

La loi provinciale prévoit la fédération d'universités ou collèges confessionnels avec l'Université Laurentienne de Sudbury. En 1960, l'Université de Sudbury (catholique), fondée en 1913, et l'Université Huntington (Eglise Unie), ayant obtenu son incorporation en 1960, se sont fédérées à l'Université Laurentienne de Sudbury. L'Université Thorneloe (anglicane) s'est jointe à la fédération en 1963.

Les accords de fédération autorisent chacune de ces universités confessionnelles à maintenir un collège à l'intérieur de la Faculté des arts et des sciences de l'Université Laurentienne de Sudbury. Actuellement, les collèges fédérés limitent leur enseignement à la philosophie et aux sciences religieuses. La philosophie est également enseignée dans le cadre du département conjoint de philosophie. Tous les étudiants obtiennent leurs grades de l'Université Laurentienne de Sudbury.

L'administration de l'université est constituée de deux organismes: le conseil des gouverneurs et le sénat. Le conseil des gouverneurs est composé de 24 membres à voix active (6 nommés par le gouvernement de l'Ontario, 6 par l'Université de Sudbury, 6 par l'Eglise Unie du Canada, et 6 par le synode du diocèse anglican d'Algoma) et de 7 membres sans voix active (2 nommés par les professeurs, 2 par le sénat, 2 par l'Association générale des étudiants et 1 par l'Association générale des étudiants de l'éducation permanente). Le sénat se compose de membres ex officio du secteur universitaire, de représentants des professeurs, des collèges fédérés, du Collège universitaire, de 8 étudiants (4 élus, 2 nommés par l'Association générale des étudiants et 2 nommés par le conseil des gouverneurs).

Installations et services

L'université est située dans les limites de la ville de Sudbury (qui a à peu près une

laboratories, offices, shops, three auditoria which can be combined to form one large auditorium, a planetarium and an astrodome; a classroom building with amphitheatre; the arts and humanities building housing faculty offices, seminar rooms and four language laboratories; the dining assembly building; and finally the administration and library tower or Ralph D. Parker building containing the library (170,000 volumes), the university's administrative offices as well as the student council offices and common rooms. All these buildings are connected and allow passage under cover from end to end of the whole complex.

To the east and southeast of the main campus are the residences of University, Huntington, Thorneloe, and Sudbury Colleges, with total accommodation for 650 men and women. A short distance from the administration and library tower, there is a complex of sports facilities including the Benjamin F. Avery physical education centre with a 50-metre swimming pool, football and soccer fields, an olympic-designed track, and tennis courts.

Student services include: a health service, a placement office, counselling services, and a foreign student adviser.

Calendars and brochures

Calendar, extension summer session calendar, admissions brochure, counsellors' handbook, folders on the professional schools, bi-monthly newsletter; available from the publications officer.

Student newspapers: Lambda, room L222; Réaction, room L221.

Courses and degrees

Note: the university uses both French and English as languages of instruction. In all cases the number of years given is beyond senior matriculation.

population de 90,000 et dont le district a environ 167,000) sur un terrain de 700 acres, à dix minutes de voiture de la ville. Le terrain va s'élevant vers le sud jusqu'à une crête rocheuse formant croissant et donnant sur trois lacs.

Les travaux des deux premières phases de la construction de l'Université Laurentienne de Sudbury sont terminés. Ils comprennent l'édifice des sciences H.J. Fraser, avec salles de cours, laboratoires, bureaux, boutiques, trois auditoriums que l'on peut transformer en une seule grande salle, un planétarium et un observatoire; un édifice des classes avec amphithéâtre; l'édifice des arts et des humanités qui loge des bureaux de professeurs, des salles de séminaires et deux laboratoires de langue; l'édifice de réception et de restauration; enfin l'édifice Ralph D. Parker, ou Tour de l'administration et de la bibliothèque qui abrite la bibliothèque (170,000 volumes), les bureaux administratifs de l'université, les bureaux du conseil des étudiants et les salles communes. Tous ces édifices communiquent entre eux et l'accès de l'un à l'autre est possible sans sortir à l'extérieur.

A l'est et au sud-est de ces édifices se situent les maisons d'étudiants de Huntington, de Thorneloe et du Collège de l'Université de Sudbury, pouvant accueillir un total de 650 étudiants.

A quelque distance de l'immeuble de la bibliothèque se trouve le centre des sports. Le centre d'éducation physique Benjamin F. Avery avec une piscine de 50 mètres, les terrains de football et de soccer, une piste de course répondant aux exigences olympiques et des courts de tennis sont en service depuis 1965.

Les services pour étudiants comprennent un service de santé, de placement, d'orientation et des étudiants étrangers.

Annuaires et brochures

On trouvera chez le responsable des publications, l'annuaire, l'annuaire des cours d'été à l'extension le dépliant sur les admissions, le guide des conseillers en orientation, les dépliants des écoles professionnelles, le bulletin bi-mensuel. Journal étudiant: salle L221, L222.

Arts
(Faculty of arts and science)

Bachelor of arts (BA).
(a) General program, normally three years. Concentrations are offered in Amerindian-Eskimo studies, economics, English, français, French, geography, German, history, Italian, Latin, Latin-American studies, mathematics, philosophy, political science, psychology, religious studies, Russian, sociology, and Spanish. Combined concentrations may be approved at the discretion of the dean. (b) Honors program, normally four years, commencing in the second year. The student is cautioned that some of the honors programs require the completion of specific courses in the first year. At the discretion of the dean, and with the approval of the department(s) concerned, specializations are offered in courses such as: economics, English, English and French, English and history, geography, history, history and philosophy, Latin, English and Latin, English and philosophy, English and Spanish, français, French, French and history, French and Latin, French and philosophy, French and Spanish, Latin and Greek, mathematics, philosophy, psychology, political science, political science and economics, political science and français, political science and Spanish, political science and philosophy, Spanish, sociology, sociology and Amerindian-Eskimo studies.

Science
(Faculty of arts and science)

Bachelor of science (BSc).
(a) General program, normally three years. Concentrations are offered in: biology, chemistry, geology, mathematics, and physics. (b) Honors program, normally four years. The first year is the same as the general degree: but students are cautioned that some of the honors programs require the completion of specific courses in the first year. Specializations are offered in: biology, chemistry, geology, mathematics, and physics.

(School of graduate studies)

Master of science (MSc).
Programs leading to a master's degree require a minimum of one academic year beyond the honors degree. Programs are offered in: biology, chemistry, geology, and physics.

Cours et grades

A noter: L'université emploie le français et l'anglais comme langues d'enseignement. Le nombre d'années indiqué ci-dessous est la durée des cours après l'immatriculation senior ou les belles-lettres.

Arts
(Faculté des arts et des sciences)

Le baccalauréat ès arts (BA).
(a) Programme général, normalement trois ans. On offre les concentrations dans les matières suivantes: allemand, anglais, économie, espagnol, études indiennes-esquimaudes, études latino-américaines, français, géographie, histoire, italien, latin, mathématiques, philosophie, psychologie, russe, science politique, sciences religieuses et sociologie. Concentration en deux matières possible avec l'approbation du doyen.
(b) Le programme spécialisé, normalement quatre ans. L'étudiant doit prendre note que certains programmes spécialisés exigent la réussite de cours particuliers en première année. Avec l'approbation du doyen et des départements concernés, l'étudiant peut prendre les spécialisations suivantes: anglais, anglais et français, anglais et histoire, anglais et latin, anglais et philosophie, anglais et espagnol, économie, espagnol, français, français et histoire, français et latin, français et philosophie, français et espagnol, géographie, histoire, histoire et philosophie, latin, latin et grec, mathématiques, philosophie, psychologie, science politique, science politique et économie, science politique et français, science politique et espagnol, science politique et philosophie, sociologie, sociologie et études indiennes-esquimaudes.

Sciences
(Faculté des arts et des sciences)

Le baccalauréat ès sciences (BSc).
(a) Programme général, normalement trois ans. Concentrations en biologie, chimie, géologie, mathématiques et physique.
(b) Programme spécialisé, normalement quatre ans. La première année est identique au programme général, mais les étudiants doivent remarquer que certains programmes spécialisés exigent la réussite de cours particuliers de la première année. On offre la spécialisation en biologie, chimie, géologie, mathématiques et physique.

Professional schools

Each of the professional schools of Laurentian University offers a program requiring four years. Professional courses are taught by the schools and non-professional courses by the faculty of arts and science. The following programs are offered:

Commerce

Bachelor of commerce (BCom).
Four years from senior matriculation; school of commerce and business administration.

A *diploma in business administration* is awarded at the successful completion of a one-year program open to those who have obtained an undergraduate degree in a discipline other than commerce or business administration.

Engineering

The school of engineering offers a general first-year and a second-year specializing in chemical, civil, metallurgical, mining, or mechanical engineering.

Language

Bachelor of science in language (BSL).
Four years from senior matriculation; school of translators and interpreters.

Nursing

Bachelor of science in nursing (BScN).
Four years from senior matriculation; school of nursing.

Physical and health education

Bachelor of physical and health education (BPHE).
Four years from senior matriculation; school of physical and health education.

(Ecole des études graduées)

Les programmes donnant droit à la maîtrise ès sciences exigent un minimum d'une année d'études après l'obtention du baccalauréat spécialisé. On offre ces programmes en biologie, chimie, géologie et physique.

Ecoles d'enseignement professionnel

Toutes les écoles d'enseignement professionnel de l'Université Laurentienne de Sudbury offrent un programme d'études de quatre ans. Ces écoles donnent l'enseignement professionnel, tandis que l'enseignement non professionnel du programme est donné par la Faculté des arts et des sciences. Les cours suivants sont offerts:

Commerce

Baccalauréat en commerce (BCom).
Quatre ans après l'immatriculation senior ou les belles-lettres, école de l'administration et du commerce.

On offre un *diplôme en administration des affaires* aux étudiants qui, ayant déjà un premier grade dans une autre matière, suivent un programme d'études d'une année en commerce et en administration des affaires.

Education physique et hygiène

Baccalauréat en éducation physique et hygiène (BPHE).
Quatre ans après l'immatriculation senior ou les belles-lettres, école d'éducation physique et d'hygiène.

Génie

L'école de génie offre une première année générale et une deuxième année de spécialisation en: génie chimique, génie civil, génie métallurgique, génie minier ou génie mécanique.

Social work

Bachelor of social work (BSW).
Four years from senior matriculation; school of social work.

Special programs

Special programs can be arranged to prepare students for entrance to professional faculties elsewhere.

An interdisciplinary program in Amerindian-Eskimo studies was approved as a BA concentration in May 1971. Under certain specified conditions, degrees may be awarded with a bilingual qualification.

Extension programs

The extension division directs a summer session on the Sudbury campus and in other northern Ontario centres, and offers part-time winter session courses in Sudbury, Blind River, Chapleau, Elliot Lake, Espanola, Kapuskasing, Kirkland Lake, Manitoulin Island, New Liskeard, Noelville, Parry Sound, Sturgeon Falls, Iron Bridge, Englehart, Onaping, and Timmins.

Preliminary year: pre-university courses are offered only through the extension division. Students may proceed in this manner to obtain grade 13 credits or raise grade 13 averages.

For university credit:

Full BA program offered.

Evening session. Undergraduate courses in arts, certain courses in science.

Summer session. Undergraduate courses in arts and certain science subjects for undergraduates proceeding to a degree and for teachers who may wish to improve their professional status.

For no university credit:

Popular courses of cultural benefit and of interest to the community are offered.

Sciences de langage

Baccalauréat en sciences du langage (BSL).
Quatre ans après l'immatriculation senior ou les belles-lettres, école de traducteurs et d'interprètes.

Sciences infirmières

Baccalauréat en sciences infirmières (BScN).
Quatre ans après l'immatriculation senior ou les belles-lettres, école des sciences infirmières.

Service social

Baccalauréat en service social (BSW).
Quatre ans après l'immatriculation senior ou les belles-lettres, école de service social.

Programmes spéciaux

Des programmes spéciaux peuvent être établis en vue de préparer les étudiants à l'admission aux écoles d'enseignement professionnel dans d'autres institutions d'enseignement.

Un programme interdisciplinaire en études indiennes-esquimaudes a été institué au mois de mai 71 comme concentration du baccalauréat. Un grade avec mention bilingue est attribué aux étudiants qui répondent à certaines conditions.

Education permanente

La division de l'extension organise les cours d'été sur le campus et dans certains centres du Nord-Ontario, et offre des cours du soir durant l'année régulière à Sudbury, Blind River, Chapleau, Elliott Lake, Englehart, Espanola, Iron Bridge, Kapuskasing, Kirkland Lake, Manitoulin Island, New Liskeard, Noelville, Onaping, Parry Sound, Sturgeon Falls et Timmins.

L'année préliminaire: la division de l'extension offre l'enseignement pré-universitaire aux étudiants qui désirent compléter leur 13e année ou rehausser leur moyenne de la 13e année.

Admission requirements

Programme complet du BA.

For a general statement regarding admission to university study, see article *Admission to university in Canada.*

Cours du soir:
matières du baccalauréat dans les arts, quelques-unes dans les sciences.

For information regarding admission to undergraduate study, consult *Requirements for admission to Canadian colleges and universities* available from Service for Admission to College and University, 151 Slater St., Ottawa, Ont., K1P 5N1, $1.50 prepaid.

Cours d'été:
matières du baccalauréat dans les arts et quelques-unes des sciences à l'intention de ceux qui s'acheminent vers le baccalauréat, et des enseignants qui désirent améliorer leurs qualifications professionnelles.

Students seeking admission to a graduate program must hold a honors bachelor's degree or its equivalent with at least second-class (B) standing in an appropriate area of study.

Sans crédit:

Enseignement destiné aux adultes qui désirent accroître leur culture personnelle et qui répond au besoin social et professionnel de la population.

Academic year

Conditions d'admission

Winter session: mid-September to early May.

Summer session: a six-week day session from early July to mid-August, and a twelve-week evening session from mid-May to mid-August.

On trouvera un exposé général sur l'admission aux études universitaires dans l'article *Admission aux universités canadiennes.*

Afin d'obtenir des renseignements sur l'admission aux études du niveau pré-grade, consultez *Conditions d'admission dans les collèges et universités du Canada* que l'on peut obtenir du Service d'admission au collège et à l'université, 151, rue Slater, Ottawa (Ontario), K1P 5N1, $1.50 port payé.

Grading system

A: 75-100%; B: 66-74%; C: 60-65%; D: 50-59%. Standing, based on the overall average received by the student, is granted at the end of each year on the following basis: first-class honors 75-100%; second-class honors 66-74%; third-class honors 60-65%; pass (general course) 50-59%.

Les candidats à l'admission dans un programme d'études supérieures doivent présenter un baccalauréat spécialisé ou son équivalent et une note d'au moins "B" dans une matière appropriée.

Fees and costs

Année universitaire

Tuition fees per year — full-time: (a) undergraduate tuition, $490; miscellaneous compulsory fees, $73; total $563; (b) graduate tuition: $485 (first year), $100 (second year); miscellaneous fees, $11.

Session d'automne: de la mi-septembre au début de mai.

Residence fees for academic year — single room on a seven-day basis, $600. Double room on a seven-day basis, $550. Board for a seven-day week, lunch and dinner only, $386.

Session d'été: une session de jour durant six semaines, du début de juillet à la mi-août, et une session de douze semaines durant la soirée, de la mi-mai à la mi-août.

Board for a five-day week (Saturday and Sunday excluded), lunch and dinner, $302.

Extension fees — in Sudbury, each full course, $110 tuition and $8 compulsory fees; for off-campus studies, each full course, $115 tuition and $7 compulsory fees.

Financial awards and assistance

All students are given consideration for a number of entrance and in-course awards, which are awarded on academic merit. The university is a participant in the Ontario student awards program.

Research institutes

The Cardio-Thoracic Research Institute was established as a cardio-thoracic or cardiovascular unit to provide facilities for study and therapy of clinical disorders of the circulatory and pulmonary systems. The cardiac research laboratories attached to the Sudbury cardiac surgical team are located in Laurentian's department of biology.

The Institute for Fine Particle Research, an interdisciplinary institute, offers short intensive postgraduate courses in fine particle science and has research facilities for studies of light scattering phenomena, sedimentation dynamics, and fine particle physics.

The Institute of Astronomy has a Spitz model, A-3-P planetarium, a 6″ Maksutov telescope, and a 22″ Newtonian telescope for visual, photographic, and photo-electric observations; and an 8″ photographic telescope.

Federated universities

Credits are transferable to Laurentian University of Sudbury.

Huntington University, Sudbury, Ontario. President: L.J. Winckel, BA, LTh, STM, ThD. Registrar: G. Hobbs, BA, BD, DèsScrel. Co-educational. United Church. Established and federated with Laurentian University of Sudbury 1960. Offers undergraduate courses in religious studies. Residence.

Système de mentions

A: 75 à 100%; B: 66 à 74%; C: 60 à 65%; D: 50 à 59%. La cote, fondée sur la moyenne générale de l'étudiant, est attribuée à la fin de chaque année selon la formule suivante: très grande distinction 75 à 100%; grande distinction 66 à 74%; distinction 60 à 65%; succès (cours général) 50 à 59%.

Droits d'inscription

Frais de scolarité annuels — étudiants à plein temps: (a) niveau pré-grade, $490; frais divers obligatoires, $73; total: $563. (b) niveau post-grade: frais de scolarité, première année, $485; deuxième année, $100; frais divers, $11.

Etudiants de l'extension à Sudbury — frais de scolarité, le cours complet, $110; droits obligatoires, $8.

Etudiants de l'extension dans les centres extérieurs — frais de scolarité, le cours complet, $115; droits obligatoires, $7.

Frais de résidence: chambre simple, 7 jours par semaine, $600. Chambre double, 7 jours par semaine, $550. Repas 7 jours par semaine (dîner et souper seulement), $386. Repas 5 jours par semaine (dîner et souper) samedi et dimanche exclus, $302.

Aide financière

L'université accorde son attention au mérite scolaire de tous les étudiants par l'attribution d'un certain nombre de bourses d'entrée et de bourses pour les étudiants inscrits dans un programme. L'université participe au programme d'Aide financière aux étudiants de l'Ontario.

Instituts de recherche

L'Institut d'astronomie possède un planétarium Spitz, A-3-P, un téléscope de 6″ Maksutov, un téléscope de 22″ Newton, pour observations visuelles, photographiques et photoélectriques; et un téléscope photographique de 8″.

Université de Sudbury/ University of Sudbury,
Sudbury, Ontario.
President: J.D. Richard, sj, PhD, LLD. Vice-
president (administration): H.L. Bertrand, sj,
BA, LPh, LTh, DrèsSc. Registrar and dean of
studies: R. Tremblay, sj, BA, LPh, LTh,
MEd. Co-educational and bilingual. Roman
Catholic (Jesuits). Established in 1913.
Federated with Laurentian University of
Sudbury on September 10, 1960. Offers
courses in philosophy and religious studies.
Residential accommodation.

Thorneloe University, Sudbury, Ontario.
President, vice-chancellor, and provost: F.A.
Peake, MA, DD. Registrar and dean of
residence: K. Winterhalder, MSc. Co-
educational. Anglican. Established 1961.
Offers undergraduate courses in religious
studies. Residence, men only.

Affiliated colleges

Degrees are awarded by Laurentian
University of Sudbury.

Algoma College, Sault Ste. Marie, Ontario.
Principal: I.W. Brown, PhD. Affiliated with
Laurentian University of Sudbury on
December 17, 1965. First-year students
enroled in September 1967. The college offers
first- and second-year level courses in arts and
first-year level courses in science during the
day, and some second- and third-year courses
through an extension program, closely
associated with Laurentian University of
Sudbury.

Nipissing College, North Bay, Ontario.
Principal: G. Zytaruk, PhD. Established in
1967 and affiliated with Laurentian
University of Sudbury. The college offers
first-year level courses in arts and science
during the day, and some second- and third-
year courses through an extension program,
closely associated with Laurentian University
of Sudbury.

Collège de Hearst, Hearst, Ontario.
Principal: M.M. Saulnier. Affiliated with the
University of Sudbury in 1957. Resident and
non-resident school. The college which is
designed for francophones students offers a
3-year course of studies leading to the BA
degree. Non-denominational.

L'Institut de recherche sur les micro-particules,
institut interdisciplinaire, offre des cours de
courte durée au niveau supérieur, et possède
des installations permettant la recherche sur
les phénomènes de la dispersion de la lumière,
la sédimentation et la physique des micro-
particules.

L'Institut de recherche cardio-thoracique
offre des installations appropriées pour la
recherche et la guérison des troubles
circulatoires et respiratoires. Les laboratoires
de recherches cardiologiques sont reliés à
l'équipe de chirurgie cardiaque de Sudbury et
font partie du département de biologie de
l'Université Laurentienne de Sudbury.

Universités fédérées

Les crédits sont transférables à l'Université
Laurentienne de Sudbury

Huntington University, Sudbury (Ont.).
Président: L.J. Winckel, BA, LTh, STM,
ThD. Secrétaire général: G. Hobbs, BA, BD,
DèsScRel. Mixte. Eglise Unie. Fondée et
fédérée avec l'Université Laurentienne de
Sudbury en 1960. Offre des cours au niveau
d'études pré-grade en sciences religieuses.
Résidence.

Université de Sudbury/ University of Sudbury,
Sudbury (Ont.).
Recteur: J.D. Richard, sj, PhD, LLD. Vice-
recteur à l'administration: H.L. Bertrand, sj,
BA, LPh, LTh, DrèsSc. Directeur des études
et secrétaire général: R. Tremblay, sj, BA,
LPh, LTh, MEd. Mixte et bilingue.
Catholique (Jésuites). Fondée en 1913.
Fédérée le 10 septembre 1960 avec
l'Université Laurentienne de Sudbury. Offre
des cours de sciences religieuses et de
philosophie. Résidence.

Thorneloe University, Sudbury (Ont.).
Recteur, vice-chancelier et principal: F.A.
Peake, MA, DD. Secrétaire général et doyen
de la résidence: R. Winterhalder, MSc. Mixte.
Anglicane. Fondée en 1961. Offre des cours
au niveau d'études pré-grade en sciences
religieuses. Résidence pour hommes.

Collèges affiliés

L'Université Laurentienne de Sudbury
décerne les grades.
Algoma College, Sault Ste Marie (Ont.).
Nipissing College, North Bay (Ont.).

Deans of faculties

Arts and science
Gerald Vallillee (acting), MA, PhD

Humanities, associate dean
To be appointed

Science, associate dean
D.H. Williamson, BSc, PhD

Social sciences, associate dean
A. Barnett, BA, MS, PhD

Directors of schools and institutes

*indicates acting directors

Commerce and administration
K.E. Loucks, BA, MBA

Engineering
A.S. Tombalakian, MASc, PhD, PEng, FCIC

Fine particle research institute
B.H. Kaye, MSc, PhD

Graduate studies
W.Y. Watson, BA, PhD

Nursing
*Margaret Lee, BScN, MA, EdD

Physical and health education
*John Dewar, BEdinPE, MA, EdD

Social work
A.C. Ashby, BA, BSW, AM

Translators and interpreters
J.F. Hendry, MA

Department heads

*indicates acting heads

Astronomy
R. Leclaire, BA, BEd, PhD

Biology
J.W. Green, BSc, MSc, PhD

Chemistry
C. Allaire, SJ, BA, MSc

Collège de Hearst, Hearst (Ont.).
Supérieur: M.M. Saulnier. Affilié en 1957 à l'Université de Sudbury. Pensionnat et externat. Le Collège de Hearst, à l'intention des étudiants de langue française, donne un programme limité de 3 ans menant au BA. Non confessionel.

Doyens des facultés

Arts et sciences
G.R. Vallillee (intérimaire), MA, PhD

Humanités, doyen adjoint
En instance de nomination

Sciences, doyen adjoint
D.H. Williamson, BSc, PhD

Sciences sociales, doyen adjoint
A. Barnett, BA, MA, PhD

Directeurs des écoles
Indique les directeurs intérimaires*

Commerce et administration
K.E. Loucks, BA, MBA

Education physique et hygiène
John Dewar, BEdinPE, MA, EdD*

Etudes graduées
W.Y. Watson, BA, PhD

Génie
A.S. Tombalakian, MASc, PhD, PEng, FCIC

Recherche sur les micro-particules, Institut de
B.H. Kaye, MSc, PhD

Sciences infirmières
Margaret Lee, BScN, MA, EdD*

Service social
A.C. Ashby, BA, BSW, AM

Traducteurs et interprètes
J.F. Hendry, MA

Directeurs des départements
Indique les directeurs intérimaires*

Anglais
Edgar Wright, BA, MA, PhD

Classical studies
*G.I. Clarke, BA, MA, BD

Economics
S. Gilani, BA, MA, PhD

English
Edgar Wright, BA, MA, PhD

French
P. Sabourin, BA, MA, DU

Geography
J. Konarek, BA, MSc

Geology
D.H. Williamson, BSc, PhD, FGS

History
*G.A. Stelter, BA, PhD

Mathematics
B.N. Lahiri, MSc, DIC, PhD

Modern languages
To be appointed

Philosophy
To be appointed

Physics
G.A. Rubin, BSc, DrRerNat

Political science
R. Segsworth, BA, MA

Psychology
Roland Farrant, BA, MA, PhD, FBPsS

Religious studies
Raymond Tremblay, BA, LTh

Sociology
G.A. Bernard, LèsL, DrSoc

Astronomie
R. Leclaire, BA, BEd, PhD

Biologie
J.W. Green, BSc, MSc, PhD

Chimie
C. Allaire, SJJ, BA, MSc

Economie
S. Gilani, BA, MA, PhD

Etudes classiques
G.I. Clarke, BA, MA, BD*

Français
P. Sabourin, BA, MA, DU

Géographie
J. Konarek, BA, MSc

Géologie
D.H. Williamson, BSc, PhD, FGS

Histoire
G.A. Stelter, BA, PhD*

Langues vivantes
En instance de nomination

Mathématiques
B.N. Lahiri, MSc, DIC, PhD

Philosophie
En instance de nomination

Physique
G.A. Rubin, BSc, DrRerNat

Psychologie
R.H. Farrant, BA, MA, PhD, FBPsS

Science politique
R. Segsworth, BA, MA

Sciences religieuses
Raymond Tremblay, BA, LTh

Sociologie
G.A. Bernard, LèsL, DrSoc

Université Laval*

Cité universitaire, Québec 10e (Qué.)

Téléphone: 418-656-2131
Prière d'adresser la correspondance d'ordre
général au secrétaire général

Total des inscriptions des étudiants à plein
temps 10,328; voir aussi la section distincte,
intitulée *Statistiques sur les universités et
collèges du Canada*

Dirigeants

Recteur
Mgr Louis-Albert Vachon, pa, VG, DTh,
DPh, LLD, DCL

Vice-recteurs
Louis-Philippe Bonneau, BA, BScapp
Fernand Gingras, BA, BPh, LTh
Larkin Kerwin, DSc
Napoléon LeBlanc, BA, MScsoc

Secrétaire général
Paul-André Laberge, BA, LèsL

Directeur général des programmes de cours
du 1er cycle
Mgr Marcel Lauzon

Registraire
Marc Boucher

Directeur de l'admission
Simon Montmigny

Directeur de l'inscription
Claude Blais, BSccom

Directeur du service des finances
Mathieu Leclerc, MSccom

Conservateur de la bibliothèque
Joseph-Marie Blanchet, BPh, BBibl

Directeur de l'éducation permanente
Maurice Barbeau, LèsL, LPéd

Directeur des cours d'été et directeur de
l'extension de l'enseignement
Anicet Greco, BA, MPh

Directeur général de la vie étudiante
Pierre Galipeau

Directeur des presses de l'université
Claude Frémont

Directeur du service du personnel
Marc Audet

Directeur des relations publiques
André Barnard, BScapp

Directeur de l'association des anciens
Ludger Saint-Pierre

Directeur du service de logement
Roger Côté

Directeur du service des activités sportives
Gaston Marcotte

Historique

L'Université Laval est à la fois la plus vieille
et la plus jeune université francophone
d'Amérique du Nord. Fondée en 1852, elle a
grandi et prospéré en vertu des pouvoirs que
lui accordait une première charte octroyée au
Séminaire de Québec. Le 8 décembre 1970, le
gouvernement de Québec accordait à
l'Université Laval une nouvelle charte qui la
constituait en une corporation d'enseignement
supérieur différente de la première, mais qui
l'habilitait à continuer l'oeuvre de cette
dernière. C'est au cours de l'été 1971 que le
lieutenant-gouverneur en conseil a promulgué
cette charte en même temps que les premiers
statuts de la nouvelle corporation préparés et
approuvés par le conseil de l'ancienne.

Les droits et pouvoirs de l'université sont
exercés par un conseil composé de 25
membres d'office et de 26 membres élus. Le
conseil exécutif voit à l'exécution des
politiques et décisions du conseil et assure
l'administration courante de l'université.

*Membre ordinaire de l'AUCC.

Installations et services

Pendant près de cent ans l'Université Laval a logé dans le vieux quartier latin de la ville de Québec. Aujourd'hui l'Université Laval est située dans la ville de Sainte-Foy en banlieue de Québec. On y trouve plusieurs édifices modernes et spacieux dont les principaux sont, par ordre d'érection: le pavillon de foresterie et de géodésie, le pavillon des sciences de l'administration, le pavillon Vandry (médecine), l'édifice du Grand Séminaire et l'église de la cité universitaire, le pavillon Vachon (sciences pures), le pavillon Pouliot (sciences appliquées), le pavillon De Koninck (sciences humaines), le pavillon de l'agriculture, le pavillon de la bibliothèque et le pavillon des sciences de l'éducation. On trouve également à la cité universitaire quatre résidences pour les étudiants (pavillons Parent, Lemieux, Lacerte et Biermans-Moraud) et un pavillon pour les activités sociales (pavillon Pollack où est située la cafétéria. En 1970 l'Université Laval a inauguré un nouveau pavillon, celui de l'éducation physique et des sports. Cet édifice conçu selon des normes d'avant-garde dans le domaine des sports, sert non seulement à l'enseignement de l'éducation physique, mais aux activités sportives des membres de la communauté universitaire.

La cité universitaire comprend aussi des pavillons de service de la Faculté d'agriculture et le laboratoire de recherches forestières du gouvernement fédéral.

Plusieurs pavillons de la cité sont reliés par un couloir souterrain qui permet aux piétons de circuler entre les pavillons, la bibliothèque, le centre sportif et le parc intérieur de stationnement.

On trouve également à la cité universitaire les bureaux de tous les services administratifs de l'université ainsi que les Presses de l'Université Laval.

La bibliothèque de l'université possède actuellement une collection de 945,246 volumes, brochures, microtextes ... et reçoit quelque 12,700 périodiques. La bibliothèque offre divers autres services parmi lesquels une cartothèque, un service d'archives, une cinémathèque, une testothèque et un centre de documentation.

A la demande des étudiants, l'Université Laval a pris en charge différents services ayant trait aux activités parascolaires des étudiants.

Ainsi, la Commission des loisirs socio-culturels offre à tous la possibilité de prendre des responsabilités ou de participer à des activités très diverses dans les domaines de la musique, de l'audio-visuel, du théâtre, des arts plastiques, du folklore, de l'information ou des activités de détente, telles: les discothèques, les spectacles, les clubs de bridge, d'échecs, etc.

La construction d'un nouveau pavillon de l'éducation physique a mis le Service des activités sportives en mesure d'offrir à des milliers d'étudiants la possibilité de participer à des sports de compétition intramuros ou interuniversitaires ou encore de s'adonner à leurs sports récréatifs préférés. Ce service offre une gamme de plus de trente-cinq activités sportives différentes.

La Direction générale de la Vie étudiante qui regroupe tous les services aux étudiants est sans cesse à la recherche de nouveaux moyens qui pourront favoriser le plein épanouissement de toutes les dimensions de la personnalité de l'étudiant. Pour ce faire, elle offre déjà les services suivants: le service des bourses et de l'aide financière; le service de santé; le service d'orientation et de counseling; le service de placement; le service aux étudiants étrangers; le service de pastorale; la commission des loisirs socio-culturels.

Annuaires et brochures

La brochure "Renseignements généraux", publiée annuellement, fournit tous les renseignements relatifs à l'admission et à l'inscription des étudiants au moins un an à l'avance, et l'énumération de tous les programmes d'études offerts par l'Université Laval.

"L'annuaire général" fournit un bref aperçu des structures de l'université et une vue d'ensemble sur les différents programmes d'études offerts dans les facultés et écoles.

"Le Rapport de l'Université", publié à la fin de chaque année universitaire, donne un compte rendu des états financiers, un aperçu des objectifs réalisés et fournit les statistiques des étudiants et des diplômés.

Sont également publiés annuellement les annuaires des facultés et écoles, les brochures "Aide financière", "Statistiques" et "Livret à l'usage des étudiants étrangers".

Durant l'année universitaire est également publié, hebdomadairement par le Service des relations publiques, le journal "Au fil des événements". On peut se procurer l'une ou l'autre des publications mentionnées en s'adressant au Service des annuaires ou au Service des relations publiques.

Cours et grades

La liste des programmes d'études à l'Université Laval est différente de celle des années antérieures. Le changement est justifié en raison de l'application intégrale, à compter de septembre 1972, des rapports de la Commission de la réforme approuvés par le conseil de l'université au sujet du régime des études de chacun des trois cyles de l'enseignement supérieur.

Seule l'énumération des programmes d'études est fournie ci-après. Les renseignements supplémentaires au sujet de ces programmes seront fournis dans une édition subséquente. En cours d'année on peut consulter la brochure "Renseignements généraux" pour de plus amples renseignements.

Programmes de cours de l'automne 1972

Les baccalauréats spécialisés:

(Arts et des lettres, Secteur des)

Arts

Baccalauréat en arts visuels (arts plastiques) *(Bartsvis)*.
Baccalauréat en arts visuels (communication graphique) *(Bartsvis)*.
Baccalauréat ès arts spécialisé en histoire de l'art *(BA)*.

Lettres

Baccalauréat ès arts ap. en études françaises (littérature canadienne) *(BA)*.
Baccalauréat ès arts spécialisé en études allemandes *(BA)*.
Baccalauréat ès arts spécialisé en études anciennes (archéologie) *(BA)*.

Baccalauréat ès arts spécialisé en études anciennes (études grecques) *(BA)*.
Baccalauréat ès arts spécialisé en études anciennes (études latines) *(BA)*.
Baccalauréat ès arts spécialisé en études anglaises (linguistique) *(BA)*.
Baccalauréat ès arts spécialisé en études anglaises (littérature) *(BA)*.
Baccalauréat ès arts spécialisé en études françaises (linguistique) *(BA)*.
Baccalauréat ès arts spécialisé en études françaises (litt. franç.) *(BA)*.
Baccalauréat ès arts spécialisé en études hispaniques *(BA)*.
Baccalauréat ès arts spécialisé en français (pour non-francophones) *(BA)*.
Baccalauréat ès arts spécialisé en traduction *(BA)*.

Musique

Baccalauréat en musique − sans mention *(BMus)*.
Baccalauréat en musique (composition) *(BMus)*.
Baccalauréat en musique (éducation musicale) *(BMus)*.
Baccalauréat en musique (histoire et littérature musicales) *(BMus)*.
Baccalauréat en musique (interprétation − chant) *(BMus)*.
Baccalauréat en musique (interprétation − flûte à bec) *(BMus)*.
Baccalauréat en musique (interprétation − flûte traversière) *(BMus)*.
Baccalauréat en musique (interprétation − guitare) *(BMus)*.
Baccalauréat en musique (interprétation − orgue) *(BMus)*.
Baccalauréat en musique (interprétation − piano) *(BMus)*.
Baccalauréat en musique (interprétation − saxophone) *(BMus)*.
Baccalauréat en musique (interprétation − violon) *(BMus)*.
Baccalauréat en musique (interprétation − violoncelle) *(BMus)*.
Baccalauréat en musique (interprétation −) *(BMus)*.
Baccalauréat en musique (rythmique) *(BMus)*.

Education

Les baccalauréats en éducation pour l'enseignement au niveau élémentaire:

Baccalauréat en éducation (enseignement élémentaire) *(BEd)*.
Majeure: pédagogie et didactique
Mineure: arts plastiques

Baccalauréat en éducation (enseignement
élémentaire) *(BEd).*
Majeure: pédagogie et didactique
Mineure: catéchèse

Baccalauréat en éducation (enseignement
élémentaire) *(BEd).*
Majeure: pédagogie et didactique
Mineure: éducation physique

Baccalauréat en éducation (enseignement
élémentaire) *(BEd).*
Majeure: pédagogie et didactique
Mineure: études anglaises

Baccalauréat en éducation (enseignement
élémentaire) *(BEd).*
Majeure: pédagogie et didactique
Mineure: études françaises

Baccalauréat en éducation (enseignement
élémentaire) *(BEd).*
Majeure: pédagogie et didactique
Mineure: géographie

Baccalauréat en éducation (enseignement
élémentaire) *(BEd).*
Majeure: pédagogie et didactique
Mineure: histoire

Baccalauréat en éducation (enseignement
élémentaire) *(BEd).*
Majeure: pédagogie et didactique
Mineure: mathématiques

Baccalauréat en éducation (enseignement
élémentaire) *(BEd).*
Majeure: pédagogie et didactique
Mineure: musique

Baccalauréat en éducation (enseignement
élémentaire) *(BEd).*
Majeure: pédagogie et didactique
Mineure: sciences naturelles

*Les baccalauréats en éducation pour
l'enseignement au niveau secondaire:*

Baccalauréat en éducation (enseignement
secondaire) *(BEd).*
Majeure: arts plastiques
Mineure: pédagogie et didactique

Baccalauréat en éducation (enseignement
secondaire) *(BEd).*
Majeure: biologie
Mineure: pédagogie et didactique

Baccalauréat en éducation (enseignement
secondaire) *(BEd).*
Majeure: catéchèse
Mineure: pédagogie et didactique

Baccalauréat en éducation (enseignement
secondaire) *(BEd).*
Majeure: chimie
Mineure: pédagogie et didactique

Baccalauréat en éducation (enseignement
secondaire) *(BEd).*
Majeure: économie familiale
Mineure: pédagogie et didactique

Baccalauréat en éducation (enseignement
secondaire) *(BEd).*
Majeure: économique
Mineure: pédagogie et didactique

Baccalauréat en éducation (enseignement
secondaire) *(BEd).*
Majeure: éducation physique
Mineure: pédagogie et didactique

Baccalauréat en éducation (enseignement
secondaire) *(BEd).*
Majeure: études allemandes
Mineure: pédagogie et didactique

Baccalauréat en éducation (enseignement
secondaire) *(BEd).*
Majeure: études anglaises
Mineure: pédagogie et didactique

Baccalauréat en éducation (enseignement
secondaire) *(BEd).*
Majeure: études françaises
Mineure: pédagogie et didactique

Baccalauréat en éducation (enseignement
secondaire) *(BEd).*
Majeure: études grecques
Mineure: pédagogie et didactique

Baccalauréat en éducation (enseignement
secondaire) *(BEd).*
Majeure: études hispaniques
Mineure: pédagogie et didactique

Baccalauréat en éducation (enseignement
secondaire) *(BEd).*
Majeure: études latines
Mineure: pédagogie et didactique

Baccalauréat en éducation (enseignement
secondaire) *(BEd).*
Majeure: géographie
Mineure: pédagogie et didactique

Baccalauréat en éducation (enseignement
secondaire) *(BEd).*
Majeure: histoire
Mineure: pédagogie et didactique

Baccalauréat en éducation (enseignement
secondaire) *(BEd).*
Majeure: hygiène
Mineure: pédagogie et didactique

Baccalauréat en éducation (enseignement secondaire) *(BEd)*.
Majeure: mathématiques
Mineure: pédagogie et didactique

Baccalauréat en éducation (enseignement secondaire) *(BEd)*.
Majeure: musique
Mineure: pédagogie et didactique

Baccalauréat en éducation (enseignement secondaire) *(BEd)*.
Majeure: physique
Mineure: pédagogie et didactique

Baccalauréat en éducation (enseignement secondaire) *(BEd)*.
Majeure: sciences de l'administration
Mineure: pédagogie et didactique

Baccalauréat en éducation (enseignement secondaire) *(BEd)*.
Majeure: sciences de la santé
Mineure: pédagogie et didactique

Baccalauréat en éducation (enseignement secondaire) *(BEd)*.
Majeure: sciences morales
Mineure: pédagogie et didactique

Les baccalauréats en éducation pour l'enseignement aux inadaptés:

Baccalauréat en éducation (enseignement aux inadaptés) *(BEd)*.
Majeure: pédagogie et didactique
Mineure: arts plastiques

Baccalauréat en éducation (enseignement aux inadaptés) *(BEd)*.
Majeure: pédagogie et didactique
Mineure: catéchèse

Baccalauréat en éducation (enseignement aux inadaptés) *(BEd)*.
Majeure: pédagogie et didactique
Mineure: éducation physique

Baccalauréat en éducation (enseignement aux inadaptés) *(BEd)*.
Majeure: pédagogie et didactique
Mineure: études anglaises

Baccalauréat en éducation (enseignement aux inadaptés) *(BEd)*.
Majeure: pédagogie et didactique
Mineure: études françaises

Baccalauréat en éducation (enseignement aux inadaptés) *(BEd)*.
Majeure: pédagogie et didactique
Mineure: géographie

Baccalauréat en éducation (enseignement aux inadaptés) *(BEd)*.
Majeure: pédagogie et didactique
Mineure: histoire

Baccalauréat en éducation (enseignement aux inadaptés) *(BEd)*.
Majeure: pédagogie et didactique
Mineure: mathématiques

Baccalauréat en éducation (enseignement aux inadaptés) *(BEd)*.
Majeure: pédagogie et didactique
Mineure: musique

Baccalauréat en éducation (enseignement aux inadaptés) *(BEd)*.
Majeure: pédagogie et didactique
Mineure: sciences naturelles

Les baccalauréats en éducation pour l'enseignement technique et professionnel

Baccalauréat en éducation (enseignement technique et professionnel) *(BEd)*.*
Majeure: techniques administratives
Mineure: pédagogie et didactique

Baccalauréat en éducation (enseignement technique et professionnel) *(BEd)*.*
Majeure: techniques biologiques
Mineure: pédagogie et didactique

Baccalauréat en éducation (enseignement technique et professionnel) *(BEd)*.*
Majeure: techniques humaines
Mineure: pédagogie et didactique

Baccalauréat en éducation (enseignement technique et professionnnel) *(BEd)*.*
Majeure: techniques physiques
Mineure: pédagogie et didactique

(Sciences appliquées, Secteur des)

Architecture

Baccalauréat en architecture *(BArch)*.

---

* L'astérisque indique que le programme est encore à l'état de projet.

Sciences agronomiques et alimentaires**

Baccalauréat ès sciences appliquées (agro-économie) *(BScapp)*.
Baccalauréat ès sciences appliquées (bio-agronomie) *(BScapp)*.
Baccalauréat ès sciences appliquées (consommation) *(BScapp)*.
Baccalauréat ès sciences appliquées (génie rural) *(BScapp)*.
Baccalauréat ès sciences appliquées (vivres) *(BScapp)*.

Sciences forestières et géodésiques

Sciences forestières: baccalauréat ès sciences appliquées (génie forestier) *(BScapp)*.
Sciences géodésiques: baccalauréat ès sciences appliquées (arpentage) *(BScapp)*.

Sciences mathématiques

Baccalauréat ès sciences de l'actuariat (administration) *(BScact)*.
Baccalauréat ès sciences de l'actuariat (économie) *(BScact)*.
Baccalauréat ès sciences de l'actuariat (mathématiques) *(BScact)*.
Baccalauréat ès sciences (informatique de génie) *(BSc)*.
Baccalauréat ès sciences (informatique de gestion) *(BSc)*.
Baccalauréat ès sciences (informatique mathématique) *(BSc)*.

Sciences physiques

Baccalauréat ès sciences appliquées (génie chimique) *(BScapp)*.
Baccalauréat ès sciences appliquées (génie civil) *(BScapp)*.
Baccalauréat ès sciences appliquées (génie électrique) *(BScapp)*.
Baccalauréat ès sciences appliquées (génie géologique) *(BScapp)*.
Baccalauréat ès sciences appliquées (génie mécanique) *(BScapp)*.
Baccalauréat ès sciences appliquées (génie métallurgique) *(BScapp)*.
Baccalauréat ès sciences appliquées (génie minier) *(BScapp)*.
Baccalauréat ès sciences appliquées (génie physique) *(BScapp)*.

_____

** Il s'agit du programme autrefois désigné sous le titre "Economie familiale".

(Sciences de la santé, Secteur des)

Baccalauréat ès sciences de la santé (diététique) *(BScsanté)*.
Baccalauréat ès sciences de la santé (ergothérapie) *(BScsanté)*.
Baccalauréat ès sciences de la santé (médecine) *(BScsanté)*.
Baccalauréat ès sciences de la santé (médecine dentaire) *(BScsanté)*.
Baccalauréat ès sciences de la santé (pharmacie) *(BScsanté)*.
Baccalauréat ès sciences de la santé (physiothérapie) *(BScsanté)*.
Baccalauréat ès sciences de la santé (sciences infirmières) *(BScsanté)*.

(Sciences humaines et sociales, Secteur des)

Baccalauréat en catéchèse *(BCat)*.
Baccalauréat en droit *(LLB)*.
Baccalauréat en éducation (administration scolaire) *(BEd)*.
Baccalauréat en éducation (orientation scolaire et professionnelle) *(BEd)*.
Baccalauréat en éducation (technologie de l'enseignement) *(BEd)*.
Baccalauréat en philosophie *(BPh)*.
Baccalauréat en psychologie *(BPsy)*.
Baccalauréat en sciences de l'administration *(BScadm)*.
Baccalauréat en service social *(BServsoc)*.
Baccalauréat en théologie *(BTh)*.
Baccalauréat ès arts spécialisé en géographie *(BA)*.
Baccalauréat ès arts spécialisé en histoire *(BA)*.
Baccalauréat ès sciences sociales (anthropologie) *(BScsoc)*.
Baccalauréat ès sciences sociales (économie) *(BScsoc)*.
Baccalauréat ès sciences sociales (politique) *(BScsoc)*.
Baccalauréat ès sciences sociales (relations industrielles) *(BScsoc)*.
Baccalauréat ès sciences sociales (sociologie) *(BScsoc)*.

(Sciences pures, Secteur des)

Baccalauréat ès sciences (biochimie) *(BSc)*.
Baccalauréat ès sciences (biologie) *(BSc)*.
Baccalauréat ès sciences (chimie) *(BSc)*.
Baccalauréat ès sciences (géologie) *(BSc)*.
Baccalauréat ès sciences (mathématiques) *(BSc)*.
Baccalauréat ès sciences (microbiologie) *(BSc)*.
Baccalauréat ès sciences (physique) *(BSc)*.

Les certificats:

Certificat d'aptitude à l'enseignement
spécialisé d'une langue seconde.
Certificat d'information professionnelle
Certificat pour l'enseignement au cours
collégial *(CEC).*
Certificat pour l'enseignement au cours
élémentaire *(CEE).*
Certificat pour l'enseignement au cours
secondaire *(CES).*

Autres programmes de premier cycle:

Baccalauréat ès arts (programme pour
adultes) *(BA).*
Junior Year Abroad

Programmes de formation professionnelle
postérieurs à un premier diplôme
universitaire:

Baccalauréat en pharmacie *(BPharm).*
Diplôme en administration *(Dipladm).*
Diplôme en droit notarial.
Doctorat en médecine *(MD).*
Licence en sciences comptables *(LSccompt).*

Programmes spéciaux

L'Institut supérieur des sciences humaines
offre quelques cours et surtout des possibilités
de recherches interdisciplinaires au niveau des
2e et 3e cycles.

Education permanente

La direction de l'Education permanente
n'offre pas de cours proprement dit. Elle
s'applique particulièrement à faciliter l'accès
des adultes aux divers programmes de
l'université.

Extension de l'enseignement universitaire

Cours de perfectionnement culturel et
professionnel. Cours dans les disciplines
suivantes: agriculture, droit, foresterie et
géodésie, lettres (langues modernes,
phonétique, traduction), médecine, musique,

sciences, sciences de l'administration, sciences
infirmières, sciences sociales, théologie,
traitement de l'information (utilisation des
ordinateurs électroniques).GEP. Cours d'été.
Certains cours de l'enseignement régulier des
trimestres d'automne et d'hiver sont repris ou
continués au trimestre d'été.

De plus un enseignement particulier est donné
dans le cadre de l'Extension de
l'enseignement: cours portant sur
l'agriculture, le français aux non-
francophones, la musique, les sciences, les
sciences de l'éducation, la théologie, ainsi que
des stages sur les techniques audio-visuelles,
des cours sur l'utilisation des ordinateurs
électroniques et des cours pratiques de
communication.

Conditions d'admission

On trouvera un exposé général sur
l'admission aux études universitaires dans
l'article *Admission aux universités
canadiennes.*

Afin d'obtenir des renseignements sur
l'admission aux études du niveau pré-grade,
consultez *Conditions d'admission dans les
collèges et universités du Canada* que l'on peut
obtenir du Service d'admission au collège et à
l'université, 151, rue Slater, Ottawa (Ont.),
K1P 5N1, $1.50 port payé.

Admission aux études des 2e et 3e cycles: le
candidat doit être titulaire du diplôme
préalable du 1er cycle, conféré par
l'Université Laval ou par toute autre
université et dont l'équivalence de grade a été
reconnue par le comité d'admission. Le
candidat doit avoir obtenu la permission de
s'inscrire à l'Ecole des gradués de la part du
comité compétent qui évalue l'aptitude à la
recherche du candidat et détermine les
conditions de son admission.

Année universitaire

L'année universitaire comprend les trimestres
d'automne et d'hiver. Le trimestre d'automne
s'étend de septembre à Noël et le trimestre
d'hiver de janvier à avril.

De plus l'université offre des cours durant
l'été. Ce trimestre s'étend du début du mois
de mai à la fin du mois d'août. Toutefois

durant ce trimestre tous les cours de l'enseignement régulier ne sont pas offerts.

Droits d'inscription

Droits de scolarité
Etudiants à temps complet $255 par trimestre – arts, catéchèse, droit, lettres, philosophie, psychologie, sciences de l'éducation, sciences sociales, théologie.

$280 par trimestre – agriculture, architecture, diététique, ergothérapie, foresterie et géodésie, pharmacie, physiothérapie, sciences, sciences de l'administration, sciences infirmières.

$330 par trimestre – médecine, médecine dentaire.

Etudiants à temps partiel $20 pour chaque cours de 15 heures.

Logement dans la cité – chambre simple: $40 par mois (par année); $15 par semaine (cours d'été seulement). Pension: $90-$100 par mois approximativement (pension libre à la cafétéria).

Logement hors de la cité – chambre simple: $10 par semaine (minimum); pension $80 à $95 par mois (approximativement).

Sports. Les étudiants à temps complet ont accès aux sports offerts par le Service des activités sportives sans frais supplémentaires. Les étudiants à temps partiel doivent payer $10 par trimestre.

Aide financière

L'Université Laval n'offre pas de bourses aux étudiants mais administre les bourses suivantes:

1er cycle des études

1er cycle des études

Agriculture: un montant annuel indéterminé est offert à un étudiant inscrit à la Faculté d'agriculture.

Cité de Québec: huit bourses sont offertes à des étudiants à temps complet résidant dans la ville de Québec.

Provinces canadiennes: une bourse couvrant les droits de scolarité est accordée à un étudiant de langue française de chacune des provinces canadiennes (sauf le Québec).

Fondation des Chevaliers de Colomb: trois bourses de $350 sont accordées aux étudiants inscrits à l'Ecole de service social.

Fondation Nicol: une bourse de $400 est offerte à un étudiant inscrit à la Faculté de droit.

2e et 3e cycles des études

Centre d'études nordiques: bourses de $1,000 à $1,500 (maîtrise) et de $2,000 (doctorat) aux étudiants diplômés désireux de poursuivre des recherches sur les territoires nordiques.

Bourses d'échange: trois bourses offertes annuellement à un étudiant d'Allemagne (Université libre de Berlin), un étudiant d'Espagne, un étudiant de Suisse (Ecole polytechnique de Zurich) désireux d'étudier à l'Université Laval dans toutes disciplines. En échange, trois étudiants de l'Université Laval peuvent aller étudier dans les universités mentionnées. La préférence est accordée aux étudiants qui connaissent la langue du pays où ils veulent aller étudier.

Centres d'études et de recherches

Centre de biomédecine
qui groupe présentement des professeurs spécialistes dans les disciplines suivantes: biochimie et immunologie, chirurgie expérimentale, médecine interne expérimentale, pathologie expérimentale.

Centre d'études nordiques.
Il a pour but d'aider les chercheurs de toutes disciplines qui effectuent des travaux de portée universelle à l'intérieur des "territoires nordiques" notamment la péninsule du Québec-Labrador. Il organise et soutient des expéditions.

Centre d'étude et de recherches en pédagogie du langage oral et écrit.
Ses objectifs principaux sont la recherche et la formation de spécialistes du langage oral et écrit, tant pour l'enseignement correctif dans les écoles que pour le travail en clinique multidisciplinaire.

Centre international de recherches sur le bilinguisme.
Le centre poursuit un double but: a) recueillir une documentation internationale et interdisciplinaire touchant le bilinguisme; b) poursuivre des recherches fondamentales sur le bilinguisme, le biculturalisme et tous les phénomènes qui s'y rattachent.

Centre de recherches sur les atomes et les molécules.
Le centre groupe les chercheurs des divers départements de l'Université Laval et des scientifiques du Centre canadien de recherche à Valcartier qui s'intéressent à la physique et à la chimie des molécules et des atomes simples.

Centre de recherches en bionique.
Ce centre est ouvert aux chercheurs de l'université et d'organismes externes dont les travaux appartiennent à la bionique ou font appel à ses méthodes. Au nombre des sujets d'études, citons l'analyse des signaux et le codage de l'information dans le système nerveux, l'électrocardiogramme, le système de commande neuro-musculaire, la régulation endocrinienne, la psychométrie.

Centre de recherches sur l'eau.
Etudie tous les problèmes qui se rapportent à l'eau: hydrologie, géographie, biologie, hydraulique, glaces, pollution, aspects socio-économiques et légaux. Le fleuve St-Laurent et la région nordique du Keewatin sont l'objet de projets immédiats.

Centre de recherches de l'état solide.
A ce centre, la priorité est donnée présentement à la science des matériaux qui comprend surtout les métaux et les céramiques. Les principales études en cours se rapportent aux propriétés électriques et magnétiques de ces composés et à la migration des atomes au cours des transformations.

Centre de recherches en nutrition.
L'objet propre de ce centre est l'acquisition par la recherche scientifique de connaissances nouvelles dans le domaine des sciences de la nutrition, la diffusion de ces connaissances et leur application à la sauvegarde de la santé et du bien-être de l'homme.

Centre de recherches en sociologie religieuse.
Son objectif est le suivant: par des études faites à l'aide de méthodes scientifiques rigoureuses et permettant une connaissance plus systématique du contexte social et religieux au Québec et au Canada, il veut contribuer à l'élaboration de la sociologie du phénomène religieux québécois et canadien,

apporter son concours à un enseignement plus éclairé de la théologie surtout morale et pastorale, et fournir des indications aux responsables de la pastorale dans le milieu.

Centre de traitement de l'information
est un centre de consultation et de recherche ouvert à tous les professeurs et étudiants. Son personnel collabore à des travaux d'analyse et de programmation, participe à la mécanisation des systèmes de classification, d'immatriculation ou de programmation de la bibliothèque et de divers services administratifs de l'université.

L'Herbier Louis-Marie
est avant tout un centre de documentation de botanique systématique mis à la disposition des facultés, des centres de recherches de l'université et des organismes scientifiques externes qui désirent consulter ses collections. Parmi les activités de l'Herbier citons les échanges de spécimens avec diverses institutions similaires au Québec, au Canada et à l'étranger.

Institut supérieur des sciences humaines.
Il a pour fonction de favoriser la recherche interdisciplinaire. Il comprend deux sections de recherches et d'enseignement: la première section est consacrée aux sciences de la culture et à l'épistémologie; la seconde est consacrée aux problèmes de développement économique et social.

Doyens des facultés

Agriculture
Victorin Lavoie

Arts
Mgr Elzéar Fortier

Droit
Hubert Reid, LLL

Foresterie et géodésie
André Lafond

Lettres
Fernand Grenier, BA, LèsL, DiplHistetGéogr

Médecine
Jean-L. Beaudoin

Philosophie
Emmanuel Trépanier

Sciences
Pierre Grenier, BSc, MSc

Sciences de l'administration
Fernand Bélanger

Sciences de l'éducation
Jean-Yves Drolet, LPéd, PhD

Sciences sociales
Yves Dubé, BA, BScapp

Théologie
Roland Beaudet, BPh, LTh

Directeurs des écoles

Architecture, Ecole d'
Paul-N. Bourque, MSc

Arts visuels, Ecole des
Omer Parent

Gradués, Ecole des
Joseph Risi, DSc

Médecine dentaire, Ecole de
Gustave Ratté

Musique, Ecole de
Lucien Brochu, BA, LMus

Pharmacie, Ecole de
Pierre Claveau, DPharm

Sciences infirmières, Ecole des
Rita Dussault (Mlle)

Service social, Ecole de
Nicolas Zay, LScsoc, LLD, MServsoc

Directeurs des centres d'études et de
recherches

Centre de biomédecine
Didier Dufour, DSc

Centre de recherches de l'état solide
Fernand Claisse, DSc

Centre de recherches en bionique
Jean-Marie Langlois, BSc, DSc

Centre de recherches en nutrition
Germain Brisson, BScAgr, MSc, PhD

Centre de recherches en sociologie religieuse
François Routhier, LPh, LTh, LScsoc

Centre de recherches sur l'eau
Alain Soucy, BSc, DIng

Centre de recherches sur les atomes et les
molécules
Garnet Woonton, MA, DSc

Centre de traitement de l'information
Louis Robichaud, MScE

Centre d'étude et de recherches en pédagogie
du langage oral et écrit
Claude Langevin, LPéd

Centre d'études nordiques
Louis-Edmond Hamelin, PhD

Centre international de recherches sur le
bilinguisme
Henri Dorion, LLL, MGéo

L'Herbier Louis-Marie
Lionel Cinq-Mars, BScAgr, MSc

Institut supérieur des sciences humaines
Fernand Dumont, MScsoc, DScsoc

Directeurs de départements et programmes
d'études

Actuariat
Gaston Paradis

Agrobiologie
Albert Alarie

Aménagement et sylviculture
Paul-Emile Vézina

Anatomie
Louis Poirier

Anesthésie
André Jacques

Anthropologie
Marc-Adélard Tremblay

Biochimie (Faculté de médecine)
Louis-Marie Babineau

Biochimie (Faculté des sciences)
Patrice Tailleur

Biologie
Lucien Huot

Catéchèse
Jean Fournier

Chimie
Ludovic Ouellet

Chirurgie
Wilfrid Caron

Diététique
Soeur Françoise Saint-Hilaire

Ecologie et pédologie
Bernard Bernier

Economie rurale
Ferdinand Ouellet

Economique
Claude Masson

Education physique
Fernand Landry

Exploitation et utilisation
Jean Poliquin

Génie chimique
Léonce Cloutier

Génie civil
Yves Giroux

Génie électrique
Denis Angers

Génie mécanique
Gratien Bouillon

Génie rural
Jacques-A. Choinière

Géodésie et cartographie
André Fréchette

Géographie
Louis Trotier

Géologie et minéralogie
Robert Ledoux

Histoire
Jean Hamelin

Informatique
Pierre Ardouin

Journalisme et information
Yves Gagnon

Langues et linguistique
Lorne Laforge

Littérature
Michel Têtu

Mathématiques
Norbert Lacroix

Médecine
Yves Morin

Médecine sociale et préventive
Jean Rochon

Microbiologie
Léo Gauvreau

Mines et métallurgie
Hector Monette

Obstétrique et gynécologie
Roger Brault

Oto-rhino-laryngologie et ophtalmologie
Paul Fugère

Pastorale
Jean-Guy Pagé

Pathologie
Jean-Louis Bonenfant

Pédiatrie
Robert Gourdeau

Pharmacologie
Corneil Radouco-Thomas

Photogrammétrie
J.-Arthur Brandenberger

Physiologie
Claude Fortier

Physiothérapie et ergothérapie
Denys Jobin

Physique
Fernand Bonenfant

Phytotechnie
Fernand Gauthier

Psychiatrie
Charles-A. Martin

Psychologie
Henri Ouellet

Radiologie
Luc Audet

Relations industrielles
Jean-Paul Deschênes

Sciences comptables
Fernand Sylvain

Sciences de la santé
Georges-Albert Bergeron

Sciences politiques
Louis Balthazar

Sociologie
André Lux

Sols
Lawrence-J. O'Grady

Vivres
Jean-Paul Julien

Zootechnie
Laurent-A. Charette

The University of Lethbridge*

Lethbridge, Alberta

Telephone: 403-327-2171
Direct general correspondence to the registrar

Total full-time student enrolment 1,409; see also separate section *Statistics on Canadian universities and colleges*

Executive and administrative officers

Chancellor
Judge L.S. Turcotte, LLB

President and vice-chancellor
W.A.S. Smith, BA, MA, PhD

Vice-president (academic)
W.E. Beckel, MSc, PhD

Registrar
J.D. Oviatt, BEd

Co-ordinator, student affairs
G.W. Russell, BA, MA

Chief librarian
D.E. Wick, MA, FLA

Controller
H. Cooper

Coordinator, information services
M.G.R. Sutherland, BA

Secretary, alumni association
Gwen West

Background

On January 1, 1967, The University of Lethbridge came into existence as an autonomous, co-educational, non-denominational, provincial university, with academic operations commencing July 1, 1967. For the previous decade university transfer courses had been offered by the Lethbridge Junior College, a regional college affiliated with The University of Alberta. By transfer of staff, students and facilities from the university section of the junior college to the university, and through agreement between the institutions regarding rental of facilities, the university was able to embark on an initially extensive program, including bachelor of arts and science (BA) and bachelor of education (BEd) degree programs. The first degrees were conferred in 1968.

A distinctive new campus and buildings have now been completed on the west side of the Old Man River.

The governing bodies of the university include a board of governors, a senate and a general faculty council. The government legislature under which the university was created and under which it presently operates is the Alberta "Universities Act".

Facilities and services

Lethbridge (population approximates 40,000) is a thriving agricultural centre located in southern Alberta within a short driving distance of the Rocky Mountains. The university is currently operating in temporary facilities on the campus of the Lethbridge Community College. Extensive planning toward a permanent campus site and over-all campus plan is underway with final planning for phase 1 completed at the present time. Occupancy of permanent campus will likely occur in the fall of 1971. The library is rapidly expanding under the supervision of a staff of professional librarians.

*Ordinary member, AUCC.

Calendars and brochures

The principal official document of the university is the academic calendar itself. Additional brochures covering various aspects of the university are available from the awards office, information office, library and the academic departments.

Courses and degrees

Arts and science
(Faculty of arts and science)

Bachelor of arts and science (BA).
A program four years post senior matriculation available in: art, biology, chemistry, economics, English, French, geography, history, mathematics, music, philosophy, physical education, physics, political science, psychology, sociology.

Within the faculty of arts and science, by careful selection of courses, several pre-professional programs are available, such as pre-med and pre-dent.

Education
(Faculty of education)

Bachelor of education (BEd).
A program four years post senior matriculation. Available specializations in both secondary and elementary education.

Extension programs

For university credit:

Evening session.
Undergraduate courses in arts, science and education.

Summer session.
Undergraduate courses in arts, science and education.

For no university credit:

A number of workshops and teach-ins are offered from time to time. Planning is underway for non-credit course offerings.

Admission requirements

For a general statement regarding admission to university study, see article *Admission to university in Canada*

For information regarding admission to undergraduate study, consult *Requirements for admission to Canadian colleges and universities* available from Service for Admission to College and University, 151 Slater St., Ottawa, Ont., K1P 5N1, $1.50 prepaid.

Academic year

Summer session: early May to mid-August.

Winter semester: early September to late December.

Spring semester: mid-January to late April.

Grading system

The university employs a letter and point system of grading as follows: A (excellent) 4; B (superior) 3; C (average) 2; D (poor) 1; F (failure) 0; *Cr (credit) no grade points; NC (no credit) 0.

*Credit/non-credit courses are offered by The University of Lethbridge to encourage students to expand their academic interests by enroling in courses outside their fields of major interest and receiving either credit (Cr) or non-credit (NC) for the course in place of the usual letter grade. A student may enrol in a maximum of two credit/non-credit courses per semester but may not enrol in, and complete successfully or otherwise, more than a total of eight for credit toward a degree.

Successful completion of class requirements results in "Cr" (credit) for the courses recorded on the student's transcript; an "NC" (no credit) is recorded if class requirements are not fulfilled. The credit/non-credit courses are not considered in computing the student's grade-point average.

Substitution of "credit" by a normal letter grade is permitted until 30 days after grades have been mailed, if requested by the student. In such cases, the letter grade is included in the student's grade-point average computation. Replacing a "credit" with a letter grade in any credit/non-credit course does not enable the student to enrol in, and complete successfully or otherwise, any more than a maximum of eight such courses.

A student may not enrol in credit/non-credit courses in his major, nor in required courses in education (i.e. required foundation courses, professional semester courses, three introductory behavioral sciences).

Fees and costs

Full-time student fees per semester, $200; students' union fees per semester, $14; part-time student fees, $65 per course. Students' union fees optional for part-time students.

Financial awards and assistance

A number of scholarships and awards are tenable at The University of Lethbridge as well as financial aid through the Queen Elizabeth scholarship fund and the Canada student loans plan.

Deans of faculties

Arts and science
P. Deane, MA, PhD

Education
R.J. Leskiw, BEd, MEd, DEd

Department chairmen

Anthropology
D.G. Bettison, BA, MA, PhD

Art
C.L. Crane, BA, MA

Biological sciences
J. Kuijt, BA, MA, PhD

Chemistry
L.G. Hepler, BSc, PhD

Economics
B.M. Bilgin, BAdmSc, MA, PhD

English
L.R. McKenzie, BA, MA, PhD

Geography
E.E. Miller, BA, MA, PhD

History
M.J. Penton, BA, MA, PhD

Mathematical sciences
D.C. Ferguson, BSc, MA, PhD

Modern languages
L.P. Cormier, BA, MA, PhD

Music
D.G. Blair, BM, MM

Philosophy
P. Butterfield, BA, MA

Physical education
J.A.P. Day, BEd, MA, PhD

Physics
J.L. Rood, BA, MA, PhD

Political science
F.Q. Quo, BA, MA, PhD

Psychology
J.T. Hamilton, BA, MA, PhD

Sociology
R.J. Dwyer, BSc, MA, PhD

Loyola College*

(Affiliated to the University of Montreal)
7141 Sherbrooke Street West, Montreal 262,
Quebec

Telephone: 514-482-0320
Direct general correspondence to the registrar

Total full-time student enrolment 3,865; see
also separate section *Statistics on Canadian
universities and colleges*

Executive and administrative officers

President
Very Rev. P.G. Malone, SJ, MA, STL, PhL

Vice-president, academic
J.C. Burke, BA, MA, PhD

Vice-president, administration
A.J. Ferrari, BComm, CA, RIA

Registrar
J. Noonan, BSc

Assistant to the president
R.P. Duder, BA, MA

Librarian
J. Princz (acting), BA, MA

Dean of students
G.P. Meyers (acting), BA, MSc

Director of alumni affairs
B.H. McCallum, BA

Director of collegial students
W.J. Cozens, BA

Director of development
J.S. Dorrance, BA, MA

Director of evening division
D.J. Potvin, BA

*Ordinary member, AUCC.

Assistant registrar (admissions)
L. Zarrelli, BA

Assistant registrar (records)
Eileen Gibbons

Dean of men
G.V. Uihlein Jr., BSc, MSc

Dean of women
M. Fraser (Miss), RN

Director of financial aid
F. Haffey (Mrs)

Student placement officer
E. Allen (Miss)

Director, physical education
E.F. Enos, BSc, MEd

Public relations director
Angela Burke (Miss), BA

Background

Loyola College has evolved from a small,
traditionalist, Jesuit college of the classical
mold with about 400 students into a complex
university-type institution with over 4,000
day students and a roughly similar number of
evening students proceeding towards degrees
of various kinds. Both teaching staff and
student body have expanded in size from a
homogeneous, English Catholic population to
a more heterogeneous, pluralistic community
ranging from Jesuits and traditional Catholics
through the spectrum of political, religious,
and ideological commitment.

Loyola College began its own separate
existence in 1899 when it was incorporated
by an act of the Quebec legislature, although
its origins can be traced back to the English
side of the Jesuit Collège Ste-Marie from
1848 on. Since 1899, its degrees have been
granted first by Laval University and later by
the University of Montreal. The arrangement
with both these universities has allowed
Loyola complete autonomy and
independence in the shaping of its curriculum
and the conduct of its examinations.

In 1943 Loyola added to its arts courses a
faculty of science, from which developed the
faculty of engineering as we know it today. A
faculty of commerce was set up in 1948. An
extension department, now known as the
evening division, and a summer school were

set up in 1957. The communication arts department was instituted in 1965.

Loyola is co-educational, supported by public and private funds, and conducted by the Fathers of the Society of Jesus.

Facilities and services

Loyola College is located on a fifty-acre site in the west-end of Montreal. The structures of the college are: the refectory building (built in 1916); the cafeteria and physical services building (1923); the administration building (1927); the chapel and auditorium (1933); the central building (1947); the Drummond science building (1962); Hingston hall (1963); the Georges P. Vanier library (1964); the physical education centre (1966); the buildings acquired for faculty, administration, and student government offices [the Hackett and Cloran buildings (1965)] and the Centennial building (1967).

The latest addition to the college is the W.F.X. Bryan building (1967). It houses 20 lecture rooms, an auditorium, two biology labs, approximately 15 psychology labs, and one of the best equipped communication arts departments in Canada, consisting of a combination T.V. studio and film studio, audio, visual, and lighting control rooms, two radio studios, a photography studio, a dark room, projection rooms, animation facilities and a multi-media room.

The 64 lecture rooms and seven seminar rooms have a total seating capacity of 3,304 and 112 respectively. The four auditoria can seat 1,265, the largest being the F.C. Smith auditorium which seats 570.

An IBM computer is used by the science faculty for research purposes and serves the registrar's office as well as certain administrative departments. Loyola also offers a BSc in computer science.

Student services include a health service, guidance and counselling, a placement office, an off-campus housing registry, cafeteria and student lounges.

Calendars and brochures

Available from the registrar: general college calendar — for university courses; collegial calendar — for two-year pre-university courses; admissions brochure.

Available from the office of the director, evening division: evening division calendars and brochures for winter and summer sessions listing major programs leading to a bachelor's degree in arts, commerce, and science; diploma programs in accountancy, business administration, data processing, labor relations, library technology, and quality control; certificate in theological studies; summer institute in the French language.

Available from the dean of student services: campus handbook.

Courses and degrees

Arts
(Faculty of arts)

Bachelor of arts (BA).
(a) General course, three years after successful completion of the pre-university CEGEP program or its equivalent, with majors in classics, communication arts, economics, English, études françaises, German, history, Italian, philosophy, political science, psychology, sociology, Spanish, theological studies, joint-major (economics-political science). (b) Honors course, three years after successful completion of the pre-university CEGEP program or its equivalent, in classics, economics, English, études françaises, history, philosophy, political science, sociology, and theological studies.

Business, see commerce below

Commerce
(Faculty of commerce)

Bachelor of commerce (BCom).
(a) General degree and major degree: to obtain a BCom(major) degree the student must have an average of 65% for courses in his chosen discipline. A student who fails to satisfy the specified average (65%) in his chosen discipline will graduate with a BCom (general) degree. With respect to both the general and major degrees, the areas of concentration are in accounting, business administration, and economics. (b) There is an honors BCom in economics.

Engineering
(Faculty of engineering)

The faculty of engineering offers in 1971-72 a program of two-cycles; a two-year collegial (CEGEP) program followed by a three-year university program. On the successful completion of the university program, students will be awarded a *bachelor of science* degree.

Although the curricula of the programs are designed to enable students to pursue advanced studies in engineering, science, or business at other universities, nevertheless, those who do not elect to do so, will find themselves well prepared for a career in industry at a high technological level. Students aspiring to practise as professional engineers are advised to register in an option described as a professional curriculum.

Science, pure
(Faculty of science)

Bachelor of science (BSc).
(a) General course, three years after successful completion of the pre-university CEGEP program or its equivalent, with a concentration chosen in any one of the following fields: chemistry, geology, mathematics or physics, but less specialized than the major course and with an emphasis on a broader choice of studies. This course is designated for students who do not plan to continue their scientific training beyond the bachelor level.

(b) Major course, three years after successful completion of the pre-university CEGEP program or its equivalent, offered in biochemistry, chemistry, computer science, geology, mathematics, physics, or psychology. Designed for students capable and willing to concentrate in a designated area; students who may develop latent talents and may perhaps with the help of a qualifying year after graduation, continue to higher degrees.

(c) Honors courses, three years after successful completion of the pre-university CEGEP program or its equivalent, in chemistry, mathematics or physics. The honors chemistry course is accredited as fulfilling all the requirements for professional membership in the Chemical Institute of Canada.

Note: The introduction of the CEGEP program in the province of Quebec has necessitated a change in the university curriculum. Effective since September 1971, Loyola is offering a three-year university program leading to bachelor's degrees in all faculties. Students admitted to the new university program will have completed a two-year pre-university program in the CEGEP, or its equivalent.

Extension programs

For university credit:

Summer and winter sessions.
Day and evening courses leading to bachelor's degrees (major) in arts, commerce, and science are presented. Eleven-course diploma programs are offered in accountancy, business administration, data processing, and labor relations to meet the needs of students who may not wish to fulfill all the requirements for a bachelor of commerce degree but are concerned mainly with acquiring an education in business areas. Full accreditation for all courses taken at the diploma level will be granted towards a bachelor of commerce degree if applicable to the program selected. Additionally, eleven-course diploma programs in library technology and quality control are available.

Certificate in theological studies.
The certificate program in theological studies provides an opportunity for mature students to up-date their theological knowledge and further their professional qualifications. Students are normally accepted into this program with a bachelor of arts degree or its equivalent. For those without a degree, the certificate will be granted upon completion of a degree program.

Summer institute in the French language.
Six-week intensive study of the French language in small groups at the elementary intermediate and advanced levels. Up to two (2) undergraduate credits may be granted upon the successful completion of the program.

Loyola High School,
a private institution, is located on the campus and offers a five-year college preparatory program for boys only.

Admission requirements

For a general statement regarding admission to university study, see article *Admission to university in Canada.*

For information regarding admission to undergraduate study, consult *Requirements for admission to Canadian colleges and universities* available from Service for Admission to College and University, 151 Slater St., Ottawa, Ont., K1P 5N1, $1.50 prepaid.

Academic year

Winter session: mid-September to early May.

Summer session: evening — early June to mid-August; day — late June to mid-August.

Grading system

Standing is graded in each subject as: A, 80-100%; B, 65-79%; C, 55-64%; D, 50-54%; failed, below 50%.

Fees and costs

Tuition fees per year — full-time students: arts general, $540; arts (communication arts), $575; commerce, $540; engineering, $595; science, $575.

Part-time: $100 per course.

Miscellaneous fees per year: $50 approximately.

Evening division and summer school: $100 per course.

Residence rates per academic year: double room— $465; single room — $540. Meals can be contracted for on a yearly basis at a cost of approximately $500.

Financial awards and assistance

Information on scholarships, bursaries, and loan funds may be obtained from the director of financial aid.

Deans of faculties

Arts
Rev. R.W. Breen, BA, STL, MS, PhD

Commerce
L.M. Bessner, BComm, CA

Engineering
G.W. Joly, BA, BEng, MEng

Science
A. Graham, SJ, BA, MA, STL

Department heads

Accountancy
L.J. Boyle, BA, BCom, MA

Biology
Rev. S. Drummond, SJ, BA, MA, PhD

Business administration
L.J. Boyle, BA, BCom, MA

Chemistry
M. Doughty, BSc, PhD

Classics
J.E. Lempkowski, BA, MA

Communication arts
Rev. J.E. O'Brien, SJ, BA, STB, STL, PhD

Computer science
D. West, BSc, BA, MA, PhD

Economics
S.A. Alvi, BA, MA, PhD

English
J. Zuckerman (acting), BA, MA, DPhil

Etudes françaises
G. Laurion, LèsL, DES, DU

Geology
E.H. Chown, BSc, MASc, PhD

History
F.G.W. Adams, BA, MA, PhD

Mathematics
A.J. Prillo, BSc, MA

Modern languages
C. Fonda, MA, PhD, MA, PhD

Philosophy
J. Morgan, BA, MA, PhD

Physics
C.E. Eappen, BSc, MSc, PhD

Political science
R. Coyte, BA, MA

Psychology
To be appointed

Sociology
J. Tascone, BA, MA

Theological studies
Rev. G. O'Brien, SJ, BA, MA, STL, STD

The University of Manitoba*

Winnipeg, Manitoba

Telephone: 204-474-8880
Direct general correspondence to the registrar

Total full-time student enrolment 12,892; see also separate section *Statistics on Canadian universities and colleges*

Executive and administrative officers

Chancellor
P.D. Curry, LLD

President and vice-chancellor
E. Sirluck, MBE, MA, PhD, LLD, FRSC

Executive assistant to the president
W.E. Alexander, BSP, MSc, PhD

Vice-president (administration)
W.J. Condo, BA

Vice-president (planning and special assignments)
W.M. Sibley, BA, MA, PhD

Vice-president (health sciences)
T.W. Fyles, MD, MSc, FRCP(C), FACP

Vice-president (research, graduate studies, and special assignments)
J.C. Gilson, BSA, MSc, PhD

Dean of students
B. Ash, BA, MA, PhD

Registrar
B.G. Browning, BA

Director of libraries
W.R. Butler, BA, MLS, MA

University College, provost
M.S. Donnelly, BA, PhD

Director, extension division
A.S.R. Tweedie, CD, MA

Director, summer and evening sessions
W.G. Stobie, MA

Comptroller
J.A. MacFarlane, BA, CA

Director, counselling service
R.I. Hudson, MA, EdD

Director, university health service
J.W. Whiteford, MD

Director of student awards and assistant to the president (student affairs)
C.E. Henry, BA, BEd

Dean of women
S.-A. Smith (Mrs), BA, MSW

Co-ordinator of overseas students' affairs
P.C. Benson

Director of residences
M.A. Kains

Communications consultant
D.R. MacFarlane (Mrs)

Executive director, alumni association
J.M. Gordon, BA

Background

The University of Manitoba was established by an act of the legislative assembly of Manitoba in 1877. Prior to the university's establishment, three church colleges were offering higher education, but did not have power to confer degrees. The new institution was conceived in the model of the University of London as an examining and degree-conferring body, with instruction being offered in affiliated colleges. The first degrees were awarded by the university in 1880. An amendment to The University Act in 1900 gave the university power to offer instruction which began in 1904 with the establishment of six professorships.

*Ordinary member, AUCC.

Present authority is that given by The University Act of 1968 providing for government by a board of governors and a senate. The University of Manitoba is a provincial university. It is non-denominational and co-educational.

Facilities and services

The university is situated in the city of Fort Garry about seven miles from the centre of the city of Winnipeg (population 534,000). The Red River forms the eastern boundary of the Fort Garry campus which consists of approximately 1,685 acres.

There are 35 teaching buildings and, as well, the facilities of two member colleges, St. John's and St. Paul's, one constituent college, University College, and an associated college, St. Andrew's, located on that site. The university also operates its own agricultural experimental station of 1,100 acres at Glenlea, 16 miles south of the Fort Garry campus. The faculties of medicine and dentistry, the school of medical rehabilitation and the school of dental hygiene are situated in close proximity to the Winnipeg General Hospital in Winnipeg.

On the Fort Garry campus there are libraries (750,000 volumes), the Canada Department of Agriculture research laboratory and science service building, the forest insect laboratory, the federal experimental swine testing station, the provincial fur farm, and the fishery research station.

There is residence accommodation for 720 men and 350 women. In addition, St. John's College provides residence facilities for 47 women and 52 men and St. Andrew's College accommodates 24 women and 80 men.

Student services include a health service, a counselling service, a housing registry, an overseas students' affairs office, cafeterias, a student union, athletic and recreational facilities, and an employment service. There is on staff a co-ordinator of overseas students' affairs who acts in a consulting relationship with the international students' organization on campus, and helps all students with individual problems.

Calendars and brochures

The following calendars are obtainable upon request at the offices of the deans or directors of the faculties or schools: faculty of agriculture, faculty of architecture, faculty of arts and science, faculty of commerce, faculty of dentistry, faculty of education, faculty of engineering, faculty of graduate studies, faculty of home economics, faculty of law, faculty of medicine, faculty of pharmacy, school of art, school of dental hygiene, school of medical rehabilitation, school of music, school of nursing, school of physical education, and school of social work.

College calendars are also available upon request from the offices of the colleges concerned: St. John's College, St. Paul's College, St. Boniface College, and University College.

In addition to the above publications the following may be obtained from the offices as indicated:

Director of summer and evening sessions: the announcement of the summer session, the announcement of the evening session;

Extension division: the announcement of the evening institute;

School of music: the syllabus of The Western Board of Music (the universities and departments of education of the provinces of Manitoba, Saskatchewan and Alberta);

Registrar's office: mature student admission announcement, out-of-province admission announcement, time-table and registration guide; student diary;

Overseas students' affairs: handbook for overseas students;

Public relations office: campus guide;

Dean's office, arts and science: arts and science: a general guide for students.

Some faculties and some departments of the university produce pamphlets additional to the calendar describing facilities and offerings.

Courses and degrees

Agriculture
(Faculty of agriculture)

Diploma in agriculture.
Two years from grade 12 or equivalent.
Applications are considered by a committee
of selection.

Diploma in dairying.
One year. No stated academic requirements
for admission. Applications are considered by
a committee of selection.

Bachelor of science in agriculture (BSA).
General course, four years from senior
matriculation. Sequences offered in
agricultural economics and farm
management, agricultural engineering,
animal science, entomology, food science,
plant science, and soil science.

(Faculty of graduate studies)

Master of science (MSc).
At least one year from a BSA degree in
agriculture. Specialization offered in
agricultural economics and farm
management, animal science, entomology,
food science, plant science, and soil science.

Doctor of philosophy (PhD).
At least two years from MSc. Available in
agricultural economics, animal science,
entomology, plant science, and soil science.

Architecture
(Faculty of architecture)

Bachelor of environmental studies (BES).
Three years from senior matriculation.

Bachelor of landscape architecture (BLA).
Two years from bachelor of environmental
studies.

Bachelor of interior design (BID).
Four years from senior matriculation.

(Faculty of graduate studies)

Master of architecture (MArch).
Three years from bachelor of environmental
studies or equivalent.

Diploma in city planning.
At least one year from first degree in arts,
engineering, or architecture.

Master of city planning (MCP).
At least two years from first degree in arts,
engineering, or architecture or one year from
diploma in city planning.

Arts
(Faculty of arts and science)

Bachelor of arts [BA or BA(Hons)].
(a) General course, three years from senior
matriculation. Major and/or minor subjects:
anthropology, classics (classical studies, Latin,
and Greek), cross-disciplinary studies,
economics, English, geography, German,
history, Icelandic, Judaic studies (Hebrew
language and literature, Judaic civilization,
Yiddish), mathematics, music, philosophy,
political studies, psychology, religion,
romance languages and literature (French,
Italian, Spanish), Slavic studies (Russian,
Polish, Ukrainian), and sociology.
(b)Honors course, four years from senior
matriculation. Available in actuarial and
business mathematics, anthropology, classics
(Latin and Greek), economics, English,
French, geography, German, history,
Icelandic, mathematics, philosophy, political
studies, psychology, Slavic studies, and
sociology.

Bachelier ès arts (BA).
Three years at St. Boniface College.

Bachelier ès arts [BA(LPh)].
Latin philosophy. Three years at St. Boniface
College.

(Faculty of graduate studies)

Master of arts (MA).
At least two years from general BA, or at
least one year from honors BA. Available in
anthropology, classics (Latin and Greek),
economics, English, French, geography,
German, history, Icelandic, mathematics,
philosophy, political studies, psychology,
Slavic studies, and sociology.

Doctor of philosophy (PhD).
At least two years from MA. Available in
economics, English, French, geography,
history, mathematics, and psychology.

Commerce
(Faculty of commerce)

Bachelor of commerce [BComm(Hons)].
Honors course, four years from senior
matriculation. Specialization available in

actuarial mathematics, quantitative methods accounting, administration, finance, industrial relations, marketing, operations research, production, and public policy.

(Faculty of graduate studies)

Master of business administration (MBA).
At least one year from BComm(Hons) degree and two years from degrees in other disciplines.

Dentistry
(Faculty of dentistry)

Diploma in dental hygiene.
Two years from senior matriculation.

Doctor of dental medicine (DMD).
Four years beyond one year in arts and science.

(Faculty of graduate studies)

Master of science (MSc).
At least one year from DMD degree. Available in dental science and oral biology; also available in orthodontics (28 months).

Doctor of philosophy (PhD).
At least two years from MSc degree. Available in oral biology.

Diploma in periodontology.
Superimposed on MSc program in oral biology. Minimum of three years.

Education
(Faculty of education)

Associateship in education.
Two years from senior matriculation: (1) the two-year integrated program in education and arts, science or other faculties; (2) one year of education and one year of arts, science, or other faculties.

Certificate in education.
Three or four years from senior matriculation: one year of education and either two years or a first degree in arts, science, or other faculties.

Bachelor of pedagogy (BPaed).
Four years from senior matriculation: two years in education and two years in arts and science or other faculties.

Bachelor of education (BEd).
Five years from senior matriculation: two years in education and a first degree in arts, science, or other faculties.

(Faculty of graduate studies)

Master of education (MEd).
At least one year from BEd degree.

Doctor of philosophy (PhD).
At least two years from a master's degree; available in educational administration.

Engineering
(Faculty of engineering)

Bachelor of science in engineering (BSc followed by appropriate affix, e.g., AE, CE, EE, GE, ME).
Four years from senior matriculation. Specialization offered in agricultural, civil, electrical, geological, and mechanical engineering.

(Faculty of graduate studies)

Master of science (MSc).
At least one year from BSc degree. Available in agricultural, civil, electrical, and mechanical engineering.

Diploma in engineering.
Normally longer than one year from a BSc degree in engineering.

Doctor of philosophy (PhD).
At least two years from MSc degree. Available in civil, electrical, and mechanical engineering.

Fine arts
(School of art)

Diploma in art.
Four years. No stated academic requirements for admission. Applications are considered by a committee of selection.

Bachelor of fine arts [BFA or BFA(Hons)].
(a) General course, three years from senior matriculation. (b) Honors course, four years from senior matriculation. Specialization offered in ceramics, drawing, graphic design, painting, print-making and sculpture.

Home economics
(Faculty of home economics)

Bachelor of home economics (BHEc).
Four years from senior matriculation.
Specialization offered in foods and nutrition,
clothing and textiles, and family studies.

(Faculty of graduate studies)

Master of science (MSc).
Specialization offered in clothing, foods,
human development, human development or
family economics and management,
nutrition, and textiles.

Interdisciplinary
(Faculty of graduate studies)

*Master of natural resources management
(MNRM).*
A minimum of two years from the bachelor's
degree.

Law
(Faculty of law)

Bachelor of laws (LLB).
Three years, full-time, beyond satisfactory
completion of at least two years of any
university course of studies. Applications are
considered by a committee of selection. Law
school admission test must be written.

(Faculty of graduate studies)

Master of laws (LLM).
One year from LLB degree.

Medical rehabilitation
(School of medical rehabilitation)

Diploma in occupational therapy.
Three years from senior matriculation.

Diploma in physical therapy.
Three years from senior matriculation.

Bachelor of occupational therapy (BOT).
One year from diploma course.

Bachelor of physical therapy (BPT).
One year from diploma course.

Medicine
(Faculty of medicine)

Doctor of medicine (MD).
Four years beyond the second year in arts
and science.

Bachelor of science in medicine [BSc(Med)].
At least one year from the second year in
medicine.

(Faculty of graduate studies)

Master of science (MSc).
At least one year from the MD degree.
Available in anatomy, biochemistry, medical
microbiology, medicine, obstetrics and
gynaecology, pathology, pediatrics,
pharmacology and therapeutics, physiology,
psychiatry, surgery.

Doctor of philosophy (PhD).
At least two years from MSc degree.
Available in anatomy, bacteriology,
biochemistry, pharmacology, and physiology.

Diploma in psychiatry.
Four years from MD degree.

Music
(School of music)

Associate in music (AMus Western Board).

Licentiate in music (LMus Western Board).

*Bachelor of music [BMus or BMus(Hons) or
BMus(Perf)].*
(a) General course, three years from senior
matriculation. (b) Honors course, four years
from senior matriculation. (c) Performance,
four years from senior matriculation.

Nursing
(School of nursing)

Bachelor of nursing (BN).
Four years from senior matriculation. A
program designed for applicants holding a
degree in a field other than nursing and for
registred nurses is offered.

Pharmacy
(Faculty of pharmacy)

Bachelor of science in pharmacy
[BSc(Pharm)].
Four years from senior matriculation (one in science plus three in pharmacy).
Specialization available in hospital pharmacy, pharmaceutical chemistry, pharmaceutics, pharmacognosy, and retail pharmacy.

(Faculty of graduate studies)

Master of science (MSc).
At least one year from bachelor's degree. Specialization in pharmaceutical chemistry, pharmaceutical microbiology, pharmacognosy, and pharmacokinetics.

Physical education
(School of physical education)

Bachelor of physical education (BPE).
Three years from senior matriculation. Applications are considered by a committee of selection.

Science
(Faculty of arts and science)

Bachelor of science [BSc or BSc(hons)].
(a) General course, three years from senior matriculation. Major subjects: botany, chemistry, computer science, geology and mineralogy, mathematics, microbiology, physics, statistics, and zoology. (b) Honors course, four years from senior matriculation. Available in actuarial mathematics, botany, chemistry, computer science, geology and mineralogy, geophysics, mathematics, microbiology, physics, statistics, and zoology.

(Faculty of graduate studies)

Master of science (MSc).
At least two years from the general degree in science or at least one year from the honors bachelor's degree in science. Available in actuarial mathematics, botany, chemistry, computer science, geology, geophysics, mathematics, microbiology, physical biology, physics, statistics, and zoology.

Doctor of philosophy (PhD).
At least two years from MSc. Available in botany, chemistry, geology, geophysics, mathematics, microbiology, physics, and zoology.

Social work
(School of social work)

Certificate in social work.
The certificate may be awarded to "special students" who successfully complete the two-year program of course work, field work and research.

Bachelor of social work (BSW).
Four years from senior matriculation.

(Faculty of graduate studies)

Master of social work (MSW).
A substantially revised program is being prepared for 1972-73.

Extension programs

For university credit:

Correspondence courses.
Courses offered in a limited number of arts and science subjects.

Evening session.
Undergraduate and graduate courses in arts, commerce, education, fine arts, music, and science.

Summer session.
Undergraduate and graduate courses offered in arts, commerce, education, fine arts, home economics, music, and science for students proceeding to a degree and for teachers who may wish to improve their professional qualifications.

For no university credit:

Extension services, extension division.
Systematic courses in the humanities and other areas of proper concern to a university on a non-credit basis.

Special short courses:
professional refresher or maintenance courses; intellectual refreshment of alumni as distinct from professional courses.

Admission requirements

For a general statement regarding admission to university study, see article *Admission to university in Canada.*

For information regarding admission to undergraduate study, consult *Requirements for admission to Canadian colleges and universities* available from Service for Admission to College and University, 151 Slater St., Ottawa, Ont., K1P 5N1, $1.50 prepaid.

Medicine — completion of two years in arts and science beyond senior matriculation with better than average standard. *Dentistry* — one year in arts and science beyond senior matriculation. *Law* — two years in arts and science beyond senior matriculation. *Pharmacy* — one year in science beyond senior matriculation. (Registration in dental hygiene, dentistry, law, medical rehabiliation, medicine, pharmacy, and physical education is restricted).

Graduate study — first degree with specified grades in appropriate subjects.

Academic year

Winter session: mid-September to early May.

Summer session: early July to mid-August.

Summer evening session: early May to end of July.

Grading system

The grading system consists of six passing grades: A +, A, B +, B, C +, C, and D. "A +" denotes exceptional accomplishment; "A", excellent; "B" and "B +", superior; "C +", better than average; "C", average and "D", marginal.

In a number of faculties and schools, special requirements in respect of averages and standing in professional subjects must be met. The faculty of medicine has recently introduced pass/fail grading in the MD program.

Fees and costs

Full-time tuition fees per year — (a) for first degree: agriculture, arts, commerce, education, home economics, law, music, nursing, physical education, science, social work, $425; interior design, $440; fine arts, $445; pharmacy, $475; engineering, $525; architecture, $540; dentistry, $550; medicine, $625; (b) for master's degree, $375 (social work $425); (c) doctor's degree, $375; thesis and degree, $80; (d) diploma courses: agriculture, $325; art, $345; dental hygiene, occupational therapy, physical therapy, $450. Student organization fees per year, $27 to $45.50.

Residence rates, board and room, per academic year, $610 to $723.

Financial awards and assistance

The major bursary funds are provided by the Manitoba Department of Youth and Education and are available only to students whose parents are domiciled in this province. In addition, industries, organizations, and various private donors place bursary funds under the administration of the university awards office.

Besides participating in the Canada student loans plan, the university has loan funds in trust; loans made from these sources are interest-free until the date set for repayment, but in each case a guarantor who is a Manitoba resident over 21 years of age and fully employed is required. There are a number of prestige awards given for academic standing in various areas of instruction. These awards vary in value from very small prizes to $1,000 maximum.

Research institutes

Agassiz Centre for Water Studies. Water resources problems and potential in northern and western Canada are being studied by representatives of the following disciplines: agricultural economics, anthropology, civil engineering, economics, food science, geography, geology, law, plant science, political science, sociology, and soil science.

Aquatic Biology Research Unit.
This group comprises participants from the Freshwater Institute of the Fisheries Research Board and from university departments. Areas of interest include fish physiology, ichthyology, limnology, and microbiology.

Centre for Settlement Studies.
The purpose of the current research program is to acquire a better understanding of the factors that help or hinder the development of an adequate quality of living for inhabitants of resource frontier communities. Participants include representatives of anthropology, city planning, economics, education, geography, home economics, law, medicine, political science, psychology, social work, and sociology.

Centre for Transportation Studies.
The aims are to give continuity and focus to a study of broad and long-range problems of the Canadian transportation system and to provide the stimulus and breadth of interdisciplinary knowledge and discussion. Co-operating departments include agricultural economics, commerce, economics, and geography.

Glenlea Research Station.
The 1,300 acre station provides facilities for: (a) fundamental and applied agricultural research of an interdisciplinary nature and (b) application of laboratory research results on a field-scale basis.

Legal Research Institute.
The objective is to promote and undertake legal research and law reform studies in Manitoba.

Manitoba Institute of Cell Biology.
The purpose of the institute is to carry out a program of research and training in the basic and clinical sciences with the object of gaining a better understanding of the nature of cancer and other diseases, by studying the underlying cellular processes.

Medieval and Renaissance Guild.
The purpose is to aid and stimulate students and faculty in medieval and renaissance studies by the institution of programs of studies, special research projects, conferences, symposia, lectures, and publications. Members include representatives from the departments of classics, English, French, German, history, Icelandic, Judaic studies, music, philosophy, political science, and Slavic studies.

Natural Resource Institute.
The institute is an interdisciplinary academic unit with a two-fold purpose, namely: (a) to seek and to develop theories and principles of natural resource management through research and scholarly endeavor; and (b) to impart the knowledge and skills of this discipline to students. The degree of master of natural resource management is offered, covering the areas of economics, resources, socio-political administration and analysis.

Northern Studies Committee.
The objective of the research program is to encourage the study of man and environment in the North.

University Field Station (Delta Marsh).
The objectives are: (a) to provide an area for research in such fields as archeology and earth sciences; botany, microbiology, and zoology; and (b) to provide facilities for teaching and for encouraging field-directed courses.

University Field Station (Star Lake).
The station is a site for teaching earth science field courses. In the planning stages at Star Lake is a geophysical observatory for seismic and magnetic recording.

Member colleges

St. John's College, Winnipeg 19, Manitoba. Warden: Rev. J.R. Brown, MA, DD. Established 1849. Co-educational. An Anglican college within the university, offering instruction in arts and science. All courses are for The University of Manitoba credit. Provides residence accommodation, dining and recreation facilities. (See separate entry.)

St. Paul's College, Winnipeg 19, Manitoba. Rector: Rev. V.J. Jensen, sj, BA, MA, STL. Established 1926. Co-educational. A Roman Catholic college within the university, offering instruction in arts and science. All courses are for The University of Manitoba credit. Provides dining and recreational facilities. (See separate entry.)

Affiliated college

Collège de Saint-Boniface, Saint-Boniface (Man.).
Recteur: Roger Saint-Denis, BA, BArp, DipIng. Fondé en 1818. Cours préparatoire et BA, BSc, ou BEd. L'enseignement est donné en langue française.

Associated college

St. Andrew's College, Winnipeg 19, Manitoba.
Principal: L. Tomaschuk, BSc, DipEd. Established 1946. Associated 1962. A college for the training of the ministry in the Ukrainian Greek Orthodox Church in Canada and the United States of America. Credits earned at this college will not transfer to a degree program at The University of Manitoba.

Approved teaching centre

Canadian Mennonite Bible College, Winnipeg 29, Manitoba.
President: Rev. Henry Poettcker, ThD. Registrar: R.A. Regehr, BA. Established 1947. Recognized by The University of Manitoba as an approved teaching centre in 1963. Co-educational. Offers courses in music and theology leading to a bachelor of theology and a bachelor of sacred music awarded by the college. The university authorized the Canadian Mennonite Bible College to offer certain of its courses each year with a student taking a maximum of seven courses at the first-year level and a maximum of three courses at the higher level, the latter to be confined to religion and music.

The authorization to offer these courses will be given each year following approval by the particular department concerned having regard to the qualifications of the proposed instructors and the content of the course. Credits in these courses may not be used to satisfy the residence requirements for The University of Manitoba degree. Students, at centres authorized to offer The University of Manitoba courses, wishing credit for courses, must comply with the admission requirements of the university, must be officially accepted by the university, and must be registered for the courses for which they

seek credit. Courses offered at the centre for credit towards a degree must not exceed 10 in number. Courses offered at the centre for credit towards a degree must not constitute a complete major in any subject.

Residential accommodation for 116 students and 15 families.

Deans of faculties

Agriculture
L.H. Shebeski, MSc, FAIC, FRSC

Architecture
R. Sellors, BArch, MArch, MAIA, FRAIC

Arts
D.J. McCarthy, BA, MA, PhD

Commerce
J.D. Mundie, BComm, MBA, PhD

Dentistry
J.W. Neilson, BA, DDS, MSc, FICD, FACD, FRCD(C)

Education
J.M. Brown, BA, BEd, MEd, EdD

Engineering
J. Hoogstraten, MSc, DEng, MEIC, PEng

Graduate studies
B.G. Hogg, BSc, MA, PhD

Home economics
L.D. Lloyd, BSc, MSc, PhD

Law
C.H.C. Edwards, LLB

Medicine
A. Naimark, BSc, MD, MSc, FRCP(C)

Pharmacy
J.R. Murray, BSc(Pharm), MSc, PhD

Science
R.D. Connor, PhD, AInstP

Directors of schools

Art
R.E. Williams, BA, MFA

Dental hygiene
M.G.E. Forgay, BA, RDH

Medical rehabilitation
Marjorie Spence (acting), ARRC, BA, MCPA

Music
L. Isaacs, BMus, ARCM

Nursing
Margaret Hart, RN, BSc, MA, EdD, FAPHA

Physical education
J. MacDiarmid, BPE, MA

Social work
C.G. Gifford, DFC, BA, MSW

Directors of centres and institutes

Agassiz centre for water studies
K. Arenson (acting)

Aquatic biology research unit
H.E. Welch (chairman), BA, MA, PhD

Centre for settlement studies
L.B. Siemens, BSA, MSc, MA

Centre for transportation studies
A.H. Soliman (executive secretary), BSc(CE),
PhD

Glenlea research station
J.D. Truscott, MSc, PhD

Legal research institute
J.M. Sharpe, BA, LLB, MA

Manitoba institute of cell biology
L.G. Israels, BA, MD, MSc, FRCP(C)

Medieval and renaissance guild
R.J. Glendinning (chairman), BA, MA,
DrPhilDes

Natural resource institute
S. Sinclair, BSA, MSc, PhD, FAIC

Northern studies committee
J.C. Gilson (acting chairman), BSA, MSc,
PhD

University field station (Delta Marsh)
Jennifer Walker-Shay, BSc, MSc, PhD

University field station (Star Lake)
W.C. Brisbin, BSc, PhD

Department heads

Accounting and finance
J.D. Blazouske, BA, BComm, MBA, CA, RIA

Actuarial and business mathematics
E.R. Vogt, BComm, FSA, FCIA, AIA

Agricultural diploma course
E.H. Lange, BSA, MSc

Agricultural economics and farm
management
A.W. Wood, BA, BSA, MSc, PhD

Agricultural engineering
G.E. Laliberte, BE, MSc, PhD, PEng

Anaesthesia
J.G. Wade, BS, MD, FRCP(C)

Anatomy
K.L. Moore, BA, MSc, PhD, FAIC

Animal science
E.W. Stringam, MSc, PhD, FAIC

Anthropology
Louise Sweet, BA, MA, PhD

Architecture
K.C. Lye, BArch, MFAinArch, MRAIC,
ASIA

Biochemistry
M.C. Blanchaer, BA, MD, CM

Botany
E.R. Waygood, BSc, MSc, PhD, FCIC

Business administration
G.D. Thomas (interim), BComm, MBA

Chemistry
R.H. Betts, BSc, MSc, PhD

City planning
V.J. Kostka, IngArch, AMTPI, MRAIC, AIP,
MTPIC

Civil engineering
A.M. Lansdown, BSc(CE), PhD, MEIC,
PEng

Classics
E.G. Berry, BA, MA, PhD

Clothing and textiles
Margaret Morton, BSc(HEc), MA

Computer science
R.G. Stanton (acting), BA, MA, PhD

Curriculum: humanities and social sciences
M.A. Bonneau, BA, BEd, MA

Curriculum: mathematics and natural
sciences
A.M. McPherson, BSc, MEd

Earth sciences
H.D.B. Wilson, BSc, MSc, PhD, FRSC

Economics
C.L. Barber, BA, MA, PhD

Educational administration
J.W. Peach, BA, BEd, MEd, PhD

Educational foundations
K. Wilson, MA, MEd, PhD

Educational psychology
Laura Baker, BA, MEd, EdD

Electrical engineering
J.P.C McMath, BSc(EE), MEIC, PEng

English
J.M. Robinson (acting), BA, MA, PhD

Entomology
A.J. Thorsteinson, BSA, PhD

Environmental studies
C.R. Nelson, Jr., BArch, MArch, MRAIC

Family studies
Lola Jackson, BHE, MSc, PhD

Food science
R.A. Gallop, MSc, PhD

Foods and nutrition
Shirley Weber, CD, BSc(HEc), MS, PhD

Geography
T.R. Weir, BA, MA, PhD

Geological engineering
W.C. Brisbin, BSc, PEng

German
R.J. Glendinning (acting), BA, MA, PhD

History
G.A. Schultz, BA, BD, MA, PhD

Icelandic
H. Bessason, CandPhil, CandMag

Immunology
A. Sehon, BSc, MSc, PhD, DSc

Interior design
Joan Harland, BArch, MA, ATCM, MIDIM

Judaic studies
Z.M. Schachter, MHL, MA, DHL

Landscape architecture
A.E. Rattray, BArch, MLA

Mathematics and astronomy
N.S. Mendelsohn, BA, MA, PhD, FRSC

Mechanical engineering
R.E. Chant, BEng, MEng, MEIC, MASME,
PEng

Medicine
J.P. Gemmell, MD, MRCP(Lond), FRCP(C)

Medical microbiology
J.C. Wilt, MD, MSc, FACP

Microbiology
H. Lees, BSc, PhD, FRSE

Obstetrics and gynaecology
T.M. Roulston, MB, BCh, BAO, FRCOG

Ophthalmology
G.M. Krolman, BSc, MD, FRSC(Edin and
Can)

Otolaryngology
W. Alexander, MD

Paediatrics
W.W. Grant (acting), BA, MD

Pathology
J.P. Wyatt, MD

Pharmacology and therapeutics
I.R. Innes, MB, ChB, MD

Philosophy
R.H. Vincent, BA, MA

Physics
A.H. Morrish, BSc, MA, PhD, FRSC

Physiology
K.R. Hughes (acting), BA, MA, PhD

Plant science
R.C. McGinnis, MSc, PhD

Political studies
K.M. Reshaur, BA, MA, PhD

Psychiatry
G.S. Sisler, MD, FRCP(C), FAPA

Psychology
A.H. Shephard, BA, MA, PhD

Public policy
S. Trachtenberg, BA, MA

Radiology
D.W. MacEwan, BSc, MD, CM, FRCP(C)

Religion
W. Klassen, AB, BD, ThD

Romance languages and literature
C.A.E. Jensen, BA, MA, PhD

Slavic studies
J.B. Rudnyckyj, MA, PhD

Social and preventive medicine
R.G. Cadham, MD, DPH

Sociology
D.L. Rennie, BSc, BA, MA, PhD

Soil science
R.A. Hedlin, BSA, MSc, PhD

Statistics
B.K. Kale (acting), BA, MA, PhD

Surgery
J.F. Lind, MD, CM, FRCS(C), FACS

Zoology
H.E. Welch, BA, MA, PhD

Marianopolis College[*]

(Affiliated to the University of Montreal)
3647 Peel Street, Montreal 112, Quebec

Telephone: 514-288-6166
Direct general correspondence to the registrar

Total full-time student enrolment 114; see also separate section *Statistics on Canadian universities and colleges*

Executive and administrative officers

President
Sister Mary MacCormack, MA

Academic dean
Sister Calista Begnal, PhD

Director of student services
Sister Clare O'Neill, MA

Chief librarian
Roman R. Grodzicky, PhD

Director of information office
Sheilagh Litchfield Johnson, BA

Accountant
André Boileau

Registrar
Sister Isabel MacDougall, MA

Background

The origins of Marianopolis College go back to the year 1908 when both Notre Dame Ladies' College and its counterpart for French-speaking young women were founded by the Sisters of the Congregation of Notre Dame. Marianopolis was the first institution in the province of Quebec for the higher education of Catholic women. The academic status of the new college was assured by an affiliation to Laval University, an arrangement which was continued until 1922. The first bachelor of arts degrees were conferred in 1912. In 1922, the affiliation was transferred to the newly chartered University of Montreal. In 1926, relinquishing its quarters in the congregation's motherhouse in favor of a new site on Westmount Avenue, the college became known as Marguerite Bourgeoys College.

As the years went on, it became evident that the two sections of Marguerite Bourgeoys College would meet the educational needs more effectively under separate administrations. Consequently in 1943 the curriculum was reorganized along the lines of the English-language universities and included programs in honors chemistry and general science. The English section of the college under the name of Marianopolis College was transferred in September 1944 to a new site on Dorchester Street. When in January 1945 fire destroyed the newly renovated building, the college moved into its present administration building on Peel Street and has since then expanded its campus by the acquisition of additional lands and buildings.

Marianopolis College was incorporated in April 1946 and in February 1961 a new and more suitable form of incorporation was secured by an act of the legislature of the province of Quebec.

Marianopolis College, which became co-educational in September 1969, is owned by the Sisters of the Congregation of Notre Dame and administered by a board of trustees. An advisory board consisting of members of the faculty, of the student body, of the alumni and of the lay community share in the direction of the college.

Facilities and services

The college is situated in downtown Montreal (population approximates 2,437,000) and is housed in six buildings. Facilities include a library (35,000 volumes) and residence accommodation.

Student services include a health service, guidance and counselling, a cafeteria, a placement service, an accident insurance

[*]Ordinary member, AUCC.

service, and a drug and birth control information centre.

Calendars and brochures

The academic calendar and general brochures are available from the director, information office.

Courses and degrees

Arts
(Faculty of arts)

Bachelor of arts (BA).
Four years from junior matriculation. Arts course with majors and/or concentrations in the following fields: applied linguistics, biology-psychology, classics, English, French, French-Spanish, history, mathematics, music, philosophy-theology, pre-medical, psychology, social sciences, sociology, Spanish.

Program is being phased out. Last degrees will be awarded in 1972.

Science
(Faculty of science)

Bachelor of science (BSc).
Four years from junior matriculation. (a) Science courses with a major or a concentration in the following fields: biology, biology-chemistry, biology-mathematics, chemistry, chemistry-mathematics, chemistry-mathematics-physics, food and nutrition, mathematics, pre-medical, textiles and design. (b) Honors course, four years from junior matriculation, available in chemistry.

Program is being phased out. Last degrees will be awarded in 1972.

Special programs

The Marianopolis CEGEP program, known as parallel M, is a unique experiment in teaching and learning methods.

Taking advantage of the small number of required courses outlined by the department of education, and the needs of present students, the program is designed to allow a student to select a core subject according to his interests, related subjects which broaden his comprehension of the core and complementary subjects to provide balance. The result is a pyramid-like pattern of choices in which orientation is decided and defined at the apex, while the center and base of the pyramid are made up of subjects which enrich the core courses.

The advantage of this approach lies in the fact that a student is free to readjust his individual program from one semester to the next in such a way that one of the related courses could become the core course, because all courses in the program form an integrated pattern. The program thus provides some degree of specialization but at the same time introduces the students to a broad spectrum of related disciplines.

The *Marianopolis College program for mature women* has been established for the purpose of helping those women who for one reason or another have not had the opportunity to attend college and who now wish to continue their educational experience. It has been designed for the woman who is actively engaged in home-making, who must have her pre-school children cared for, and who must take her family responsibilities into account when planning study and classes.

The program offers: (a) a convenient way of beginning academic work after an absence of years; (b) guidance in formulating a realistic plan for continuing education based upon personal interests, needs and aptitudes; (c) professional assistance in adjusting to the multiple roles of wife-mother-student; (d) infant and pre-school child care on the campus at no cost to the student mothers. It is open to women of all ages and has been planned specifically to encourage married women to work at a pace compatible with the rest of their lives.

The courses in the program have been selected to introduce formal study in multiple disciplines while keeping in mind the specific interests and needs of the adult woman. Classes will be held from 9:00 - 12:00 each weekday morning from late September to mid-April, and students will attend four or five mornings each week according to their individual programs. In all, a participant will take a minimum of four courses each semester for a total of 12 class hours per week. Her CEGEP program would thus be

achieved in a slightly longer than usual period of time, but she would be studying with a group of women who are, like herself, combining several roles at once.

An important feature of this program is the child care centre. A mother may rest assured while attending classes that her infant or pre-schooler is being well cared for by a professionally trained staff under the supervision of a nursery school expert.

Dynamics of society and culture is an interdisciplinary program of five courses meeting all the standards of the college program but having the added advantage of being closely related to each other in content and integrated in procedures. Faculty and students work together planning all aspects of the program.

The program centers around courses in English, sociology, history, religious studies and political science.

Admission requirements

For a general statement regarding admission to university study, see article *Admission to university in Canada*.

For information regarding admission to undergraduate study, consult *Requirements for admission to Canadian colleges and universities* available from Service for Admission to College and University, 151 Slater St., Ottawa, Ont., K1P 5N1, $1.50 prepaid.

Academic year

Mid-September to early May.

Grading system

All grading is done by letters. Appropriate equivalents: A, 80-100%; B, 70-79%; C, 60-69%; D, 50-59%; F, below 50%.

Fees and costs

Tuition fees per year: arts, $550; science,

$600; CEGEP-equivalent, $400. Miscellaneous and student fees per year depend on course.

Residence rates, room and board per year, $900.

Financial awards and assistance

Financial aid for students who attend Marianopolis College is available in the form of scholarships, bursaries, and loans. Academic achievement and promise, character, participation in extra-curricular activities and financial need are factors governing selection of candidates.

Entrance scholarships are granted on a competitive basis to students completing junior and senior matriculation. These scholarships can be renewed for succeeding years to candidates who maintain a high level of academic achievement.

A student interested in any of the above should communicate with the chairman, committee on scholarships, Marianopolis College.

Dean of faculty

Academic dean
Sister Calista Begnal, PhD

Department heads

English language and literature
Paul Aldus, BS, MA, PhD

History and the social sciences
Agnes Fergusson, BA, MA

Modern languages
Madeleine Ellis, BA, MA, PhD

Natural sciences and mathematics
Catherine Westbury, BSc, DSc, PhD

Philosophy and theology
Josephine McQueen (co-chairman), BA, PhD
George Di Giovanni (co-chairman), BA, MA, STB

McGill University*

P.O. Box 6070, Montreal 101, Quebec

Telephone: 514-392-4311
Direct general correspondence to the registrar

Total full-time student enrolment 15,178; see also separate section *Statistics on Canadian universities and colleges*

Executive and administrative officers

Chancellor
Donald Hebb, BA, MA, PhD, DSc, DHL, LLD, FRS, FRSC

Chairman of the board of governors
S.M. Finlayson, BSc

Principal and vice-chancellor
Robert Bell, MA, PhD, DSc, FRSC, FRS

Vice-principal (academic)
Michael Oliver, MA, PhD

Vice-principal (administration and professional affairs)
S.B. Frost, BD, MTh, DPhil, DD, DLitt

Acting vice-principal, Macdonald College and acting dean, agriculture
Harold Klinck, BSA, MSc, PhD

Director, finance
Allan McColl, DFC, BCom, CA

Secretary of the board of governors
J.H. Holton, BCom

Secretary of senate and registrar
C.M. McDougall, DSO, BA

University treasurer
N.D. Johnston, BCom

Comptroller
John Armour, AACCA

Chief accountant
R.G. Kuranoff

Director, university libraries
Keith Crouch, BA, MA, BLS

Director, educational development
G.C.B. Cave, BA, MA, PhD, FCIC

Executive director of the graduates' society
Lorne Gales, BA, BCL

Director, admissions office
R.C. Coleman, DSO, MC, BA, LLB

Schools liaison officer
J.F. Stewart, BA

Director, centre for continuing education
E.C. Webster, MA, PhD

Director, athletics, physical education and recreation
H.E. Griffiths, MA, BCom

Warden, Royal Victoria College
To be appointed

Director, personnel services
P.M. Matthews, BA, MSc

Student counsellor and director, student aid office
J.S. Kennedy, BA, BD

Director, information office
Andrew Allen (acting)

Director, McGill-Queen's University Press
Robin Strachan, BA, MA

Director, university health service
J.G. Lohrenz, MD, DipPsychiat

Director, business operations
Charles E. Noel, BComm, CA

Director, physical plant
A.D. Elliott, MM, BEng

Superintendent, buildings and grounds
P.A. Cunningham

*Ordinary member, AUCC.

Constituent colleges

Macdonald College, Ste-Anne de Bellevue,
Que., (postal address: Macdonald College
800, Que.).
Acting vice-principal: Harold Klinck, BSA,
MSc, PhD. Registrar: Jean David, LSA, PhD.
Secretary-bursar: W.C. Shipley, BSc(Agr),
MA. Dean of students: to be appointed.
Founded in 1907 by Sir William Macdonald.
Residential college composed of faculty of
agriculture (co-educational), and school of
food science (women only). Institute of
parasitology, attached to faculty of graduate
studies and research, also at Macdonald
College.

Royal Victoria College, 3425 University St.,
Montreal, Que.
Warden: to be appointed. Main building
(Hurlbatt wing) erected in 1899 under terms
of endowment created by the Rt. Hon. Baron
Strathcona and Mount Royal for the
education of women at McGill. A west wing
(Vaughan) was added in 1930-31 and an east
wing in 1948-49; the Muriel Roscoe wing
was opened in 1964. Now houses the faculty
of music. West wing and Roscoe wing
accommodate 225 women students. All
women undergraduates of McGill are
members of the college whether they are in
residence or not, and women's activities
centre in it. Not a teaching college.

Background

In 1813, the Hon. James McGill, a leading
merchant and prominent citizen of Montreal,
died, and in his will left 46 acres of land and
£10,000 to the already existing "Royal
Institution for the Advancement of
Learning", for the purpose of founding a
college or university. As a result, a royal
charter was granted in 1821 and the
University of McGill College was opened in
1829 with teaching in the faculties of
medicine and arts. The first degree was
awarded in 1833. The university is non-
denominational and for many years has been
co-educational in most of its 12 faculties and
six schools.

A general supervisory power in the university
is retained by the Crown and is exercised
through the Governor-General as visitor. The
members of the board of governors constitute
"The Royal Institution for the Advancement
of Learning" while the senate is the highest
academic authority of the university.

Facilities and services

Eleven of the faculties of McGill are situated
in Montreal (population approximates
2,489,000), where the university campus lies
on the lower slopes of Mount Royal.
Macdonald College at Ste-Anne de Bellevue,
about 25 miles from Montreal, is an
incorporated college of the university, and
houses the faculty of agriculture and the
school of food science.

The Montreal campus has an area of 75 acres
and contains 85 buildings, including teaching
buildings, administration buildings, students'
centre, and men's and women's residences.
The university library includes the McLennan
library and various faculty and departmental
libraries in other buildings. The Osler library
of the history of medicine contains about
20,000 volumes and has, as a nucleus, the
8,000 volumes bequeathed to McGill by one
of its most famous pupils and teachers, Sir
William Osler. The several libraries of the
university now contain more than 1,250,000
volumes and 50,000 pamphlets and receive
about 23,000 periodicals, government
publications, and transactions of various
literary and scientific societies. The McCord
museum houses the university's extensive
collection of Canadiana. The Redpath
museum of natural history is used for
reference and research. In addition there are
specialized collections such as the Rutherford
collection of experimental physics and the
anatomical, medical, pathological and
biological museums.

Macdonald College consists of approximately
1,600 acres with 30 buildings including
residences, students' centre, indoor skating
rink, gymnasia, swimming pools and other
sports facilities. The campus proper consists
of 200 acres and contains the orchard,
horticulture plots, and poultry ranges. In
addition there are the stock farm, the
agronomy and the college farms. The
Morgan arboretum, established in 1947, has
700 acres of woodland devoted to the study
of woodlot management and the place of
the woodlot in the eastern Canadian farm
economy. The Lyman entomological museum

contains the best insect collection in Canadian universities. The Brace Research Institute devoted to the study of the engineering aspects of arid land development and the Institute of Parasitology are also housed on the Macdonald campus.

In 1958, on the death of Brigadier A. Hamilton Gault, McGill inherited Mont St. Hilaire, a property consisting of 2,285 acres, which is used for research in meteorology, geography, geology, horticulture, entomology, botany, zoology, and for other academic purposes.

Student services include health, guidance, counselling, and placement services, student aid office, a rooms registry, cafeterias, a bookstore, and a students' centre. The Sir Arthur Currie memorial gymnasium, the Percival Molson memorial stadium, and the McConnell winter stadium provide facilities for summer and winter sports.

Calendars and brochures

The General announcement and Renseignements généraux as well as separate announcements for each faculty or school are available from the registrar's office.

Courses and degrees

(N.B. CEGEP represents the initials for "Collège d'enseignement général et professionnel" [*college of general and vocational education.*])

Agriculture
(Faculty of agriculture)

Bachelor of science in agriculture [BSc(Agr)].
Three years post CEGEP or equivalent. Major areas of study: agricultural sciences (agricultural economics, animal science, general agriculture, plant sciences, soil science); biological sciences (botanical sciences, zoological sciences, environmental biology, microbiology); renewable resources development (wildlife resources, environment conservation, public service and administration, resource economics and management, community resource development, agricultural land planning development).

Bachelor of science in agricultural engineering [BSc(AgrEng)].
Three years post CEGEP or equivalent.

Diploma in agriculture.
Two years after graduation from high school. Mature students also considered. Training in modern agricultural practice.

(Faculty of graduate studies and research)

Master of science (MSc).
At least one year from a BSc(Agr) or BSc(AgrEng). Offered in agricultural chemistry, agricultural engineering, agronomy, animal science (animal genetics, animal pathology, animal physiology and nutrition), biochemistry, entomology, horticulture, microbiology, parasitology, plant pathology, soil science, wildlife biology, and woodlot management.

Master of arts (MA).
At least one year after BSc, offered in agricultural economics.

Doctor of philosophy (PhD).
At least two years from MSc. Offered in agricultural chemistry, agricultural engineering, agronomy, animal science (animal genetics, animal pathology, animal physiology and nutrition), biochemistry, entomology, microbiology, parasitology, plant pathology, and soil science.

Architecture
(School of architecture, faculty of engineering)

Bachelor of science (architecture) [BSc(Arch)].
Three years post CEGEP or equivalent.

Bachelor of architecture (BArch).
Four years post CEGEP or equivalent or a minimum of one year after BSc (Arch).

(Faculty of graduate studies and research)

Master of architecture (MArch).
At least one year from BArch. Offered in architectural design, housing design and community planning.

Arts
(Faculty of arts)

Bachelor of arts (BA).
Three years post CEGEP or equivalent in honors, major and general courses in descending degree of specialization. Honors in anthropology, art history, classics, economics, English, French, geography, German, history, Italian, Latin, linguistics, mathematics, philosophy, political science, psychology, Russian, sociology, Spanish, and certain paired combinations of these subjects.

Majors in African studies, anthropology, economics, economics and political science, English, French, French Canada studies, geography, German, history, industrial relations, Italian, Jewish studies, linguistics, mathematics, North American studies program, political science, psychology, religious studies, Russian, sociology, and Spanish.

(Faculty of graduate studies and research)

Master of arts (MA).
At least one year from BA. In most departments an honors BA is required. Offered in anthropology, art history, classics, economics, education, English, French, geography, German, history, Islamic studies, Italian language and literature, linguistics, mathematics, philosophy, political science, psychology, religious studies, Russian, sociology, and Spanish.

Doctor of philosophy (PhD).
At least three years from bachelor's degree or two years from master's degree. Offered in anthropology, economics, English, French, geography, German, history, Islamic studies, linguistics, management, mathematics, philosophy, political science, psychology, religious studies, Russian, sociology and Spanish.

Business, see management

Dentistry
(Faculty of dentistry)

Doctor of dental surgery (DDS).
Five years post CEGEP or equivalent. The first year of the five is a dental preparatory year in arts or science.

(Faculty of graduate studies and research)

Diploma in restorative dentistry and prosthodontics.
One year after DDS or equivalent degree

Divinity, see religious studies

Education
(Faculty of education)

Bachelor of education (BEd).
Three years post CEGEP or equivalent. General and major courses in physical education and home economics. Graduates qualify for the class I interim teacher's certificate from the Quebec Department of Education.

McGill diploma in education.
One year after university degree. Graduates qualify for the class I interim teacher's certificate from the Quebec Department of Education. Also available for music specialists with bachelor of music degree with major in school music.

Class II diploma in education.
One year post CEGEP or equivalent. For kindergarten, technical-vocational education or business education specialists. Graduates qualify for the class II teacher's certificate from the Quebec Department of Education.

(Faculty of graduate studies and research)

Master of arts in education (MA).
After undergraduate degree of minimum of second-class standing plus McGill diploma in education or equivalent, or BEd degree or equivalent. Not less then two years of full-time study or the equivalent in summer school and part-time work. Thesis is required. Offered in social foundations of education, counsellor education, educational administration, educational psychology, and physical education.

Master of education (MEd).
After undergraduate degree of minimum of second-class standing plus McGill diploma in education or equivalent, or BEd degree or equivalent. Not less than two years of full-time study. Internship or other practical experience required. Offered in counsellor education, educational administration, special education, teaching of reading, and teaching subjects.

Doctor of education (DEd).
After MEd (counsellor education) or equivalent degree: minimum of two years of full-time study, plus summer school between the two academic years. Offered in counsellor education.

Engineering
(Faculty of engineering)

Bachelor of engineering (BEng).
Three years post CEGEP or equivalent.
Specialization in chemical, civil, electrical,
mechanical, metallurgical, mining
engineering and applied geophysics. Special
honors courses in electrical and mechanical
engineering.

(Faculty of graduate studies and research)

Diploma in arid land development.
One year from undergraduate degree.

Master of engineering (MEng).
At least one year from BEng. Offered in
chemical, civil, electrical, mechanical,
metallurgical, and mining engineering and
applied geophysics.

Master of engineering (mining)
[MEng(Mining)].
At least one year after the graduate diploma
or at least two years from BEng. Dissertation
required.

Master of science (MSc).
At least one year from bachelor's degree.
Offered in computer science, electrical
communications, fluid mechanics, metallurgy,
mining engineering and applied geophysics.

Doctor of philosophy (PhD).
At least three years from bachelor's or two
years from master's degree. Offered in
chemical, civil, electrical, electrical
communications, mechanical, metallurgical,
and mining engineering and applied
geophysics.

Centre for continuing education.
Graduate diplomas in chemical, civil,
electrical, mechanical and mining
engineering. No thesis required. Evening
classes.

Food science
(School of food science, faculty of
agriculture)

Bachelor of science in food science [BSc(FSc)].
Three years post CEGEP or equivalent.
Major area of study: food and consumer
sciences (consumer education and home
economics, dietetics and nutrition, food
biochemistry, food management, food
technology, general food and consumer
sciences).

Law
(Faculty of law)

Bachelor of civil law (BCL).
Three years after completion of BA degree or
post CEGEP or equivalent or one year after
LLB degree.

Bachelor of laws (LLB).
Three years after completion of BA degree or
one year after BCL degree.

(Faculty of graduate studies and research)

Diploma in air and space law.
One session after completion of BCL degree
or equivalent professional standing. No thesis
required.

Master of civil law (MCL).
At least one year after completion of BCL
degree.

Master of laws (LLM).
Two years or sometimes one year after
completion of first degree in law. Offered in
air and space law and comparative and
foreign law.

Doctor of civil law (DCL).
Three years after first degree in law.

Library science
(Graduate school of library science,
professional division, faculty of graduate
studies and research)

Master of library science (MLS).
Two years following bachelor's degree.

Management
(Faculty of management)

Bachelor of commerce (BCom).
Three years post CEGEP or equivalent.
General; honors courses in economics,
political science, and accounting and
economics; major courses in economics,
industrial relations or mathematics.

(Faculty of graduate studies and research)

Master of business administration (MBA).
At least two years after BA, BSc, BEng,
BCom, etc.

Master of commerce (MCom).
Two years from BCom. One year of full-time study and one year in a chartered accountant's office.

Doctor of philosophy (PhD).
At least three years from master's degree.

(Centre for continuing education)

Diploma in management.
At least three years after BA, BSc, BEng, BCom, or BCL. Evening classes.

Medicine
(Faculty of medicine)

Doctor of medicine and master of surgery (MD,CM).
Five years post CEGEP or equivalent. The first of the five is a preparatory year with further studies in physical and biological sciences and humanities.

(Faculty of graduate studies and research)

Master of science (MSc).
At least one year from MD. Offered in anatomy, biochemistry, epidemiology and health, experimental medicine, experimental surgery, human communication disorders, neurology, neurosurgery, otolaryngology, pathology, pharmacology and therapeutics, physiology, psychiatry, and diagnostic and therapeutic radiology.

Master of science (applied) [MSc(Appl)].
At least two years from bachelor's degree. Available in human communication disorders.

Doctor of philosophy (PhD).
At least three years from MD or two from master's degree. Offered in anatomy, biochemistry, epidemiology and health, experimental medicine, experimental surgery, microbiology and immunology, neurology and neurosurgery, pathology, pharmacology and therapeutics, and physiology.

(Faculty of medicine)

Graduate diploma in medicine.
Four years following MD degree and one year's internship. Offered in anaesthesia, neurology, psychiatry, radiology, and urology. Five years following MD degree and one year's internship for neurosurgery. Graduate diploma in epidemiology, one year from medical or dental degree.

Music
(Faculty of music)

Licentiate in music (LMus).
Three years after high school leaving for instrumentalists and singers who are able to pass a special audition at advanced level.

Concert diploma.
Two-year post-licentiate or equivalent course for specially gifted instrumentalists and singers who are able to pass a special audition.

Bachelor of music (BMus).
Three years post CEGEP or equivalent and special McGill entrance examinations in practical and theoretical subjects in music. Major courses in composition, performance, school music, and history and literature of music.

(Faculty of graduate studies and research)

Master of musical arts (MMA).
Two years from BMus. Offered in either composition or musicology.

Nursing
(School for graduate nurses, faculty of medicine)

Bachelor of nursing (BN).
Two years from hospital training school diploma in nursing provided the candidate has full senior matriculation or equivalent.

Bachelor of science in nursing [BSc(N)].
Three years post CEGEP or equivalent. Students are prepared for positions in hospitals and public health agencies.

(Faculty of graduate studies and research)

Master of science (applied) [MSc(Appl)].
Two years from BN. Designed to prepare the specialist in nursing.

Master of nursing (teaching) [MN(Teaching)].
One year from BSc(N). Open to highly qualified graduates of the basic nursing university program. Prepares teachers of nursing.

Physical and occupational therapy
(School of physical and occupational therapy, faculty of medicine)

Bachelor of science in occupational therapy [BSc(OccTher)].
Three years post CEGEP or equivalent.

Bachelor of science in physical therapy [BSc(PhysTher)].
Three years post CEGEP or equivalent.

Religious studies
(Faculty of religious studies)

Bachelor of theology (BTh).
Three years post CEGEP or equivalent.

(Faculty of graduate studies and research)

Master of arts (MA).
Two years post BA or BTh.

Doctor of philosophy (PhD).
At least three years after BTh. Specialization in church history, comparative study of religion, New Testament, Old Testament, philosophy and psychology of religion, and historical theology, including theological ethics.

Science, applied, see engineering

Science, pure
(Faculty of science)

Bachelor of science (BSc).
Three years post CEGEP or equivalent in honors, major and general courses in descending degree of specialization. Honors in anatomical sciences, biochemistry, biochemistry and chemistry, biology (animal behavior, biomedical sciences, cell biology, microbial genetics, ecology, palaeobiology, comparative physiology), biophysics, botany*, chemistry, chemistry and physics, crystallography, genetics*, geochemistry, geography, geological sciences, geology and physics (geophysics), mathematics, mathematics and physics, meteorology, microbiology and immunology, physics, physiology, psychology, and zoology*. Majors in biochemistry, cell biology, chemistry, geography, geological sciences, mathematics, meteorology, microbiology and immunology, physics, psychology, and zoology*.

(Faculty of graduate studies and research)

Diploma in geological sciences.
One year from bachelor's degree.

Master of science (MSc).
At least one year from bachelor's degree; in most departments an honors BSc is required. Offered in anatomy, biochemistry, botany*, chemistry, computer science, crystallography, genetics*, geography, geological sciences, geophysics, glaciology, marine sciences, mathematics, meteorology, microbiology and immunology, physics, physiology, psychology, and zoology*.

Master of science (applied) [MSc(Appl)].
At least two years from bachelor's degree. Offered in geological sciences (mineral exploration) and psychology. No thesis required.

Doctor of philosophy (PhD).
At least three years from bachelor's degree or two years from master's degree. Offered in anatomy, biochemistry, botany, chemistry, genetics, geography, geological sciences, marine sciences, mathematics, meteorology, microbiology and immunology, pharmacology, physics, physiology, psychology, and zoology*.

Social work
(Faculty of arts)

Bachelor of social work (BSW).
Three years post CEGEP or equivalent.

(School of social work, professional division, faculty of graduate studies and research)

Master of social work (MSW).
At least one year after BSW.

Diploma in advanced practice.
One year after MSW.

Special programs

African studies program, French Canada studies program, school of human communication disorders, North American studies program, urban studies program, biomedical engineering unit, Brace research

*Now part of the department of biology.

institute, centre for developing area studies, aviation medical research unit, East Asian studies, Jewish studies program, general course on the environment, intensive agriculture and water pollution research project, MA and PhD programs in communications. Other programs are also available through research institutes (see separate section).

Extension programs

For university credit:

Evening classes.
Some advanced courses in civil, electrical, chemical, and mechanical engineering for credit toward the MEng degree or the graduate diploma in engineering.
A series of courses in management and business administration is available leading in three years to a diploma in management. Candidates must be graduates with BA, BSc, BEng, or BCL.
Night courses are also offered for university graduates wishing to qualify as high school teachers.

Summer schools.
A number of day courses including accountancy, biology, chemistry, Chinese, education, management, English, screen study, French, and geography are available. Director of summer session: Prof. G.W.E. McElroy.

For no university credit:

Diploma and certificate courses not requiring matriculation.
English-French, French-English translation courses leading in three years (minimum) to a diploma.

Courses at the university level.
Courses in engineering subjects (mathematics, mechanics, strength of materials, hydraulics, and occasionally others at a higher level). Language courses (English, French, German, Italian, Russian, Spanish). Accountancy courses in preparation for the CA, CGA, and RIA examinations. Courses for certificates in administration, insurance, marketing, retail, systems design and transportation management. Courses for the ACIS and FCIS (Chartered Institute of Secretaries). A

certificate for pathologists trained in cytology and a certificate for technicians in diagnostic cytology are also offered.

Miscellaneous courses.
A number of popular courses are offered (e.g., appreciation of art and of music, introduction to English literature, philosophy, psychology, sociology, etc.) for which no academic prerequisite is specified. Also a number of technical and semi-technical courses are offered for the benefit of particular groups as a community service. Italian and Spanish and also business management diploma courses.

Summer courses.
Evening course in French, English, accountancy, and management. Day seminars in executive and staff development and industrial relations.

Admission requirements

For a general statement regarding admission to university study, see article *Admission to university in Canada.*

For information regarding admission to undergraduate study, consult *Requirements for admission to Canadian colleges and universities* available from Service for Admission to College and University, 151 Slater St., Ottawa, Ont., K1P 5N1, $1.50 prepaid.

For admission to graduate study a student must have completed the equivalent of an honors degree at McGill with specified grades in appropriate subjects.

Application for admission to most departments in the faculty of graduate studies and research should be made to the dean by July 3.

Academic year

Winter session: mid-September to early May (June, for medicine and dentistry and other professional schools).

Summer session: in some subjects, July to mid-August.

Grading system

Arts, science: all courses carry a credit rating. The earned grade point for each course is the product of the credit rating of the course and the grade rating attained. A — (80-100%), 4; B — (65-79%), 3; C — (55-64%), 2; D — (45-54%), 1; F — (0-44%), 0. Standing is determined on the basis of a grade point average (GPA) computed by dividing the sum of the grade points earned for the year by the total course credits attempted.

Engineering: each course is assigned a course weight. The earned grade point average is defined by the ratio: sum of the products (course weight) X grade points = sum of the course weights. A — excellent, 4; B — very good, 3; C — good, 2; D — conditional pass, 1; F — failed, 0.

Medicine: S — satisfactory, 60-100%; F — failed, under 60%. *Dentistry*: pass — 60-100%; fail — under 60%. *Graduate studies and research*: pass mark 65%.

College equivalent programs: A — 80-100%; B — 65-79%; C — 55-64%; D — 45-54%; failure — under 45%.

Fees and costs

Fees per year, including tuition and miscellaneous fees: agriculture (degree) $525, (diploma) $65 for children of farmers of Quebec, eastern Ontario and the Maritime provinces, others $375; architecture $746, BSc(Arch) $746; arts $638; dentistry $690 (lab. equipment not included); education, BEd $638, PE major $658, HEc major $550, diplomas, classes I and II $500; engineering $740; food science $525; graduate studies, except MBA, MLS 2, and MSW $652, MBA $717, MLS 2 $312, MSW $654; law $635; management, (BCom) $643; medicine 1st, 2nd and 3rd years $800, 4th year $805; music, (degree) $638, concert diploma $655, licentiate $595; nursing, BN $615, BSc(N) $615; physical and occupational therapy, $610; religious studies $585; science, $703; BSW, $638; partial courses, $150 per course; Quebec students in 1st or 2nd year of college equivalent programs on Montreal campus, $460, except college equivalent programs in management, $465; Quebec students in college equivalent programs on Macdonald campus, $475; non-Quebec students in college equivalent programs pay standard university fees for the appropriate course.

Board and residence — men: $914 to $1,209; women: $985 to $1,305.
(All fees are subject to possible changes.)

Financial awards and assistance

Fellowships and assistantships are available in the faculty of graduate studies and research. Application through the dean of the faculty. In the undergraduate faculties, application for entrance scholarships for Canadian students only are made through the admissions office. Bursaries and loans are available through the student aid office. The scholarships announcement giving further details may be obtained from the registrar's office.

Provincial and federal aid: address inquiries to student aid, c/o department of education in the appropriate provincial capital. Quebec students are not eligible to apply for federal aid but should apply for provincial aid to: Student Aid Service, Parliament Buildings, Quebec 4, Quebec.

Research institutes, centres, and programs

Allan Memorial Institute of Psychiatry.
A psychiatry institute for teaching, research, and treatment. McGill University undertakes responsibility for the training and teaching facilities, and the Royal Victoria Hospital for the clinical work. Teaching covers both undergraduate instruction and advanced postgraduate training. Research facilities are provided for clinical and laboratory studies of clinical conditions and biochemical, physiological, and psychological study of various aspects of behavioral disorders in animal and man.
Director: Dr. M. Dongier.

Anthropology of Development Program.
The program co-ordinates and furthers research and teaching on the process of socio-economic development as it affects small communities in the Canadian North and in low-income countries.
Director: Professor R.F. Salisbury.

Arctic Institute of North America.
An international organization, the Montreal office (and headquarters) of which has since 1945 occupied space provided by McGill University. It fosters research in all scientific disciplines both natural and social, on northern North America, and maintains a reference library, a map collection and a small museum. It co-operates with the university in the McGill-Arctic Institute-Carnegie program which assists graduate students in northern studies.
Director: Montreal Office: Kenneth de la Barre.

Aviation Medical Research Unit.
The unit deals with physiology of orientation, vision and postural control.
Director: Professor Melvill Jones.

Bellairs Research Institute.
At this institute, located in Barbados, research is conducted in marine biology, geology, geography, and tropical climatology.
Director: Professor F. Sander.

Biomedical Engineering Unit.
The unit operates both in the faculties of engineering and medicine to carry out research and to train graduate students. Its work concentrates especially on neuromuscular control systems, sensory and neural communication theory, eye movements and electronystagmography and hospital information systems.
Director: Professor J.H. Milsum.

Brace Research Institute.
This institute is concerned with the desalinification of sea water and the development of arid lands. It maintains field research projects throughout the West Indies, where experimental facilities are available for desalinification and wind and solar energy. It offers a graduate diploma course in "engineering aspects of arid land development", and collaborates with other engineering departments at McGill in research problems of mutual interest.
Director: Professor G.T. Ward.

Centre for Developing Areas Studies, The.
This centre is instrumental in co-ordinating and expanding, on an interdisciplinary basis, social science activities at McGill, especially in relation to south Asia, west Africa, and the West Indies. It offers facilities for basic research and administers technical research assistance in its special areas under arrangements with the government of Canada.
Director: to be appointed.

Centre for Learning and Development.
The centre was established in 1969 to help improve the learning environment, teaching practices and learning methods at all levels of education. At present its activities focus on university education and include dissemination of relevant information, consultation, workshops, and research.
Director: Professor M.L. Goldschmid.

Dairy Herd Analysis Service (livestock population genetics).
Research in the dynamics of domesticated livestock population with particular emphasis on the physiological and environmental factors that affect the estimation of the relative genetic merit of individual and groups of animals.
Director: Professor J.E. Moxley.

East Asian Studies Program.
Since 1968 the centre has been acting as a co-ordinating entity in the stimulation of courses, acquisition of library and promoter of the department of east Asian languages and literatures. In addition, the centre has sponsored the McGill Chinese language summer school.
The framework within which all of these activities are pursued is the humanistic tradition of scholarships with primary emphasis on the modern period of both China and Japan. Though the centre has ceased to exist, the program of teaching will continue.
Director: Professor John Trentman.

Financial Research Institute.
The institute maintains price, fundamental, and economic computerized data files and accessing languages for the use of its corporate and university members.
President: Richard Hamilton.

Foster Radiation Laboratory.
Research interests include charged particle reaction studies on light and medium mass nuclei using 100 MeV cyclotron and Tandem van de Graaff accelerators; and decay scheme analysis of radio-active isotopes.
Director: Professor R.B. Moore.

French Canada Studies Program.
This program was established in 1963 for the study of French Canada at the undergraduate and graduate levels by research, and extension and public education programs. It has included in its program the award of fellowships, a large number of research projects, and the improvement of the collection of French Canadiana in the McLennan library.
Assistant director: Professor Jean-Louis Roy.

Gastrointestinal Research Laboratory.
The laboratory conducts the following
projects: structural chemistry of
gastrointestinal mucin, absorption of metal
ions, deficiency of trace elements in
coelenterates, gastrointestinal microbiological
flora and synthesis of gastric detoxicants.
Director: Professor Stanley Skoryna.

Gault Estate, The: Mont St. Hilaire.
The estate is a legacy from the late Brig.
Hamilton Gault of 2,200 acres of forested
mountain. At present it is being used chiefly
as a field research station in botany, zoology,
geography, and geology. It also provides
recreational facilities for staff and students.
There is accommodation for up to 32 persons
in the laboratory-dormitory block, built in
1963.
Acting warden and director of the nature
centre: Alice Johannsen.

Industrial Relations Centre, The.
The centre provides information, evening
seminars, research on industrial relations;
offers fellowships and research training;
publishes newsletters surveying developments
in industrial relations in Canada, as well as
research reports; maintains documents library
of all Canadian collective bargaining
agreements. Membership from community
includes crown corporations and government
agencies, industrial firms, hospital and labor
unions.
Director: Mrs. Frances Bairstow.

Institute for Mineral Industry Research.
Research at this institute consists of rock
penetration studies, mineral dressing
processes, and all aspects of the mining
environment, including dust, ventilation,
noise and underground illumination.
Director: Professor F.T.M. White.

Institute of Air and Space Law.
An academic organization for graduate study
and independent research in international air
law, open only to those already holding law
degrees or to members of the bar. Students in
the institute may proceed to the LLM degree.
Director: Professor E. McWhinney.

Institute of Comparative and Foreign Law.
The institute is established within the faculty
of law of McGill University as a centre for
comparative legal studies providing facilities
for graduate work, advanced studies and field
research in private and public law. In private
law the main emphasis is placed upon the
concepts of the civil law systems of
continental Europe and Quebec and of the

Anglo-American-Canadian common law. In
public law special attention is given to
comparative constitutional law.
Director: Dr. H.R. Hahlo.

Institute of Islamic Studies.
McGill University's institute is concerned
with the disciplined study of Islamic
civilization throughout the scope of its history
and its geographical spread. It gives attention
to the origins of Islam, to the rise of the
civilization in which Islamic faith was the
vivifying factor, to the forces which shaped
the civilization and the changes it has
undergone. It is also concerned with the
contemporary dynamics of the Islamic world
as Muslims seek to relate their heritage from
the past to the radical situation of modernity.
Director: Professor C.J. Adams.

Institute of Parasitology.
A co-operative venture of the National
Research Council and the university for the
study of parasitology in man and animals. It
also co-operates with public authorities in the
practical applications of parasitology. It
accepts qualified students who wish to
proceed to the MSc or the PhD degree. The
institute is housed at Macdonald College, Ste-
Anne de Bellevue, near Montreal.
Director: Professor K.G. Davey.

Institute of Pathology.
The institute is active in a broad research
program into the biology of disease. The staff
are individual investigators in their field of
choice which includes the nature of
connective tissue in health and disease,
respiratory disease, cardiovascular disease,
liver disease, haematoligic disease, and study
of the role of amino transferases in health
and disease.
Director: Professor R.H. More.

Institute of Theoretical Physics.
Present interests include fundamental field
theory, particle physics and dispersion theory,
high and low energy nuclear physics,
superconductivity and other areas of solid
state physics.
Director: Professor P.R. Wallace.

Jewish Studies Program.
This program was established in 1968 on an
interdisciplinary basis. The aims of the
program include making Jewish culture and
thought available to students through courses
within several departments as well as to those
students who seek a measure of
specialization.
Chairman: Professor H.M. Bracken.

Lyman Entomological Museum: Macdonald College.
Located on the Macdonald campus of McGill University, Ste-Anne de Bellevue, Quebec, in association with the department of entomology. Second only to the Canadian national collection in both specimens and numbers of species; world-wide in scope. Current research is primarily on orthoptera (grasshoppers and related groups). Has extensive facilities for research, but relatively little space for display purposes.
Chairman: Professor D.K. McE. Kevan.

Management Development Institute.
The institute, an ancillary operation of the faculty of management, offers courses and seminars designed to help middle and senior management people keep abreast of current developments in analytical and decision-making techniques, and to provide executives with a better appreciation of the integrative problems of general management.
Director: R.N. Morrison.

Marine Sciences Centre, The.
The centre is inter-departmental in scope, emphasizing the inter-disciplinary nature of the science of oceanography. Excellent laboratory and library facilities are available, and opportunities for field work exist in the Arctic, the Gulf of St. Lawrence, the Canadian eastern seaboard, and at the Bellairs Research Institute in Barbados. Special research interests include the physics of sea ice, the energy exchange between atmosphere and hydrosphere, marine climatology, the dynamics of sea water, marine bacteria, growth and life cycles of marine organisms, marine productivity, marine biogeography and sedimentation.
Chairman: Professor M.J. Dunbar.

McGill Cancer Research Unit.
The unit is supported by the National Cancer Institute of Canada. Principal field of research is the study of a control of cell division using chemo- and radio-therapeutic agents.
Director: to be appointed.

McGill Sub-Arctic Research Laboratories, Schefferville, Quebec.
This laboratory at Knob Lake in the heart of Labrador-Ungava provides facilities for research in most aspects of physical geography. It is staffed by five resident assistants, and a resident director.
Director: to be appointed.

McGill University Project for Deaf Children.
This bilingual research project, begun in 1966, tries to determine methods of identifying deafness in early infancy and evaluating training procedures which can be used in the rehabilitation of young deaf children. The type of research undertaken includes research on prosthetic devices such as frequency transposing hearing aids.
Director: Professor Daniel Ling.

Montreal Neurological Institute.
The Montreal Neurological Institute and Montreal Neurological Hospital provide undergraduate and graduate teaching in neurology, neurosurgery, and the basic neurological disciplines, research in both basic and applied sciences related to the nervous system, as well as clinical care for patients with organic diseases and lesions of the nervous system.
Director: to be appointed.

Morgan Arboretum, The: Macdonald College.
Established in 1947 and located at Macdonald College, the arboretum has 700 acres of woodland devoted to the study of woodlot management and the place of the woodlot in the eastern Canadian farm economy. About 100 acres have been planted in reforestation projects. In addition, the arboretum, in spite of its short history, has Canada's best collection of examples of all Canadian and many foreign species of trees and shrubs of interest from the view of pulpwood, timber, and landscaping.
Curator: Professor J.D. MacArthur.

Phonetics Research Laboratory.
Research in acoustic phonetics and speech perception. Spectrographic analysis of speech, production of synthesized speech by means of an electronic vocal analog. Languages investigated include English, French, Cree, Mohawk, Czech, Hungarian.
Director: Professor André Rigault.

Pulp and Paper Research Institute of Canada.
Separately incorporated non-profit research organization affiliated with McGill University and also with the Canadian Pulp and Paper Association and the federal Department of Forestry but with its own board of control. Supported by the Canadian pulp and paper industry. Principal field of research: pulp and paper technology, including woodlands research, mechanical and chemical pulping, paper making, process control, product quality and environmental pollution. Also provides facilities to graduate students working in pulp and paper technology and technical services for pulp and paper industry.
Director: Dr. Pierre Gendron.

Shastri Indo-Canadian Institute.
McGill University is a founding member of
the Shastri Indo-Canadian Institute, a co-
operative, voluntary organization,
incorporated in Ottawa, whose members are
Canadian colleges and universities with an
interest in Indian studies. Its objectives are to
enhance the mutual understanding between
India and Canada by supporting and
promoting development of Indian studies at
Canadian institutions of higher learning. This
is presently being done by the provision of
fellowships for persons residing in Canada to
conduct scholarly research in the humanities
and social sciences and by the acquisition of
Indian publications for scholarly use in
Canada.

Social Sciences Statistics Laboratory.
The laboratory is intended to promote
quantitative research and teaching by
members of the department of anthropology,
economics, political science, and sociology. At
present efforts are being directed towards
facilitating the use of the computer centre
facilities at McGill. The laboratory's facilities
include a programmer, a system of computer
programs, and a databank.

Soil Mechanics Laboratory.
Research interests include fundamental soil
mechanics, soil-water inter-action, soil
dynamics and soil-structure inter-action, soil
stability and constitution behaviors, and
other related problems in soil engineering.
Director: Professor Raymond Yong.

Wellcome Anaesthesis Research Department.
Electrophysiological and neurochemical
studies on synaptic transmission in the brain:
the aim is to identify the naturally occurring
chemical transmitter and receptor substances
and to analyze their modes of action.
Director: Professor K. Krnjevic.

Affiliated colleges

The Montreal Diocesan Theological College,
3473 University Street, Montreal, Quebec.
Principal: Rev. Monroe Peaston, MA, BD,
ThD. Anglican. For men only. Founded in
1873. Residential accommodation for 34
single students. There are also 13 apartments
for married students. Offers courses in
theology leading to a certificate for
ordination granted by the college, and
courses leading to the degree of bachelor of
theology (BTh), which is awarded by the
university.

The Presbyterian College of Montreal, 3495
University Street, Montreal, Quebec.
Acting principal: Rev. Ritchie Bell, BA, DD.
Presbyterian. For men only. Established in
1865. Offers course in theology leading to the
diploma of the college and the degree of
bachelor of divinity (BD), which are awarded
by the college. Residential accommodation
for 34 men students.

The United Theological College of Montreal,
3473 University Street, Montreal, Quebec.
Principal: J.A. Boorman, BA, MA, PhD.
United Church. Co-educational. Founded in
1926. Offers courses in theology leading to a
certificate for ordination granted by the
college, and courses leading to the degree of
bachelor of theology (BTh), which is
awarded by the university.

Deans of faculties

Agriculture
Harold Klinck (acting), BSA, MSc, PhD

Arts
Robert Vogel, BA, MA, PhD

Dentistry
Ernest Ambrose, DDS, FACD, FICD

Education
C. W. Hall, MA

Engineering
G.L. d'Ombrain, BSc(Engin), PhD, DIC,
AGCI, MIEE, MAIEE

Graduate studies and research
W.F. Hitschfeld, BASc, PhD

Law
J.W. Durnford, BA, BCL

Management
H.I. Ross, OBE, CA, BA, MA, LLD, DScCom

Medicine
Maurice McGregor, MB, BCh, MD,
MRCP(L), FRCP(C)

Music
Helmut Blume, MusB

Religious studies
George Johnston, MA, BD, PhD, DD

Science
E.J. Stansbury, MA, PhD

Students
E. Pedersen, BA, MA, PhD

Directors of schools

Architecture
John Bland, BArch, AMTPI, FRAIC,
ARIBA, RCA

Food science
Helen Neilson, MBE, BHS, MSc

Graduate nurses
Elizabeth Logan, BSc, MN

Library science
Virginia Murray, MA, EdD, BLS

Physical and occupational therapy
Guy Fisk, BA, MD, CM, DTMandH,
FRCP(C)

Social work
David Woodsworth, MA, PhD

Department heads

Agricultural chemistry
R.H. Common, BSc, MAgr, PhD, DSc,
FRSC, FRIC, FCIC, FAIC

Agricultural economics
D.L. MacFarlane, BSA, MSc, PhD

Agricultural engineering
J.R. Ogilvie, BSc(Agr), MSA

Agricultural physics
R.H. Douglas, BSc, MA, PhD

Agronomy
H.R. Klinck, BSA, MSc, PhD

Anaesthesia
P.R. Bromage, MB, BS, FFARCS

Anatomy and histology
C.P. Leblond, MD, PhD, FRS, FRSC

Animal science
H.F. MacRae, BSc(Agr), MSc, PhD

Anthropology
B.G. Trigger, BA, PhD

Art history
R.N. Bertos (acting), MA, PhD

Biochemistry
A.F. Graham, BSc, MSc, PhD, DSc

Biology
G.A. MacLachlan, MA, PhD

Catholic studies
T. Francoeur, BA, MA, DEd,
DipPastoralTheol

Chemical engineering
G.A. Ratcliff, MA, PhD, FICE

Chemistry
L. Yaffe, MSc, PhD, FCIC, FRSC

Civil engineering and applied mechanics
R.G. Redwood, BSc, MASc, PhD

Classics
A. Schachter, BA, MA, DPhil

Economics
J.G. Smith, BA, MA, PhD

Educational administration
R.E. Lavery, BA, BEd, PhD

Educational psychology
H.A. Stutt (acting), BA, BEd, MEd

Education, counsellor
A. Adkins, BA, ThB, MA, DEd

Education, elementary
Franga Stinson, BA, MA

Education, graduate division and educational
research
L.B. Birch, BSc, MA, FBPsS

Education in art
E. Jacques

Education in English
J.M. O'Hara, BA, BEd, MA

Education in mathematics and the sciences
H. Lead, BSc, MSc, PhD

Education in music
Lois McDonald, BMus, MA

Education in second languages
J. Lobelle, MA

Education in the social sciences
D.C. Smith, BEd, MA, PhD

Education, social foundations of
R. Magnuson, BA, MA, PhD

Electrical engineering
G.W. Farnell, BASc, SM, PhD

English
D.F. Theall, AB, MA, PhD

Entomology
D.K. McE. Kevan, BSc, AICTA, PhD, FRSE

Epidemiology and health
J.C. McDonald, MD, DPH, SM, DIH,
MRCP, FRCP(C)

French language and literature
J. Ethier-Blais, BA, LèsL, DèsL, DES

Geography
J.B. Bird, MA

Geological sciences
C.W. Stearn, BSc, MS, PhD, FRSC

German
A. Arnold, DLet

History
P.D. Marshall, BA, MA, PhD

History of medicine
D.G. Bates, BA, MD

Horticulture
C.D. Taper, BSA, MSA, PhD

Italian
A. d'Andrea, DottFil

Linguistics
C.D. Ellis, BA, MA, PhD

Mathematics
E.M. Rosenthall, MSc, PhD

Mechanical engineering
B.G. Newman, MA, PhD, FRAeS

Medicine, clinical and experimental
J.C. Beck, MD, CM, MSc, DipIntMed,
FRCP, FRCP(C), FRSC

Metallurgical engineering
W.M. Williams, MSc, PhD

Meteorology
S. Orvig, BSc, MSc, PhD

Microbiology (Macdonald College)
R. Knowles, BSc, PhD

Microbiology and immunology
J.W. Stevenson (acting), MDCM

Mining engineering and applied geophysics
F.T.M. White, BE

Music, applied
H. Blume, MusB

Music, performance
R. Lawton, BMus, MMus

Music, theoretical
Paul Pedersen, BA, MusM

Neurology and neurosurgery
To be appointed

Obstetrics and gynaecology
G.B. Maughan, MSc, MD, CM, FACS

Ophthalmology
S.T. Adams, BA, MDCM

Otolaryngology
J.D. Baxter, MSc, MD, CM

Paediatrics
Mary Ellen Avery, AB, MD

Pathology
R.H. More, MSc, MD

Pharmacology and therapeutics
M. Nickerson, AB, ScM, PhD, MD

Philosophy
J. Trentman, MA, PhD

Physical education
R. Wilkinson, BSc(PE), MA, DPE

Physics
J.M. Robson, MA, ScD, FRSC

Physiology
D.V. Bates, MBBChir, MD, MRCP

Plant pathology
R.H. Estey, BSc(Agr), BEd, MS, DIC, PhD

Political science
H.M. Waller, SB, MS, PhD

Psychiatry
H.E. Lehmann, MD, FRSC

Psychology
G.A. Ferguson, BA, MEd, PhD, FRSC

Radiology, diagnostic
R.G. Fraser, MD, DipRad, FRCP

Radiology, therapeutic
J.J. Hazel, BSc, MDCM

Russian and Slavic studies
J.G. Nicholson, MA, PhD

Sociology
D.N. Solomon, MA, PhD

Soil science
A.F. MacKenzie, BSA, MSc, PhD

Spanish
S. Lipp, BS, MS, PhD

Surgery
L.D. MacLean, BSc, MD, PhD

Woodlot management and Morgan
arboretum
J.R. Bider, BSc, MSc, PhD

McMaster University*

Hamilton, Ontario

Telephone: 416-522-4971
Direct general correspondence to the registrar

Total full-time student enrolment 7,928; see also separate section *Statistics on Canadian universities and colleges*

Executive and administrative officers

Chancellor
L.T. Pennell, PC, BA, LLB, LLD

President and vice-chancellor
H.G. Thode, CC, MBE, MSc, PhD, DSc, LLD, FRS, FRSC, FCIC

Vice-president academic (arts)
W.F. Hellmuth, BA, PhD

Vice-president academic (health sciences)
J.R. Evans, MD, DPhil, FRCP(C), FACP

Vice-president academic (science and engineering)
A.N. Bourns, BSc, PhD, DSc, FRSC, FCIC

Vice-president administration
D.M. Hedden, BSc

Registrar
J.P. Evans, BCom, MA

Assistant to the president
M. Zack, MA

Assistant to the president (student awards)
W.N. Paterson, BA

Assistant to the president (fund raising) and presidential consultant (communications and special projects)
T.W.D. Farmer, BA

Principal, Divinity College
I.C. Morgan, ThM, DD, BA, BD

Dean of adult education
W.J. McCallion, MA

Dean of students
L.A. Prince

University librarian
W.B. Ready, BA, DipEd, MA, MLA, ALA

Information officer
Gilbert Murray, BA

Background

Named after Senator William McMaster, who bequeathed substantial funds to endow a Christian school of learning, McMaster University was established by an act of the Ontario legislature in 1887. From then until 1957 it was governed by the Baptist Convention of Ontario and Quebec. Teaching began in Toronto in 1890, and the first degrees were conferred in 1894.

The university moved to Hamilton in 1930. In 1948 it was reorganized into three colleges: Divinity College; University College (arts); and Hamilton College (science) which was non-denominational and operated under its own board of governors as an affiliated college. In 1957 the Baptist Convention withdrew from legal control of the university, and the university and Hamilton College became one, non-denominational corporation. McMaster Divinity College was at the same time incorporated as an affiliated theological college.

McMaster University is governed by a board of governors and a senate.

In 1967 the constituent colleges were dissolved and replaced by a divisional structure composed of the divisions of arts, science and engineering, and health sciences. The division of arts was divided into three faculties: business, humanities and social sciences. The division of science and engineering is composed of two faculties: science and engineering; and the division of health sciences consists of the faculty of medicine. These revisions were implemented during the academic year 1967-68.

*Ordinary member, AUCC.

Facilities and services

The university possesses a large campus in the west-end of the city, its lands being bordered by tracts of parkland forming part of the extensive acreage of the Royal Botanical Gardens, in whose program the university co-operates. There are 34 permanent buildings, and another two under construction. There are several temporary buildings. Among the permanent buildings are the Mills memorial library with a capacity for 720,000 volumes, a nuclear research building, a research greenhouse, facilities for administration and for students and alumni activities, a linear accelerator building, a modern physical education complex, and eight student residences that will accommmodate 975 men and 875 women.

Student services include a health service, guidance and counselling service, housing registry, refectory, student union, and employment service.

Calendars and brochures

Principal calendars: arts and science; school of nursing; faculty of engineering; faculty of medicine; school of graduate studies; school of adult education; divinity college.

Several brochures are available on request from the high school relations officer. Write c/o office of the registrar.

Courses and degrees

Arts
(Faculty of humanities and faculty of social sciences)

Bachelor of arts (BA).
(a) Pass course, three years from senior matriculation. Available in anthropology, business, economics, English, fine arts, French, geography, German, history, Italian, Latin, philosophy, political science, psychology, religion, Russian, sociology, Spanish. (b) Honors course, four years from senior matriculation. Available in anthropology, classics, economics, English, fine arts, French, geography, German, history, Latin, philosophy, political science, psychology, religion, sociology, Spanish, and combinations of these.

(School of graduate studies)

Master of arts (MA).
A minimum of one year from an honors bachelor's degree. Available in social anthropology, classics, economics, English, French, geography, German, Greek, history, Latin, philosophy, political science, psychology, religious sciences, Russian, and sociology.

Doctor of philosophy (PhD).
A minimum of three years from an honors bachelor's degree or two years from a master's degree. Available in economics, English, history, political science, religious sciences, Roman studies, and sociology.

Business, see commerce below

Commerce
(Faculty of business)

Bachelor of commerce (BCom).
Honors degree, four years from senior matriculation.

(School of graduate studies)

Master of business administration (MBA).
A minimum of two curriculum years beyond a bachelor's degree. Available in the school of business in regular session or part-time evening classes.

Engineering
(Faculty of engineering)

Bachelor of engineering (BEng).
Four years from senior matriculation. Available in chemical, civil, electrical, mechanical, and metallurgical engineering, and engineering physics.

Bachelor of engineering and management (BEngM).
Five years from senior matriculation. Joint program with faculty of business.

(School of graduate studies)

Master of engineering (MEng).
A minimum of one year from a bachelor's degree in engineering. Available in chemical,

civil, electrical, mechanical, and metallurgical engineering.

Doctor of philosophy (PhD).
A minimum of three years from an honors bachelor's degree or two years from a master's degree. Available in chemical, civil, electrical, mechanical and metallurgical engineering.

Medicine
(Faculty of medicine)

Bachelor of science in medicine [BSc(Med)].
A one-year program which may be taken by students transferring to McMaster after three years of an honors science course at another unversity.

Doctor of medicine (MD).
A three-year (thirty-three month) program following an acceptable bachelor's degree or three years of an honors program.

(School of graduate studies)

Master of science (medical science) (MSc).
A minimum of one year from an honors bachelor's degree in science.

Doctor of philosophy (medical science) (PhD).
A minimum of three years from an honors bachelor's degree or two years from the MSc degree.

Music
(Faculty of humanities)

Bachelor of music (MusBac).
Honors degree, four years from senior matriculation.

Nursing education
(School of nursing, faculty of science)

Bachelor of science in nursing (BScN).
Four years from senior matriculation.

Physical education
(Faculty of social sciences)

Bachelor of physical education (BPE).
A combined four-year program from senior matriculation leading to BA/BPE degrees.

Science, applied, see engineering

Science, pure
(Faculty of science)

Bachelor of science (BSc).
(a) Pass course, three years from senior matriculation. Available in biology, chemistry, computer science, geography, geology, mathematics, physics, psychology. (b) Major course, four years from senior matriculation. Available in applied mathematics and computer science, biochemistry, chemistry, geology, mathematics, metallurgy and materials science, and physics. (c) Honors course, four years from senior matriculation. Available in applied chemistry, applied mathematics and computer science, applied mathematics and theoretical physics, biochemistry, biology, chemistry, geography, geology, mathematics, metallurgy and materials science, physics, psychology, science and combinations of these.

(School of graduate studies)

Master of science (MSc).
Minimum of one year from an honors bachelor's degree. Available in biochemistry, biology, biophysics, chemical physics, chemistry, geography, geology, materials science, mathematics, medical sciences, metallurgy, molecular biology, and physics.

Doctor of philosophy (PhD).
Minimum of three years from an honors bachelor's degree or two years from a master's degree. Available in biochemistry, biology, chemical physics, chemistry, geochemistry, geography, geology, materials science, mathematics, medical sciences, metallurgy, molecular biology, physics, and psychology.

Social work
(School of social work, faculty of social sciences)

Bachelor of social work (BSW).
A combined four-year program from senior matriculation leading to BA/BSW degrees.

Theology
(McMaster Divinity College)

Master of divinity (MDiv).
Three years from a bachelor's degree and comprehensive examinations.

Master of religious education (MRE).
Two years from bachelor's degree.

Special programs

In 1971-72, the faculty of social sciences is continuing its experimental year I program. Participation in the program requires a student to take 18 units (equivalent to three of his five year I classes) of work which will involve him in a highly integrated combination of lectures, seminars, tutorials, and individual sessions with a group of faculty members drawn from the social sciences.

Extension programs

For university credit:

Teaching certificates.
Type A and type B, and type B "endorsed". Evening classes. Leading to pass BA. Evening classes in Hamilton and adjacent centres.

Summer school.
Courses leading to BA.

For no university credit:

Certificate courses not requiring matriculation.
Certificates in business, corrections, foremen, manpower development, metallurgy of iron and steel, personnel management, retail administration, and social welfare.

Adult education services.
A wide selection of courses to meet adult education and community service needs.

Calendars available.

Admission requirements

For a general statement regarding admission to university study, see article *Admission to university in Canada.*

For information regarding admission to undergraduate study, consult *Requirements for admission to Canadian colleges and universities* available from Service for Admission to College and University, 151 Slater St., Ottawa, Ont., K1P 5N1, $1.50 prepaid.

For admission to the MD program, students must have completed, or must be in, the third year of a degree program at a recognized university and have written the medical college admission test.

For admission to graduate study, students must have obtained an honors bachelor's degree with specified grades in appropriate subjects.

For admission as candidates for the MDiv and MRE degrees, students must have obtained a bachelor's degree.

Academic year

Winter session: mid-September to mid-May.

Summer session: early July to mid-August.

Grading system

Standing is graded as first-class honors (I): 75-100%; second- class honors (II): 66-74%; third-class honors (III): 60-65%; credit (c): 50-59%; failure (F): below 50%.

The experimental program in the faculty of social sciences only will assign grades as follows: first-class grade; second-class grade; pass; fail.

Fees and costs

Tuition fees per year: a) first degree — arts, $490; science, $495; engineering, $545; nursing, $470; medicine, $340 per semester (program consists of eight semesters); supplementary fees (compulsory) total $52.50, and include charges for athletics, students' union, etc; b) master's degree — first year, $405; subsequent, $105; three years part-time, $486; any additional (if needed), $45; c) doctorate — first two years, $405 per year; on-campus study thereafter, $105; MDiv, MRE courses, $200 per year.

Residence fees (room only), $600 per academic year.

Financial awards and assistance

Students, who qualify, may apply for financial assistance under the Ontario student awards program. A student, who completes at one sitting, with an average of 75% the credits required for admission, may qualify for a matriculation scholarship.

For a complete listing of scholarships and bursaries available, write to the office of the assistant to the president (student awards) for the booklet on scholarships and awards.

Research institutes

Centre for Applied Research and Engineering Design.
An industrially oriented, applied research and design institute established in 1967 which undertakes projects for specific industries on a consultant basis.

Institute for Materials Research.
A unit formed to meet the needs of interdisciplinary work in the area of materials research. It has no degree-granting authority.

Research Unit in Biochemistry, Biophysics, and Molecular Biology.
The unit offers graduate training in biophysics leading to the MSc degree.

Affiliated college

McMaster Divinity College, Hamilton, Ontario.
Principal: Rev. I.C. Morgan, BA, BD, ThM, DD. Baptist. Co-educational. Established in 1957. Has its own board of trustees and senate, the latter awarding certificates and diplomas only. Academic degrees in course and honorary degrees are awarded by the university. Offers courses in theology leading to the certificate in theology, the diploma in divinity, the master of divinity (MDiv), and the master of religious education (MRE).

Deans of faculties

Business
W.J. Schlatter, AM, PhD, CPA

Engineering
L.W. Shemilt, BASc, MSc, PhD

Humanities
A.G. McKay, MA, AM, PhD, FRSC

Medicine
J.R. Evans, MD, DPhil, FRCP(C), FACP

Science
D.R. McCalla, BSc, MSc, PhD

Social sciences
S.J. Frankel, BA, MA, PhD

Directors of schools, centres and institutes

Centre for applied research and engineering design
M.C. de Malherbe, DIC, PhD, DiplIng

Data processing and computing centre
G.L. Keech, BASc, MSc, PhD

Institute for materials research
J.A. Morrison, MSc, PhD

Nursing
Dorothy Kergin, BSc, MPH, PhD

Physical education
A.J. Smith, CD, BSA, MEd

Research Unit in Biochemistry, Biophysics
and Molecular Biology
K.B. Freeman, BSc, PhD

Social work
H.L. Penny, DiplTheol, BA, MSW

Department heads

Anatomy
J.E. Anderson, MD

Anesthesia
F.J. Wright, MD, CM

Applied mathematics
G. Field, BSc, BSc, PhD

Biochemistry
R.H. Hall, BA, MA, PhD

Biology
S.T. Bayley, BSc, PhD

Chemical engineering
C.M. Crowe, BEng, PhD

Chemistry
R.H. Tomlinson, BSc, PhD, FCIC

Civil engineering
A.A. Smith, BSc, PhD

Classics
H.F. Guite, MA

Clinical epidemiology and biostatistics
D.L. Sackett, BA, BSc, MD, MS

Commerce
W.J. Schlatter, AM, PhD, CPA

Economics
J.E.L. Graham, BA, MA, BLitt

Electrical engineering
S.S. Haykim, BSc, PhD, DSc

Engineering physics
J. Shewchun, BASc, MASc, PhD

English
R.N. Shrive, CD, BA, MA, PhD

Family medicine
J. Hay, MD, CM

Fine arts
P.H. Walton, BA, AM, PhD

Geography
L.J. King, MA, PhD

Geology
R.J. Burley, BSc, MSc, PhD

German
J.B. Lawson, BA, MA

History
E. Cappadocia, MA, PhD

Mathematics
T. Husain, MA, PhD

Mechanical engineering
G.F. Round, BSc, PhD, FCIC

Medicine
E.J.M. Campbell, BSc, MB, BS, MD, PhD,
FRCP, FRCP(C)

Metallurgy and materials science
G.R. Piercy, MASc, PhD

Music
A. Walker, BMus, DMus

Neurosciences (neurobiology)
J. Diamond, BSc, PhD, MB, BS

Nursing education
Dorothy Kergin, BSc, MPH, PhD

Obstetrics and gynecology
F.L. Johnson, MD, FRCS(C), FACOG

Pathology
J.F. Mustard, MD, PhD, FRCP(C)

Pediatrics
A. Zipursky, MD, BSc, FRCP(C)

Philosophy
J.E. Thomas, BA, BD, MA, PhD

Physical education
Rose Hill, BPHE, MA

Physics
M.W. Johns, MA, PhD, FRSC

Political science
H.H. Lentner, BS, MA, PhD

Psychiatry
N.B. Epstein, MD, CM, FAP, FAPA

Psychology
P.L. Newbigging, BA, MA, PhD

Radiology
W.P. Cockshott, MD, DMRD

Religion
E.P. Sanders, BA, BD, ThD

Romance languages
B. Blakey, MA, PhD

Russian
K. Denner (acting), MA, PhD

Social work
H.L. Penny, DiplTheol, BA, MSW

Sociology and anthropology
P.C. Pineo, BA, MA, PhD

Surgery
C.B. Mueller, AB, MD, FACS

Memorial University of Newfoundland*

St. John's, Newfoundland

Telephone: 709-753-1200
Direct general correspondence to the registrar

Total full-time student enrolment 6,378; see also separate section *Statistics on Canadian universities and colleges*

Executive and administrative officers

Chancellor
The Hon. G.A. Frecker, BA, BE, LLD, DPaed, Ddel'U

President and vice-chancellor
The Rt. Hon. The Lord Taylor of Harlow, BSc, MD, FRCP

Vice-president (academic) and pro vice-chancellor
M.O. Morgan, MA, LLD

Deputy vice-president and dean of arts and science
L. Harris, BA(Ed), MA, PhD

Assistant vice-president for administration and comptroller
W.H.M. Selby, LLB, FACCA, ACIS

Registrar
H.T. Renouf, JP, FCIS

Director, counselling centre
C.F. Preston, BD, MA, PhD

Associate dean of education
W.G. Rowe, BA, MA

*Ordinary member, AUCC.

Associate dean of medicine
K.B. Roberts, MA, MB, BS, DPhil, FRCP(C), FRCP

Assistant dean of junior studies (science)
E.J.F. Hodgett, BSc, PostgradCertEd

Assistant dean of arts
I.A.F. Bruce, MA, DipEd, PhD

Director, student affairs
J.D. Eaton, BPHE, MA, PhD

Director, student teaching
H.A. Cuff, BA(Ed), MEd

Director, educational television
D.B. Starcher, BA, MM

Director, centre for audio-visual education
G. Fizzard, BA(Ed), MA

Director, extension
D. Snowden, BJ

Director, public relations
G.B. Woodland

Director, summer session and extra-mural studies
A.H. Roberts, BA, EdM, EdD

Master, Paton College
S.J. Carew, BSc, BE, DEng

University librarian
D.L. Ryan, AB, MS

Director, Marine sciences research laboratory
D. Idler, BA, MA, PhD

Dean of women
Sarah Drinkwater (Mrs), BA, MA

Background

Memorial University of Newfoundland developed from Memorial University College which was founded in 1925 as a memorial to the men of Newfoundland and Labrador who died in the first world war. During the first ten years of the college, the Carnegie Corporation of New York provided annual grants towards defraying general expenses.

Memorial University was established by an act of the provincial legislature in 1949. The first degrees were awarded in 1950. The university is a provincial, co-educational institution; administration is in the hands of

a board of regents, while academic matters are in the charge of the various faculty councils and the senate.

Facilities and services

The campus is located on a 100-acre site near the northern limits of the city of St. John's, (population approximates 101,000), the provincial capital. There are four academic buildings, 11 temporary academic buildings, an administration building which also houses several academic departments, a major library building (over 250,000 volumes, and 300,000 microforms), nine residences accommodating 335 women and 586 men, a dining hall, and a students' centre.

Affiliated residential colleges with buildings adjacent to the campus are St. John's, Queen's, and Coughlan. The Marine sciences research laboratory is located at Logy Bay, ten minutes' drive from campus.

Calendars and brochures

University calendar and summer session calendar are available from the division of public relations. The Muse, student weekly newspaper available by subscription. Write The Muse at above address.

Courses and degrees

Architecture see engineering

Arts
(Faculty of arts and science)

Bachelor of arts (BA).
(a) General course, four years from junior matriculation. (b) Honors course, 4 1/2 years from junior matriculation. Specialization possible in classics, economics, English, folklore, French, geography, German, history, linguistics, mathematics, philosophy, political science, psychology, religious studies, sociology and anthropology, and Spanish.

Master of arts (MA).
At least one year from BA. Available in economics, English, folklore, French, geography, German, history, linguistics, mathematics, philosophy, political science, psychology, sociology and anthropology.

Doctor of philosophy (PhD).
Minimum of three years from bachelor's degree or two years from master's degree with at least one year in residence. Available in English and folklore.

Note: A doctoral program in mathematics is planned for the academic year 1972-73.

Commerce
(Faculty of arts and science)

Bachelor of commerce (BCom).
(a) General course, five years from junior matriculation. (b) Honors course, five years from junior matriculation. Specialization possible in accounting, economics, finance and management, industrial relations, marketing, and quantitative method.

Education
(Faculty of education)

Bachelor of arts (education) [BA(Ed)].
Four years from junior matriculation.

Bachelor of education (BEd) and *bachelor of arts (BA)* or *bachelor of science (BSc)* or *bachelor of physical education (BPE).*
Five years from junior matriculation.

Graduate diploma in education.
One year from bachelor's degree in arts, science, or commerce.

Master of education (MEd).
Minimum of fourteen calendar months full time from first degree, by course of instruction and thesis after research in approved topic; or by course of instruction and an approved project and report; or by course of instruction and an approved internship program with a report. Available in curriculum and instruction, educational administration, and guidance and counselling.

Engineering
(Faculty of engineering and applied science)

Bachelor of engineering (BEng).
Students enter junior divison after junior matriculation. Degree obtainable four years after junior division.

Master of engineering (MEng).
Minimum of two semesters full time from first degree, by course of instruction and thesis after research in approved topic, or by course of instruction and project report of professional calibre on engineering problem.

Doctor of philosophy (PhD).
Minimum of three years from bachelor's degree or two years from master's degree. Available in ocean engineering.

Forestry
(Faculty of engineering and applied science)

Forestry diploma
discontinued; program modified to fit engineering program. Now called pre-forestry program and meets the needs of other Canadian university programs.

Interdisciplinary studies

Master of philosophy (MPhil).
The degree is awarded upon completion of course of instruction and examinations. Candidates must be full-time students for a minimum of 16 months. Specialization available in economics, German, history, linguistics, mathematics, political science, sociology and anthropology.

Medicine
(Faculty of medicine)

Bachelor of medical science (BMS).
Five years from junior matriculation.

Master of science in medicine (MSc).
At least one year from bachelor's degree.

Doctor of philosophy in medicine (PhD).
Three years from bachelor's degree, or two years from master's degree.

Nursing
(Faculty of arts and science)

Bachelor of nursing (BN).
Five years from junior matriculation.

Physical education
(Department of physical education and athletics).

Bachelor of physical education (BPE).
Four years from junior matriculation.

Science, applied see engineering or forestry

Science, pure
(Faculty of arts and science)

Bachelor of science (BSc).
(a) General course, four years from junior matriculation. (b) Honors course, 4 1/2 years from junior matriculation. Specialization possible in biochemistry, biology, chemistry, geography, geology, mathematics, physics, and psychology.

Master of science (MSc).
At least one year from BSc. Available in biochemistry, biology, chemistry, geography, geology, and physics.

Doctor of philosophy (PhD).
Minimum of three years from bachelor's degree or two years from master's degree with at least one year in residence. Available in biochemistry, biology, chemistry, geology, and physics.

Social work
(Faculty of arts and science)

Bachelor of social work (BSW).
Five years from junior matriculation.

Special programs

Co-operative engineering program.
In 1969 Memorial University inaugurated the co-operative engineering program which provides for alternate periods of working in industry and studying on campus over a five-year period for students.

Students entering university with deficiencies in some subjects may be required to take a foundation course to upgrade such deficiencies. This will necessitate staying in university one extra term (May-July) to catch up with first-year course.

Extension programs

For university credit:

Evening and off-campus courses for university credit.
Undergraduate classes offered during the fall and winter semesters on campus and at 26 centres across the province in arts, commerce, education, science, and social work.

Summer session.
Courses are offered for undergraduates proceeding to a degree and for teachers who may wish to improve their professional qualifications by working towards graduate degrees and diplomas in education. Subjects offered are chiefly in arts, education, and science; also a limited number in nursing and social work.

For no university credit:

The extension service offers a large number of courses both on campus and off campus throughout the province — all non-credit. The courses lie in business, fine arts, human relations, liberal studies, public administration, and technical and professional studies. Over 2,000 people enrol in these courses throughout the province.

Admission requirements

For a general statement regarding admission to university study, see article *Admission to university in Canada.*

For information regarding admission to undergraduate study, consult *Requirements for admission to Canadian colleges and universities* available from Service for Admission to College and University, 151 Slater St., Ottawa, Ont., K1P 5N1, $1.50 prepaid.

For admission to medicine students must have completed a minimum of two years with appropriate selection of subjects in arts and science beyond junior division.

For admission to graduate study a student must have obtained a first degree with specified grades in appropriate studies.

Academic year

1st semester — mid-September to end of December.

2nd semester — early January to end of April.

3rd semester — end of April to end of July.

(3rd semester usually used only by students studying in junior division — first-year students.)

Limited courses are available at all degree levels as far as exigencies of the departments will permit.

Grading system

Degrees awarded to students who have obtained an average of at least one point per subject taken. Grades range: F (45% and below or failure to write an examination without acceptable cause); D (50%, a pass, but without a point); C (55%, 60%, one point per course); B (65%, 70%, 75%, 2 points per course); and A (80%, 85%, 90%, 95%, 100%, 3 points per course).

Fees and costs

Applications for entry must be accompanied by certified cheque or money order for $30.

Tuition fees per semester: full-time undergraduate includes bachelor, diploma, and foundation programs, $250. Graduate students: diploma in education, $200; master's program, $300; doctorate program, $500; a semester fee of $50 per semester is charged all graduate students. For partial students: $50 per course per semester. Student organization fees — undergraduate, $8 per semester; graduate, $15 per annum.

Residence rates: double room per semester, $180; single room per semester, $205; meal charge per semester — 3 meals per day, $200; 2 meals per day, $148.

Financial awards and assistance

There are the usual number of scholarships and bursaries available for students, both resident and non-resident of this province. The provincial government, for residents only, provides, either in whole or in part, tuition and other fees where a student can demonstrate need. The university offers a number of studentships up to $700 each for students reading for honors degrees in various departments. For graduate students there are $2,800 graduate fellowships offered each year. For both cases students may be required to perform certain departmental duties.

Research institutes

The Institute of Social and Economic Research,
established in 1961, is concerned with research in economics and social questions arising in Newfoundland and Labrador because of its unique historical, geographical, and economic position. The insti composed of researchers who have joint appointments with any of several departments whose studies are allied with the institute. It is an integral, not an autonomous, appendage of the university. It has initiated a publications program and provides specialized information for both the university and the general public.

The Institute for Research in Human Abilities was established in 1967 and was designed to study human learning from both the theoretical and applied points of view. Members of the institute may hold joint appointments with university departments, especially the department of psychology.

Affiliated colleges

Queen's College, St. John's, Newfoundland. Provost: Rev. G.H. Earle, MA. A theological

college to train priests for the Anglican Church of Canada. Residences for men and women adjoin the college which is located on grounds adjacent to the campus.

St. John's College, St. John's, Newfoundland. A Roman Catholic residential college for men only adjacent to the university campus.

St. Bride's College, Littledale, Newfoundland on the southern outskirts of St. John's. Principal: Sister Teresina Bruce, BA, BSc, MA, PhD. This Roman Catholic college provides courses at the first- and second-year levels of Memorial University for girls. Residence for women only.

Coughlan College, St. John's Newfoundland. A United Church of Canada residential college for men and women adjacent to the university campus.

Christian Brothers College, Mono Mills, Ontario.

Deans of faculties

Arts and science
L. Harris, BA(Ed), MA, PhD

Education
G.A. Hickman, BA, MA, EdD

Engineering and applied science
A.A. Bruneau, BASc, DIC, PhD

Graduate studies
F.A. Aldrich, AB, MSc, PhD

Junior studies
A.M. Sullivan, BA(Ed), BA, MA, PhD

Medicine
I. Rusted, BA, MSc, MD, CM, FRCP(C), FACP

Director of school

Nursing
Joyce Nevitt, BScN, MA

Department heads

Anaesthesia
C.D. Green, BSc, MD, MS

Biochemistry
L.A.W. Feltham, BSc, MA, PhD

Biology
M. Laird, BSc, MSc, PhD, DSc

Chemistry
J.M.W. Scott, BSc, PhD

Classics
J.B. Ashley, BA, MA, PhD

Commerce
E.M. Peter, MBA, PhD, CA

Continuing medical education
A.M. House, MD, CRCP(C)

Curriculum and instruction
G. Murphy, BEd, MEd, PhD

Economics
S.S. Mensinkai, BA, MA, PhD

Educational administration
P.J. Warren, BA, BSc, MEd, PhD

Educational foundations
W.J. Gushue, BA(Ed), EdD

Educational psychology, guidance and
counselling
H.H. Way, BA, MA, MSc, EdD

Engineering co-ordination
P.V. Young, BSc(Eng), ARSM, PEng, CEng

English
D.G. Pitt, BA, MA, PhD

Folklore
H. Halpert, BS, MA, PhD

Geography
W.F. Summers, BSc, MSc, PhD

Geology
E.R.W. Neale, BSc, MS, PhD, FRSC

German and Russian
H.H. Jackson, BA, LLD

History
G.E. Panting, BA, MA

Linguistics
J. Hewson, BA, MèsA, Ddel'U

Mathematics
W.J. Blundon, BA, MA

Medicine
A.R. Cox, BA, MD, FRCP(C)

Obstetrics and gynecology
G.H. Flight, MD, CM, FRCS(C)

Pathology
M.G. Lewis, MB, BS, MD

Pediatrics
J.M. Darte, MD, FRCP(C), DMRT

Philosophy
J.G. Dawson, MA, PhL, STB

Physical education and athletics
M.J. Foster, BA(Ed), DipPhyEd, MSc

Physics
S.W. Breckon, BSc, PhD

Political science
H.J. Whelan, BA, MA

Postgraduate medical education
W.H. Marshall, MD, PhD, MRCP

Psychiatry
J. Hoenig, MD, MRCP, DPM

Psychology
D.S. Hart, MA, PhD

Radiology
C.J. Hodson, MB, BS, DMRE, FFR, FRCP

Religious studies
M.F. Hodder, BA, DipinTh,
PostgradDipinTh, STM, ThD

Romance languages
C.S. Barr, BA, MA

Social work
N. Flachs, BA, MSW, PhD

Sociology and anthropology
J.A. Tuck, AB, PhD

Surgery
J.B. Littlefield, AB, MD, FACS

Université de Moncton*

Moncton, Nouveau-Brunswick

Téléphone: 506-855-2070
Prière d'adresser la correspondance d'ordre
général au secrétaire général

Total des inscriptions des étudiants à plein
temps 3,149; voir aussi la section distincte,
intitulée *Statistiques sur les universités et
collèges du Canada*

Dirigeants

Chancelier
J.L. Levesque, DScCom, DLL, CEcPol

Recteur
Adélard Savoie, BA, BScSoc, CR, LLD

Vice-recteur académique
Helmut Schweiger, BA, MA, PhD

Vice-recteur administratif
Médard Colette, BA, MScCom, CA

Secrétaire général
Léandre Bourque, MScComm, MBA, CA

Directeur des services administratifs
Arthur Girouard, MScCom

Bibliothécaire
Agnez Hall, BA, BBibl

Directeur de la recherche
B.T. Newbold, BSc, DSc, FRIC, FCIC

Directeur des affaires extérieures
En instance de nomination

Directeur des affaires étudiantes
Gilles Nadeau, BA, MPs

Préposé aux admissions
Luc Lévesque, BA, BEd, MEd

Préposé aux dossiers
Claude Gagnon, BScCom

Directeur du service d'information
Roland Tessier, BA

Directeur de personnel
Léonide Comeau, BA

Historique

L'Université de Moncton, créée par acte de la
législature du Nouveau-Brunswick le 19 juin
1963, plonge ses racines dans un siècle
d'histoire. Ses origines remontent à 1864,
date de la fondation du Collège Saint-Joseph
qui obtenait, quatre ans plus tard, le pouvoir
de conférer des grades universitaires. Deux
autres institutions de langue française dans la
province recevaient des pouvoirs identiques:
le Collège du Sacré-Coeur de Bathurst, en
1900, et le Collège Saint-Louis
d'Edmundston, en 1947. D'autres collèges de
langue française établis dans la province
étaient rattachés, pour fins universitaires, à
l'une ou l'autre de ces trois institutions.

Au mois de mai 1961, le gouvernement
provincial créait une commission royale pour
enquêter sur l'enseignement supérieur.
Prenant connaissance de la multiplicité des
institutions françaises pour desservir une
population relativement restreinte, la
commission recommanda la création d'une
université centrale de langue française à
laquelle seraient affiliées les trois institutions
possédant antérieurement des chartes; à ces
collèges seraient annexés les autres
établissements existants. L'ensemble des
collèges affiliés et annexés constituerait la
faculté des arts de l'université. Le
gouvernement provincial adopta cette
formule par une mesure d'initiative
ministérielle votée à l'assemblée législative
au mois de juin 1963.

L'université est catholique et mixte. Depuis le
mois de juin 1967 elle est administrée par un
conseil de gouverneurs. Un sénat universitaire
constitue l'autorité suprême en tout ce qui
concerne l'enseignement.

*Membre ordinaire de l'AUCC.

Installations et services

La cité universitaire est idéalement située au centre de la ville de Moncton (population, 55,000), sur un terrain de 400 arpents. L'université dispose actuellement de cinq immeubles d'enseignement (sciences, arts, éducation, sciences infirmières, commerce), d'une bibliothèque centrale, de deux résidences, d'une patinoire et d'un centre social. Le collège pédagogique provincial est aussi situé sur le campus.

Les services organisés à l'intention des étudiants sont les suivants: services religieux, santé, orientation, consultation, placement, aide financière, logement, cafétéria, librairie, piscine, corps école des officiers, et boîte à chansons.

Annuaires et brochures

Le secrétariat général assure la distribution de l'annuaire général de l'université ainsi que d'une brochure intitulée "Modalités d'inscription et programmes d'études".

Seule la faculté des arts publie son propre annuaire, lequel peut être obtenu en écrivant directement au secrétariat de la faculté des arts.

Le secrétariat de l'extension de l'enseignement distribue les annuaires des cours offerts à temps partiel durant les sessions d'hiver et d'été, tandis que le département des affaires étudiantes assure la diffusion de tout renseignement dont l'étudiant a besoin pour guider son choix et connaître les formalités à remplir en vue de son admission et de son inscription à l'université. Ce département renseigne aussi l'étudiant sur l'organisation matérielle de la vie étudiante.

Cours et grades

Note: L'université emploie le français comme langue d'enseignement. En éducation permanente, quelques cours sont offerts aux adultes anglophones.

Arts
(Faculté des arts)

Baccalauréat ès arts (BA).
Quatre ans après les études secondaires. Avec mention en anglais, art dramatique, beaux-arts, biologie, chimie, économie, éducation physique, français, géographie, histoire, latin, musique, philosophie, psychologie, sciences politiques, service social et sociologie.

(Etudes graduées)

Maîtrise ès arts (MA).
Au moins deux ans après le BA avec mention. Offert en français, histoire et philosophie.

Commerce
(Ecole de commerce)

Baccalauréat ès sciences commerciales (BScCom).
Avec mention en administration ou en comptabilité. Quatre ans après l'immatriculation junior ou l'équivalent; deux ans après le baccalauréat ès arts ou ès sciences.

Maîtrise en gestion des affaires (MBA).
Etre détenteur d'un premier baccalauréat, préférablement le BScCom.

Education
(Ecole d'éducation-psychologie)

Baccalauréat d'enseignement à l'élémentaire (BEE).
Deux ans après l'obtention du brevet d'enseignement du Nouveau-Brunswick. S'obtient par cours à plein temps ou à temps partiel.

Baccalauréat en éducation (BEd).
Un an après le baccalauréat ès arts ou ès sciences.

Baccalauréat en éducation-physique (BEdPhy).
Quatre ans après l'immatriculation junior.

(Etudes graduées)

Maîtrise en éducation (MEd).
Avec spécialisation en administration scolaire, orientation, psychologie éducationnelle, enseignement secondaire. Un an après le baccalauréat en éducation.

Maîtrise ès arts en éducation [*MA(Ed)*].
Un an après le baccalauréat en éducation.
Thèse.

Génie
(Faculté des sciences)

Baccalauréat ès sciences appliquées (BScA).
Génie civil et industriel; cinq ans après les
études secondaires.

Psychologie
(Ecole d'éducation-psychologie)

Maîtrise en psychologie (MPs).
Trois ans après le baccalauréat ès arts ou ès
sciences. Deux ans après le BA mention
psychologie.

Maîtrise ès arts en psychologie [*MA(Ps)*].
Trois ans après le baccalauréat ès arts ou ès
sciences. Deux ans après le BA mention
psychologie. Thèse.

Sciences pures
(Faculté des sciences)

Baccalauréat ès sciences (BSc).
Quatre ans après les études secondaires. (a)
Avec spécialisation en physique ou en chimie.
(b) Avec mention en physique, chimie
organique, biologie, physico-chimie,
biochimie, mathématiques, pré-médecine.

(Etudes graduées)

Maîtrise ès sciences (MSc).
Au moins une année après le BSc avec
spécialisation. Offerte en physique, en chimie
et en biochimie.

Sciences domestiques
(Ecole des sciences domestiques)

*Baccalauréat en sciences domestiques
(BScDom)*.
Avec mention en enseignement ou nutrition et
diététique. Quatre ans après les études
secondaires.

Sciences infirmières
(Ecole des sciences infirmières)

Baccalauréat en sciences infirmières
[*BSc(Inf)*].
Quatre ans après les études secondaires. Pour
les infirmières diplômées le programme
comporte trois années d'études.

Sciences sociales
(Ecole des sciences sociales)

Baccalauréat en service social (BSSoc).
Programme de quatre ans après les études
secondaires.

(Etudes graduées)

Maîtrises ès arts (MA)
en sociologie, économie.
Programme de deux ans après le baccalauréat
ès arts avec mention en économie ou en
sociologie.

Education permanente

Cours conduisant à un grade

Cours d'extension.
Cours du soir à l'université et dans des centres
extra-muros.

Cours d'été.
Trois instituts spécialisés sont organisés pour
la session d'été 1971, destinés aux enseignants
des écoles publiques. Les cours offerts sont les
suivants: géographie, mathématiques
secondaires et musique.

Cours spéciaux.
Enseignement du français au niveau
secondaire (méthode Dwane); problèmes
spécifiques d'apprentissage (conseillé aux
professeurs des "classes spéciales"); Sablier;
nouvelles mathématiques. Cours conduisant
au baccalauréat ès arts, au baccalauréat en
éducation dans les trois collèges affiliés; et à
la maîtrise en éducation à l'université.

Cours qui ne conduisent pas à un grade

Cours.
Conversation française, formation de chef,
administration publique, vente d'immeubles.
Service d'éducation populaire par l'université
et par les collèges affiliés.

Conditions d'admission

On trouvera un exposé général sur l'admission aux études universitaires dans l'article *Admission aux universités canadiennes.*

Afin d'obtenir des renseignements sur l'admission aux études du niveau pré-grade, consultez *Conditions d'admission dans les collèges et universités du Canada* que l'on peut obtenir du Service d'admission au collège et à l'université, 151, rue Slater, Ottawa (Ont.), K1P 5N1, $1.50 port payé.

Pour être admis aux études supérieures, l'étudiant doit avoir obtenu un premier grade universitaire dans les matières appropriées.

Année universitaire

Session régulière: de la mi-septembre à la fin d'avril.

Cours d'été: du 2 juillet environ à la mi-août.

Système de mentions

Minimum exigé dans chaque matière: 60%. Moyenne générale de promotion annuelle: 60%.

Droits d'inscription

Etudiants à temps complet: toutes les facultés, $525; exceptions: psychologie et sciences, $600.

Etudiants à temps partiel: $20/crédit pré-grade. $25/crédit post-grade.

Frais particuliers: première demande d'admission, $5; association des étudiants, $30; reprise d'examens, $5 – $10; logement des étudiants (avec pension), $800 par année.

Aide financière

Les gouvernements fédéral et provinciaux, certaines compagnies, fondations et sociétés et l'université elle-même offrent des bourses ou des prêts aux étudiants réguliers incrits à l'Université de Moncton.

Etudiants du niveau pré-grade:

a) Gouvernement fédéral:

1. Ministère des Affaires indiennes et du Nord canadien
2. Ministère des Affaires des anciens combattants.
3. Ministère de la Défense nationale – plan ROTP.
4. Régime fédéral de prêts aux étudiants canadiens.

b) Provinces canadiennes:

Les étudiants peuvent obtenir de l'aide financière en s'adressant au ministère de l'Education de leur province respective.

c) Nouveau-Brunswick:

Des bourses de $200 chacune sont offertes aux élèves qui terminent leur cours secondaire et qui ont obtenu une moyenne de 70% et plus aux examens provinciaux d'immatriculation.

Les étudiants s'inscrivant pour la première fois en première année d'un cours universitaire peuvent obtenir, selon le besoin, un prêt-bourse maximum de $1,600. Les étudiants des autres années, incluant les étudiants inscrits à des études supérieures, peuvent obtenir un prêt-bourse maximum de $1,200.

d) Province de Québec:

1. Ministère de l'Education
2. Ministère des Affaires culturelles.
3. Service de Réadaptation professionnel des handicapés.

e) Université de Moncton:

Une somme totale d'environ $60,000 est administrée par le Service d'aide financière aux étudiants de l'université. Ces fonds proviennent de l'université elle-même ainsi que de sociétés et compagnies.

Pour renseignements ou l'obtention de formules de demande, s'adresser au directeur du service d'aide financière aux étudiants, Université de Moncton, Moncton, N.-B.

Pour tout renseignement, s'adresser au Service d'aide financière, département des affaires étudiantes, Université de Moncton, Moncton, N.-B.

Etudiants gradués:

a) Gouvernement fédéral:

1. Conseil des arts du Canada.
2. Conseil national de recherches.
3. Bourses de l'OTAN.
4. Société royale du Canada.

b) Province du Nouveau-Brunswick:

1. Ministère de la Jeunesse.
2. Ministère de la Santé.

c) Province de la Nouvelle-Ecosse:

Bourses couvrant les frais de scolarité accordées aux étudiants de la province inscrits en éducation.
S'adresser au ministère de l'Education, boîte postale 578, Halifax, N.-E.

d) Province de Québec:

Ministère de la Santé.
Bourses accordées aux étudiants du Québec inscrits en psychologie.
S'adresser au ministère de la Santé, les services psychiatriques, a/s M. Dominique Médard, directeur, Hôtel du gouvernement, Québec (P.Q.).

e) Sociétés et compagnies:

1. The New Brunswick Electric Power Commission.
2. Union du Canada.
3. New Brunswick Teachers' Association.
4. Ordre impérial des filles de l'empire (IODE).
5. The Atlantic Provinces Inter-University Committee on the Sciences (APICS).
6. Rotary Foundation Fellowship.
7. Gulf Oil Canada Limitée.
8. Imperial Oil Limited.

f) Université de Moncton:

Un certain nombre d'étudiants gradués peuvent obtenir des postes d'assistant dans l'enseignement, la correction, les laboratoires, etc.

Collèges affiliés

Ces institutions sont directement rattachées à l'université; elles offrent un cours de huit années, dont les quatre premières sont au niveau secondaire; les quatre dernières, au niveau collégial, visant l'obtention du baccalauréat ès arts de l'université.

Collège Saint-Joseph, Moncton, N.-B.
Directeur des études: Maurice Chamard, csc, BA, LèsL. Catholique. Mixte. Fondé en 1864. Charte d'incorporation en 1868. Amendements: 1871 et 1873. Refonte de la charte en 1894. En vertu d'un amendement en 1898, l'institution recevait le titre d'université. En 1963, Saint-Joseph était affilié à la faculté des arts de l'Université de Moncton. Le collège est maintenant installé sur le campus central.

Collège de Bathurst, Bathurst, N.-B.
Directeur des études: Raymond Woodworth, cjm, BA, MEd. Catholique. Mixte. Fondé à Caraquet en 1899 sous le nom de Collège du Sacré-Coeur. Charte d'incorporation en 1900. Après l'incendie de 1915, l'institution fut transférée à Bathurst. Amendement à la charte en 1920. En 1941, le gouvernement provincial octroyait à l'institution le titre d'université. En 1963, en vertu d'un amendement à la charte, l'institution devenait le Collège de Bathurst. Quatre années du cours conduisant au baccalauréat ès arts.

Collège Saint-Louis, Edmundston, N.-B.
Directeur des études: Jean-Guy Lachance, cjm, BA, LPh, certScS. Catholique. Pour jeunes gens. Fondé en 1946. Charte d'incorporation en 1947 donnant à l'institution le statut d'université. En 1963, en vertu d'un amendement à la charte, l'établissement devenait le Collège Saint-Louis. Enseignement offert: les quatre années des études conduisant au baccalauréat ès arts.

Collèges annexés

Ces institutions sont rattachées par la faculté des arts, plus concrètement par l'intermédiaire de l'un des deux collèges affiliés.

Collège Maillet, Saint-Basile, N.-B.
Directrice: Soeur Anne-Marie Savoie, rhsj,
MA. Catholique. Pour jeunes filles. Fondé en
1949. Quatre années d'études conduisant au
baccalauréat ès arts. Annexé au Collège Saint-
Louis.

Collège Jésus-Marie, Shippegan, N.-B.
Directrice: Soeur Ghislaine Côté, rjm, BA,
BPh, LPh. Catholique. Pour jeunes filles.
Fondé en 1960. Quatre années d'études
conduisant au baccalauréat ès arts. Annexé au
Collège de Bathurst.

Doyens des facultés

Arts
Maurice Chamard, csc, BA, LèsL

Sciences
Victor Ross, BA, BScA, MScA, DSc, IngP

Directeurs des écoles

Commerce
Léandre Bourque, BScCom, MScCom, MBA,
CA

Education-psychologie
En instance de nomination

Sciences domestiques
Ghislaine Cormier, ndsc, BScDom, DtP, MA,
PhD

Sciences infirmières
Huberte Richard, BScN, MScN

Sciences sociales
Aurèle Young, BA, LScEcon

Chefs de département

Administration
Jean-Claude Ladouceur, BEd, MCom, Epost-
grad

Anglais
Joseph Casey, BA, BEd, MA

Arts visuels
Claude Roussel

Biologie
Rafael Candela, LMéd, DMéd

Chimie
Mool Chand Mehra, BSc, MSc, DSc

Comptabilité
Gaétan Baril, BScCom, MScCom,
MScCompt, MBA, CA

Economie
Emmanuel Sajous, BA, LDr, DES, DES,
DScEcon

Education
Aldéo Renaud, BA, BEd, MEd, PhD

Education-physique
Vance Toner, BA, MSc

Français
Melvin Gallant, BScCom, LèsL

Génie
Jean-René Longval, BScA, MScA, PhD

Histoire-géographie
Khaled Belkhodja, BA, LèsL, MA, DES,
CAPES

Langues modernes
Normand Vautour, BA, Diplenphonétique

Musique
Brian Ellard, BMus, MA

Philosophie
Serge Morin, BA, BPh, MA, DPh

Physique-mathématiques
Fernand Girouard, BSc, PhD

Psychologie
Gérard Cormier, BA, BPs, MA

Psycho-social
Pierre Dion, BA, LOP, PhD

Sciences politiques
Philippe Doucet, BA, MA

Sciences religieuses
Fernand Arsenault, BA, BScSoc, LTh, DTh

Sciences secrétarielles
Pauline Landry, ndsc, BScCom, MCom

Service social
Normand Doucet, BA, MA

Sociologie
Baliah Naidu, MA, MA, DSoc

Université de Montréal*

Case postale 6128, Montréal 101 (Québec)

Téléphone: 514-343-6111
Prière d'adresser la correspondance d'ordre général au secrétaire général

Total des inscriptions des étudiants à plein temps 13,132; voir aussi la section distincte, intitulée *Statistiques sur les universités et collèges du Canada*

Dirigeants

Chancelier
Marcel Piché, CR, LLL

Recteur
Roger Gaudry, BScA, DSc, LLD, FSRC

Vice-recteur exécutif
Paul Lacoste, MA, LPh, Ddel'U, LLL

Vice-recteur à la recherche
Maurice L'Abbé, LSc, MA, PhD

Vice-recteur aux affaires académiques
André Archambault, BPhm, DPhm

Vice-recteur à l'administration
Roger Larose, BPhm, LScsoc

Secrétaire général
Jacques Girard, LLL, LLM

Registraire
Claude St-Arnaud, LSc, MSc, PhD

Directeur des services
Jacques Lucier, MA

Directeur des finances
Poste vacant

Directeur du fonds de développement
André Bachand, LLL, LSccom, MS

Directeur des services aux étudiants
Yves Thérien, BPh

Directeur de l'éducation permanente
Gaëtan Daoust, LPh, DPh, DTh

Directeur des bibliothèques
Daniel Reicher, BA, MLS

Directeur du centre de calcul
Jacques St-Pierre, LSc, PhD, PhD

Directeur du centre des techniques audio-visuelles
Jean Cloutier, LLL

Directeur du service d'information et de consultation psychologique
Roger-E. Lapointe, PhD

Directeur du service du personnel enseignant
Juliette Barcello, LLL, MA

Directrice des presses de l'Université de Montréal
Danièle Ros

Directeur du bureau de l'information
Louis-Martin Tard

Directeur du service de l'équipement
O-Jean Gratton, BScA

Directeur du service du personnel
Pierre Dupras, MA

Directeur du service des achats
Georges Bourgeois

Directeur du service de santé
Jean-Guy Hébert, MD, CSPQ, FRCP(C)

Directeur des sports
Gérald Simon, DMS

Directeur du centre social
Poste vacant

Archiviste
Luc-André Biron

Historien de l'université
Léon Lortie, DSc, LLD, FSRC

Aumônier
Michel Buron, ptre

*Membre ordinaire de l'AUCC.

Historique

En 1876, à la suite d'une demande faite par Mgr Ignace Bourget, évêque de Montréal, en vue d'obtenir une université catholique pour sa ville épiscopale, la sacrée congrégation de la Propagande proposa à l'Université Laval d'établir à Montréal une succursale où l'on donnerait la même formation qu'à Québec. L'enseignement fut inauguré en 1878 dans les facultés de théologie et de droit; en 1879 dans la faculté de médecine; en 1887 dans la faculté des arts. En vertu de la constitution apostolique Jamdudum, du 2 février 1889, la succursale devint pratiquement indépendante de la maison de Québec. Elle recevait encore ses grades du conseil universitaire de Québec, mais elle possédait une administration locale complète.

En 1919 et 1920, la succursale fut dotée de son autonomie entière, de droit et de fait; elle prit le nom d'Université de Montréal et conféra ses premiers grades en 1921. Dans l'ordre canonique, elle fut d'abord régie, à partir du 8 mai 1919, par un rescrit préparatoire à une bulle pontificale. La charte civile lui a été octroyée par la législature provinciale de Québec, le 14 février 1920. Le 30 octobre 1927, elle recevait de Rome la bulle définitive. Une nouvelle charte administrative est entrée en vigueur le 5 juin 1950.

L'université comptait, en 1920, les facultés de théologie, de droit et de médecine, une faculté des arts qui groupait des enseignements très divers mais fragmentaires; des écoles de pharmacie, de chirurgie dentaire, et de médecine vétérinaire. Par affiliation, l'Ecole polytechnique, l'Ecole des hautes études commerciales et l'Institut agricole d'Oka lui étaient rattachés. Enfin, une dernière catégorie, celle des institutions annexées, comprenait l'enseignement dit moderne, l'enseignement de la musique et de l'art ménager.

Pour compléter ses cadres essentiels, l'Université de Montréal fonda coup sur coup une faculté des lettres, une faculté des sciences, une école des sciences sociales, économiques et politiques et une faculté de philosophie. Elle réunit les collèges de jeunes gens et de jeunes filles dans une faculté des arts.

Depuis le 1er septembre 1967, l'université a une nouvelle charte qui en fait une institution à caractère public. Elle est dirigée par un conseil de vingt-quatre membres dont huit sont nommés par le gouvernement du Québec, cinq par l'assemblée universitaire, deux après consultation de l'assemblée des étudiants, et deux après consultation de l'association des diplômés, ainsi que deux nommés par le modérateur des facultés ecclésiastiques, c'est-à-dire l'archevêque de Montréal.

L'Université de Montréal est une institution mixte.

Installations et services

Le campus de l'Université de Montréal s'étend sur le versant nord-ouest du Mont-Royal. Sa superficie est de 158 acres. Outre l'immeuble principal, on compte de nombreux pavillons dont ceux de l'Ecole polytechnique, du centre social, des facultés de droit et de sciences sociales, des hautes études commerciales. Seuls, sont situés hors du campus, l'Ecole de réadaptation, l'Ecole de médecine vétérinaire et le département d'éducation physique.

Les bibliothèques appartiennent en propre à l'université et comptent 682,000 volumes. A ce chiffre, si l'on ajoute les bibliothèques des grandes écoles affiliées, le nombre total des publications dans les bibliothèques universitaires est de près de 1,300,000 volumes.

L'université dispose d'un service de placement, d'un service de santé, d'un centre sportif, d'un service de bourses et prêts aux étudiants, d'un service d'évaluation et de consultation psychologique (SEICUM), d'un service d'accueil aux étudiants, de logement hors campus, trois résidences pouvant loger chacune 186 étudiants, 174 étudiantes, 186 étudiants, et d'un centre communautaire.

Le centre communautaire comprend deux pavillons: l'un d'eux abrite la caisse populaire, la coopérative, etc., tandis que les restaurants et les salons se trouvent dans le second pavillon. Depuis l'année dernière, il y existe une section animation qui réalise divers programmes sociaux et culturels de concert avec les étudiants. Le centre sportif comprend un stade d'hiver (patinoire et salles d'exercice), une pente de ski, un stade de football ainsi que de nombreuses salles pour les joueurs. On loue également piscine et

gymnases à l'extérieur. Le service de santé dispense des premiers soins en tout temps, des examens médicaux, consultations psychiatriques, psychothérapie individuelle ou de groupe, physiothérapie, etc. Le SEICUM offre des tests psychologiques d'aptitudes, d'intérêts et de personnalité; il comprend aussi une section orientation et consultation; offre les avantages d'un counselling psychologique. Nous avons de plus des correspondants pour informer les étudiants des services mis à leur disposition, les familiariser avec la vie sur le campus, identifier leurs besoins, revendications, etc. Le service d'accueil a pour but de répondre aux besoins des étudiants tant étrangers que canadiens. Il facilite leur intégration et leur adaptation au monde universitaire et fournit à ceux qui le désirent des renseignements d'ordre non universitaire.

Annuaires et brochures

Annuaire général; annuaires de faculté. Renseignements généraux (registraire). Forum (hebdomadaire, bureau de l'information).

Cours et grades

Le diplôme d'études collégiales (DEC) décerné par les collèges d'enseignement général et professionnel (CEGEP) est l'unique condition d'admission dans les facultés universitaires.

Note: Sauf aux cours d'anglais, la langue d'enseignement est le français. Aux examens on peut cependant se servir de la langue anglaise.

Beaucoup de documentation étant disponible en anglais seulement, il est utile d'avoir une bonne connaissance de cette langue.

Administration des affaires
(Ecole des hautes études commerciales)

Baccalauréat en administration des affaires (BAA).
Trois ans après le DEC ou l'équivalent.

Maîtrise en administration des affaires (MAA).
Un an après le BAA ou deux ans après un

premier grade spécialisé d'une autre discipline: avec ou sans mémoire.

Administration de la santé
(Ecole de santé publique)

Maîtrise en administration de la santé (MAS).
Deux ans après un baccalauréat spécialisé ou la licence; mémoire.

Architecture
(Faculté de l'aménagement)

Baccalauréat en architecture (BArch).
Quatre ans après le DEC ou l'équivalent.

Baccalauréat en architecture paysagiste (BAP).
Quatre ans après le DEC, ou l'équivalent.

Baccalauréat en design industriel (BDI).
Quatre ans après le DEC, ou l'équivalent.

Maîtrise en aménagement [MAm(Arch)].
Un an après le BArch ou l'équivalent; mémoire.

Doctorat en aménagement (PhD).
Deux ans après une maîtrise en aménagement, ou l'équivalent.

Chirurgie dentaire
(Faculté de chirurgie dentaire)

Doctorat en chirurgie dentaire (DDS).
Quatre ans après le DEC, ou l'équivalent.

Baccalauréat en hygiène dentaire (BHD).
Majeur en hygiène dentaire et mineur en éducation.

Certificat en orthodontie.
Cours postscolaire pour praticiens: 21 mois au minimum, après le DDS.

Certificat en pédodontie.
Deux ans après le DDS, avec stages.

Maîtrise ès sciences en orthodontie [MSc(orthodontie)].
Vingt-quatre (24) mois au minimum, après le DDS; un an après le certificat en orthodontie; mémoire.

Maîtrise en biologie dentaire [MSc(biologie dentaire)].
Deux ans après le DDS, le MD ou le

baccalauréat ès sciences (option biologie), ou l'équivalent.

Commerce, voir administration des affaires

Droit
(Faculté de droit)

Licence en droit (LLL).
Trois ans après le DEC ou un diplôme équivalent.

Maîtrise en droit (LLM).
Un an après la LLL; mémoire.

Doctorat en droit (LLD).
Un an après la LLM; thèse.

Ecole normale supérieure
(Sciences de l'éducation)

Un *mineur de éducation,* combiné à un *majeur* de l'une des disciplines suivantes: sciences, lettres, diététique, musique, sciences religieuses, a remplacé la licence d'enseignement secondaire.

Diplôme de l'Ecole normale supérieure (DENS).
Un an et un stage après le premier grade spécialisé des facultés des lettres, de philosophie, des sciences et de théologie.

Education physique

Baccalauréat ès sciences (éducation physique) [*BSc(Edphys)*].
Trois ans après le DEC.

Maîtrise ès sciences (éducation physique) [*MSc(Edphys)*].
Deux ans après le BSc(Edphys).

Etudes médiévales
(Institut d'études médiévales de la faculté de philosophie)

Maîtrise ès arts en sciences médiévales [*MA(sciences médiévales)*].
Un an après une maîtrise, deux ans après un premier grade spécialisé; mémoire.

Philosophiae doctor en sciences médiévales [*PhD(sciences médiévales)*].
Deux ans après la MA (sciences médiévales) ou l'équivalent; thèse.

Génie
(Ecole polytechnique)

Baccalauréat ès sciences appliquées et diplôme d'ingénieur (BScA).
Quatre ans après le DEC et l'examen d'admission. Le diplôme fait mention de l'option choisie par l'étudiant: génie chimique, civil, électrique, géologique, mécanique, métallurgique, minier, ou physique.

Maîtrise ès sciences appliquées (MScA).
Un an après le BScA (avec un minimum de 70% des points dans l'ensemble des matières); mémoire. Offerte en génie chimique, civil, électrique, géologique, mécanique, métallurgique, minier, nucléaire et physique.

Maîtrise en ingénierie (MIng).
Grade professionnel dans les mêmes disciplines. Minimum un an après le BScA.

Doctorat ès sciences appliquées (DScA).
Deux ans après la MScA; thèse. Offert en génie chimique, civil, électrique, géologique, mécanique, métallurgique, minier, nucléaire et physique.

Diplôme d'études complémentaires.
Un an après le BScA. Cours de perfectionnement.

Hygiène
(Ecole de santé publique)

Diplôme en hygiène publique (DHP).
Un an. Le cas de chaque candidat est étudié par le conseil qui décide de son admission comme élève régulier.

Maîtrise ès sciences en hygiène (MScH).
Un an après le MD, DDS, DMV, BSc spécialisé, ou BScA. Mémoire dans la spécialité environnement.

Doctorat ès sciences en hygiène (DScH).
Deux ans après la MScH; thèse.

Lettres
(Faculté des lettres)

Un baccalauréat,
avec sujet majeur dans l'une des disciplines
suivantes: géographie, grec, histoire, langue et
littérature anglaises, langue et littérature
françaises, latin et mineur en éducation,
remplace la licence d'enseignement
secondaire. Voir Ecole normale supérieure.

Baccalauréat en traduction (BTrad).
Trois ans après le DEC.

Baccalauréat ès arts (BA).
Trois ans après le DEC.

Baccalauréat ès arts spécialisé
dans l'une des disciplines suivantes: études
allemandes, études anglaises, études
classiques, études françaises, études
hispaniques, études italiennes, russes et
slaves, géographie, histoire, histoire de l'art,
linguistique.

Baccalauréat ès arts spécialisé
avec sujet majeur et sujet mineur selon une
combinaison des spécialités ci-avant.

Baccalauréat ès arts général [BA(lettres)].
Programme choisi dans trois spécialités, à
parts égales.

Maîtrise en bibliothéconomie (MBibl).
Deux ans après un premier grade spécialisé ou
l'équivalent.

Maîtrise ès arts (MA).
Au moins un an après le BA spécialisé;
mémoire. Offerte dans les mentions suivantes:
études anglaises, études classiques, études
françaises, géographie, histoire, histoire de
l'art, linguistique et langues modernes,
littérature comparée.

Maîtrise en traduction (MTrad).
Un an après le BTrad ou deux ans après le
premier grade spécialisé.

Philosophiae doctor (PhD).
Au moins deux ans après la MA; thèse. Offert
dans les mêmes disciplines que celles de la
MA.

Médecine
(Faculté de médecine)

Doctorat en médecine (MD).
Cinq ans après le DEC ou l'équivalent.

Maîtrise ès sciences (MSc).
Un an après le MD ou le BSc spécialisé;
mémoire. Offerte en anatomie, biochimie,
pharmacologie, pathologie, médecine et
chirurgie expérimentales, microbiologie et
immunologie, sciences cliniques et sciences
neurologiques.

Philosophiae doctor (PhD).
Deux ans après la MSc; thèse. Offert dans les
mêmes spécialisations que la maîtrise.

Médecine vétérinaire
(Ecole de médecine vétérinaire)

Doctorat en médecine vétérinaire (DMV).
Quatre ans après le DEC.

Maîtrise en sciences vétérinaires (MScV).
Un an après le DMV. Mémoire.

Médiévales, Etudes, voir Etudes médiévales

Musique profane ou sacrée
(Faculté de musique)

Baccalauréat en musique spécialisé (BMus).
Trois ans après le DEC. Mentions:
interprétation, composition et techniques
d'écriture, histoire et langues musicales.

Baccalauréat ès arts (BA)
avec sujet majeur. Trois ans après le DEC. Le
sujet mineur peut être choisi dans une autre
faculté.

Baccalauréat en musique (BMus)
général.

Maîtrise en musique (MMus).
Deux ans après le BMus; mémoire.

Doctorat en musique (DMus).
Deux ans après la MMus; thèse.

Notariat
Mêmes études que le droit.

Nursing

Baccalauréat en nursing (BNurs).
a) Section de base: le cours est de trois ans après le DEC et est destiné aux candidats qui désirent allier à la formation infirmière une culture générale plus étendue.

b) Section des infirmières: le cours est d'une durée de deux ans pour les candidates détentrices d'un diplôme d'infirmière.

Maîtrise en nursing (MNurs).
Deux ans après le BNurs; mémoire. Dans les spécialités suivantes: administration du nursing à l'hôpital, éducation en nursing, nursing en médecine et chirurgie, psychiatrie et hygiène mentale.

Nutrition
(Institut de diététique et de nutrition)

Baccalauréat ès sciences (nutrition) [BSc(nut)].
Trois ans après le DEC.

Baccalauréat ès sciences (BSc).
Sujet majeur: alimentation. Sujet mineur: éducation. Trois ans après le DEC. Remplace la licence d'enseignement secondaire.

Maîtrise ès sciences (nutrition) [MSc(nut)].
Au moins un an après le BSc(nut) ou le BSc d'autres institutions canadiennes ou américaines équivalent au BSc(nut); mémoire.

Optométrie
(Ecole d'optométrie)

Licence en optométrie (LScO).
Trois ans après le DEC.

Pharmacie
(Faculté de pharmacie)

Baccalauréat ès sciences (pharmacie) [BSc(phm)].
Quatre ans après le DEC, ou l'équivalent.

Diplôme en pharmacie d'hôpital.
Un an après le BSc(phm).

Maîtrise ès sciences (MSc).
Au moins un an après le BSc(phm), ou l'équivalent; mémoire. Dans les options suivantes: chimie médicinale, pharmacie, pharmacognosie, pharmacodynamie biochimie.

Doctorat (PhD).
Deux ans après la MSc dans la spécialité choisie: mêmes options que pour la maîtrise.

Philosophie
(Faculté de philosophie)

Baccalauréat en philosophie (BPh).
Trois ans après le DEC ou l'équivalent.

Maîtrise ès arts (philosophie) [MA(Ph)].
Un an après le BPh ou l'équivalent; mémoire.

Philosophiae doctor (philosophie) [PhD(Ph)].
Deux ans après la MA(Ph); thèse.

Psychologie
(Faculté de philosophie, Institut de psychologie)

Baccalauréat ès sciences (psychologie) [BSc(Ps)].
Trois ans après le DEC.

Baccalauréat ès sciences (psychoéducation) [BSc(psed)].
Trois ans après le DEC.

Maîtrise ès arts (psychologie) [MA(Ps)].
Un an après le BSc(Ps) ou l'équivalent; mémoire.

Maîtrise en orientation (MOr).
Un an après le BSc(Ps); mémoire.

Maîtrise en psychoéducation (MPsed).
Un an après le BSc(psed); mémoire.

Maîtrise en psychologie (MPs).
Un an après le BSc(Ps); mémoire.

Philosophiae doctor en psychologie [PhD(Ps)].
Deux ans après la MA(Ps) ou l'équivalent; thèse.

Doctorat en psychologie (DPs).
Deux ans après la MPs; thèse.

Réadaptation
(Ecole de réadaptation)

Baccalauréat ès sciences (ergothérapie) [BSc(erg)].
Trois ans après le DEC.

Baccalauréat ès sciences (physiothérapie)
[*BSc(physio)*].
Trois ans après le DEC.

Baccalauréat ès sciences (orthophonie et audiologie) [*BSc(orthoetaudio)*].
Trois ans après le DEC.

Maîtrise en orthophonie et audiologie (MOA).
Un an après le BSc(orthophonie et audiologie); mémoire.

Sciences appliquées, voir génie

Science de l'éducation
(Faculté des sciences de l'éducation)

La faculté décerne un *baccalauréat ès sciences,* cours général en *éducation* et deux *baccalauréats spécialisés,* l'un en orthopédagogie et l'autre en éducation préscolaire et enseignement élémentaire. *(BScEd–BSc spécialisé).*

Cours spécialisés:
durée de cours – trois ans.

Baccalauréat ès sciences (éducation)
[*BSc(Ed)*].
Cours général.

Baccalauréat ès sciences (orthopédagogie)
[*BSc(ortho)*].

Baccalauréat ès sciences (éducation préscolaire et enseignement élémentaire)
[*BSc(éducprésensélém)*].

Maîtrise en éducation (MEd).
Un an après le BSc; mémoire.

Maîtrise ès arts (enseignement) [*MA(ens)*].
Douze mois avec stages après un premier grade spécialisé.

Maîtrise ès arts (MA).
Un an après un bacalauréat spécialisé.

Doctorat (PhD).
Deux ans après la maîtrise; thèse.

Sciences pures
(Faculté des sciences)

Baccalauréat ès sciences (spécialisé) (BSc).
Trois ans après le DEC ou l'équivalent. Le diplôme fait mention de la spécialisation en

biochimie, biologie, chimie, géologie, informatique, mathématiques, physique, ou mathématiques et physique.

Une moyenne des deux tiers des points au cours de chacune des deux dernières années est nécessaire pour avoir droit au grade de BSc spécialisé.

Baccalauréat ès sciences (BSc)
avec sujet majeur et sujet mineur. Trois ans après le DEC. On peut combiner les options mentionnées plus haut.

Note: un sujet majeur en chimie, mathématiques, physique ou sciences naturelles, suivi d'un sujet mineur en éducation, remplacent la licence d'enseignement secondaire.

Maîtrise ès sciences (MSc).
Au moins un an après le BSc (spécialisé) de l'ordre de la maîtrise projetée, ou l'équivalent; plus une année préparatoire ou des cours complémentaires dans le cas du BSc avec majeur et mineur; mémoire. Offerte en biochimie, botanique, chimie, géologie, informatique, mathématiques, physiologie, physique, zoologie. Les détenteurs d'un BSc spécialisé ou de la LèsL (linguistique) sont admissibles à la MSc (informatique).

Doctorat (PhD).
Au moins deux ans de recherche dans un laboratoire de la faculté après la MSc de l'ordre du doctorat projeté; thèse. Offert dans les mêmes spécialisations que la maîtrise.

Sciences sociales
(Faculté des sciences sociales)

Baccalauréat ès sciences (spécialisé) (BSc).
Trois ans après le DEC ou l'équivalent. Le diplôme fait mention de la spécialisation en anthropologie, criminologie, démographie, économique, politique, relations industrielles, service social, ou sociologie.

Maîtrise ès sciences (MSc).
Un an après le BSc de la faculté; mémoire. Offerte dans les mêmes spécialisations que le baccalauréat.

Diplôme d'études africaines.
Un an après un grade délivré par une des facultés de droit, des lettres, des sciences sociales ou l'équivalent.

Philosophiae doctor (PhD).
Au moins deux ans après la MSc de la faculté; thèse. Offert dans les mêmes spécialisations que la maîtrise.

Théologie
(Faculté de théologie)

Baccalauréat en théologie (BTh).
Trois ans après le DEC.

BA spécialisé (études bibliques — théologie).

BA sujet majeur
(études bibliques — théologie — sciences de la religion) et sujet mineur.

Baccalauréat en théologie pastorale (BThPast).

Baccalauréat ès arts général [BA(général)].

Maîtrise ès arts (MA).
Un an après l'un des baccalauréats. Mentions: études bibliques, pastorales, ou théologiques.

Philosophiae doctor (PhD).
Deux ans après la MA, avec les mêmes mentions.

Licence en théologie (LTh).
Deux ans après le BTh. Grade canonique.

Doctorat en théologie (DTh).
Un an après la LTh; thèse. Grade canonique.

Urbanisme
(Faculté de l'aménagement)

Maîtrise en urbanisme.
Cinq semestres après le BArch, le BScA, le BSc ou la LèsL (géographie), ou l'équivalent.

Service d'éducation permanente

Le secteur des grades et certificats:
chacun de ces programmes comprend 30 crédits et est couronné par un certificat de l'Université de Montréal: animation, animation de la vie étudiante, animation pédagogique des bibliothèques, aptitude à l'enseignement de l'éducation physique au niveau élémentaire, cytotechnologie, enseignement du français au niveau élémentaire, enseignement du français au niveau secondaire, enseignement des mathématiques et des sciences au niveau élémentaire, études catéchétiques, gestion d'hôpital, information scolaire et professionnelle, loisir, pédagogie audio-visuelle, recherche opérationnelle; relations industrielles, relations publiques, sciences familiales, traduction.

Le secteur des cours de promotion culturelle:
ces cours de culture et de perfectionnement, tout comme ceux de la promotion du travail, s'adressent aux personnes désireuses de poursuivre leur éducation, d'acquérir ou de parfaire leurs connaissances. On y trouve des cours de langue, de civilisation, en sciences humaines, et de littérature. Baccalauréat ès sciences (BSc).
Regroupement approuvé de trois certificats.

Conditions d'admission

On trouvera un exposé général sur l'admission aux études universitaires dans l'article *Admission aux universités canadiennes.*

Afin d'obtenir des renseignements sur l'admission aux études du niveau pré-grade, consultez *Conditions d'admission dans les collèges et universités du Canada* que l'on peut obtenir du Service d'admission au collège et à l'université, 151, rue Slater, Ottawa (Ontario), K1P 5N1, $1.50 port payé.

En règle générale, tout candidat qui désire s'inscrire comme étudiant régulier doit justifier d'une connaissance suffisante de la langue française et avoir obtenu le diplôme d'études collégiales (DEC) ou son équivalent. Les étudiants des facultés professionnelles qui n'exerceront pas leur profession dans la province de Québec devront avoir été régulièrement admis à l'étude dans leur pays d'origine.

Année universitaire

Session régulière: du début du mois de septembre à la fin d'avril.

Cours de vacances (soir): du 11 mai, environ, au 23 juin; (jour): du 2 juillet, environ, à la mi-août.

Système de mentions

Etudes pré-grade: succès, 60%; distinction, 70%; grande distinction, 80% et plus.

Droits d'inscription

Pour les cours par année: étudiants à temps complet — administration de la santé, $646; administration des affaires (commerce), $446; aménagement (architecture et urbanisme), $546; chirurgie dentaire, $596; droit, $496; éducation physique, $496; études médiévales, $496; génie (sciences appliquées), $496; lettres, $496; médecine, $696; médecine vétérinaire, aucun frais; nursing, $546; nutrition, $496; optométrie, $546; pharmacie, $546; philosophie, $496; psychologie, $496; réadaptation, $496; santé publique (hygiène), $496; sciences de l'éducation, $496; sciences pures, $546; sciences sociales, $496; service social, $496; théologie, $496. Etudiants à temps partiel (pour chaque cours): cours théoriques, par crédit, $19.50; cours avec laboratoire, $27.

Frais divers ou variables: pour examen du dossier lors d'une première demande d'admission, $15; pour l'usage du vestiaire, $2 (par année); pour étudiants provenant d'un pays étranger, $15; droits de reprise d'examen, une matière, $2 — plusieurs matières, $5.

Logement des étudiants, environ $375 par année (sans pension), pour une chambre à un lit.

Aide financière et bourses

Le service des bourses et de l'aide financière fournit toute information pouvant être obtenue sur le ministère de l'Education, le prêt d'honneur. L'université dispose également de bourses et prêts donnés par les associés de l'université, diverses compagnies, clubs sociaux, etc.

Centres de recherche

Banque de terminologie.
Centre de recherches Caraïbes.
Centre de recherches en développement économique.
Centre de recherches en sciences neurologiques.
Centre de recherches mathématiques.
Centre de recherches sur la croissance humaine.
Centre de sondage.
Centre international de criminologie comparée.

Ecoles affiliées

L'université confère les diplômes et les grades aux étudiants de ces écoles qui, soumises à ses règlements d'ordre universitaire, ne relèvent pas de son administration.

Ecole des hautes études commerciales, 5255, avenue Decelles, Montréal 250 (Québec). Directeur: Roger Charbonneau, LSccom, CA, MBA. Fondée en 1907 par le gouvernement de la province de Québec. Affiliée depuis 1915 à l'université dont elle est en fait la faculté de commerce. L'école décerne: (1) le baccalauréat en administration des affaires (BAA); (2) la maîtrise en administration des affaires (MAA).

Ecole polytechnique, 2500, avenue Marie-Guyard, Montréal 26 (Qué.). Directeur: Roger-P. Langlois, SM, BScA, Ing. Fondée en 1873, on l'annexa à la faculté des arts de l'Université Laval en 1887. Après quelques années, il parut de plus en plus évident qu'il fallait la doter d'une corporation indépendante pour veiller de plus près à ses intérêts, et le 8 janvier 1894 le gouvernement sanctionna le projet d'incorporation. Actuellement l'école est affiliée à l'Université de Montréal dont elle est en fait la faculté des sciences appliquées. Les étudiants peuvent s'inscrire à l'une des huit options du programme d'études qui conduit au diplôme d'ingénieur avec mention de l'option choisie; en outre, l'Université de Montréal accorde en même temps que le diplôme d'ingénieur le grade de bachelier ès sciences appliquées. L'école possède aussi un centre de recherche spécialement destiné aux recherches en sciences appliquées dans les diverses branches du génie. Les étudiants peuvent y approfondir leurs connaissances scientifiques et techniques et obtenir, moyennant les

conditions ordinaires, les grades de maîtrise et de doctorat ès sciences appliquées.

Doyens des facultés et écoles

Aménagement
Guy Desbarats, BArch, AIRAC

Arts
Pierre Décary, pd

Chirurgie dentaire
Jean-Paul Lussier, DDS, PhD, FACD

Diététique et de nutrition, Institut de
Claire Dalmé, MNS

Droit
Pierre Carignan, LLL, MA

Droit public, Institut de recherches en
Gilles Pépin

Hautes études commerciales
Roger Charbonneau, LSccom, CA, MBA

Lettres
René de Chantal, BA, LèsL, Ddel'U

Médecine
Pierre Bois, MD, PhD

Médecine vétérinaire
Ephrem Jacques, BA, DMV

Médiévales, Institut d'études
Jean Gagné, DPh

Musique
Jean Papineau-Couture, BMus

Nursing
Alice Girard, DIH, BScPHN, LScsoc, MA, DipHA

Pharmacie
Julien Braun, BPhm, PhD

Philosophie
David Bélanger, DPh

Optométrie, Ecole d'
Claude Beaulne, LSco

Polytechnique, Ecole
Roger-P. Langlois, MS, BScA, Ing

Psychologie, Institut de
R.P. Noël Mailloux

Réadaptation, Ecole de
Gustave Gingras, MD

Sciences
Serge Lapointe, BSc, MSc, PhD

Sciences de l'éducation
Michel Plourde, LTh, DèsL

Sciences sociales
Philippe Garigue, BScécon, PhD

Théologie
Richard Brosseau, pss, DPh, LTh

Directeurs des départements

Administration scolaire
Philippe Dupuis

Administration de la santé
Gilbert Blain

Africaines, Programmes d'études
Gérald Berthoud

Anatomie
Pierre Bois

Anatomie et physiologie animales
Olivier Garon

Anglais
Philip Stratford

Anthropologie
Guy Dubreuil

Architecture
Jean-Luc Poulin

Bibliothéconomie
Richard-K. Gardner

Biochimie
Walter Verly

Biologie
Jean-Guy Pilon

Biologie dentaire
Zdenek Mézl

Chimie
R.H. Marchessault

Chirurgie
Maurice Parent

Classiques, Etudes
Paul-Eugène Lortie

Criminologie
André Normandeau

Démographie
Jacques Henripin

Dentisterie de restauration
G.-Hervé Deschênes

Dentisterie préventive
Jean-Paul Lussier, DDS, PhD, FACD

Français
Normand Leroux

Géographie
Gilles Boileau

Géologie
Jacques Béland

Histoire
Roland Lamontagne

Histoire de l'art
Poste vacant

Hygiène des milieux
Jacques Nantel

Informatique
Pierre Robert

Linguistique et langues modernes
André Clas

Mathématiques
Poste vacant

Médecine
René Pelletier

Médecine et chirurgie expérimentales
Hans Selye

Microbiologie et immunologie
Sorin Sonea

Obstétrique-gynécologie
Michel-J. Bérard

Orientation
Dominique Erpicum

Orthodontie
Claude Baril

Orthopédagogie
Ali Haramein

Pathologie

Pathologie et microbiologie
André Lagacé

Pédiatrie
Jacques Ducharme

Pharmacologie
G.L. Plaa

Philosophie
Venant Gauchy

Physiologie
Poste vacant

Physique
R.J.A. Lévesque

Physique nucléaire, Laboratoire de
Pierre DePommier

Prosthodontie
Jean Nadeau

Psychiatrie
Gérard Beaudoin

Radiologie
Jean-Louis Léger

Réadaptation
Gustave Gingras

Relations industrielles
Jean-Réal Cordin

Sciences biologiques
Lucien Auclair

Sciences économiques
Gérald Marion

Sciences pédagogiques
Robert Tousignant

Sciences politiques
Gilles Lalande

Service social
Jacques Alary

Sociologie
Robert Sévigny

Stomatologie
Gérard deMontigny

Urbanisme, Institut d'
Iskandar Gabbour

Mount Allison University*

Sackville, New Brunswick

Telephone: 506-536-2040
Direct general correspondence to the registrar

Total full-time student enrolment 1,347; see also separate section *Statistics on Canadian universities and colleges*

Executive and administrative officers

Chancellor
H.R. Crabtree, BSc, LLD

President
L.H. Cragg, MA, PhD, DCL, DSc, FCIC

Vice-president (academic)
Cyril Poole, MA, PhD

Vice-president (administration)
Anthony Bailey, OBE

Registrar
Donald Cameron, BSc

Director, public relations and director, department of extension
R.J. Hickey, MA

Librarian
E.E. Magee, BA, BSc, MLS

Dean of students
A. Groenenberg, BA, BTh, BD, MA

Information officer
H. Daley

Associate dean of students
J. MacLeod, BA, MRE

Executive director of alumni
D.W. MacLauchlan, BSc, PhD

Director of development
K.A. Ross, FCIS

Director of physical education and athletics
Warren Lutes, BSc, MSc

Background

Mount Allison Wesleyan College, founded in 1843 as an academy, was in 1858 granted the power to confer degrees by the legislature of the province of New Brunswick. The original university faculties were those of arts and science. In 1875, a faculty of theology was added and the schools of applied science and home economics were established in 1903. After church union in 1925, an arrangement was made with Pine Hill Divinity Hall, Halifax, by which the theological subjects, except for the first year, should be taught at Pine Hill. In 1937, the conservatory of music and the Owens School of Fine Arts, previously under separate administration, were added to the faculties of the university.

While the university is directly connected with the United Church of Canada, it is conducted on non-sectarian principles. In 1913 the name was changed to Mount Allison University and at the same time the name of the corporation was changed to the Regents of Mount Allison. In 1963, the name of the corporation was changed to Mount Allison University.

University teaching began in 1859 and the first degrees were granted in 1863. The university is privately endowed and co-educational.

The direct government of the university is vested in a board of regents, entrusted with the general management of affairs, and a senate, charged with regulating the strictly educational concerns of the university. There is also a faculty council which gives consideration to certain academic matters before they are dealt with by the senate.

Facilities and services

The university is located on a hilltop in the centre of Sackville and overlooks the Tantramar Marshes. The campus comprises

approximately 100 acres. There are nine teaching buildings, a library (164,600 volumes), a chapel, an art gallery, administration facilities, a convocation hall (seating capacity 1,550), a rink, a gymnasium, a students' centre, a swimming pool, and playing fields. Mount Allison is basically a residential college. Three residences for women accommodate 456 students. Six residences for men accommodate 553 students.

Student services include health, employment, housing, counselling, and a university centre. Recreation facilities are provided in all residences and in a students' centre.

Campus organizations serving students from abroad are the foreign students' club and World University Service of Canada.

Calendars and brochures

The university calendar, and various academic brochures (science, music, scholarships and bursaries) are available through the registrar's office. Summer school and extension department calendar available through the extension department.

Courses and degrees

Arts
(Faculty of arts)

Bachelor of arts (BA).
Four years from junior matriculation. Honors available in biology, Canadian studies, chemistry, economics, English, French, geology, German, Greek, history, Latin, mathematics, music, philosophy, physics, political science, and psychology.

Business, see commerce below

Commerce
(Faculty of arts)

Bachelor of commerce (BComm).
Four years from junior matriculation, with specialization in accounting, economics, or mathematics.

Education
(Faculty of arts)

Bachelor of education (BEd).
One year after graduation in arts, science, or commerce.

Engineering
(Faculty of science)

Certificate in engineering.
First three years of engineering course from junior matriculation. Arrangements have been made with other Canadian universities to permit holders of this certificate to attain their engineering degree in an additional two years. After two years (beyond junior matriculation) students may enter the architecture course at Nova Scotia Technical College.

Fine arts
(Faculty of arts)

Bachelor of fine arts (BFA).
Four years from junior matriculation.

Home economics
(Faculty of science)

This degree program is not offered in 1971-72 and may not be available in 1972-73.

Music
(Faculty of arts)

Bachelor of music (BMus).
Four years from junior matriculation.

Bachelor of arts with major in music (BA).
Four years from junior matriculation.

Bachelor of music education (BMEd).
One year following BA with major in music, or equivalent.

Science, applied, see engineering above

Science, pure
(Faculty of science)

Bachelor of science (BSc).
Four years from junior matriculation. Honors
available in biology, chemistry, geology,
mathematics, and physics.

Master of science (MSc).
Usually 18 months from an honors bachelor's
degree in science. Available in chemistry.

Secretarial science
(Faculty of arts)

*Bachelor of arts with secretarial certificate (BA
with secretarial certificate).*
Four years from junior matriculation.

Theology
(Faculty of arts and Pine Hill Divinity Hall)

Bachelor of arts (BA).
Four years in arts from junior matriculation
at the university and three years at Pine Hill
Divinity Hall.

Extension programs

For university credit:

Correspondence courses.
Courses offered in a number of arts subjects.

Evening classes.
Courses offered by regular faculty members
in arts and education subjects.

Summer school.
Undergraduate course in arts, science, and
education.

For no university credit:

Special summer school programs.
The United Nations seminar for high school
students, summer art workshop, instrumental
music camp, music teachers' refresher course,
summer school of ballet.

Admission requirements

For a general statement regarding admission
to university study, see article *Admission to
university in Canada.*

For information regarding admission to
undergraduate study, consult *Requirements
for admission to Canadian colleges and
universities* available from Service for
Admission to College and University, 151
Slater St., Ottawa, Ont., K1P 5N1, $1.50
prepaid.

For admission to courses leading to a first
degree in education, a bachelor's degree is
required.

Academic year

Winter session: mid-September to early May.

Summer session: early July to mid-August.

Grading system

Standing is graded in each subject by division
— division I: 80-100%; division II: 70-79%;
division III: 60-69%; pass: 50-59%; failure:
below 50%.

Fees and costs

Fees for tuition and other activities for all
full-time undergraduate programs are $695
per annum. Part-time fees (per subject) are
$125. Education and post-graduate
programs, $685.

Residence fees, room and board, $875-$975.

Financial awards and assistance

The university awards a substantial number
of entrance scholarships for new students.
The value of the scholarships ranges from
$400 to $1,500 per year and many of them
are renewable. These scholarships are based

on the candidate's academic record and in some cases financial need is taken into account. Bursaries are also available to students demonstrating financial need.

Dean of faculty

Arts and science
A.J. Motyer, BA, MA

Department heads

Biology
D. Fensom, BASc, FRIC

Canadian studies
G.F.G. Stanley, BA, BLitt, MA, DPhil, DèsL, DLit, LLD

Chemistry
L.R.C. Barclay, BSc, MSc, PhD

Classics
J.E.A. Crake, BA, MA, PhD

Commerce
N. de Vos, BA, BComm, CA

Economics and political science
W.B. Cunningham, BA, MA, PhD

Education
G.G. Manson, BA, BEd, MEd, PhD

Engineering
R.A. Boorne, BASc

English
L.A. Duchemin, BA, MA, PhD

Fine arts
L. Harris, RCA, OSA

Geology
J.C.G. Moore, BA, MSc, PhD

German
F. Haberl, BA, MA, PhD

History
G. Adams, BA, MA, PhD

Mathematics
W.S.H. Crawford, BA, MA, PhD

Music
G. Proctor, BA, MMus, PhD

Philosophy
R. Stanway, BA, MA, PhD

Physics
D.P. Crawford, BSc, MSc, PhD

Psychology and sociology
E.G. Nichols, MSc, PhD

Religion
E.R. Hay, BA, BD, MA, PhD

Romance languages
A.B. Fancy, BA, MA

Secretarial studies
A. Adams, BA

Mount Saint Vincent University*

Halifax, Nova Scotia

Telephone: 902-453-4450
Direct general correspondence to the registrar

Total full-time student enrolment 944; see also separate section *Statistics on Canadian universities and colleges*

Executive and administrative officers

Chancellor
His Excellency, Most Reverend James Hayes, JCD, DD, Archbishop of Halifax

President
Sister Catherine Wallace, PhD

Registrar
Jean Hartley, MSc

Administrative assistant
Michael Merrigan, MEd

Dean of women
Sister Mary Burns, MSc

Director, summer school and continuing education and extension
Mary Cutler, BA

Director of public relations
Harry Etheridge

Librarian
Marjorie Kelley, AB, MSinLS

Business officer
Maureen Lyle, AASA

Background

Mount Saint Vincent University was granted a charter by the legislature of the province of Nova Scotia in 1925. Since 1914, it had been a junior college working under agreement with Dalhousie University to give the first two years of the arts course. The first degrees were awarded in 1927.

Present authority is that given by a new charter granted by the Nova Scotia legislature in 1966. The university is pre-eminently a women's university, but men are admitted as non-resident students. The charter provides for government by a board of governors appointed chiefly by the council of the Sisters of Charity (the university corporation) with members named also by the university alumnae and the governor-in-council.

In September 1969, an agreement was made with Dalhousie University, to be implemented over a period of five years. Each university is now represented on the senate of the other and committees are working toward the awarding of joint degrees.

Facilities and services

Mount Saint Vincent University is situated in Rockingham, a residential suburb of the city of Halifax (population 200,000). The university has two teaching buildings, a library (80,000 volumes), and residence accommodation for 500 women students.

Student services include a health service, guidance and counselling, some placement service, and a cafeteria.

Courses and degrees

Arts

Bachelor of arts (BA).
Four years from junior matriculation. Three years from senior matriculation. Areas of emphasis: business, language and literature, philosophy, social science, sociology, and

---

*Ordinary member, AUCC.

theology. Majors may be taken in business-economics, economics, English, history, mathematics, modern languages, political studies, psychology, and sociology.

Master of arts (MA).
At least two years or four summers from the bachelor's degree. Available in education and home economics education.

Business

Diploma in medical secretarial science.
Two years from junior or senior matriculation.

Diploma in secretarial studies.
Two years from junior or senior matriculation.

Education

Junior diploma in education.
One year following two years beyond junior matriculation in arts, science, or commerce. Prepares students for elementary school teaching.

Senior diploma in education.
One year following three years beyond junior matriculation in arts, science, or commerce. Prepares students for elementary school teaching.

Diploma courses in education are to be phased out.

Bachelor of education (BEd).
One year from a first bachelor's degree. Prepares students for both elementary and secondary school teaching and business teaching.

Home economics

Bachelor of science in home economics (BScHEc).
Four years from either junior or senior matriculation. Specialization offered for teaching, in dietetics, and in other fields.

Nursing

Bachelor of science in nursing (BScN).
Four calendar years from senior matriculation.

Science

Bachelor of science (BSc).
Four years from junior matriculation. Majors offered in chemistry and biology.

Special program

A psycho-educational centre for the diagnosis and remedial treatment of reading problems.

Extension programs

For university credit:

Evening classes.
Undergraduate classes in arts and science. Graduate classes in education and home economics education.

Summer school.
Undergraduate classes in arts and science. Graduate classes in education and home economics education.

For no university credit:

Business administration, catechetics, contemporary drama, fashion and design, journalism, and psychology of counselling.

Admission requirements

For a general statement regarding admission to university study, see article *Admission to university in Canada.*

For information regarding admission to undergraduate study, consult *Requirements for admission to Canadian colleges and universities* available from Service for Admission to College and University, 151 Slater St., Ottawa, Ont., K1P 5N1, $1.50 prepaid.

For admission to graduate study a student must have obtained a first degree, a specified number of credits in the major subject, and the fulfilment of certain prerequisite courses.

Academic year

Winter session: mid-September to early May.

Summer session: early July to mid-August.

Intersession: mid-May to late June.

Grading system

Numerical grading is used. Merit is indicated as follows — section I: 85-100%; section II: 70-84%; pass: 50-69%; failure: below 50%. One unit of credit is given for a two-semester course; one-half unit for a one-semester course.

Fees and costs

Full-time tuition fees per year: undergraduate, $582.75; graduate study, $150 per course. Part-time fees (per subject), $120.

Board and room, $825-$900.

Financial awards and assistance

Merit scholarships available to undergraduates have been made possible through the generosity of the Sisters of Charity and of benefactors who wish to assist the university to achieve its aim of providing higher education for women.

Entrance scholarships are awarded on academic achievement. Scholarships ranging from $250 to full tuition are available to all applicants. No special application is necessary for scholarships. On application to the university the scholastic record of each applicant is considered and scholarships awarded accordingly.
The Canada Student Loans Plan is available to students who can demonstrate need of financial assistance to undertake or continue university studies. In addition to the loan, a Nova Scotia student may obtain a bursary, up to a maximum of $600, which is not repayable.

Dean of faculty

Academic dean
Sister Margaret Molloy, MA

University of New Brunswick*

Fredericton, New Brunswick

Telephone: 506-475-9471
Direct general correspondence to the registrar

Total full-time student enrolment 5,102; see also separate section *Statistics on Canadian universities and colleges*

Executive and administrative officers

Chancellor
Sir Max Aitken, Bart, DSO, DFC, LLD

President and vice-chancellor
J.O. Dineen, BSc, MSc, LLD, DSc

Vice-president (academic)
W.C.D. Pacey, BA, PhD, FRSC

Vice-president (administration)
B.F. Macaulay, BSc, LLD

Registrar
D.C. Blue, MA, MEd

Librarian
G.E. Gunn, BA, MA, MLS, PhD

Dean of women
J.P. Kidd (Mrs), BA

Dean of men's residences
P.C. Kent, BA, BEd, MSc

Alumni secretary
E.W. Roberts, BScF

Director of development and assistant to the president
R.W. McBrine, BA, BJ, MA

Director of information
A. Pacey, BA

Background

The University of New Brunswick was established by the governor and council of New Brunswick on December 13, 1785, as the Academy of Arts and Science. It was transformed into the College of New Brunswick by provincial charter in 1800, and, by royal charter, it became King's College in 1828. In 1859, it was again reconstituted, and given the name University of New Brunswick. The first degrees were awarded in 1828.

The University of New Brunswick is a co-educational, non-denominational publicly-supported institution. It is governed by a board of governors, a senate and faculty councils.

The first course in engineering at a Canadian university was offered at UNB in 1854, and in 1908 a course in forestry was introduced.

A commission on post-secondary education in the province was established in 1967, primarily to study the financial needs of the provincial universities and to advise the government with regard to the granting of financial assistance for university purposes.

Facilities and services

The university has two campuses: one in the capital city, Fredericton (population, 25,000) and a second campus in Saint John (population, 95,000). There are over 40 buildings on the campus, including those for the New Brunswick Teachers' College (English-speaking division), Saint Thomas University, a Roman Catholic co-educational university affiliated with UNB, the Maritime headquarters of the federal Department of Fisheries and Forestry, and the headquarters building of the New Brunswick Teachers Association.

*Ordinary member, AUCC.

The campus in Fredericton has three major libraries (general, law, engineering), as well as individual departmental libraries (over 325,000 volumes in all). The Saint John campus consists presently of three buildings: one for arts, one for science, and a combined library-administration building. The parent campus has eight men's residences accommodating 800 men, and four women's residences providing accommodation for 500 women. The campus in Saint John does not provide residence accommodation for students.

Calendars and brochures

The following calendars and/or brochures are published annually: general university calendar, school of graduate studies calendar, faculty of law calendar, summer session calendar, freshman bulletin, faculty publications and research resources summary.

Courses and degrees

Arts
(Faculty of arts)

Bachelor of arts (BA).
(a) General course, four years from junior matriculation. A student must choose a major in one or two subjects in upper years. Twenty credits required. (b) Honors course, four years from junior matriculation. Honors available in anthropology, biology, chemistry, economics, English, French, geology, German, Greek, history, Latin, mathematics, philosophy, physics, political science, psychology, sociology, Spanish, and combinations of most of these.

(School of graduate studies)

Master of arts (MA).
Two academic years from bachelor's degree. Residence requirement may be shortened on recommendation of department or departments concerned. Available in classics, economics, English, French, German, history, mathematics, philosophy, political science, psychology and sociology.

Doctor of philosophy (PhD).
At least three years from bachelor's degree or two years from master's degree. Presently available in English, history, and mathematics.

Business administration
(Faculty of arts)

Bachelor of business administration (BBA).
Twenty-three credits required, eight in business, two in mathematics: electives available in arts, science and business administration.

Certificate in business administration - management certificates.
A five-credit program, through extension, including three business and one economics credit.

Education
(Faculty of education)

Bachelor of physical education (BPE).
Four years from junior matriculation. Twenty-three credits required, eleven in arts and science, the remainder professional. Gymnasia, swimming pools, ice-rink and outdoor facilities for activity training are good.

Bachelor of teaching (BT).
Four programs available: a) elementary; b) industrial; c) home economics; d) commercial. All programs largely restricted to graduates from either New Brunswick Teachers' College or New Brunswick Institute of Technology.

Bachelor of education (BEd).
One year following recognized bachelor's degree. Practice teaching is required in part of the program, except for those who already hold a teacher's license. Core program with electives.

(School of graduate studies)

Master of education (MEd).
Minimum of one year from bachelor of education degree. A report and oral examination required. Program may be entirely in education, or with arts or science electives, or half in education and half in an academic discipline.

Engineering
(Faculty of engineering)

Bachelor of science in engineering (BScE).
Five years from junior matriculation, four years from senior matriculation. Specialization offered in chemical, civil, electrical, mechanical and surveying

engineering. First three years of mining engineering also offered.

Bachelor of science in forest engineering (BScFE).
A five-year program offered jointly by the faculties of engineering and forestry. It includes basic arts and science courses, as well as forestry and engineering subjects.

Diploma in surveying engineering.
A one- or two-year program intended primarily for overseas students. Courses selected are based on the individual student's background and needs.

(School of graduate studies)

Master of engineering (MEng).
At least three academic terms from bachelor of science in engineering. Available in chemical, civil, mechanical, and surveying engineering.

Master of science in engineering (MScE).
At least one year from bachelor of science in engineering. Available in chemical, civil, electrical, mechanical and surveying engineering.

Master of science in computer science (MScCS).
At least one year from previous degree.

Doctor of philosophy (PhD).
At least three years from a bachelor's degree. Presently available in chemical, electrical, and surveying.

Forestry
(Faculty of forestry)

Bachelor of science in forestry (BScF).
Five years from junior matriculation, four years from senior matriculation. Specialization in forest entomology, forest engineering, forest products, silviculture, forest pathology, and forest management.

(School of graduate studies)

Master of forestry (MF).
A minimum of one year after bachelor of science in forestry.

Master of science in forestry (MScF).
A minimum of one year after bachelor of science in forestry.

Law
(Faculty of law)

Bachelor of laws (LLB).
Three years from bachelor's degree in arts, business administration, commerce or science. Students in arts or business administration at the university may be admitted at the conclusion of the penultimate year of a first-degree course. Students in arts at St. Thomas University may be admitted to the first year in law.

Nursing
(Faculty of nursing)

Bachelor of nursing (BN).
Four years from junior matriculation. Number of students restricted. Program includes arts, science required courses and electives as well as theory and practice of nursing. Clinical work is a very important part of the training.

Degree program for registered nurses (BN).
A three-year generalized nursing program for registered nurses who meet university entrance requirements. Fourteen arts and science courses and four nursing courses are minimum. Field work may be required. Two years may be taken through extension. The final year must be on campus.

Science
(Faculty of science)

Bachelor of science (BSc).
Four years from junior matriculation, three years from senior matriculation. Honors courses available in biology, chemistry, geology, mathematics, physics, and general science.

(School of graduate studies)

Master of science (MSc).
At least two years from bachelor's degree in arts or in science. Available in biochemistry, biology, botany, chemistry, geology, mathematics, physics, physiology, and zoology.

Doctor of philosophy (PhD).
At least three years from bachelor of science. Presently available in biology, chemistry, geology, mathematics, microbiology, and physics.

Combined courses

Combined courses in arts and law enable
students to obtain two degrees in less time
than if the two courses were taken separately.

Extension programs

For university credit:

Undergraduate classes offered during the
winter session at various centres in arts,
science, business administration, and
education.

Summer session:
Courses are offered for undergraduates
proceeding to a degree and for teachers who
may wish to improve their professional
qualifications by working towards graduate
degrees and diplomas in education.

Extension programs:
Courses are offered in arts, science, education
and business for credit in Saint John,
Fredericton and a number of other centres.
Occasionally, these are offered in co-operation
with other universities.

For no university credit:

In addition to management certificate
courses, a few courses are offered on a non-
credit basis, particularly in art. The university
is presently reviewing its extension program.

Admission requirements

For a general statement regarding admission
to university study, see article *Admission to
university in Canada.*

For information regarding admission to
undergraduate study, consult *Requirements
for admission to Canadian colleges and
universities* available from Service for
Admission to College and University, 151
Slater St., Ottawa, Ont., K1P 5N1, $1.50
prepaid.

Academic year

Winter session: early September to end of
April.

Summer session: early July to mid-August.

Grading system

Generally in percentage marks. 1st division —
75% and above; 2nd division — 65-74%; 3rd
division — 50-64%; below 50% — fail.

In the faculties of law, engineering and
forestry, a student must maintain a weighted
average of 55%. Marks over 35% may be
allowed as fail-credits.

In education, a student must maintain an
average of 55%.

Fees and costs

Tuition fees per year — full-time:
undergraduate — arts, business, engineering
(1st year), forestry, law, physical education
(1st year), science, $612; education, nursing,
physical education (2nd to 4th year),
teaching, $587; engineering (2nd to 5th
year), $642.

Miscellaneous compulsory fees per year:
undergraduates and graduates, $35.

Residence rates, board and room: single,
$925; double, $850; multiple, $800.

Financial awards and assistance

The university maintains a financial aid and
awards office which deals with awards,
financial aid and scholarships for both
graduate and undergraduate students. It is
also concerned with research grant funds,
scholarships, bursaries and university loans.

Research institutes

The Bio-Engineering Institute
deals with the interaction between man and
modern technology (man-machine systems),
and the development of electronic controls
for artificial limbs. Other work includes
analysis of muscle function, mathematical
modelling of human operators, development
of improved methods of fitting and aligning
artificial limbs, investigation of training
techniques for voluntary control of skeletal
muscles, and development of improved
electrodes for electro-physiological
monitoring.

Muskeg Research Institute.
The institute brings the knowledge and
experience of biologists, geologists, foresters
and engineers to bear on national and
international research and development
problems in connection with organic terrain,
commonly called muskeg.

Fire Science Centre.
The centre aims to promote interdisciplinary
studies on combustion and heat transfer
phenomena, with special emphasis on fires,
including natural and controlled forest fires.

Water Resources Development Centre.
This has been established to bring about a co-
operative program of water resources
research in the Atlantic provinces in co-
operation with government agencies.

Affiliated institutions

St. Thomas University.
Established in Chatham, N.B. in 1910, as St.
Thomas College. Received a university
charter in 1934 and was changed in name to
St. Thomas University in 1960. Moved to the
UNB campus in 1964. Offers the degrees of
bachelor of arts, bachelor of education and
bachelor of teaching. Co-educational Roman
Catholic institution.
President: Very Rev. Msgr. D.C. Duffie, BA,
BCL, JCD, LLD.

Maritime Forest Ranger School.

Deans of faculties

Arts
T.J. Condon, BA, MA, PhD

Education
R.J. Love, BA, MA, BPaed, DPaed

Engineering
L.G. Jaeger, MA, PhD

Forestry
J.W. Ker, BASc, MF, DFor, DSc

Graduate studies
R.J. Kavanagh, BSc, MASc, PhD, DIC

Law
W.F. Ryan, QC, BA, BCL, LLM, LLD

Nursing
M.G. McPhedran, BA, MA

Science
Mervyn Franklin, BSc, PhD

Directors of schools

Extension services
J.F. Morris, BA, MA

Summer school and extension
R.J. Love, BA, MA, BPaed, DPaed

Department heads

Anthropology and sociology
D.R. Pullman, BEd, MA, PhD

Biology
B.G. Cumming, BSc, PhD

Business administration
P.T. Kehoe, BComm, MBA, LLB

Chemical engineering
J.J.C. Picot, BE, MSc, PhD

Chemistry
Zdenek Valenta, DiplIngChem, MSc, PhD

Civil engineering
I.M. Beattie, BSc, MS

Classics and ancient history
L.C. Smith, PhD

Computer science
W.D. Wasson, BSc, SM

Economics
P.F.M. McLoughlin, BA, PhD

Electrical engineering
R.E. Burridge, BSc, MS, PhD

English
D.R. Galloway, MC, MA

Geology
N. Rast, BA, PhD

German and Russian
Abram Friesen, Drphil

History
J.K. Chapman, BA, MA, PhD

Mathematics
B.O.J. Tupper, BSc, PhD

Mechanical engineering
E.E. Wheatley, BSc, MSc

Philosophy
N.W. MacGill (acting), MA

Physical education
G.B. Thompson (acting), BPE, MSc

Physics
M.A. Edwards (acting), BSc, MSc, PhD

Political science
S.I. Pobihushchy, BA

Psychology
J.A. Easterbrook, BA, MA, PhD

Romance languages
A.J. Shaw, BA, MA

Surveying engineering
A.C. Hamilton, BASc, MASc

Notre Dame University of Nelson*

Nelson, British Columbia

Telephone: 604-352-2241
Direct general correspondence to the registrar

Total full-time student enrolment 646; see
also separate section *Statistics on Canadian
universities and colleges*

Executive and administrative officers

Chancellor
Hugh Keenleyside, MA, PhD, DSc, LLD,
FRHistS, FRGS

President
C.L. Kaller, BEd, MA, PhD

Executive vice-president
Reverend Bede MacEachen, SA, STL, MA,
JCL

Registrar
E.D. Baravalle, BSc

Dean of students
D.R. Forbes, BA, PhD

Librarian
R. Welwood, BA, BLS

Director of information
To be appointed

Background

Notre Dame College was founded in 1951 by
the Most Reverend Martin Johnson, Bishop
of Nelson. The college was affiliated first in
1951, as a junior college, to Gonzaga
University of Spokane, Washington; and
then in 1961 to Saint Francis Xavier
University of Antigonish, Nova Scotia. The
latter arrangement ended in 1963 when an
act of the British Columbia legislature raised
Notre Dame College to the status of a
chartered university, with full power to grant
all degrees, changing the name to Notre
Dame University of Nelson. The first degrees
were conferred in 1964.

Originally operated by the Roman Catholic
diocese of Nelson, the university now
functions under the direction of a board of
governors and a board of advisors. The
board of governors is the main policy-making
body in the structure of the university, while
the function of the board of advisors is to
advise the board of governors on all matters
relating to business and financial affairs, and
development of the university. There is, in
addition, the academic committee which
receives, considers, and makes
recommendations with respect to all
academic matters of the university. The
academic committee deals more directly with
the day-to-day operation of the university
than does the board of governors.

Facilities and services

The campus is located on the outskirts of the
city of Nelson and covers an area of
approximately 42 acres, with present
buildings covering only 19 acres of the total
site. In addition to the original building
erected in 1954, the university has added a
three-storey classroom and administration
building, a chapel, a women's residence
accommodating 180 students, and three
men's residences accommodating 550
students. There is also a building consisting
of the student cafeteria, gymnasium, athletic
offices, student union offices, and student
lounge. The university library is presently
located in a complex of four pre-fabricated
buildings, and contains approximately 45,000
volumes. A student placement service is
provided on campus by Canada Manpower.

*Provisional member, AUCC.

Calendars and brochures

Calendars and summer school brochures available at registrar's office.

Courses and degrees

Bachelor of arts (BA).
(a) General course, four years from junior matriculation. (b) Major course, four years from junior matriculation. Available in economics, English, French, history, mathematics, philosophy, psychology, and sociology.

Bachelor of education (BEd).
Elementary, four years from junior matriculation.

Bachelor of science (BSc).
(a) General course, four years from junior matriculation. (b) Major course, four years from junior matriculation. Available in botany, chemistry, mathematics, physics, and zoology.

Bachelor of science (medical records)
[BSc(MR)].
Four years from junior matriculation.

Bachelor of fine arts (BFA).
Four years from junior matriculation.

Bachelor of secretarial arts (BSA).
Four years from junior matriculation.

Associate degree in medical or general
secretaryship.
Two years from junior matriculation.

Extension programs

For university credit:

Notre Dame University offers evening courses and summer session courses for credit in any degree program. These courses change from year to year and are usually offered on the basis of demand by the students. The university does not offer a full bachelor's degree program by correspondence, evening courses, or summer sessions.

For no university credit:

The extension department of the university sponsors a liberal arts home study program for interested parties. In addition, there are day and evening classes offered for which no credit is given. From time to time, workshop sessions are sponsored for a special segment of the community which desires such assistance. An extensive offering in fine arts is offered each summer.

Admission requirements

For a general statement regarding admission to university study, see article *Admission to university in Canada.*

For information regarding admission to undergraduate study, consult *Requirements for admission to Canadian colleges and universities* available from Service for Admission to College and University, 151 Slater St., Ottawa, Ont., K1P 5N1, $1.50 prepaid.

Academic year

The academic year begins approximately September 7 for new students with classes beginning September 14. The academic year closes with graduation on approximately May 4.

Summer session.
Seven weeks starting the first week of July.

Grading system

86-100%, excellent, first-class standing; 75-85%, definitely above average, second-class standing; 60-74%, average, pass standing; below 60%, failing; 50-60%, supplemental permissible; below 50%, no supplemental.

Fees and costs

(a) Full-time students' tuition, $460; (b) part-time students' tuition, $90; (c) foreign students' tuition, $660; application fee, $35.

Room and board, $93.75 per month.

Financial awards and assistance

B.C. government scholarships and bursaries listed in the calendar; write registrar's office.

Dean of faculty

Studies
D.V. George, BSc, PhD

Director of school

Medical records
Ula Harris (Miss), MFA, RRL

Department heads

Education
M. Hassemer (Miss), BS, MA, PhD

Fine arts
To be appointed

History and social science
J.M. MacAulay, BA, BEd, MA

Literature and language
Marvin Singleton, BA, MA, PhD, JD

Natural sciences and mathematics
D.S. Sahri, MSc, PhD

Philosophy
M.L. Brown, MA

Professional studies
Sr. Mary Ellen, BComm, MBA

Religious studies
Reverend Bede MacEachen, STB
STL, MA, JCB, JCL

Nova Scotia Agricultural College*

Truro, Nova Scotia

Telephone: 902-895-1571
Direct general correspondence to the registrar

Total full-time student enrolment 194; see also separate section *Statistics on Canadian universities and colleges*

Executive and administrative officers

Principal
W.A. Jenkins, DrPA

Vice-principal
J.E. Shuh, MSA

Registrar
Parker Cox, MA

Librarian
B.S. Sodhi, MA, DipLSc

Background

Nova Scotia Agricultural College was established in 1905 under the terms of an act of the legislative assembly of the province passed in 1899. The college took over the work of the school of agriculture, which had been set up in 1885, and the school of horticulture, which had its origin in 1893. Teaching at the college began in 1905 and the first diplomas were awarded in 1906.

Nova Scotia Agricultural College is a provincial institution. It is non-denominational and co-educational. It operates under the direction of the Nova Scotia Department of Agriculture and Marketing.

Facilities and services

The college is situated in Bible Hill, a suburb of Truro, with a site of 350 acres of which about 25 acres compose the main campus. There are eight teaching buildings, farm buildings and three residences accommodating 510 men. The library contains 2,500 volumes.

Student services include a medical service (nurse and doctor only), informal guidance and counselling, a cafeteria in residence, an employment service, and a canteen service. Headquarters for the Department of Agriculture and Marketing extension services.

Calendars and brochures

Annual undergraduate calendar.

Courses and degrees

Agriculture

Diploma.
Two years from senior matriculation and three years from junior matriculation. Graduates usually proceed for further studies to Macdonald College, the University of Guelph, the University of Maine or the Nova Scotia Technical College.

Extension services and courses below university level

For no university credit:

Technician course.
Diploma awarded to students taking a two-year technician course and completing appropriate in-service training.

*Ordinary member, AUCC.

Technology course.
Diploma awarded to students taking a third year after completing technician course.

Admission requirements

For a general statement regarding admission to university study, see article *Admission to university in Canada.*

For information regarding admission to undergraduate study, consult *Requirements for admission to Canadian colleges and universities* available from Service for Admission to College and University, 151 Slater St., Ottawa, Ont., K1P 5N1, $1.50 prepaid.

Academic year

Mid-September to early May.

Grading system

Actual marks obtained appear on transcripts. High honors: 80-100%; honors: 75-79%. Pass mark - degree course: 50%; technician course: 50%.

Fees and costs

Full-time tuition fees per year: (a) university course, $400; (b) technician course, no tuition, and technology course, no tuition for students from the Atlantic provinces. Miscellaneous fees: $39-$44.

Room and board in residence: $690 per year.

Financial awards and assistance

Scholarships based on academic achievement and varying from half tuition to full tuition plus $200 are available from several sources to students registered in any year of the degree course. Full tuition is provided for technician course students from the Atlantic provinces by the province of residence.

Dean

Technical and vocational training
A.D. Ells, MA

Department heads

Agricultural engineering
D.E. Clark, BSA, MSA

Agronomy
J.S. Bubar, BSc(Agr), MSc, PhD

Animal science
L.M. Cock, BSc(Agr), MSc, PhD

Biology
A.E. Roland, BA, MA, PhD

Chemistry
W.M. Langille, BSc, MSc

Economics and business management
W.A. Jenkins, BSc(Agr), MSc, DrPA

English and social sciences
Parker Cox, BA, MA

Horticulture
To be appointed

Mathematics and physics
I.M. Fraser, BSc, MA

Physical education
K.S. Marchant, BPEd

Nova Scotia College of Art and Design*

6152 Coburg Road, Halifax, Nova Scotia

Telephone: 902-429-1600
Direct general correspondence to the college

Total full-time student enrolment 388; see also separate section *Statistics on Canadian universities and colleges*

Executive and administrative officers

President
G.N. Kennedy, AOCA, BFA, MFA

Vice-president for development and chairman, design division
Richard Wright, BA

Dean
James Davies, BA, MA, PhD

Business manager
A.J. MacDonald

Registrar
Susan Giesler

*Provisional member, AUCC.

Background

The Nova Scotia College of Art and Design is a co-educational independent institution of higher education chartered by act of the provincial legislature. It was established as the Victoria School of Art and Design, 1887; renamed the Nova Scotia College of Art, 1925; renamed the Nova Scotia College of Art and Design, 1969. The college receives its principal financial support from the province of Nova Scotia. Government of the college is vested in a board of governors of 19 members, including government appointees, students, faculty, alumni, and elected members.

Four-year programs of study lead to the bachelor's degree in fine art or design. The college first awarded the bachelor's degree in 1970. The diploma in fine art is a four-year program and the diploma in graphic design requires three years. A student may also include in the degree program, courses which will qualify him to receive the Nova Scotia Teacher's Certificate as an art specialist.

Facilities and services

The main building of the college is located at 6152 Coburg Road, immediately adjacent to Dalhousie University. The college also occupies several adjacent houses and large painting and weaving studios about a mile away from the main building.

The principal studio areas open to students in fine art include ceramics, jewellery, painting, photography, printmaking, projects, sculpture, and weaving. The design program offers specialization in environmental design and communication design, including design of printed materials and audio-visual communication. Students at the college may arrange to take courses at Dalhousie University and at other universities in the city.

The college library, a specialized collection in art and design, contains about 9,000 volumes. Libraries of the other universities in the city are also available to students of the college.

The Anna Leonowens Gallery, named for one of the founders of the college, the famous teacher of the children of the King of Siam, presents a series of exhibitions that are open to the public throughout the year.

The college does not provide residential accommodations.

Calendars and brochures

Printed material about the college may be obtained by addressing enquiries to the admissions secretary.

Courses and degrees

Design

The *bachelor of design degree (BDes)* is granted in environmental design or in communication design. The degree requires a four-year program of study. Either program allows the student a considerable range of choice of areas in which to specialize. The student in communication design may study graphic design, the design of film or other audio-visual communications, or the design of mixed-media communications. Students in environmental design may be concerned with problems of industrial design, interior design, or the design of exterior spaces, systems and relationships.

The *diploma in graphic design* [*Associate of the Nova Scotia College of Art and Design (ANSCAD)*] is a three-year program of study with specialization in graphic design.

Fine art

The *bachelor of fine arts degree (BFA),* offered in fine art and in fine art and education requires a four-year program of study. Three courses, normally taken in the first year, are specifically required for the degree of fine art. The remaining courses are selected by the student from the various courses of study available at the college, and from courses available at other universities in the city. The degree program in fine art and education requires five additional courses, normally taken during the last five semesters of the student's program of study. Completion of this program qualifies the student to receive the Nova Scotia Teacher's Certificate as an art specialist.

The *bachelor of arts degree in art education* is a four-year program designed principally for students transferring to the college from other institutions of higher education. It also qualifies the student for the teacher's certificate.

The *diploma in fine art* [*Associate of the Nova Scotia College of Art and Design (ANSCAD)*] requires four years of study, almost entirely in studio courses.

Special programs

Summer trimester:
The college offers a summer trimester of 14 weeks from May until August. Students who do not desire to enrol in the entire trimester may select courses lasting for one-quarter or one-half of the term, beginning in May, June, early July, or late July.

Off-campus study:
A student may receive credit for a program of study undertaken while travelling or at a place away from the college which may offer particular advantages for the work which he is pursuing. A student proposing an off-campus program of study for credit will arrange a plan with individual faculty members. Each proposal for such study is subject to approval of the appropriate faculty body.

Lithography workshop:
The lithography workshop of the college provides an opportunity for advanced students of lithography to work with the master printmaker of the college, and with artists who visit the college for the purpose of having their work printed in the workshop.

Extension programs

Courses in various areas of art and design are offered, without credit, for adults and children in the Halifax area. The college does not offer credit courses under the extension program, but persons not regularly enroled in the college may seek admission to regular classes of the college as special students, for either part-time or full-time study.

Admission requirements

For a general statement regarding admission to university study, see article *Admission to university in Canada*.

For information regarding admission to undergraduate study, consult *Requirements for admission to Canadian colleges and universities* available from Service for Admission to College and University, 151 Slater St., Ottawa, Ont., K1P 5N1, $1.50 prepaid.

Academic year

The college year includes three terms: September to December; January to April; May to August. Students may be admitted beginning with any term.

Grading system

The college records as *Credit* those courses which are satisfactorily completed. Courses which are not satisfactorily completed receive no credit and are not entered on the student's permanent record.

Fees and costs

Tuition, full-time enrolment (11 to 20 credits) — $287.50 per semester, $575 per year. Tuition fee, part-time students, per credit — $27 per semester. Registration fee (payable 1st semester of registration of each academic year) — Nova Scotia resident, $10 per year; out-of-province resident, $25 per year. Studio fee, full-time student — $27 per semester, $54 per year. Studio fee, 1 to 9 credits, per credit — $3 per semester. Student council fee — $10 per semester, $20 per year.

Other expenses are estimated as follows: room and board, out-of-town students — $450 per semester, $900 per year; class supplies — $100 per semester, $200 per year; personal expenses — $150 per semester, $300 per year.

Financial awards and assistance

Students of the college are granted aid by the college toward their educational expenses according to their financial needs, and the availability of college funds, subject to the following conditions:

1. The student requesting aid must use the resources of the Canada Student Loans Plan and any applicable provincial bursary plan, to the extent that he is eligible. Students who are not from Canada may also be considered for financial aid under a modified policy and within the limitations of available funds.

2. The college assesses a student's need for assistance according to the determination used by the Canada Student Loans Plan.

3. A reasonable portion of the aid will be offered as remuneration for employment with the college and the remainder will be given as remission of fees.

Division chairmen

Design
Richard Wright, BA

Interdisciplinary
David Sewell, BFA, MA

Media and workshops
Guenter Karkutt

Nova Scotia Technical College *

P.O. Box 1000, Halifax, Nova Scotia

Telephone: 902-429-8300
Direct general correspondence to the registrar

Total full-time student enrolment 567; see also separate section *Statistics on Canadian universities and colleges*

Executive and administrative officers

Chancellor
C.H. Simpson, BSc, LLD, FASCE

President
A.E. Steeves (acting), BSc, MSc

Registrar
V.F. O'Connor, CD, BSc

Director, extension
A.E. Creelman, BEng, MASc

Alumni secretary
C.H. Miller, BEng, MASc, PhD

Bursar
C.R. Lloyd

Dean of students
A.E. Steeves, BSc, MSc

Librarian
M.R. Hussain, MA, MSLS

Placement officer
P.C. Hamilton, BSc

Public relations officer
Mary Barker (Miss)

Background

The Nova Scotia Technical College was authorized by an act of the provincial legislature in 1907. Teaching began in 1909 and the first degrees were awarded in 1910. In 1947 the act of 1907 was repealed and replaced by two new acts which separated engineering education and secondary technical education and provided for the establishment of graduate studies. The college now confines its activities to work at the university level.

The college is non-denominational and co-educational. It is governed by a board of governors, the controlling body in all matters pertaining to the college, and a senate and faculty councils which are responsible for academic policy.

Facilities and services

The college is located in the heart of the city of Halifax (1969 population 123,000; with environs, 249,500), the provincial capital, on a site of 13 acres. There are 11 buildings containing classrooms, laboratories, a computer centre, research facilities, the administration, a gymnasium, a common room, a library (36,000 volumes), and a men's residence, the M.M. O'Brien hall for 132 students.

Calendars and brochures

Calendar of the college, annual. Bulletin of graduate studies, annual. Obtainable from the office of the registrar.

Courses and degrees

Architecture
(Faculty of the school of architecture)

Bachelor of architecture (BArch).
Four years after transfer from university with

*Ordinary member, AUCC.

appropriate credits (see admission requirements). This is a co-operative program.

(Faculty of graduate studies)

Master of architecture (MArch).
At least one year from BArch.

Engineering
(Faculty of engineering)

Bachelor of engineering (BEng).
Two years after transfer with diploma from Acadia, Dalhousie, Mount Allison, Prince Edward Island, St. Francis Xavier, or Saint Mary's universities. Specialization offered in agricultural (in co-operation with the Nova Scotia Agricultural College only), chemical, civil, electrical, industrial, mechanical, metallurgical, and mining engineering.

(Faculty of graduate studies)

Graduate programs offered in all fields of engineering listed for BEng, except agricultural.

Master of engineering (MEng).
At least one year from bachelor's degree in engineering.

Doctor of philosophy (PhD).
At least two years from the master's degree in engineering, or three years from the bachelor's degree in engineering.

Extension programs

For no university credit:

The department of extension offers refresher, general, and specialist courses in the evenings for architects and engineers. Special courses for specific groups or industries can be arranged. These can be concentrated or extended courses and given at the college or on industry premises.

Admission requirements

For a general statement regarding admission to university study, see article *Admission to university in Canada.*

For information regarding admission to undergraduate study, consult *Requirements for admission to Canadian colleges and universities* available from Service for Admission to College and University, 151 Slater St., Ottawa, Ont., K1P 5N1, $1.50 prepaid.

Architecture, undergraduate.
A student must present a transcript showing that he has successfully completed the first two years in any course of study at any university, one mathematics course is desirable or an entrance examination may be required, as well as a letter of recommendation from the university, before he will be admitted into the Co-op One year of the architectural program. Students from other institutions recognized by the faculty of the school of architecture may be accepted into the Co-op One year of architecture.

Engineering, undergraduate.
A student must have a transcript forwarded from one of the following universities, showing the successful completion of the uniform engineering course and award of certificate, for transfer to the junior year of engineering: Acadia, Dalhousie, Mount Allison, Prince Edward Island, St. Francis Xavier, and Saint Mary's. Students from other universities wishing to transfer to the college must have a transcript forwarded for assessment of equivalency of credits and a letter of recommendation from the dean of their previous university.

For agricultural engineering, the student must have a transcript forwarded from the Nova Scotia Agricultural College showing successful completion of the course given.

Postgraduate.
A student must have a first degree with high standing in the appropriate studies and supply the documentation required by the application forms.

Academic year

Architecture, undergraduate – September to August for Co-op One, January to December for Co-op Two, both with three terms, September to May for Co-op Three with two terms.

Engineering, undergraduate – September to May with two terms.

Graduate studies — twelve months with normal commencement in September.

industrial research for public and private industry in the Atlantic provinces.

Grading system

Standing is graded in each subject as follows: A — excellent (80-100%); B — good (70-79%); C — acceptable (60-69%); D — conditional (50-59%); E — failure (30-49%); F — complete failure (0-29%).

Deans of faculties

Engineering
O. Cochkanoff (acting), BASc, MASc, PhD

Graduate studies
M.R. Foran, BSc, MSc, PhD

Fees and costs

Tuition fees per year — full-time: (a) undergraduate, $325 per term; (b) graduate, $650 minimum.

Miscellaneous compulsory fees: undergraduate engineering, $35; undergraduate architecture, $35; graduate, $50.

Residence rates, board and room, $450 in double, $487.50 in single, per term.

Directors of schools

Architecture
P. Manning, AADipl, PhD

Atlantic Industrial Research Institute
T.J. Gray, BSc, PhD

Department heads

Applied mathematics
J.H. Ahrens, DAE, DrNatSc

Bio-resources engineering
W. Carson, BSc, MSc, PhD

Chemical engineering
G.D. MacKay, BEng, MEng, PhD

Civil engineering
G.G. Meyerhof, BSc, MSc, PhD, DSc, FRSC

Electrical engineering
O.K. Gashus, BSc, PhD

Industrial engineering
B. Worrall, BSc, PhD

Mechanical engineering
O. Cochkanoff, BASc, MASc, PhD

Mining and metallurgical engineering
K.V. Gow, BASc, MSc, PhD

Financial awards and assistance

Canada student loans plan available to Canadian citizens, and to landed immigrants of one-year residence who intend to remain in Canada after their graduation. For residents of Quebec, the Quebec student assistance scheme is applicable.
Undergraduate: several industrial scholarships to the amount of tuition fees, or more, may be applied for after registration. Graduate: most major fellowships in the appropriate fields are tenable at the college; grants in aid of research to professors from varied sources are available for support of students; a limited number of teaching assistantships are available for awarding after registration.

Research institute

The Atlantic Industrial Research Institute is an adjunct to the college with its aims to encourage, co-ordinate, direct, and administer programs and contracts of engineering and

Ontario Institute for Studies in Education*

252 Bloor Street West, Toronto 5, Ontario

Telephone: 416-923-6641
Inquiries concerning graduate studies in education should be directed to the co-ordinator of graduate studies, and general inquiries to the office of the director

Total full-time student enrolment 377; see also separate section *Statistics on Canadian universities and colleges*

Executive and administrative officers

Chairman, board of governors
H. Pullen, BA, BPaed, EdD, FCIS, FCCT

Director
R.W.B. Jackson, BA, PhD, LLD, FRSS, FCP

Assistant director
J.H.M. Andrews, MA, PhD

Co-ordinator of graduate studies
G.E. Flower, MA, EdD, FCCT

Supervisor, computing services group
Douglas Dinniwell, MA

Head, editorial
John Main, BEd

Director, educational clinic
To be appointed

Chief librarian
Shirley Wigmore, MLS

Background

The Ontario Institute for Studies in Education was established in July 1965, by an act of the Ontario legislature, and is under the management and control of an independent board of governors, which reports to the minister of education. It combines in one organization the former departments of educational research and graduate studies of the University of Toronto's Ontario College of Education and the Ontario Curriculum Institute.

The objects of the institute are to study matters and problems relating to or affecting education, to disseminate the results of educational studies and assist in their implementation, and to establish and conduct courses leading to certificates of standing and graduate courses in education. Although it was chartered as a college with the right to grant degrees, the institute has entered into an agreement of affiliation with the University of Toronto, so that its graduates receive University of Toronto degrees.

The institute is organized internally into 10 academic departments, each concerned with conducting research in a particular field of education and with the development of better educational methods and materials. The departments include: adult education, applied psychology, computer applications, curriculum, educational administration, educational planning, history and philosophy of education, measurement and evaluation, sociology in education, and special education. Specialized programs of graduate study are offered in each of these departments, and are co-ordinated by the office of the co-ordinator of graduate studies. The facilities of the institute enable advanced graduate students to be involved directly in research or development programs in their particular field of scholarly interest. A degree program is offered in the field of higher education.

Facilities and services

The institute is housed in a new, 12-storey building on Bloor Street West near St. George Street, in the centre of Toronto; (the population of metropolitan Toronto is just

*Ordinary member, AUCC.

over 2 million). The campus of the University of Toronto is within easy walking distance, and the resources and services of its library are available to graduate students at OISE. The institute's own library houses a large collection specializing in education, with growing strength in related social sciences. Extensive reference materials and some 2,200 serial titles are available.

Special display centres for audio-visual materials and curriculum resources are being developed, including equipment for viewing and listening. Staff and students of OISE have access to six computers via teletype terminals. A collection of statistical programs is available for data analysis. Programmers are available for consultation, and will write programs for computer users at standard OISE rates. The institute also has a PDP-9 computer and a time-shared PDP-8. The institute has an editorial division which provides editorial assistance to staff and students.

Residence accommodation can be obtained at the University of Toronto, but the number of rooms available for graduate students is rather limited. The university's housing service will assist students to find off-campus accommodation.

Calendars and brochures

OISE bulletin, graduate degrees in education, University of Toronto. Published every February, the bulletin describes admission requirements and programs of study for the forthcoming academic year. Available from the institute's office of graduate studies.

Ontario Institute for Studies in Education. This booklet gives brief descriptions of a few typical research and development projects up to March 1971 and provides background and purposes of OISE. Available from the office of the director.

Annual reports. Complete accounts of each year's activities, including publications, are published annually.

Courses and degrees

Education

Master of education (MEd).
One regular academic session and one summer if pursued on a full-time basis. This degree can be taken on a part-time basis but must be completed within six years from first enrolment as an MEd candidate. Admission is based on either a four-year or a three-year BA, or equivalent, with second-class standing or better in the final year, teacher certification and one year of teaching experience.

Master of arts (MA).
One academic year plus a thesis from a four-year BA or equivalent, two years from a three-year BA or equivalent, with second-class standing or better in the final year. One-third of a year advanced standing will be granted in a two-year program for teacher certification. The time limit for completion of the degree is five years from commencement of program at the four-year BA level or equivalent. A year of residence is required for this degree.

Master of philosophy (PhilM).
One year of residence is required beyond an MA in the department of educational theory at the University of Toronto. One year and one summer are required for students with a masters degree in the same field of specialization but from other academic institutions. Two years of residence are required from a four-year BA in a relevant discipline. The degree must be completed within one year after the residence requirements have been fulfilled.

Doctor of philosophy (PhD).
At least two years of residence are required beyond the MA if continuing in a relevant area of specialization. The degree must be completed within six years of the date of PhD first enrolment after a relevant MA.

Extension programs

For no university credit:

During the regular academic session a considerable number of courses are scheduled after hours for part-time students. The summer session offers courses primarily for MEd programs, although under certain

circumstances MA and PhD students may also take summer courses for degree credit.

Admission requirements

For a general statement regarding admission to university study, see article *Admission to university in Canada.*

For information regarding admission to undergraduate study, consult *Requirements for admission to Canadian colleges and universities* available from Service for Admission to College and University, 151 Slater St., Ottawa, Ont., K1P 5N1, $1.50 prepaid.

A minimum of second-class standing in the final year of an appropriate undergraduate degree is required for admission to graduate programs in educational theory. For detailed requirements for various degree programs, see pages 21 to 28 of the OISE bulletin.

Academic year

Winter session: mid-September to end of April.

Summer session: early July to mid-August, with required pre-session reading and post-session papers.

Grading system

Seven-point grading system as follows: A + — 9, A — 8, A- — 7, B + — 6, B — 5, B- — 4 and F — failure.

Fees and costs

Tuition fees per year; full-time $485. Miscellaneous compulsory fees per year: men — $40; women — $20.

Financial awards and assistance

There are two types of awards available for full-time students: fellowships, with no work requirements; ranging assistantships, with a work requirement carrying a maximum value of $1,800. Each $500 of assistantship requires the equivalent of two and one-half hours per week over 40 weeks. Students may be awarded either a fellowship or an assistantship, or a combination of both.

Research institute

OISE

is itself a research institute. In addition to their teaching duties, staff members in its 10 academic departments carry out programs of research and development in education on a large scale. Strong emphasis is placed on interdisciplinary projects; as a result, the research and development program can be described under headings other than those provided by the department titles. In a recent reclassification of the institute's projects, certain priority areas for research and development were identified, taking account of OISE capability in relation to educational need: (1) innovative approaches to the learning situation; (2) problem solving and learning in children; (3) methods of educational policy decision-making and implementation; (4) development of Canadian educational materials and encouragement of bilingualism in students; (5) effective implementation of educational change; (6) development of special programs and curricula; (7) development of departmental programs to maximize particular areas of expertise; (8) emphasis on interdisciplinary approaches to research and development; (9) international studies in education.

Co-ordinators

Field development
K.F. Prueter, BA, BPaed, EdD

Graduate studies
G.E. Flower, MA, EdD, FCCT

Research and development studies
David Brison, EdD

Department chairmen

Adult education
Alan Thomas, PhD

Applied psychology
John Weiser, EdD

Computer applications
Leslie McLean, PhD

Curriculum
Ralph Garry, PhD

Educational administration
Robin Farquhar, PhD

Educational planning
Vincent D'Oyley, EdD

History and philosophy of education
Trevor Wigney

Measurement and evaluation
To be appointed

Sociology in education
Jan Loubser, PhD

Special education
Harry Silverman, PhD

Université d'Ottawa*

University of Ottawa*

Ottawa (Ontario), K1N 6N5

Ottawa, Ontario, K1N 6N5

Téléphone: 613-231-3311
Prière d'adresser la correspondance d'ordre général au registraire

Total des inscriptions des étudiants à plein temps 8,243; voir aussi la section distincte, intitulée *Statistiques sur les universités et collèges du Canada*

Telephone: 613-231-3311
Direct general correspondence to the registrar

Total full-time student enrolment 8,243; see also separate section *Statistics on Canadian universities and colleges*

Executive and administrative officers

Direction et personnel administratif

Grand chancelier
L'honorable Madame Georges-P. Vanier, CP, CC, DCL, DScSoc, LLD

Recteur et vice-chancelier
Roger Guindon, omi, BA, LPh, DTh, LLD

Vice-recteur à l'enseignement et à la recherche
Maurice Chagnon, LPh, MA, PhD

Vice-recteur (affaires administratives)
Allan Gillmore, BA

Vice-recteur adjoint (planification et services scolaires)
Jean-Marie Joly, PhD

Vice-recteur adjoint (affaires administratives)
Jack McCarthy, CA, ACIS

Vice-recteur adjoint (services aux étudiants)
Trefflé Lacombe

Secrétaire
Roland Trudeau, omi, BA, LPh, MBA

Registraire
Georges-L. Amyot, BA

Chancellor
The Honorable Madame Georges-P. Vanier, PC, CC, DCL, DScSoc, LLD

Rector and vice-chancellor
Roger Guindon, omi, BA, LPh, DTh, LLD

Vice-rector (academic)
Maurice Chagnon, LPh, MA, PhD

Vice-rector (administration)
Allan Gillmore, BA

Assistant vice-rector (academic planning and services)
Jean-Marie Joly, PhD

Assistant vice-rector (administration)
Jack McCarthy, CA, ACIS

Assistant vice-rector (student services)
Trefflé Lacombe

Secretary
Roland Trudeau, omi, BA, LPh, MBA

Registrar
Georges-L. Amyot, BA

Administrator of campus libraries
Paul-Emile Drouin, omi, LPh, LTh, MA, MLS

*Membre ordinaire de l'AUCC.

*Ordinary member, AUCC.

Administrateur des bibliothèques de
l'université
Paul-Emile Drouin, omi, LPh, LTh, MA,
MLS

Directeur, admissions
Kenneth Ferren, BTh, MA, MEd

Directeur, aide financière à l'étudiant
Charles-L. Laurin, LScCom

Directeur, association des anciens
H.-Olivier Pelletier, BA

Directeur, aumônerie
Louis-de-Gonzague Raby, omi, BA, LTh

Directeur, centre de communications et de
moyens didactiques
Bernard LeTremble

Directeur, dossiers et statistiques scolaires
J.G. Wright, BA

Directeur, extension de l'enseignement
universitaire
Gérard Forcier, omi, MA(Econ)

Directeur, Les éditions de l'Université
d'Ottawa
Léopold Lanctôt, omi, BA, LPh, LTh, LDC

Directeur, logement et cantines
J.A.B. Campbell

Directeur, planification et construction
Witold Kubasiewicz, DiplIng(Arch)

Directeur, relations extérieures
Gérard Boss, BA

Directeur, service de placement
Fernand-M. Villemaire

Directeur, service de santé
William Howe, MD

Directeur, service des finances
Rhéo Brisson, CA

Historique

Le Collège de Bytown, future Université
d'Ottawa, fut fondé en 1848 par les
Missionnaires Oblats de Marie-Immaculée.
Erigée en corporation en 1849, l'institution
prit le nom de Collège d'Ottawa en 1861.
Quelques années plus tard, soit en 1866, le
collège se voyait octroyer une charte
d'université par le gouvernement d'Union. En
1889, le Pape Léon XIII accordait à

Director, admissions
Kenneth Ferren, BTh, MA, MEd

Director, alumni association
H.-Olivier Pelletier, BA

Director, communications and instructional
media centre
Bernard LeTremble

Director, chaplain services
Louis-de-Gonzague Raby, omi, BA, LTh

Director, financial services
Rhéo Brisson, CA

Director, housing and food services
J.A.B. Campbell

Director, placement office
Fernand-M. Villemaire

Director, planning and construction
Witold Kubasiewicz, DiplIng(Arch)

Director, public relations
Gérard Boss, BA

Director, student financial aid
Charles-L. Laurin, LScCom

Director, health services
William Howe, MD

Director, student records and statistics
J.G. Wright, BA

Director, university extension
Gérard Forcier, omi, MA(Econ)

Director, University of Ottawa Press
Léopold Lanctôt, omi, BA, LPh, LTh, LDC

Background

The University of Ottawa was founded as the
College of Bytown in 1848 by the Missionary
Oblates of Mary Inmaculate. Incorporated in
1849, it became the College of Ottawa in
1861 and was raised to the rank of a
university in 1866 by an act of the union
government. In 1889, it became a pontifical
university by decree of Pope Leo XIII. The
revised civil charter was approved by the
Ontario legislature in 1933. The amended
pontifical charter was given a new approval
by Rome in 1934.

l'université une charte pontificale. La charte civile remaniée était sanctionnée par la législature d'Ontario en 1933. La charte pontificale amendée recevait une nouvelle approbation de Rome en 1934.

Au mois de juillet 1965, les facultés de théologie et de droit canonique furent groupées sous l'Université Saint-Paul, institution fédérée à la nouvelle Université d'Ottawa avec représentation au sénat. L'administration de l'Université d'Ottawa passa à un bureau de gouverneurs mais le sénat conserva la responsabilité des décisions dans le domaine de l'enseignement universitaire.

Installations et services

L'université occupe, dans la capitale nationale, une bonne partie du quartier de la Côte de Sable. Le campus couvre une superficie de 42 acres et s'étend sur une longueur d'environ un mille, le long de la rive est du canal Rideau. D'ici une vingtaine d'années, la superficie du campus atteindra 83 acres. On y compte actuellement dix édifices contenant salles de cours et laboratoires, six édifices temporaires et trois résidences d'étudiants. Les collections des 18 bibliothèques de faculté, d'école et de département totalisent plus de 425,000 volumes.

Les services aux étudiants comprennent une librairie, un service de placement, un service de consultation, un service de santé, un service de logement, une patinoire intérieure et un gymnase.

Annuaires et brochures

S'adresser au bureau des admissions

Annuaire général; admission au baccalauréat; aide financière; arts; bibliothéconomie; common law; cours d'été; cours du soir; cours par correspondance; droit civil; éducation; éducation physique et récréation; études supérieures*; formation des enseignants; médecine; philosophie; psychologie; renseignements généraux; sciences de la gestion; sciences et génie; sciences infirmières; sciences sociales; vie étudiante**.

* S'adresser à l'Ecole des études supérieures
**S'adresser au directeur des services aux étudiants

In July 1965 the faculties of theology and canon law were grouped as Saint Paul University, federated to the new University of Ottawa, with representation in its senate. Government of University of Ottawa was vested in a board of governors, the senate retaining authority to control academic policy.

Facilities and services

The university is situated in the Sandy Hill district of Ottawa and will, in the future, extend over a distance of one mile along the east bank of the Rideau Canal. The campus at present covers an area of 42 acres, but will expand to cover 83 acres within 20 years. There are ten teaching buildings, six temporary buildings, 18 faculty, school, and departmental libraries (with holdings totalling over 425,000 volumes) and three student residences.

Student services include a bookstore, a placement service, a counselling service, a student health service, a housing bureau, an indoor skating rink and a gymnasium.

Calendars and brochures

Direct requests to the office of admissions.

General calendar; arts; common law; correspondence courses; droit civil; education; evening division; financial aid; formation des enseignants; general information; graduate studies*; library science; management sciences; medicine; nursing; physical education and recreation; science and engineering; social sciences; student life**; summer session; philosophy; psychology; undergraduate admission.

* Direct requests to the school of graduate studies.
**Direct requests to the director of student services.

Courses and degrees

Note. The languages of instruction are French and English.

Cours et grades

N.B. Les langues d'enseignement sont le français et l'anglais.

Administration correctionnelle, voir criminologie

Administration d'affaires, voir sciences de la gestion

Administration hospitalière, voir hospital administration (texte anglais)

Administration publique, voir sciences de la gestion

Arts
(Faculté des arts)

Baccalauréat ès arts (BA).
(a) Général, quatre ans après l'immatriculation junior. (b) Avec concentration, quatre ans après l'immatriculation junior. Concentrations possibles: allemand, arts plastiques, civilisations grecque et romaine, communications sociales, English, espagnol, études slaves, géographie, grec, histoire, latin, lettres françaises, mathématiques, musique, philosophie, psychologie, science économique, science politique, sciences domestiques, sciences religieuses, sociologie, théâtre. (c) Prémédical, quatre ans après l'immatriculation junior. (d) Avec spécialisation, cinq ans après l'immatriculation junior. Domaines de spécialisation: anglais*, arts plastiques, communications sociales, English, espagnol, études latines, géographie, histoire, langue et littérature françaises, langues et littératures slaves, linguistique, linguistique-traduction*, musique, sciences religieuses, théâtre. (e) Avec spécialisation, cinq ans après l'immatriculation junior, comportant la conjugaison de deux disciplines: l'une, "majeure", du niveau de spécialisation; l'autre, "mineure", du niveau de concentration.

*Programme d'études destiné exclusivement aux francophones

Arts
(Faculty of arts)

Bachelor of arts (BA).
(a) General, four years from junior matriculation. (b) With concentration, four years from junior matriculation. Possible concentrations: classical civilization, economics, English, French*, geography, German, Greek, history, home economics, Latin, lettres françaises, mathematics, music, philosophy, political science, psychology, religious studies, Slavic studies, social communications,EP. sociology, Spanish, theatre arts, visual arts. (c) Premedical, four years from junior matriculation. (d) Honors, five years from junior matriculation. Fields of specialization: English, French language and literature*, geography, history, langue et littérature françaises, linguistics, linguistics-translation*, music, religious studies, Roman studies, Slavic languages and literatures, social communications, Spanish, theatre arts, visual arts. (e) Honors, five years from junior matriculation, combining two disciplines: a "major", at honors level; a "minor", at concentration level.

*Program for English-speaking students only

(School of graduate studies)

Master of arts (MA).
At least one year from honors BA. Available in ancient history, applied linguistics, English, geography, history, Latin, Latin-Greek, lettres françaises, regional planning, religious studies, Slavic studies, translation.

Doctor of philosophy (PhD).
At least two years from MA. Available in same disciplines as MA, except in ancient history, Latin-Greek, linguistics, regional planning, translation.

Business administration, see management sciences

Canon law*
(Faculty of canon law)

Bachelor of canon law (BCL).
Two years from a baccalaureate degree or the equivalent.

*Civil degrees. Saint Paul University confers ecclesiastical degrees.

(Ecole des études supérieures)

Maîtrise ès arts (MA).
Au moins un an après le BA avec
spécialisation. Offerte en English, études
slaves, géographie, histoire, histoire ancienne,
latin, latin-grec, lettres françaises, linguistique
appliquée, planification régionale, sciences
religieuses, traduction.

Doctorat en philosophie (PhD).
Au moins deux ans après la maîtrise. Offert
dans les mêmes disciplines que la maîtrise,
sauf en histoire ancienne, latin-grec,
linguistique, planification régionale,
traduction.

Beaux-arts
(Faculté des arts)

Certificat en beaux-arts.
Deux ans après l'immatriculation junior.
Disciplines: arts plastiques, théâtre anglais,
théâtre français.

Certificat supérieur en beaux-arts.
Trois ans après l'immatriculation junior.
Disciplines: les mêmes que pour le premier
certificat.

Bibliothéconomie, voir library science (texte
anglais)

Coopération internationale
(Faculté des sciences de la gestion)

Diplôme en coopération internationale.
Un an après le baccalauréat ou l'équivalent.

Criminologie
(Faculté de psychologie, Ecole des études
supérieures)

*Maîtrise en administration correctionnelle
(MAC).*
Deux ans après le baccalauréat. Sans thèse.

Maîtrise ès arts en criminologie [MA(Crim)].
Deux ans après le baccalauréat. Thèse.

(School of graduate studies)

Master of canon law (MCL).
One year from the BCL. No thesis.

Master of arts in canon law [MA(CL)].
One year from the BCL. Thesis.

Doctor of philosophy in canon law [PhD(CL)].
At least one year from master's degree in
canon law.

Commerce, see management sciences

Correctional administration, see criminology

Criminology
(Faculty of psychology, school of graduate
studies)

Master of correctional administration (MCA).
Two years from a baccalaureate degree. No
thesis.

Master of arts in criminology [MA(Crim)].
Two years from a baccalaureate degree.
Thesis.

Dietetics-home economics
(Faculty of arts)

*Honors bachelor of science in dietetics
[BSc(Diet)].*
Five years from junior matriculation.

*Honors bachelor of science in home economics
[BSc(HEcon)].*
Five years from junior matriculation.

Droit, see French text

Education
(Faculty of education)

Bachelor of education (BEd).
One year from a baccalaureate degree. The
BEd program constitutes the preparatory year
of the master's program.

Diététique-sciences domestiques
(Faculté des arts)

Baccalauréat ès sciences avec spécialisation en diététique [*BSc(Diét)*].
Cinq ans après l'immatriculation junior.

Baccalauréat ès sciences avec spécialisation en sciences domestiques [*BSc(ScDom)*].
Cinq ans après l'immatriculation junior.

Droit
(Faculté de droit, section de droit civil)

Licence en droit (LLL).
Trois ans après le BA ou un diplôme jugé équivalent.

(Ecole des études supérieures)

Maîtrise en droit (LLM).
Au moins un an après la licence en droit ou un diplôme jugé équivalent. Thèse.
Concentrations: droit privé, droit public.

Doctorat en droit (LLD).
Au moins un an après la maîtrise en droit. Thèse.

Droit canonique*
(Faculté de droit canonique)

Baccalauréat en droit canonique (BDC).
Deux ans après un baccalauréat ou l'équivalent.

(Ecole des études supérieures)

Maîtrise en droit canonique (MDC).
Un an après le baccalauréat en droit canonique. Sans thèse.

Maîtrise ès arts en droit canonique [*MA(DC)*].
Un an après le baccalauréat en droit canonique. Thèse.

Doctorat en philosophie en droit canonique [*PhD(DC)*].
Au moins un an après la maîtrise en droit canonique.

(School of graduate studies)

Master of education (MEd).
Two years from a baccalaureate degree or one year from BEd. No thesis.
Concentrations: educational administration, educational foundations, measurement and experimentation, psychopedagogy, school counselling.

Master of arts in education [*MA(Ed)*].
Two years from a baccalaureate degree or one year from BEd. Thesis. Concentrations: same as for MEd.

Doctor of philosophy (PhD).
At least one year from MA(Ed) or equivalent.

Engineering
(Faculty of science and engineering)

Bachelor of applied science (BASc).
Five years from junior matriculation. Available in chemical, civil, electrical, and mechanical engineering.

(School of graduate studies)

Master of engineering (MEng).
At least one year from BASc. Available in chemical, civil, electrical, and mechanical engineering. Engineering report.

Master of applied science (MASc).
At least one year from BASc. Available in chemical, civil, electrical, and mechanical engineering. Thesis.

Doctor of philosophy (PhD).
At least two years from MASc. Available in same disciplines as MASc, except in mechanical engineering.

Fine arts
(Faculty of arts)

Certificate in fine arts.
Two years from junior matriculation. Available in English theatre arts, French theatre arts, visual arts.

Advanced certificate in fine arts.
Three years from junior matriculation. Available in same fields as for first certificate.

---

*Grades civils. L'Université Saint-Paul confère les grades ecclésiastiques.

Education
(Faculté d'éducation)

Baccalauréat en éducation (BEd).
Un an après un baccalauréat. Les études du
BEd constituent l'année propédeutique de la
maîtrise en éducation.

(Ecole des études supérieures)

Maîtrise en éducation (MEd).
Deux ans après un baccalauréat ou un an
après le BEd. Sans thèse. Concentrations:
administration scolaire, counselling scolaire,
fondements théoriques de l'éducation, mesure
et expérimentation, psychopédagogie.

Maîtrise ès arts en éducation [MA(Ed)].
Deux ans après un baccalauréat ou un an
après le BEd. Thèse. Concentrations: les
mêmes que pour la maîtrise sans thèse.

Doctorat en philosophie (PhD).
Au moins un an après la maîtrise ès arts en
éducation ou l'équivalent.

Education physique
(Ecole d'éducation physique et de récréation)

*Baccalauréat en éducation physique
(BEdPhys).*
(a) Général, trois ans après l'immatriculation
senior. (b) Avec spécialisation, quatre ans
après l'immatriculation senior.

*Baccalauréat ès sciences en kinanthropologie
[BSc(Kin)].*
Quatre ans après l'immatriculation senior.

*Baccalauréat ès sciences en récréologie
[BSc(Réc)].*
Quatre ans après l'immatriculation senior.

(Ecole des études supérieures)

Maîtrise en éducation physique (MEdPhys).
Au moins un an après le BEdPhys avec
spécialisation. Sans thèse. Condition
préalable: brevet d'enseignement permanent
valide ou deux années d'expérience valable
dans le domaine de l'éducation physique.

*Maîtrise ès sciences en kinanthropologie
[MSc(Kin)].*
Au moins un an après le BEdPhys avec
spécialisation ou le BSc(Kin). Thèse.

Home economics, see dietetics-home
economics

Hospital administration
(Faculty of management science, school of
graduate studies)

Master of hospital administration (MHA).
At least two years from a bachelor's degree or
equivalent: one year of study on campus, one
year in residence at a hospital, and a six-week
post-residency session on campus.

International co-operation
(Faculty of management sciences)

Diploma in international co-operation.
One year from a baccalaureate or an
equivalent degree.

Kinanthropology, see physical education

Labor relations, see management sciences

Law
(Faculty of law, common law section)

Bachelor of laws (LLB).
Three years from an approved degree or,
exceptionally, from the second year of an
approved degree course beyond senior
matriculation.

Library science
(Library school)

Bachelor of library science (BLS).
At least one year from BA or equivalent
degree.

(School of graduate studies)

Master of library science (MLS).
At least one year from BLS.

Management sciences
(Faculty of management sciences)

Certificate in business administration.
One year from senior matriculation.

Génie, voir engineering (texte anglais)

Kinanthropologie, voir éducation physique

Law, voir le texte anglais

Médecine, voir medicine (texte anglais)

Musique
(Faculté des arts)

Baccalauréat en musique avec spécialisation (BMus).
Cinq ans après l'immatriculation junior.
Domaines de spécialisation: composition, éducation, exécution, musicologie.

Pastorale
(Faculté de théologie, Ecole des études supérieures)

Maîtrise en pastorale (MPast).
Deux ans après le BA ou l'équivalent. Sans thèse. Options: pastoral counselling, pastorale familiale.

Philosophie
(Faculté de philosophie)

Baccalauréat ès arts avec mention philosophie [BA(Ph)].
Deux ans après la première année d'une faculté des arts, ou l'équivalent.

Baccalauréat ès arts avec spécialisation en philosophie [BA(spPh)].
Un an après le BA avec mention philosophie.

(Ecole des études supérieures)

Maîtrise ès arts en philosophie [MA(Ph)].
Deux ans après le BA avec mention philosophie ou un an après le BA avec spécialisation en philosophie.

Doctorat en philosophie (DPh).
Un an ou deux ans après la maîtrise ès arts en philosophie.

Certificate in labor relations in the public service.
One year from senior matriculation.

Certificate in public administration.
One year from senior matriculation.

Advanced certificate in public administration.
One year from first certificate in that field.

Bachelor of management sciences (BManSc).
(a) General, three years from senior matriculation. (b) Honors, four years from senior matriculation. Specialization: operations research.

Honors bachelor of commerce (BCom).
Four years from senior matriculation.

Honors bachelor of public administration (BPubAd).
Four years from senior matriculation.

Diploma in management sciences.
At least one year from a baccalaureate degree.

(School of graduate studies)

Master of management sciences (MManSc).
At least two years from a baccalaureate degree.

Medicine
(Faculty of medicine)

Doctor of medicine (MD).
Four years from BA(Premed) or BSc with appropriate options or first two years of honors BSc in biology.

Diploma in postgraduate training in psychiatry.
Two years from MD.

(School of graduate studies)

Master of science (MSc).
At least one year from honors BSc or from MD. Available in anatomy, biochemistry, histology and embryology, microbiology and immunology, pathology, pharmacology, physiology.

Doctor of philosophy (PhD).
Two or three years from MSc; three or four years from honors BSc or from MD. Available in same disciplines as MSc.

Psychologie
(Faculté de psychologie, Ecole des études
supérieures)

Maîtrise en psychologie (MPs).
Trois ans après le BA ou le BSc, y compris un
an de pratique. Sans thèse.

Maîtrise ès arts en psychologie [MA(Ps)].
Trois ans après le BA ou le BSc. Thèse.

Doctorat en philosophie (PhD).
Au moins deux ans après la maîtrise. Offert en
counselling, psychologie, psychologie
clinique, psychologie clinique de l'enfant,
psychologie scolaire, psychopédagogie.

Récréologie, voir éducation physique

Relations de travail, voir sciences de la
gestion

Sciences, voir science (texte anglais)

Sciences commerciales, voir sciences de la
gestion

Sciences de la gestion
(Faculté des sciences de la gestion)

Certificat en administration d'affaires.
Un an après l'immatriculation senior.

Certificat en administration publique.
Un an après l'immatriculation senior.

*Certificat supérieur en administration
publique.*
Un an après le certificat dans la même
discipline.

*Certificat en relations de travail dans la
fonction publique.*
Un an après l'immatricultion senior.

*Baccalauréat en sciences de la gestion
(BScGest).*
(a) Général, trois ans après l'immatriculation
senior. (b) Avec spécialisation, quatre ans
après l'immatriculation senior. Spécialisation:
recherche opérationnelle.

Mission studies
(Faculty of theology, school of graduate
studies)

*Master of arts in mission studies
[MA(MissStud)].*
Two years from BA degree or equivalent.

Music
(Faculty of arts)

Honors bachelor of music (BMus).
Five years from junior matriculation. Fields
of specialization: composition, education,
musicology, performance.

Nursing
(School of nursing)

*Bachelor of science in nursing education
[BSc(NEd)].*
Two years from diploma in nursing.
Prerequisite: senior matriculation.

*Bachelor of science in public health nursing
[BSc(PHN)].*
Two years from diploma in nursing.
Prerequisite: senior matriculation.

Bachelor of science in nursing (BScN).
Four years from senior matriculation.

Pastoral studies
(Faculty of theology, school of graduate
studies)

Master of pastoral studies (MPast).
Two years after BA or equivalent degree. No
thesis. Options: pastoral counselling,
pastorale familiale.

Philosophy
(Faculty of philosophy)

*Bachelor of arts with a major in philosophy
[BA(Ph)].*
Two years after the first year in a faculty of
arts, or the equivalent.

*Honors bachelor of arts in philosophy
[HonBA(Ph)].*
One year from the BA with a major in
philosophy.

Baccalauréat en administration publique avec spécialisation (BAdPub).
Quatre ans après l'immatriculation senior.

Baccalauréat en sciences commerciales avec spécialisation (BCom).
Quatre ans après l'immatriculation senior.

Diplôme en sciences de la gestion.
Au moins un an après le baccalauréat.

(Ecole des études supérieures)

Maîtrise en sciences de la gestion (MScGest).
Au moins deux ans après le baccalauréat.

Sciences domestiques, voir diététique-sciences domestiques

Sciences infirmières, voir nursing (texte anglais)

Sciences missionnaires
(Faculté de théologie, Ecole des études supérieures)

Maîtrise ès arts en sciences missionnaires [MA(ScMiss)].
Deux ans après le BA ou l'équivalent.

Sciences sociales
(Faculté des sciences sociales)

Baccalauréat en sciences sociales (BScSoc).
(a) Général, trois ans après l'immatriculation senior. (b) Avec spécialisation, quatre ans après l'immatriculation senior. Domaines de spécialisation: science économique, science politique, sociologie.

(Ecole des études supérieures)

Maîtrise ès arts (MA).
Au moins un an après le BScSoc avec spécialisation. Offerte en science économique, science politique, sociologie.

Doctorat en philosophie (PhD).
Au moins un an après la maîtrise ès arts. Offert en science économique, science politique.

(School of graduate studies)

Master of arts in philosophy [MA(Ph)].
Two years from BA with a major in philosophy or one year from HonBA(Ph).

Doctor of philosophy (DPh).
One or two years from the MA(Ph).

Physical education
(School of physical education and recreation)

Bachelor of physical education (BEdPhys).
(a) General, three years from senior matriculation. (b) Honors, four years from senior matriculation.

Bachelor of science in kinanthropology [BSc(Kin)].
Four years from senior matriculation.

Bachelor of science in recreology [BSc(Rec)].
Four years from senior matriculation.

(School of graduate studies)

Master of physical education (MPhysEd).
At least one year from honors BPhysEd. No thesis. Prerequisite: valid permanent teaching certificate or two successful years of experience in the field.

Master of science in kinanthropology [MSc(Kin)].
At least one year from honors BPhysEd or from BSc(Kin). Thesis.

Psychiatry, see medicine

Psychology
(Faculty of psychology, school of graduate studies)

Master of psychology (MPs).
Three years from BA or BSc, including one year of practice. No thesis.

Master of arts in psycholgoy [MA(Ps)].
Three years from BA or BSc. Thesis.

Doctor of philosophy (PhD).
At least two years from master's degree. Available in psychology, clinical psychology, child clinical psychology, counselling, experimental psychology, school psychology.

Théologie*
(Faculté de théologie)

Baccalauréat en théologie (BTh).
Trois ans après le BA ou l'équivalent.

(Ecole des études supérieures)

Maîtrise en théologie (MTh).
Un an après le BTh. Sans thèse.
Concentrations: missiologie, pastorale,
théologie systématique fondamentale.

Maîtrise ès arts en théologie [MA(Th)].
Un an après le BTh. Thèse. Concentrations:
les mêmes que pour la maîtrise sans thèse.

Doctorat en philosophie en théologie
[PhD(Th)]
Au moins un an après la maîtrise.

Education permanente

Sauf indication contraire, pour tout
renseignement s'adresser au Département de
l'extension de l'enseignement universitaire.

Cours universitaires:

Cours par correspondance.
En vue du BA seulement. Les candidats
doivent suivre au moins huit cours en
résidence (cours d'été, cours du soir).

Cours du soir.
(a) Niveau du baccalauréat. Cours donnés à
l'université et aux centres d'enseignement
extérieurs suivants, en Ontario: Barry's Bay,
Cornwall, Hawkesbury, Pembroke et
Renfrew. (b) Niveau des études supérieures.
Cours donnés à l'université seulement.
S'adresser à l'Ecole des études supérieures. (c)
Certificat en administration d'affaires,
certificat en administration publique, certificat
supérieur en administration publique,
certificat en relations de travail dans la
fonction publique. S'adresser à la Faculté des
sciences de la gestion. (d) Certificat en beaux-
arts, certificat supérieur en beaux-arts.
Disciplines: arts plastiques, théâtre anglais,
théâtre français.

Public administration, see management
sciences

Recreology, see physical education

Science
(Faculty of science and engineering)

Bachelor of science (BSc).
(a) General, four years from junior
matriculation. (b) With major, four years
from junior matriculation. Available in
biochemistry, biology, chemistry, computer
science, geology, mathematics, physics,
physics-mathematics. (c) Honors, five years
from junior matriculation. Available in same
disciplines as BSc with major.

(School of graduate studies)

Master of science (MSc).
At least one year from honors BSc. Available
in biochemistry, biology, chemistry, geology,
mathematics, physics.

Doctor of philosophy (PhD).
At least two years from MSc. Available in
same disciplines as MSc.

Social sciences
(Faculty of social sciences)

Bachelor of social sciences (BSocSc).
(a) Pass, three years from senior
matriculation. (b) Honors, four years from
senior matriculation. Available in economics,
political science, sociology.

(School of graduate studies)

Master of arts (MA).
At least one year from honors BSocSc.
Available in economics, political science,
sociology.

Doctor of philosophy (PhD).
At least one year from MA degree. Available
in economics and political science.

*Grades civils. L'Université Saint-Paul
confère les grades ecclésiastiques.

Cours d'été.
(a) Niveau du baccalauréat. Cours donnés à l'université et aux centres d'enseignement extérieurs suivants, en Ontario: Cornwall, Hawkesbury, Pembroke et Renfrew. (b) Niveau des études supérieures. Cours donnés à l'université seulement. S'adresser à l'Ecole des études supérieures.

Cours télévisés.
En vue du BA seulement. Les candidats doivent suivre au moins huit cours en résidence (cours d'été, cours du soir).

Cours extra-universitaires:

Cours du soir.
Opérations de banque. Cours donnés en collaboration avec l'Institute of Canadian Bankers et conduisant au diplôme décerné par cet organisme.

Cours d'été.
(a) Droit comparé. Cours d'une durée de trois semaines. S'adresser au Centre canadien de droit comparé, Université d'Ottawa. (b) Bibliothéconomie. Cours spéciaux en vue d'un certificat de compétence en administration d'une petite bibliothèque.

Conditions d'admission

On trouvera un exposé général sur l'admission aux études universitaires dans l'article *Admission aux universités canadiennes.*

Afin d'obtenir des renseignements sur l'admission aux études du niveau pré-grade, consultez *Conditions d'admission dans les collèges et universités du Canada* que l'on peut obtenir du Service d'admission au collège et à l'université, 151, rue Slater, Ottawa (Ontario), K1P 5N1, $1.50 port payé.

Pour être admis en première année de common law, le candidat doit avoir complété, après l'immatriculation senior, au moins deux années d'un programme d'études conduisant à un premier grade.

Pour être admis en première année de droit civil, le candidat doit détenir le baccalauréat ès arts ou un diplôme jugé équivalent.

Pour être admis en première année de médecine, le candidat doit détenir le baccalauréat ès arts (avec études

Theology*
(Faculty of theology)

Bachelor of theology (BTh).
Three years from BA or equivalent degree.

(School of graduate studies)

Master of theology (MTh).
One year from BTh. No thesis. Concentrations: fundamental systematic theology, missiology, pastoral studies.

Master of arts in theology [MA(Th)].
One year from BTh. Thesis. Concentrations: same as for MTh.

Doctor of philosophy in theology [PhD(Th)].
At least one year from master's degree.

Extension programs

Unless otherwise indicated, direct inquiries to the department of university extension.

For university credit:

Correspondence courses.
Towards BA degree only. Students must take at least eight courses in residence (evening division, summer session).

Evening division.
(a) Undergraduate level. Courses given at the university and at the following off-campus centres: Barry's Bay, Cornwall, Hawkesbury, Pembroke, and Renfrew, Ontario. (b) Graduate level. Courses given at the university only. Address inquiries to the school of graduate studies. (c) Certificate in business administration, certificate in public administration, advanced certificate in public administration, certificate in labor relations in the public service. Address inquiries to the faculty of management sciences. (d) Certificate in fine arts, advanced certificate in fine arts. In following fields: English theatre arts, French theatre arts, visual arts.

Summer session.
(a) Undergraduate level. Courses given at the university and at the following off-campus centres: Cornwall, Hawkesbury, Pembroke,

**Civil degrees. Saint Paul University confers ecclesiastical degrees.

prémédicales) ou le baccalauréat ès sciences (avec les options appropriées) ou avoir complété les deux premières années du baccalauréat ès sciences avec spécialisation en biologie.

L'admission aux cours supérieurs exige que le candidat soit titulaire d'un premier grade et qu'il ait obtenu les notes requises dans les matières appropriées au programme d'études choisi.

Année universitaire

Année régulière: de la mi-septembre à la fin d'avril.

Cours d'été: du début de juillet à la mi-août.

Système de mentions

Au niveau du baccalauréat: A, 75-100%; B, 66-74%; C, 60-65%; D, 50-59%; F, 30-49% (échec avec droit de reprise); (*), moins de 30% (échec sans droit de reprise).

Droits d'inscription

Etudiants à temps complet.
Les droits indiqués comprennent les frais de scolarité et les frais accessoires. (a) Baccalauréat, par année: pré-universitaire (arts, génie, sciences), $486; arts, bibliothéconomie (BLS), diététique-sciences domestiques, droit, éducation (BEd), éducation physique et récréation, philosophie, sciences commerciales, sciences de la gestion, sciences infirmières, sciences sociales, $536; génie, pré-médecine (arts), sciences, $611; médecine, $706. (b) Etudes supérieures (y compris l'année propédeutique): par trimestre, $258.

Etudiants à temps partiel.
Frais de scolarité. (a) Baccalauréat: chaque cours, $100-$130; chaque demi-cours, $50. (b) Etudes supérieures: chaque cours de 4 crédits ou plus, $120; chaque cours de 3 crédits ou moins, $60.

Frais de logement.
Par année, $400-$480.

and Renfrew, Ontario. (b) Graduate level. Courses given at the university only. Address inquiries to the school of graduate studies.

For no university credit:

Evening division.
(a) Courses in banking, offered in co-operation with the Institute of Canadian Bankers and leading to the diploma granted by the institute. (b) Courses in industrial management and administration, offered in co-operation with the Canadian Industrial Management Association, Ottawa branch, and leading to the certificate granted by the association.

Summer session.
(a) Program in comparative law. Duration: three weeks. Address inquiries to the Canadian and Foreign Law Research Centre, University of Ottawa. (b) French summer school. Courses at the beginners', intermediate, and advanced levels.

Admission requirements

For a general statement regarding admission to university study, see article *Admission to university in Canada.*

For information regarding admission to undergraduate study, consult *Requirements for admission to Canadian colleges and universities* available from Service for Admission to College and University, 151 Slater St., Ottawa, Ont., K1P 5N1, $1.50 prepaid.

Applicants for admission to first year common law must have completed, beyond senior matriculation, at least two years of a program leading to a first degree.

Admission to first year of droit civil requires that the applicant hold the BA degree or a degree deemed to be equivalent.

Applicants for admission to first year medicine must hold the BA(premed) or the BSc (with appropriate options) or have completed the first two years of the honors BSc in biology.

For admission to graduate study, applicants must have obtained a first degree with specified grades in appropriate subjects.

Aide financière

Les gouvernements fédéral et provinciaux, de nombreuses compagnies, fondations et associations offrent des bourses et des prêts aux étudiants inscrits à temps complet aux cours de baccalauréat et aux études supérieures.

L'université elle-même attribue chaque année, à l'admission, un certain nombre de bourses d'excellence aux candidats admis aux études à temps complet. Les bourses accordées aux élèves des écoles secondaires admis à l'année pré-universitaire ou à la première année d'un cours de baccalauréat sont renouvelables pendant quatre ans. Dans le cas des candidats admis à s'inscrire en bibliothéconomie, en common law, en criminologie, en droit civil, en éducation ou en médecine, les bourses d'admission ne sont pas renouvelables.

En outre, l'université offre annuellement une vingtaine de bourses d'excellence aux étudiants pré-diplômés inscrits à temps complet qui ont obtenu, aux épreuves de fin d'année, des résultats au-dessus de la moyenne.

Pour plus de renseignements, consulter la brochure sur l'aide financière.

Université fédérée

Université Saint-Paul, Ottawa (Ontario) cf. mention particulière.

Collèges affiliés

L'Université d'Ottawa confère les grades.

Notre Dame of Canada College, Wilcox, Saskatchewan. Recteur: Athol Murray. Doyen, Faculté des arts: Christopher Mansbridge. Catholique. Mixte. Fondé et affilié en 1933. Pensionnat et externat. Programme d'études conduisant au BA destiné aux anglophones.

St. Charles Scholasticate, Battleford, Saskatchewan. Recteur: Adam Exner, OMI. Doyen des études: Martin Moser, OMI. Collège catholique pour hommes. Fondé et affilié en 1939. Externat. Programme d'études conduisant au BA destiné aux anglophones.

Academic year

Regular session: from mid-September to the end of April.

Summer session: from the beginning of July to mid-August.

Grading system

At the undergraduate level: A, 75-100%; B, 66-74%; C, 60-65%; D, 50-59%; F, 30-49% (failure with supplemental privileges); (*), less than 30% (failure without supplemental privileges.

Fees and costs

Full-time students. The amounts shown include both the tuition fees and the incidental fees. (a) Undergraduate programs, per year: pre-university (arts, engineering, science), $486; arts, commerce, dietetics-home economics, education (BEd), law, library science (BLS), management sciences, nursing, philosophy, physical education and recreation, social sciences, $536; engineering, pre-medicine (arts), science, $611; medicine, $706. (b) Graduate programs (including the preparatory year): per trimester, $258.

Part-time students. (a) Undergraduate programs: each course, $100-$130; each half-course, $50. (b) Graduate programs: each course of four credits or more, $120; each course of three credits or less, $60.

Residence fees (room only). Per year: $400-$480.

Financial awards and assistance

The federal government and the provincial governments, as well as numerous companies, foundations, and associations, offer scholarships, bursaries, and loans to full-time students registered in undergraduate and graduate programs.

The university itself awards each year a limited number of admission scholarships to applicants admitted to full-time studies.

Doyens des facultés

Arts
Joseph-Marie Quirion, omi, BA, LPh, BTh, MSc(Econ), ACIS

Droit (section de common law)
Thomas Feeney, CR, BA, LLB

Droit (section de droit civil)
Gérald Beaudoin, BA, LLL, MA(Droit), DiplESD

Education
Lionel-P. Desjarlais, BA, BPéd, MA, PhD

Etudes supérieures (Ecole des)
Paul Hagen, MB, FCIC

Médecine
J.-Jacques Lussier, BA, MSc, MD, PhD, FICS

Philosophie
Gilles Cazabon, omi, BA, LPh, LTh, DPh

Psychologie
Raymond-H. Shevenell, omi, LPh, MA, PhD, DEd

Sciences de la gestion
Joseph Debanné, DiplIng, MSc

Sciences et génie
Antoine D'Iorio, BSc, PhD, MSRC

Sciences sociales
Denis Carrier, MScCom, DiplES(ScPol), DUP

Directeurs des écoles

Bibliothéconomie
Peter Harvard-Williams, MA

Education physique et récréation
W.A.R. Orban, BSc, MS, PhD, FACSM

Sciences infirmières
Yolande Proulx, sco, RN, BScNEd, MS

Directeurs des départements

Administration hospitalière
John Babson, AB, MBA, PhD

Entrance scholarships awarded to secondary school students admitted to the pre-university year or to the first year of an undergraduate program are renewable for four years. Scholarships awarded to applicants admitted to a program in common law, criminology, droit civil, education, library science, or medicine are not renewable.

In addition, the university offers annually some 20 scholarships to registered full-time undergraduate students whose achievement, at final examinations, has been above average.

For futher information, see the brochure on financial aid.

Federated university

Saint Paul University, Ottawa, Ontario. See separate entry.

Affiliated colleges

Degrees are conferred by the University of Ottawa.

Notre Dame of Canada College, Wilcox, Saskatchewan.
Rector: Athol Murray. Dean of arts: Christopher Mansbridge. Catholic. Co-educational. Founded and affiliated in 1933. Resident and day students. Courses lead to BA degree.

St. Charles Scholasticate, Battleford, Saskatchewan.
Rector: Adam Exner, OMI. Dean of studies: Martin Moser, OMI. Catholic. Men only. Founded and affiliated in 1939. Day students. Courses lead to BA degree.

Deans of faculties

Arts
Joseph-Marie Quirion, omi, BA, LPh, BTh, MSc(Econ), ACIS

Education
Lionel-P. Desjarlais, BA, BPéd, MA, PhD

Graduate studies (School of)
Paul Hagen, MB, FCIC

Administration publique
William Dymond, MA, PhD

Anatomie
Marc Colonnier, BA, BPh, MD, MSc, PhD

Anesthésie
Lloyd Hampson (intérimaire), MD

Beaux-arts
Françoys Bernier, BA

Biochimie
Donald Layne, MSc, PhD

Biologie
Quentin LaHam, BA, MS, PhD

Chimie
Hans Baer, DrRerNat, FCIC

Chirurgie
J.B. Ewing, MD, FRCSEd, FRCSCan, FACS, FICS

Coopération internationale
Louis Sabourin, BA, LLL, DiplLittCont, DiplScPol, PhD

Counselling-clinique
Raymond-H. Shevenell, omi, LPh, MA, PhD, DEd

Criminologie
Tadeusz Grygier, DiplScPol, LLM, PhD, FBPS

Diététique-sciences domestiques
Lucie Blondeau (intérimaire), cnd, BScD, MS, PhD

Education physique
Stewart Davidson, BSc(PE), MA, EdD

English
Paul Marcotte, MA, PhD

Epidémiologie et médecine sociale
John Last, MD, DiplPH, FRSM, FAPHA

Etude de l'enfant
Agatha Sidlauskas, MA, PhD

Etudes anciennes
Colin Wells, MA, DPhil

Etudes slaves
Constantine Bida, PhD

Génie chimique
Benjamin C.-Y. Lu, MASc, PhD

Law (common law section)
Thomas Feeney, QC, BA, LLB

Law (droit civil section)
Gérald Beaudoin, BA, LLL, MA(Droit), DiplESD

Management sciences
Joseph Debanné, DiplIng, MSc

Medicine
J.-Jacques Lussier, BA, MSc, MD, PhD, FICS

Philosophy
Gilles Cazabon, omi, BA, LPh, LTh, DPh

Psychology
Raymond-H. Shevenell, omi, LPh, MA, PhD, DEd

Science and engineering
Antoine D'Iorio, BSc, PhD, FRSCan

Social sciences
Denis Carrier, MScCom, DiplES(ScPol), DUP

Directors of schools

Library science
Peter Harvard-Williams, MA

Nursing
Yolande Proulx, sco, RN, BScNEd, MS

Physical education and recreation
W.A.R. Orban, BSc, MS, PhD, FACSM

Department heads

Anaesthesia
Lloyd Hampson (acting), MD

Anatomy
Marc Colonnier, BA, BPh, MD, MSc, PhD

Biochemistry
Donald Layne, MSc, PhD

Biology
Quentin LaHam, BA, MS, PhD

Chemical engineering
Benjamin C.-Y. Lu, MASc, PhD

Chemistry
Hans Baer, DrRerNat, FCIC

Génie civil
J.D. Scott, MS, PhD

Génie électrique
Clément Lemyre, BScA, PhD, DIC

Génie mécanique
Poste vacant

Géographie
Jean-Bernard Racine (intérimaire), LèsL,
DU(Aix)
Rolf Wesche (intérimaire), MA, PhD

Géologie
Donald Hogarth (intérimaire), MASc, PhD

Histoire
Cornelius Jaenen, MA, BEd, PhD

Histologie et embryologie
Leonard-F. Bélanger, BA, MD, MMSc,
MSRC

Informatique
Louis Birta (intérimaire), BASc, MS, PhD

Kinanthropologie
Maurice Jetté, MS(PhysEd), PhD

Lettres françaises
Eugène-M. Roberto, DLett

Linguistique et langues modernes
Guy Rondeau, BPéd, MA, DLett

Mathématiques (sciences et génie)
Victor Linis, DiplMath, MSc, PhD

Mathématiques et sciences générales (arts)
Léopold Vachon (intérimaire), BA, BScCom,
LScCom

Médecine
R.K. Smiley, BA, MD, FRCPCan

Microbiologie et immunologie
J.C.N. Westwood, BA, MB

Musique
Françoys Bernier, BA

Obstétrique et gynécologie
Gilles-D. Hurteau, BA, MD, FRCSCan,
FACOG

Ophtalmologie
A.G. Watson, MB, FRCSCan, FACS

Oto-rhino-laryngologie
G.-Guy Laframboise, BA, MD, FRCSCan

Child psychology
Agatha Sidlauskas, MA, PhD

Civil engineering
J.D. Scott, MS, PhD

Classical studies
Colin Wells, MA, DPhil

Clinical counselling
Raymond-H. Shevenell, omi, LPh, MA, PhD,
DEd

Commerce
A.W.J. Craig, BCom, MBA, PhD

Computer science
Louis Birta (acting), BASc, MS, PhD

Criminology
Tadeusz Grygier, DiplScPol, LLM, PhD,
FBPS

Dietetics-home economics
Lucie Blondeau (acting), cnd, BScD, MS,
PhD

Economics
John Kuiper

Electrical engineering
Clément Lemyre, BScA, PhD, DIC

English
Paul Marcotte, MA, PhD

Epidemiology and community medicine
John Last, MD, DiplPH, FRSM, FAPHA

Fine arts
Françoys Bernier, BA

General-experimental psychology
William Barry, BA, MPs, PhD

Geography
Jean-Bernard Racine(acting), LèsL, DU(Aix)
Rolf Wesche (acting), MA, PhD

Geology
Donald Hogarth (acting), MASc, PhD

Histology and embryology
Leonard-F. Bélanger, BA, MD, MMSc,
FRSCan

History
Cornelius Jaenen, MA, BEd, PhD

Hospital administration
John Babson, AB, MBA, PhD

Pathologie
Desmond Magner, MD, BSc(Med),
FRCPCan

Pédiatrie
Dominick Conway, MA, MD, FRCPCan

Pharmacologie
George Ling, MA, PhD

Physiologie
Geza Hetenyi, MD, PhD

Physique
John Woolley, PhD

Psychiatrie
Charles Roberts, BSc, MD

Psychologie générale-expérimentale
William Barry, BA, MPs, PhD

Radiologie
Conway Don, MB, BA, DiplMR(D), FFR

Recherche opérationnelle et planification
Oussama Achou, DiplIng, LMath, DiplES,
PhD

Récréologie
Jean-Marc Beauchesne, BA, MS

Science économique
John Kuiper

Science politique
Jean-Pierre Gaboury, MA, DScPol

Sciences commerciales
A.W.J. Craig, BCom, MBA, PhD

Sciences religieuses
Maurice Giroux, omi, MA, LPh, DTh

Sociologie
Rodolphe-J.-H. Bietlot, LPhL, DèsL(Sociol)

International co-operation
Louis Sabourin, BA, LLL, DiplLittCont,
DiplScPol, PhD

Kinanthropology
Maurice Jetté, MS(PhysEd), PhD

Lettres françaises
Eugène-M. Roberto, DLett

Linguistics and modern languages
Guy Rondeau, BPéd, MA, DLett

Mathematics (science and engineering)
Victor Linis, DiplMath, MSc, PhD

Mathematics and general science (arts)
Léopold Vachon (acting), BA, BScCom,
LScCom

Mechanical engineering
To be appointed

Medicine
R.K. Smiley, BA, MD, FRCPCan

Microbiology and immunology
J.C.N. Westwood, BA, MB

Music
Françoys Bernier, BA

Obstetrics and gynaecology
Gilles-D. Hurteau, BA, MD, FRCSCan,
FACOG

Operations research and planning
Oussama Achou, DiplIng, LMath, DiplES,
PhD

Ophthalmology
A.G. Watson, MB, FRCSCan, FACS

Oto-rhino-laryngology
G.-Guy Laframboise, BA, MD, FRCSCan

Paediatrics
Dominick Conway, MA, MD, FRCPCan

Pathology
Desmond Magner, MD, BSc(Med),
FRCPCan

Pharmacology
Georgè Ling, MA, PhD

Physical education
Stewart Davidson, BSc(PE), MA, EdD

Physics
John Woolley, PhD

Physiology
Geza Hetenyi, MD, PhD

Political science
Jean-Pierre Gaboury, MA, DScPol

Psychiatry
Charles Roberts, BSc, MD

Public administration
William Dymond, MA, PhD

Radiology
Conway Don, MB, BA, DiplMR(D), FFR

Recreology
Jean-Marc Beauchesne, BA, MS

Religious studies
Maurice Giroux, omi, MA, LPh, DTh

Slavic studies
Constantine Bida, PhD

Sociology
Rodolphe-J.-H. Bietlot, LPhL, DèsL(Sociol)

Surgery
J.B. Ewing, MD, FRCSEd, FRCSCan, FACS,
FICS

University of Prince Edward Island*

Charlottetown, Prince Edward Island

Telephone: 902-892-4121
Direct general correspondence to the registrar

Total full-time student enrolment 1,755; see also separate section *Statistics on Canadian universities and colleges*

Executive and administrative officers

Chancellor
Hon. Mr. Justice T.A. Campbell, MA, LLD

President and vice-chancellor
R.J. Baker, BA, MA, LLD

Registrar
M.F. Hennessey, BA, BEd

Assistant registrar (admissions)
Louise Gay (Mrs)

Librarian
M. Crockett, BA, BLS

Dean of women
Eileen Hornby, BA, MSc

Comptroller
G.D. Clough, BCom, CA

Information officer
Marita McNulty (Mrs)

Director of student counselling
J.A. Blanchard, BA, BEd, MA

Director of student services
J. Griffith, BA

Financial aid and liaison officer
R.J. LeClair, BA

Athletic director
E. Hilton, BCom

Student placement officer
M.S. Kelly, BA

Development officer
Earl Nicholson

Background

The University of Prince Edward Island was established by an act of the legislature of Prince Edward Island in April 1969, and Prof. R.J. Baker was appointed its first president.

The new, public, non-denominational university is a merger of two institutions of higher learning, Prince of Wales College established in 1834, and St. Dunstan's University established in 1855.

The 18-member board of governors of the University of Prince Edward Island is under the chairmanship of Hon. Mr. Justice C. St. Clair Trainor. Under the university act the chancellor, the president of the university, the president of the college of applied arts and technology, six members of the university community, and nine members appointed by the lieutenant-governor-in-council constitute the board. There are two members from the student body on the board. The 24-member senate includes six members from the student body of the university.

Enrolment at the University of Prince Edward Island, which began its second academic year in September 1970, was 1,755 students. Courses offered lead to degrees in arts, science, business administration, and education. The first degrees of UPEI were conferred at convocation exercises held on May 15, 1970. The full-time teaching staff during the 1970-71 academic session totaled approximately 150 persons.

*Ordinary member, AUCC.

Facilities and services

The university campus is situated at the northern boundary of Charlottetown on the Trans-Canada highway. Its campus occupies approximately 50 acres upon which there are four teaching buildings, a library (75,000 volumes approximately), five residences accommodating about 250 men and 200 women. During 1970-71 one residence accommodating 100 men was maintained downtown. For 1971-72 it is anticipated that the only departments to be maintained downtown will be home economics and music. The university's sports facilities include a gymnasium, two football fields, and an arena with an artificial ice plant.

Calendars and brochures

University calendar for the regular academic session, September to May. University calendar for summer sessions, May – June, 1 July – mid-August. Incidental brochures.

Calendars and brochures are available at the registrar's office.

Courses and degrees

Arts
(Faculty of arts)

Bachelor of arts (BA).
General degree with a major. Four years from junior matriculation. Available in economics, English, history, modern languages, music, philosophy, political science, psychology, religious studies, and sociology.

Business administration
(Faculty of arts)

Bachelor of business administration (BBA).
Four years from junior matriculation.

Education
(Faculty of education)

Bachelor of education (BEd).
Four years from junior matriculation or one year from BA or BSc.

Diploma in education.
Two years from junior matriculation.

Engineering
(Faculty of science)

Diploma in engineering.
Three years from junior matriculation. The diploma admits students to the fourth year of a five-year course leading to the bachelor of engineering degree at Nova Scotia Technical College, Halifax.

Home economics
(Faculty of science)

Bachelor of science (BSc).
Four years from junior matriculation.

Music
(Faculty of arts)

Bachelor of music (BMus).
Four years from junior matriculation.

Science, pure
(Faculty of science)

Bachelor of science (BSc).
General degree with a major. Four years from junior matriculation. Available in biology, chemistry, home economics, mathematics, and physics.

Extension programs

For university credit:

Evening courses.
Courses offered at the university and by extension in several centres in the province, mainly in arts, business administration, and education.

Summer sessions.
Courses are offered for undergraduates proceeding to a degree and to teachers who may wish to improve their professional qualifications. Subjects offered are chiefly in arts and education, but a limited number of science, business administration, and home economics courses are also offered.

For no university credit:

A limited number of non-credit courses are offered during the evening and summer sessions.

Admission requirements

For a general statement regarding admission to university study, see article *Admission to university in Canada.*

For information regarding admission to undergraduate study, consult *Requirements for admission to Canadian colleges and universities* available from Service for Admission to College and University, 151 Slater St., Ottawa, Ont., K1P 5N1, $1.50 prepaid.

Academic year

Winter session: mid-September to mid-May.

Summer sessions: mid-May to end of June and early July to mid-August.

Grading system

All grades are given on a credit basis. A passing mark in each subject is 50%. Successful results are classified as follows: first-class (80% and over), second-class (70-79%), and passed (50-69%).

Fees and costs

Tuition and other fees per year, $110 per six semester hour course. Student union fee, $40.

Room and board (semi-private), $850 per year.

Deans of faculties

Arts
J. Smith, BA, MA

Education
E.L. Edmonds, BA, MA, MA(Educ), PhD

Science
J.R. Duffy, BA, MSc, PhD

Directors of schools

Extension
I.P. MacDonald, BSc, MEd

Summer session
D.J. O'Connell, BA, MA

Department heads

Biology
E.L. Drake, BSc, MSc, PhD

Business administration
J.J. Revell, BCom, MBA

Chemistry
G.E. Palmer, BSc, MA, PhD

Classics
J.H. Quincey, MA

Economics
D.J. O'Connell, BA, MA

Engineering
D.J. Gillis, BSc, BEng, MEng

English
F.J. Ledwell, BA, MA

Fine arts
A. Arsenault, BA, MA

History
F.W.P. Bolger, BA, STL, MA, PhD

Home economics
Doris Anderson, BSc, MSc

Mathematics
J.I. Dowling, BSc, MSc

Modern languages
A.I.R. Galloway, MA, DipEd

Music
F.A. Reesor, BMus, MMus, AMus

Philosophy
V. Smitheram, BA, PhilM

Physics
W.C. Lin, BSc, MSc, PhD

Political science
R. Gool, BA, MA

Psychology
K.L. Ozmon, BA, MA, PhD

Religious studies
T.M. MacLellan, BA, DPh, STD

Sociology
S. Dasgupta, BSc, MSc, PhD

Université du Québec*

2525, boulevard Laurier Québec 10 (Qué.)

Téléphone: 418-651-7220

Prière d'adresser toute correspondance d'ordre général au secrétariat général, Université du Québec, 2525, boulevard Laurier, Québec 10 (Qué.)

Total des inscriptions des étudiants à plein temps 6,873; voir aussi la section distincte, intitulée *Statistiques sur les universités et collèges du Canada*

Dirigeants

Président
Alphonse Riverin, MScSoc, MScCom, MBA, DScEcon

Vice-président à l'administration et aux finances
Gérald Martin, BA, LLL, MBA

Vice-président à l'enseignement
Maurice Boisvert, BA, BPh, BScA, MSc, DSc

Vice-président à la planification
Pierre Martin, BA, LLL

Vice-président à la recherche
Louis Berlinguet, BSc, DSc, MSRC

Vice-président aux communications
Louis Brunel (par intérim), BA, LScCom

Secrétariat général
Robert Tessier, BA, BScSoc

Adjoint au secrétaire général
J.C.G. Regalbuto, BA

Archiviste
Michel Clauser

Coordonnateur à la bibliothèque
P.E. Filion

Directeur, service de l'information
Michel Dumas, BA, LPh

Le Centre d'études universitaires de Rimouski:

Directeur général
Alcide Horth, BA, BSc, MSc, DSc

Secrétaire général et registraire
Bertrand Lepage, BA, LSc

Directeur de l'admission et des inscriptions
Bertrand Lepage, BA, LSc

Directeur des affaires étudiantes
Roland Dorval, BA, LPed, BMed

Directeur du service audio-visuel
Hector Frenette

Directeur de la bibliothèque
Gérard Mercure

Directeur de l'éducation permanente
André Bernier

Directeur des études
Pascal Parent

Directeur de l'informatique
Roland Guihur

Directeur des services administratifs
Jacques Plante, BCom, MCom

L'Ecole nationale d'administration publique (Québec):

Directeur
Roland Parenteau, BA, LScCom, DiplEtPol

Secrétaire général
Claude Archambault, BA

Directeur des études
André Gélinas, MA, MSc

L'Institut national de la recherche scientifique (Québec):

Président
Louis Berlinguet, BSc, DSc, MSRC

Directeur
Charles-E. Beaulieu, BA, BScA, DSc

*Membre provisoire de l'AUCC.

Directeur administratif
Roland Dugré, BScA

Secrétaire général
Guy Reeves

L'Université du Québec à Chicoutimi:

Recteur
André Desgagné, BA, LPh, LLD, DES, CR

Vice-recteur à l'enseignement et à la recherche
Laurent Larouche, BA, LPh, LTh, BSc, MSc

Vice-recteur à la planification
Paul-Gaston Tremblay, BA, MScCom

Vice-recteur à l'administration et aux finances
Charles Chamard, MScCom

Secrétaire général
André Lemieux, BLet

Registraire
Laurent Massé, BA, BPed, BSc

Directeur de l'admission
Richard Tremblay

Directeur des approvisionnements
Jean Coutu, MScCom

Directeur du service audio-visuel
J.N. Jacob

Directeur de l'équipement
Gilles Bergeron

Directeur de l'extension et de l'enseignement
Antoine Lavallée

Directeur des finances
Guy Lemay

Directeur de l'informatique
Gilbert Touzot

Directeur des services aux étudiants
J.P. Gagnon

L'Université du Québec à Montréal:

Recteur
Léo Dorais, LPsycho, MBA, PhD

Vice-recteur à l'enseignement et à la recherche
René Hurtubise, BA, LLL, MA, MA

Vice-recteur à l'administration et aux finances
Luc Bernier, BA, BScCom, LScCom, CA

Vice-recteur aux communications
Alexis Zinger, BSc, MSc, PhD

Secrétaire générale
Lise Langlois (Mlle), BA, LLL

Registraire
Denis Laforte

Directeur de l'admission
Claude Clark

Directeur des achats
Maurice Bernard

Directeur de l'animation artistique
Jean Brousseau

Directeur de l'animation sportive
J.G. Prescott

Directrice des archives
Hélène Solyak

Directeur de l'entretien
André Boulet

Directeur des finances
Robert Dionne, BA, MScCompt, RIA

Directeur de l'inscription
J.M. Goyette

Directeur des relations publiques
M.A. Gagnon

Directeur de la santé
Georges Charest

Directeur du service socio-économique
Jean-Marie Rabin, BA, BPed

L'Université du Québec à Trois-Rivières:

Recteur
Gilles Boulet, BTh, LTh, MèsL, LPh, DES

Vice-recteur à l'enseignement et à la recherche
Livia Thür (Mme), LLL, LLD, LScPol,
LScEc

Vice-recteur aux communications
André Brousseau, BA, BPed, MA

Vice-recteur à l'administration et aux finances
François Soumis, LScCom

Vice-recteur aux affaires étudiantes
Jean-Guy Béliveau, BA, BPed, LPed

Directeur de la bibliothèque
Maurice Auger

Directeur des finances
Bernard Lorrain

Directeur de la pastorale
Gilles Marchand

Directeur des services aux étudiants
Jean-Paul Bettez, BA, BPed, LPed, CertEtSup

Directeur des sports
J.F. Grenier

Historique

L'Université du Québec a été constituée le 18 décembre 1968 par l'assemblée nationale du Québec. C'est une université publique gérée, cependant, par une corporation distincte de l'état.

L'université est administrée par l'assemblée des gouverneurs, composée du président, de trois personnes du milieu socio-économique, des recteurs de chaque université constituante, de trois membres du corps professoral, de deux étudiants, de quatre vice-présidents et de trois directeurs d'instituts de recherche ou d'école supérieure.

Elle constitue un réseau d'établissements d'enseignement supérieur et de recherche.

L'Université du Québec se compose actuellement de trois universités constituantes, à Chicoutimi (établie le 19 mars 1969; population de Chicoutimi 36,000), Trois-Rivières (établie le 19 mars 1969; population de Trois-Rivières 65,000), et Montréal (établie le 9 avril 1969; population de Montréal 2,500,000); d'une école supérieure, l'Ecole nationale d'administration publique (établie le 26 juin 1969; population de Québec 400,000); d'un institut de recherche, l'Institut national de la recherche scientifique (établi le 16 décembre 1969; population de Québec 400,000), du Centre d'études universitaires de Rimouski (établi le 3 septembre 1969; population de Rimouski 28,000) et la direction des études universitaires de l'Université du Québec dans l'Outaouais.

Annuaire

On peut obtenir un exemplaire de l'Annuaire général de l'université en s'adressant au secrétariat général, Université du Québec, 2525, boulevard Laurier, Québec 10 (Qué.).

Cours et grades

Structures des programmes de premier cycle:

L'Université du Québec offre deux genres de programmes au niveau du premier cycle: le baccalauréat général et le baccalauréat spécialisé. La structure d'accueil pour les deux programmes est la même: le diplôme d'études collégiales (du ministère de l'Education du Québec) ou l'équivalent.

Le baccalauréat général comprend un minimum de 30 cours; le baccalauréat spécialisé comprend un minimum de 14 cours de spécialisation entre 3 et 6 cours libres et un bloc de cours complémentaires pour un total minimum de 30 cours.

Habituellement, un étudiant s'inscrit à cinq cours par session. Le baccalauréat comporte donc six sessions.

Programme de premier cycle 1971-72:

Chicoutimi

Baccalauréat spécialisé

Administration

Administration *(BSpAdm)*.
Administration (sciences comptables) [*BSpAdm(sciences comptables)*].

Arts et sciences humaines

Arts plastiques *(BSpArtsPl)*.
Géographie *(BSpGéogr)*.
Histoire *(BSpH)*.
Lettres (études françaises) [*BSpL(études françaises)*].
Philosophie *(BSpPh)*.
Psychologie *(BSpPs)*.

Sciences de l'éducation

Education physique *(BSpEdPh)*.
Enfance inadaptée *(BSpEnfInad)*.
Enseignement élémentaire *(BSpEnsEl)*.
Enseignement secondaire (administration) [*BSpEnsSec(administration)*].
Enseignement secondaire (anglais)

[*BSpEnsSec(anglais)*].
Enseignement secondaire
(biologie) [*BSpEnsSec(biologie)*].
Enseignement secondaire (chimie)
[*BSpEnsSec(chimie)*].
Enseignement secondaire (géographie)
[*BSpEnsSec(géographie)*].
Enseignement secondaire (histoire)
[*BSpEnsSec(histoire)*].
Enseignement secondaire (lettres françaises)
[*BSpEnsSec(lettres françaises)*].
Enseignement secondaire (mathématiques)
[*BSpEnsSec(mathématiques)*].
Enseignement secondaire (physique)
[*BSpEnsSec(physique)*].
Sciences de l'éducation *(BSpScdel'Ed)*.

Sciences pures, appliquées et de la santé

Biologie [*BSpSc(biologie)*].
Chimie [*BSpSc(chimie)*].
Génie chimique [*BSpScA(génie chimique)*].
Génie électrique [*BSpScA(génie électrique)*].
Génie médical [*BSpScA(génie médical)*].
Génie physique [*BSpScA(génie physique)*].
Mathématiques [*BSpSc(mathématiques)*].
Physique [*BSpSc(physique)*].

Montréal

Baccalauréat spécialisé

Famille de formation des maîtres

Enseignement de la sexologie
[*BSpEns(sexologie)*].
Enseignement de l'éducation physique
[*BSpEns(éducation physique)*].
Enseignement élémentaire (BSpEnsEl).
Enseignement enfance inadaptée
(BSpEnfInad).
Enseignement préscolaire et élémentaire
(BSpEnsPrésc), (BSpEnsEl).
Information scolaire et professionnelle
(BSpInformScoletProf).

Famille des arts

Arts plastiques (BSpArtsPl).
Arts plastiques (gravure)
[*BSpArtsPl(gravure)*].
Arts plastiques (peinture)
[*BSpArtsPl(peinture)*].
Arts plastiques (sculpture)
[*BSpArtsPl(sculpture)*].
Design 2D [*BSpDesign(2D)*].

Design 3D [*BSpDesign(3D)*].
Histoire de l'art *(BSpHdel'art)*.
Musique *(BSpMus)*.

Famille des lettres

Animation culturelle *(BSpAnimCult)*.
Animation culturelle esthétique
[*BSpAnimCult(esthétique)*].
Animation culturelle études étrangères
[*BSpAnimCult(études étrangères)*].
Animation culturelle études littéraires
[*BSpAnimCult(études littéraires)*].
Animation culturelle études théâtrales
[*BSpAnimCult(études théâtrales)*].
Animation culturelle linguistique
[*BSpAnimCult(linguistique)*].
Education culturelle *(BSpEdCult)*.
Education culturelle esthétique
[*BSpEdCult(esthétique)*].
Education culturelle études étrangères
[*BSpEdCult(études étrangères)*].
Education culturelle études littéraires
[*BSpEdCult(études littéraires)*].
Education culturelle études théâtrales
[*BSpEdCult(études théâtrales)*].
Education culturelle linguistique
[*BSpEdCult(linguistique)*].
Information culturelle *(BSpInformCult)*.
Information culturelle esthétique
[*BSpInformCult(esthétique)*].
Information culturelle études étrangères
[*BSpInformCult(études étrangères)*].
Information culturelle études littéraires
[*BSpInformCult(études littéraires)*].
Information culturelle études théâtrales
[*BSpInformCult(études théâtrales)*].
Information culturelle linguistique
[*BSpInformCult(linguistique)*].
Lettres (études françaises) [*BSpL(études
françaises)*].
Linguistique *(BSpLing)*.
Recherche culturelle *(BSpRechCult)*.
Recherche culturelle esthétique
[*BSpRechCult(esthétique)*].
Recherche culturelle études étrangères
[*BSpRechCult(études étrangères)*].
Recherche culturelle études littéraires
[*BSpRechCult(études littéraires)*].
Recherche culturelle études théâtrales
[*BSpRechCult (études théâtrales)*].
Recherche culturelle linguistique
[*BSpRechCult(linguistique)*].

Famille des sciences

Biologie [*BSpSc(biologie)*].
Chimie [*BSpSc(chimie)*].
Enseignement professionnel
(électrotechnique)
[*BSpEnsProf(électrotechnique)*].
Enseignement professionnel (techniques de la
mécanique) [*BSpEnsProf (techniques de la
mécanique)*].
Enseignement secondaire (biologie)
[*BSpEnsSec(biologie)*].
Enseignement secondaire (chimie)
[*BSpEnsSec(chimie)*].
Enseignement secondaire (mathématiques)
[*BSpEnsSec(mathématiques)*].
Enseignement secondaire (physique)
[*BSpEnsSec(physique)*].
Géographie-physique [*BSpSc(géographie-
physique)*].
Géologie [*BSpSc(géologie)*].
Mathématiques [*BSpSc(mathématiques)*].
Physique [*BSpSc(physique)*].

Famille des sciences économiques et administratives

Administration *(BSpAdm)*.
Economique *(BSpEc)*.
Enseignement secondaire (administration)
[*BSpEnsSec(administration)*].

Famille des sciences humaines

Enseignement secondaire (géographie)
[*BSpEnsSec(géographie)*].
Enseignement secondaire (histoire)
[*BSpEnsSec(histoire)*].
Enseignement secondaire (latin)
[*BSpEnsSec(latin)*].
Enseignement secondaire (latin-grec)
[*BSpEnsSec(latin-grec)*].
Enseignement secondaire (sciences
religieuses) [*BspEnsSec(sciences religieuses)*].
Géographie humaine *(BSpGéogHum)*.
Histoire *(BSpH)*.
Lettres classiques (études anciennes)
[*BSpLCl(études anciennes)*].
Lettres classiques (latin) [*BSpLCl(latin)*].
Lettres classiques (latin-grec) [*BSpLCl(latin-
grec)*].
Philosophie *(BSpPh)*.
Psychologie *(BSpPs)*.
Relations humaines *(BSpRelHum)*.
Science politique *(BSpScPol)*.
Sciences religieuses *(BSpScRel)*.
Sociologie *(BSpSoc)*.
Travail social *(BSpTravSoc)*.

Rimouski

Baccalauréat spécialisé

Famille des lettres et sciences humaines

Etudes françaises [*BSpL(études françaises)*].
Etudes françaises-géographie
Etudes françaises-histoire
Géographie-administration
Géographie-biologie
Géographie-études françaises
Géographie-histoire
Géographie-mathématiques
Histoire-études françaises
Histoire-géographie

Famille des sciences de l'administration

Administration *(BSpAdm)*.

Famille des sciences de l'éducation

Enseignement élémentaire et préscolaire
(BSpEnsEl), *(BSpEnsPrésc)*.
Enseignement enfance inadaptée
(BSpEnfInad).
Enseignement secondaire (administration)
[*BSpEnsSec(administration)*].
Enseignement secondaire (biologie)
[*BSpEnsSec(biologie)*].
Enseignement secondaire (chimie)
[*BSpEnsSec(chimie)*].
Enseignement secondaire (études anglaises)
[*BSpEnsSec(études anglaises)*].
Enseignement secondaire (études françaises)
[*BSpEnsSec(études françaises)*].
Enseignement secondaire (géographie)
[*BSpEnsSec(géographie)*].
Enseignement secondaire (histoire)
[*BSpEnsSec(histoire)*].
Enseignement secondaire (mathématiques)
[*BSpEnsSec(mathématiques)*].
Enseignement secondaire (physique)
[*BSpEnsSec(physique)*].
Enseignement secondaire (sciences
religieuses)

Famille des sciences pures

Biologie [*BSpSc(biologie)*].
Biologie-administration
Biologie-chimie
Biologie-mathématiques
Biologie-physique
Chimie [*BSpSc(chimie)*].
Chimie-biologie
Chimie-mathématiques
Chimie-physique
Mathématiques [*BSpSc(mathématiques)*].
Mathématiques-administration
Mathématiques-biologie
Mathématiques-chimie
Mathématiques-physique
Physique [*BSpSc(physique)*].
Physique-biologie
Physique-chimie
Physique-mathématiques

Famille des sciences religieuses

Théologie *(BSpTh)*.

Trois-Rivières

Baccalauréat spécialisé

Famille des arts et des sciences humaines

Arts plastiques *(BSpArtsPl)*.
Génagogie *(BSpGénagogie)*.
Géographie *(BSpGéogr)*.
Histoire *(BSpH)*.
Langue moderne (études anglaises)
[*BSpLangMod(études anglaises)*].
Lettres (études françaises) [*BSpL(études françaises)*].
Lettres (études québécoises) [*BSpL(études québécoises)*].
Lettres classiques (grec) [*BSpLCl(grec)*].
Lettres classiques (latin) [*BSpLCl(latin)*].
Lettres classiques (latin-grec) [*BSpLCl(latin-grec)*].
Linguistique *(BSpLing)*.
Musique *(BSpMus)*.
Philosophie *(BSpPh)*.
Psychologie *(BSpPs)*.
Récréologie *(BSpRécréol)*.
Théologie *(BSpTh)*.

Famille des sciences de l'administration et de l'économie

Administration *(BSpAdm)*.
Administration (sciences comptables) [*BSpAdm(sciences comptables)*].
Economique *(BSpEc)*.
Recherche opérationnelle *(BSpROp)*.

Famille des sciences de l'éducation

Education physique *(BSpEdPh)*.
Enfance inadaptée *(BSpEnfInad)*.
Enseignement élémentaire *(BSpEnsEl)*.
Enseignement préscolaire *(BSpEnsPrésc)*.
Enseignement (éducation physique) [*BSpEns(éducation physique)*].
Enseignement (enfance inadaptée) [*BSpEns(enfance inadaptée)*].
Enseignement (musique) [*BSpEns(musique)*].
Enseignement secondaire (administration) [*BSpEnsSec(administration)*].
Enseignement secondaire (anglais) [*BSpEnsSec(anglais)*].
Enseignement secondaire (arts plastiques) [*BSpEnsSec(arts plastiques)*].
Enseignement secondarei (biologie) [*BSpEnsSec(biologie)*].
Enseignement secondaire (chimie) [*BSpEnsSec(chimie)*].
Enseignement secondaire (histoire) [*BSpEnsSec(histoire)*].
Enseignement secondaire (géographie) [*BSpEnsSec(géographie)*].
Enseignement secondaire (lettres françaises) [*BSpEnsSec(lettres françaises)*].
Enseignement secondaire (mathématiques) [*BSpEnsSec(mathématiques)*].
Enseignement secondaire (physique) [*BSpEnsSec(physique)*].
Enseignement secondaire (sciences religieuses) [*BSpEnsSec(sciences religieuses)*].
Enseignement technique
Sciences de l'éducation *(BSpScdel'Ed)*.

Famille des sciences pures, appliquées et de la santé

Biologie [*BSpSc(biologie)*].
Biologie humaine [*BSpSc(biologie humaine)*].
Biochimie [*BSpSc(biochimie)*].
Chimie [*BSpSc(chimie)*].
Génie chimique [*BSpScA(génie chimique)*].
Génie électrique [*BSpScA(génie électrique)*].
Génie médical [*BSpScA(génie medical)*].
Génie physique [*BSpScA(génie physique)*].
Mathématiques [*BSpSc(mathématiques)*].
Nursing [*BSpSanté(nursing)*].
Physique [*BSpSc(physique)*].

Programmes de formation culturelle et professionnelle

Ces programmes sont administrés par l'université en collaboration directe avec les associations et instituts professionnels concernés qui définissent les seuils d'accueil aux programmes. Ordinairement, on tient compte, pour ce qui est de l'admission des étudiants à ces programmes, de l'expérience et de la vie professionnelle et on s'appuie, règle générale, sur le diplôme de fin d'études secondaires.

En outre, l'un ou l'autre des diplômes, brevets ou certificats décernés, sont accessibles à des catégories d'étudiants très particuliers.

Le Centre d'études universitaires de Rimouski.

Brevet de l'Institut des banquiers canadiens
Certificat des agents d'assurance (A.D.A.)
Certificat en formation religieuse
Certificat en sciences de l'administration
Certificat en sciences de l'éducation
Diplôme de la Société des comptables en administration et prix de revient (R.I.A.)
Diplôme de l'Association des comptables généraux du Québec (C.G.A.)

L'Université du Québec à Chicoutimi.

Brevet de l'Institut des banquiers canadiens
Certificat en sciences comptables
Certificat en sciences de l'administration
Diplôme de la Société des comptables en administration et prix de revient (R.I.A.)
Diplôme de l'Association des administrateurs d'hôpitaux de la province de Québec
Diplôme de l'Association des comptables généraux du Québec (C.G.A.)
Diplôme de l'Institut des officiers municipaux

L'Université du Québec à Trois-Rivières.

Brevet de l'Institut des banquiers canadiens
Certificat de technicien supérieur I
Certificat de technicien supérieur II
Certificat en administration pour le personnel des caisses populaires
Certificat en comptabilité industrielle
Certificat en mathématiques
Certificat en psycho-pédagogie
Certificat en recouvrement de crédits
Certificat en sciences comptables
Certificat en sciences de l'administration
Diplôme de la Société des comptables en administration et prix de revient (RIA)
Diplôme de l'Association des comptables généraux licenciés
Diplôme de l'Institut des officiers municipaux

Cours d'été.

La plupart des cours qui se donnent l'été (1972) peuvent s'intégrer soit au programme universitaire soit au programme des brevets d'enseignement.

Conditions d'admission

On trouvera un exposé général sur l'admission aux études universitaires dans l'article *Admission aux universités canadiennes.*

Afin d'obtenir des renseignements sur l'admission aux études du niveau pré-grade, consultez *Conditions d'admission dans les collèges et universités du Canada* que l'on peut obtenir du Service d'admission au collège et à l'université, 151, rue Slater, Ottawa (Ont.), K1P 5N1, $1.50 port payé.

Etudes de deuxième cycle:
baccalauréat spécialisé ou l'équivalent avec moyenne cumulative d'au moins B ou l'équivalent.

Etudes de troisième cycle:
maîtrise dans la discipline choisie ou l'équivalent.

Année universitaire

L'enseignement à l'Université du Québec se donne sur une base de sessions — trois sessions par année.

Session d'automne: septembre à décembre.

Session d'hiver: janvier à mai.

Session d'été: juin à août.

Système de mentions

A — excellent; B — très bien; C — bien; D — passable; E — échec; I — incomplet; S — exigence satisfaite; X — abandon autorisé.

Pour fin de calcul de la moyenne cumulative, la valeur numérique accordée à chacune des lettres est la suivante: A — 4; B — 3; C — 2; D — 1; E — 0. Ce système a été adopté

provisoirement par l'assemblée des gouverneurs de l'université.

Frais

Les frais de scolarité sont de $50 par cours. Habituellement l'étudiant à temps complet s'inscrit à cinq cours par session, donc $250 par session.

Aide financière

On peut distinguer deux sortes d'aide financière aux étudiants: le régime de prêts-bourses du ministère de l'Education du Québec, les bourses décernées soit par l'université soit par des associations, instituts ou compagnies.

Service d'aide aux étudiants du ministère de l'Education

Des prêts maxima de $700 et des bourses maxima de $1,100 sont consentis aux étudiants du premier cycle universitaire, aux conditions suivantes: l'étudiant doit être citoyen canadien, être domicilié et avoir résidé au Québec depuis au moins un an, être étudiant à temps complet et avoir besoin d'aide financière. Les étudiants étrangers qui, à titre d'immigrants, demeurent au Québec depuis un an sont admissibles à ce régime de prêts-bourses.

Bourses de l'Université du Québec. Deux bourses de la Compagnie de papier Rolland Limitée ($500 chacune); trois bourses "I.B.M. — Thomas J. Watson Memorial" ($500 chacune).

Bourses de l'Université du Québec à Chicoutimi. Une bourse de la compagnie Alcan Limitée ($500); une bourse du Cercle des Affaires d'Alma ($500); une bourse du Club Social "Alcan Recherche et Développement" ($100).

Bourses de l'Université du Québec à Trois-Rivières. Dix bourses de la Commission des Affaires étudiantes de l'université ($100).

Instituts ou centres de recherche

La recherche à l'Université du Québec se fait soit dans les centres de recherche et les départements des universités constituantes, soit dans les centres de recherche rattachés à l'Institut national de la recherche, soit à l'Ecole nationale d'administration publique.

Institut national de la recherche scientifique.
Centre de recherche des sciences de la santé
Centre de recherche en énergie
Centre de recherche en ingénierie des télécommunications
Centre de recherches urbaines et régionales
Centre québécois des sciences de l'eau

Université du Québec à Chicoutimi.
Centre de recherche du moyen-nord
Centre de recherche en productivité biologique

Université du Québec à Montréal.
Centre de recherche en didactique
Centre de recherche en écologie

Université du Québec à Trois-Rivières.

Centre de recherche des sciences de la santé, efficience physique et psycho-sociologique.
Directeur: Hugues Lavallée
Axes de recherche: efficience physique et psycho-sociologique des individus dans les domaines du travail et des sports.
Centre de recherche à la santé et aux sports.
Le programme de recherche comprend, entre autres, les projets suivants:
. efficience physique, psychologique et sociologique des enfants de quatre à treize ans soumis à des activités physiques et des sports contrôlés;
. comportement de l'enfance exceptionnelle;
. l'efficience physique selon le milieu et les conditions de travail;
. la valeur des tournois de hockey pee wee-mosquito;
. la valeur des équipements pour prévenir les blessures dans les différents sports de contact.
Domaine de recherche: efficience physique et psycho-sociologique chez l'enfant et l'adolescent.
Programme de recherche:
. projet longitudinal (dix ans) sur la croissance psycho-somatique des enfants de quatre à treize ans soumis à un minimum d'activités physiques et de pratique de sports contrôlée;
. évaluation des facteurs inhérents à la pratique des sports de compétition qui peuvent avoir une influence psycho-somatique chez l'enfant et l'adolescent;

. évaluation des tests de psychologie de l'effort chez l'enfant;
. recherche sur le métabolisme intermédiaire à l'effort chez l'enfant.

Centre de recherche en communication humaine.
Directeur: Reynald Rivard
Axes de recherche: communication humaine — théorie et thérapie de la communication.
Les recherches entreprises au centre le sont à partir d'un schéma issu des travaux de Wiener, Lewin et Innis. Cette méthode de travail permet au centre d'entreprendre des études concernant un grand nombre de secteurs de l'activité.
Le programme de recherche porte sur la construction d'un modèle contemporain de la communication humaine et sur sa vérification expérimentale dans les domaines de la psychologie, de l'administration, de la pédagogie et de la pastorale.
Programme de recherche:
. construction d'un modèle du processus de la communication humaine;
. détermination des codes et des média propres à rendre efficace la communication entre l'homme et certains oiseaux;
. influence du feedback magnétoscopique en thérapie familiale;
. les modes de communication dans les familles canadiennes-françaises dont l'un des enfants est bègue;
. étude analytique d'une méthode d'apprentissage en lecture rapide.

Centre de recherche en histoire des religions et de la pensée.
Directeur: Alexis Klimov
Axes de recherche: histoire des religions et de la pensée — histoire des religions, archéologie, art et esthétique.
Ce centre se spécialise dans les domaines suivants:
. études anciennes (recherche bibliographique et philosophique, Sénèque et son temps);
. histoire des religions (symbolisme, religion orientale: bouddhisme et brahmanisme, langues anciennes; sanscrit et hébreux; études des phénomènes mystiques en rapport avec les données de la para-psychologie contemporaine);
. archéologie (archéologie préhistorique du Québec, fouilles et musée);
. esthétique et histoire de l'art (théâtre expérimental).
Domaine de recherche: études anciennes — histoire des religions, archéologie préhistorique; art et esthétique.
Programme de recherche:
. la civilisation gréco-romaine;
. bibliographie exhaustive de Sénèque;
. la religion de Virgile;

. bibliographie des études anciennes à partir de 1896;
. les subordonnées complétives en latin;
. dictionnaire des symboles;
. études sur l'hindouisme;
. revue Helios;
. fouilles archéologiques au Québec (Abitibi et Mauricie);
. recherches sur l'esthétique du Moyen-Age;
. recherches sur la psychologie de l'art.

Centre de recherche en loisirs.
Directeur: Michel Bellefleur
Axes de recherche: récréologie, civilisation du loisir, changements technologiques/loisirs.
Le centre favorise à court terme trois projets de recherche:
. une étude du marché du travail pour les professionnels en loisirs;
. une études sur les loisirs étudiants à l'intérieur d'une école de type (polyvalente);
. une étude sur les loisirs adolescents en milieu urbain.
Deux autres études seront mises en marche incessamment. L'une portera sur l'aménagement du territoire en fonction d'une utilisation rationnelle de nos ressources régionales du "plein air". L'autre s'attaquera au phénomène socio-culturel de la chanson québécoise au point de vue sciences humaines.
Domaine de recherche: le développement de l'ensemble des connaissances scientifiques nécessaires à la perception du phénomène loisir et de son implication en tant que champ de développement d'une discipline professionnelle.
Programme de recherche:
. étude des loisirs de plein air dans la région économique de Trois-Rivières;
. étude analytique sur le statut de l'organisation actuelle et sur les modalités possibles d'organisation des loisirs pour la municipalité de Trois-Rivières;
. enquête sociologique sur le phénomène loisir dans la municipalité de Ste-Foy;
. étude sur des besoins de perfectionnement (éducation permanente) pour les professionnels en loisir du Québec;
. étude sur les différents modes d'intervention politique en loisir;
. l'étude sémantique du langage spécialisé propre au loisir.

Centre de recherche prospective en éducation.
Directeur: Gérard Marier
Axes de recherche: recherche prospective pertinente au développement des systèmes d'éducation en relation avec la société.
L'orientation du centre est nettement prospective et les recherches multidisciplinaires s'organisent autour de thèmes généraux, la violence, la préparation

au marché du travail, les rapports maître-
élèves.
Les projets à court terme sont:
. le carrefour des étudiants du Québec (Tome
I déjà paru);
. la publication d'un ouvrage sur l'avenir des
étudiants et les étudiants de l'avenir;
. la cueillette d'une documentation
prospective;
. la mise en place d'une équipe québécoise de
spécialistes et d'étudiants qui s'interrogent
constamment sur l'avenir;
. la mise à jour de la carte scolaire afin
d'assurer aux recherches prospectives une
base convenable;
. la recherche théorique sur l'animation socio-
culturelle.
Domaine de recherche: prospective en
éducation.
Programme de recherche:
. droits, responsabilités et aspirations des
membres de la communauté scolaire;
. l'environnement des universitaires à Trois-
Rivières;
. mutation des modèles culturels chez les
jeunes québécois de 1970 à 1980;
. l'errance chez les jeunes québécois.

Autres institutions

Service universitaire Nord-Ouest québécois
(rattaché à l'Université du Québec à Trois-
Rivières).

*Service universitaire dans l'Outaouais
québécois.*

Doyens

Centre d'études universitaires de Rimouski:

Premier cycle
Yves-Marie Dionne, MA, LTh, LSc

Ecole nationale d'administration publique:

Directeur des études
André Gélinas, MA, MSc

Université du Québec à Chicoutimi:

Premier cycle
Albert Joris, CertScCom, ScEc, DScEc

Université du Québec à Montréal:

Premier cycle
Jacques Peltier, BEc, BPh, BTh, MA

Etudes supérieures
Maurice Brossard, BSc, PhD

Université du Québec à Trois-Rivières:

Premier cycle
Christian Demers, BA, BSc(phy)

Directeurs des centres

Institut national de la recherche scientifique:

Centre de l'énergie
Brian Gregory, BASc, PhD

Centre de recherches en sciences de la santé
Didier Dufour

Centre des recherches urbaines et régionales
Gérald Fortin, PhD

Centre québécois des sciences de l'eau
Michel Slivitzky, BScA, MSc

Directeurs des départements

Centre d'études universitaires de Rimouski:

Sciences économiques et administratives
Albert Joris, DSc, Ec

Sciences humaines et lettres
Gilles Lamontagne, BA, DiplLittFranç

Sciences pures
Michel Champagne

Sciences religieuses
Jean Drapeau, BA, DTh

Université du Québec à Chicoutimi:

Bibliothèque
Raoul Lapointe

Sciences de l'éducation
André Caille

Sciences économiques et administratives
Michel Legault

Sciences humaines
Jean-Paul Vincent, LTh, MA, LèsLet

Sciences pures et appliquées
J.P. Paquet

Sciences religieuses
Marcel Bouchard

Université du Québec à Montréal:

Economique
Vely Leroy, PhD

Etudes littéraires
Paule Leduc, Doct

Histoire
Alfred Dubuc, DLet

Mathématiques
Claude Janvier

Psychologie
Hans Neidhard, Doct

Sciences politiques
Jacques Levesque, Doct

Sciences religieuses
Anita Caron, Doct

Université du Québec à Trois-Rivières:

Biologie-chimie
Marcel Lefebvre, BA, BSc, MSc

Ingénierie
Jean-Luc Dion, BSc, MSc

Lettres
Armand Guilmette, BA, BPh, LPed, LLL,
DES, DèsLet

Mathématiques
Louise Matin (Mlle), BA, BSc, MSc

Philosophie
Jean Langlois, BA, LPh, LTh, DPh

Physique
André-Guy Lacerte, BSc, MSc

Psychologie et sciences de l'éducation
Raymond Champagne

Sciences de l'administration et de
l'économique
Gilles Arès

Sciences humaines
Maurice Carrier, BA, MA

Théologie
Jean-Marie Levasseur

Queen's University at Kingston*

Kingston, Ontario

Telephone: 613-546-3871
Direct general correspondence to the registrar

Total full-time student enrolment 8,087; see also separate section *Statistics on Canadian universities and colleges*

Executive and administrative officers

Chancellor
J.B. Stirling, SM, CD, BA, BSc, LLD, DSc

Rector
A. Broadbent, BA

Vice-chancellor and principal
J.J. Deutsch, BCom, LLD

Vice-principal, administration
R.L. Kennedy, MC, BSc, MS

Vice-principal, academic
G.A. Harrower, BSc, PhD

Vice-principal, finance
D.H. Bonham, BA, BCom, LLB, LLM, CA

Vice-principal, health sciences
E.H. Botterell, OBE, MD, MS, FRCS(C)

Vice-principal, development and information
James Courtright, BA, BSc

Registrar
G.C. Leech, OBE, CD, BSc(EE)

Assistant registrar, admissions
H.W. Sterne, DSO, MBE, CO

---

*Ordinary member, AUCC.

Assistant registrar, student awards
D.N. Ellis, BA

Assistant registrar, statistics and records
R. Ziola, BA, BCom

Bursar
T.H.R. Parkinson, BCom, MBA, CA

Librarian
D.A. Redmond, BSc, BLS, MS(LS)

Director, university extension
M.R. Wardle, BSc, MSc

Dean, student affairs
Stewart Webster, MA, PhD

Dean of women
To be appointed

Director, student health services
H.W. Greenidge, CD, MD, CM, CRCP(C)

Director, public relations
L.T. Moore, BA

Director, men's residences
G. McGrath, BA, MA

Director, alumni fund
Ernest E. Hurlbut, BA

Secretary, alumni association
H.J. Hamilton, BA

Background

Queen's College was founded by the Presbyterian Church of Canada in connection with the Church of Scotland primarily to provide educational opportunity for the youth of a growing economy and for a ministry trained within the country. On October 16, 1841, Queen Victoria issued a Royal Charter to "Queen's College at Kingston". The first session opened on March 7, 1842, and the first degrees were awarded in June 1847.

The only denominational requirement was that the principal be a Presbyterian minister and that trustees and staff subscribe to the Westminster Confession of Faith. The denominational requirements were gradually eliminated by successive acts of parliament. The Dominion of Canada Act of 1912, essentially a new charter, removed the last trace of them. The faculty of theology became Queen's Theological College and the original Queen's College at Kingston became

Queen's University at Kingston, a non-
denominational and co-educational
institution.

Facilities and services

Queen's University at Kingston (population
of Kingston approximates 60,000), has 34
teaching buildings; an administration
building; a library (850,000 volumes), a law
library (66,000 volumes); an education
library (30,000 volumes); well-equipped
laboratories for the basic and applied sciences
and a psychological laboratory; an
experimental station some 15 miles from
Kingston provides special opportunity for
research in land and water biology; the
Kingston general hospital, the Hotel-Dieu
and the Kingston psychiatric hospital are
centres for clinical teaching in medicine.
There is residence and dining accommodation
for 1,114 women and 1,105 men (the dining
hall in the women's residence also
accommodates women students lodging out
of residence), an art centre, a music library, a
new gymnasium complex with a swimming
pool of olympic size, a synchroton laboratory,
a computing centre, and foreign language
laboratories. Queen's University radio
station, CFRC, is owned by the university
and operated by the student radio club under
the supervision of the director of radio and a
professor of electrical engineering.

Student services include a health service,
housing office, employment bureau,
bookstore, and students' union with dining
hall, coffee shop, reading, study, and common
rooms.

Calendars and brochures

Queen's University publishes the following
calendars and brochures, copies of which
may be obtained by writing to the registrar.
Entrance and matriculation scholarships
bulletin; faculty of applied science; faculty of
arts and science; faculty of education; faculty
of law; faculty of medicine; handbook
admissions bulletin; school of business
(undergraduate and graduate); school of
graduate studies; school of nursing; school of
rehabilitation therapy; summer school and
extramural; theological college.

Courses and degrees

Arts
(Faculty of arts and science)

Bachelor of arts (BA).
(a) General course, three years from senior
matriculation. Concentration possible in art
history, biochemistry, biology, chemistry,
classical studies, commerce, drama,
economics, English, film, French, geography,
German, Greek, history, Italian, Latin,
mathematics, music, philosophy, physics,
political studies, psychology, religion,
Russian, sociology, and Spanish. (b) Honors
course, four years from senior matriculation.
Available in art history, biology, classics,
economics, English, French, geography,
German, Greek, history, Latin, mathematics,
music, philosophy, physics, political studies,
psychology, Russian, sociology, and Spanish.

Bachelor of music (BMus).
Four years from senior matriculation.

Bachelor of art education (BAE).
Four years from senior matriculation.

(School of graduate studies)

Master of arts (MA).
Ordinarily, one year from honors BA.
Available in classics, economics, English,
French, geography, German, history,
mathematics, philosophy, political studies,
psychology, Spanish.

Diploma in clinical psychology.
Given at the end of the first year of a PhD
program.

Doctor of philosophy (PhD).
Normally two years from master's degree.
Available in economics, English, French,
German, history, mathematics, philosophy,
political studies, and psychology.

Business
(School of business)

Bachelor of commerce (BCom).
Four years from senior matriculation.

Diploma in business administration.
One year from bachelor's degree in arts,
science or engineering.

Master of business administration (MBA).
Two years from bachelor's degree in arts,
science or engineering. Designed for
graduates seeking careers in professional
management and administration.

Master of public administration (MPA).
A university degree and substantial
administration experience, or having
graduated with a better than average
standing in either arts, law or commerce.

Commerce see business above

Divinity
(Queen's Theological College)

Bachelor of divinity (BD).
Three years from BA.

Bachelor of theology (BTh).
Four years.

Education

Bachelor of education (BEd).
Admission requirements are proof of
graduation with an approved degree.

Master of education (MEd).
Honors bachelor's degree followed by BEd
degree and 2 years' teaching.

Engineering, see science, applied

Law
(Faculty of law)

Bachelor of laws (LLB).
Three years from: (a) three years of
university degree course beyond junior
matriculation, or (b) two years of university
degree course beyond senior matriculation, or
(c) a bachelor's degree.

Master of laws (LLM).
One year full-time program, admission
restricted to 40. Proof of graduating with a
high standing from a recognized university.

Medicine
(Faculty of medicine)

Doctor of medicine (MD).
A total of six years from senior matriculation
(the two pre-medical years have now been
discontinued). These are followed by one
year internship.

(School of graduate studies)

Master of science (MSc).
Normally at least one year from MD degree
with a minimum of second class honors
standing. Available in anatomy,
biochemistry, community health and
epidemiology, medicine, microbiology and
immunology, paediatrics, pathology,
pharmacology, physiology, and surgery.

Diploma in radiology (diagnosis) [DMR(D)].
Two years. Candidates with the MD degree
are accepted under the general regulations of
the school of graduate studies and research.
Studies for the DMR(D) program lead to
certification or fellowship by the Royal
College of Physicians and Surgeons of
Canada after three years of diagnostic
radiology. The Royal College requires an
additional year which may be spent either in
isotopes in the department, or in medicine or
surgery, or six months of either plus six
months of pathology.

Diploma in anaesthesia.
Applicants with the MD degree are accepted
under the general regulations of the school of
graduate studies and research. All graduate
students who complete three years' training in
the department of anaesthesiology, one of
which shall be either internal medicine or a
basic science, will be a candidate for the
diploma in anaesthesia, on examination,
granted by the university.

The postgraduate course satisfies the
requirements for examination for the
certificate and fellowship (in anaesthesia)
degree of the Royal College of Physicians
and Surgeons of Canada.

In addition, postgraduate work is offered in
obstetrics and gynaecology, psychiatry and
urology.

Nursing
(School of nursing)

A four-year integrated program leading to
the *bachelor of nursing science* is offered to

high school graduates. Registered nurses are required to complete a three-year program. The one-year diploma course in public health nursing has been discontinued.

Physical education

(School of physical and health education and faculty of arts and science)

Bachelor of arts (BA) and *bachelor of physical and health education (BPHE)*.
Four years from senior matriculation.

Rehabilitation therapy

(School of rehabilitation therapy)

Diploma in physical or *occupational therapy*.
Enrolment limited to 25. Secondary school honors graduation diploma or equivalent required. Three-year program.

Students may return after two years' clincial practice and take a fourth year leading to a BSc(PT) or BSc(OT). A straight four-year degree program will be offered in the near future.

Science, applied

(Faculty of applied science)

Bachelor of science (BSc).
Four years from senior matriculation. Available in chemical, civil, electrical, mechanical, metallurgical, and mining engineering, and in chemistry, geological sciences, mathematics and engineering, and physics. Students graduating with first- and second-class honors standing on the work of the third and fourth years are awarded the BSc with honors.

(School of graduate studies)

Master of science in engineering [MSc(Eng)].
Ordinarily, one year from BSc with at least second-class honors standing. Available in chemical, civil, electrical, mechanical, metallurgical, and mining engineering, and in chemistry, geological sciences, mathematics, and physics.

Diploma in engineering.
One year from BSc. Available in some branches of engineering. Programs are substantially the same as those for the master's degree except that five or six graduate courses are required and there is no research or thesis.

Doctor of philosophy (PhD).
Two years from master's degree. Available in chemistry, chemical, civil, electrical, mechanical, metallurgical, and mining engineering, geological sciences, mathematics, and physics.

Science, natural

(Faculty of arts and science)

Bachelor of arts (BA).
General course, three years from senior matriculation. Concentrations possible in the experimental sciences.

Bachelor of science (BSc).
Honors course, four years from senior matriculation. Available in biochemistry, biology, chemistry, geography, geology, life sciences, mathematics, mathematics and computing science, microbiology and immunology, physics, and physiology.

(School of graduate studies)

Master of science (MSc).
Ordinarily, one year from BSc with at least second-class honors standing. Available in anatomy, biochemistry, biology, chemistry, community health and epidemiology, computing science and information, geography and mathematics, geology, medicine, microbiology and immunology, pathology, pharmacology, physiology, psychiatry, and surgery.

Doctor of philosophy (PhD).
Two years from master's degree. Available in anatomy, biochemistry, biology, chemistry, geological sciences, mathematics, microbiology and immunology, pathology, pharmacology, physics, and physiology.

Extension programs

For university credit:

Extramural courses.
Undergraduate courses are offered by correspondence or in local tutorial groups. It is not possible to take a degree entirely by correspondence. Residence requirements must be fulfilled by attending four summer schools or one regular winter session and two

summer schools. Two courses taken with a tutorial group (see below) will count as one summer school. Tutorial centres, includes Oshawa, Cobourg, Belleville, Brockville,

Madoc; a program of fortnightly lectures by university staff. Kingston has more frequent night classes.

Summer school.
Courses in a large number of arts and science subjects.

Summer school in Bermuda.
Regular degree courses are given each summer in Bermuda with university instructors in charge.

For no university credit:

Summer school.
School of English for French-speaking Canadians and others.

Admission requirements

For a general statement regarding admission to university study, see article *Admission to university in Canada.*

For information regarding admission to undergraduate study, consult *Requirements for admission to Canadian colleges and universities* available from Service for Admission to College and University, 151 Slater St., Ottawa, Ont., K1P 5N1, $1.50 prepaid.

For admission to a first degree in law, students must have either completed three years of university degree course beyond junior matriculation, or completed two years of university degree course beyond senior matriculation, or hold a bachelor's degree. For admission to the BD courses, a BA degree. For admission to graduate study, a student must have obtained a degree or degrees with specified grades.

Academic year

Winter session: September to May.

Summer session: early July to mid-August.

Grading system

Standing is graded as follows for all faculties: grade A, 80-100%; grade B, 65-79%; grade C, 50-64%; grade E, 35-49%; grade F, below 35%.

Fees and costs

Tuition fees per year: full-time (a) for first degree — arts, commerce, law, 1st year nursing, $500; pure science, physical and health education, nursing, medicine (pre-medical years), rehabilitation therapy, $500; engineering (1st and 2nd years) $575; medicine (medical years), engineering (3rd and 4th years), $625; (b) for master's degree — arts, science, $242.50 per term or $485 per year; business administration, $495; (c) for doctorate — $242.50 per term or $485 per year; (d) for graduate diploma — medical radiology — $242.50 per term or $485 per year plus $100 fee for a two-term year.

Student activities per year: $61 to $86 depending on faculty. Extramural course, $85; summer school course, $115; course taken as an extension tutorial class, $115.

Residence fees for men: (room and board) — arts and science (first year), single $1,078, double $1,016; arts and science (second, third and fourth years), single $1,059, double $997; pre-medical (second year), single $1,059, double $997; medicine (first, second and third years), single $1,257, double $1,183; applied science (first year), single $976, double $919; applied science (second, third and fourth years), single $1,006, double $948.

Earl Street residence (senior students, room only): arts and science (third and fourth years), $542; applied science (third and fourth years), $514; commerce (third and fourth years), $552; medicine (first, second and third years), $642; law, $635.

West campus residence (co-ed, room only): fees as above in Earl Street residence.

Residence fees for women: (room and board) single $956, double $916.

Financial awards and assistance

Queen's University offers a large number of scholarships and bursaries as well as other kinds of financial aid. Detailed information is contained in the university calendars or may be obtained by writing directly to the assistant registrar (student awards).

Research institutes

Centre for French Area Studies.
The centre was established in 1967 to co-ordinate and develop interdisciplinary studies and research in areas where French is the main language of communication.
Its present membership includes specialists in the language, literature, history, and politics of France and French Canada.

Institute of Commonwealth and Comparative Studies.
The Queen's University Institute of Commonwealth and Comparative Studies was established in 1963 to concentrate, co-ordinate, and encourage interdisciplinary studies in comparative Commonwealth and other areas at the undergraduate and graduate levels.
Programs of study may be arranged within the current course offerings and regulations of the participating departments and faculties. At the present time, the institute is sponsored jointly by the departments of economics, English, French, geography, history, political studies, and the faculty of law.

Institute of Local Government.
The institute is associated with the department of political studies. Its staff conducts research and teaches graduate and undergraduate students in provincial and local governments. The institute has an extensive library.

Institute for Economic Research.
Conferences, research, and publications on topics in economics are organized by the Institute for Economic Research.

Institute of Intergovernmental Relations.
This institute, also associated with the department of political studies, was established to provide a centre for research into the problems of intergovernmental relations in Canada and elsewhere. The institute provides students in several disciplines with an opportunity for directed study in intergovernmental relations.

The Industrial Relations Centre.
The varied facilities of the centre are available to undergraduate and graduate students. Industrial relations has formed an important part of work at Queen's for many years. Hence students wishing to concentrate in this field can draw upon these specialized resources.
The program of the centre is built upon five functions: 1) participation in undergraduate and graduate instruction; 2) undertaking of a continuing program of research and publication; 3) conducting of seminars and conferences; 4) maintenance of policy-oriented relationships with government, industry, and labour; 5) maintenance of a specialized, industrial relations reference library.
The centre's research programs offer opportunities for summer employment and research experience. The specialized library is also particularly valuable to those students engaged in special study and research in industrial relations and labor economics.

Canadian Institute of Guided Ground Transportation.
The Canadian institute for research and education in ground transportation was established in June 1970 by four founders — Queen's University, Canadian National Railway, Canadian Pacific Railway and the Canadian Transport Commission. Its main functions are: (a) to seek solutions to some of the problems that face Canada's railway industry; (b) to provide additional opportunities in research and education for students, university staff, and employees of industry and government; (c) to increase the supply of persons competently trained in fields relating to guided ground transportation; (d) to establish a reference centre which will facilitate national co-ordination within the industry.

Centre for Metal and Mineral Technology.
A centre for industrial research in the science of metal and mineral technology. Statistics are drawn from physics, chemistry, mining and earth sciences.

Affiliated college

Queen's Theological College, Kingston, Ontario.
Principal: Rev. Donald Mathers, MA, BD,

PhD, DD. Registrar: Rev. Charles Parker, BA, BD. United Church. Co-educational. Established 1912, when the faculty of theology was separated from the university and incorporated as Queen's Theological College. Offers courses in theology leading to the bachelor of divinity (BD) and bachelor of theology (BTh) degrees awarded by the university.

Deans of faculties

Applied science
R.J. Uffen, BASc, MA, PhD, DSc, FRSC, FGSA

Arts and science
R.L. Watts, BA, MA, DPhil

Business
R.J. Hand, BCom, MBA

Education, McArthur College of
V.S. Ready, BA

Graduate studies and research
R.L. McIntosh, BA, MSc, PhD, FRSC, FCIC

Law
D.A. Soberman, BA, LLB

Medicine
D.O. Waugh, BSc, MD, CM, MSc, PhD, FRCP(C)

Nursing
Jean Hill, AB, BA, MSc, EdD

Directors of schools

Physical and health education
D.F. Macintosh, BEd, MS, PhD

Rehabilitation therapy
D.C. Symington, MB, ChB

Department heads

Anaesthesiology
S.L. Vandewater, MD, FRCP(C), FACA

Anatomy
A.A. Travill, MB, BS, MRCS, LRCP, MSc(Med)

Art history and art education
G.E. Finley, BA, MA, PhD

Biochemistry
P.H. Jellinck, BA, BSc, MSc, PhD

Biology
B.N. Smallman, BA, MA, PhD, FRSC

Chemical engineering
R.H. Clark, BSc(Eng), PhD

Chemistry
W. MacF. Smith, BSc, PhD, PhD, FCIC

Civil engineering
A. Brebner, BSc(Eng), PhD, MICE

Classics
S.E. Smethurst, BA, MA

Commerce
R.J. Hand, BCom, MBA

Community health and epidemiology
Robert Steele, MD, DPH, FAPHA

Computing and information science
S.D. Baxter, BSc, ScM, PhD

Drama
J.A. Euringer, BA

Economics
D.C. Smith, BA, MA, PhD

Electrical engineering
C.H.R. Campling, BSc, SM

Engineering
A.J. Coleman, BA, MA, PhD

Engineering drawing
W.G. Stinson, BSc

English language and literature
J.M. Stedmond, BA, MA, PhD

French language and literature
G.W. Ireland, MA

Geography
R.T.H. Smith, BA, MA, PhD

Geological sciences
H.R. Wynne-Edwards, BSc, MA, PhD, FRSC

German language and literature
A.W. Riley, BA, PhD

Hebrew
C.H. Parker, BA, BD

History
J.A. Leith, BA, MA, PhD

Law
D.A. Soberman, BA, LLB, LLM

Mathematics
A.J. Coleman, BA, MA, PhD

Mechanical engineering
P.G. Hill, BSc, MSc, ScD

Medical jurisprudence
D.L. Wilson, MA, MD, CM, FRCP(C),
FACP

Medicine
E.R. Yendt, MD, FRCP(C)

Metallurgy and metallurgical engineering
W.B. Mackay, BSc(EE), BMetE, MS, PhD

Microbiology and immunology
F.H. Milazzo, BS, MS, PhD

Mining engineering
A. Bauer, BSc, PhD

Music
I. Anhalt

Obstetrics and gynaecology
J.A. Low, MD, FRCS(C)

Ophthalmology
D.A. Rosen, BSc, MD, CM, FRCS(C), FACS

Otorhinolaryngology
D.M.L. Williams, MRCS, FRCS

Paediatrics
A.M. Bryans, MS, FRCP(C), FAAP

Pathology
N. Kaufman, MBE, BSc, MD, CM

Pharmacology
G.S. Marks, BSc, MSc, DPhil

Philosophy
A.R.C. Duncan, MA

Physical and health education
D. deF. Macintosh, BEd(PE), MS(PE), PhD

Physics
A.T. Stewart, BSc, MSc, PhD

Physiology
J.D. Hatcher, MD, PhD

Political studies
J.W. Grove, BSc, DPA

Psychiatry
T.J. Boag, MD, ChB, CRCP(C)

Psychology
W.R. Thompson, BA, MA, PhD

Radiology
S.L. Fransman, MD, FCCP, FRCP(C)

Rehabilitation medicine
D.C. Symington, MB, ChB

Religion
D.M. Mathers, MA, BD, PhD, DD

Russian language and literature
A.W. Riley, BA, PhD

Sociology
J. Lele, BA, MA, PhD

Spanish language and literature
A.M. Fox, BA, MA, PhD

Surgery
J.R. McCorriston, BA, MD, CM, MSc,
FRCS(C), FACS

Therapeutic radiology
S. Lott, BA, MD, DMRT, CRCP

Urology
A.W. Bruce, MB, ChB, FRCS, FRCS(C)

Royal Military College of Canada*

Kingston, Ontario

Telephone: 613-545-7236
Direct general correspondence to the registrar

Total full-time student enrolment 542; see also separate section *Statistics on Canadian universities and colleges*

Executive and administrative officers

Commandant
Brigadier General (L) W.K. Lye, MBE, CD, ADC, PSC, RMC, CE, BSc, PEng

Director of studies
J.R. Dacey, MBE, BSc, MSc, PhD, FCIC

Director of cadets and military training
Lieutenant-Colonel (A) R.A. White, CD, PSAC, RMC, BASc

Director, administration
Lieutenant-Colonel (A) D.M. Youngson, CD, RMC, BScCE, PEng

Chief librarian
J.W. Spurr, BA, BEd

Registrar
R.E. Jones, MA, PhD

Information officer
Captain P.T. Haydon, CD

Background

The Royal Military College of Canada had its beginning in 1874 when the Dominion government decreed by act of parliament that there be established in one of the garrison towns of Upper Canada "an institution for the purpose of imparting a complete education in all branches of military tactics, fortification, engineering, and a general scientific knowledge of the military profession, and for qualifying officers for command and for staff appointments".

The site selected was the old naval dockyard on Point Frederick immediately east of Kingston. The college was opened in June 1876. The title "Royal" was conferred on the college by Queen Victoria in 1878. The college was closed in 1942 for the duration of the war and reopened in 1948 as a tri-service college.

It is for men only and is non-denominational. A degree-granting charter was obtained from the Ontario legislature in March 1959 for the conferment of degrees in arts, science, and engineering. The first degrees were awarded in 1959.

The college is one of the three Canadian military colleges and is maintained and administered by the Department of National Defence. The minister of National Defence is, ex officio, president of the Canadian military colleges, and chancellor of the Royal Military College of Canada.

Facilities and services

The college is situated east of Kingston on a peninsula comprising approximately 110 acres. It has 10 teaching buildings, including laboratories and workshops, a library (130,000 volumes), two gymnasia, a student facilities building that includes a swimming pool, four dormitories and several other administrative and athletic buildings. All cadets are in residence, with complete living facilities provided.

*Ordinary member, AUCC.

Calendars and brochures

Calendar and counsellors' handbook available from the registrar.

Courses and degrees

Arts

Bachelor of arts (BA).
(a) Honors course, four years from senior matriculation. Courses of study are available in economics and commerce, English, French, history, international studies, political and economic science, emphasis politics, or emphasis economics. (b) General course, four years from senior matriculation. Courses of study are available in commerce, economics, English, French, history, international studies, and politics.

(Graduate studies and research division)

Master of arts (MA).
Minimum one year from honors BA. Available in the departments of economics and politics, history and war studies.

Engineering

Bachelor of engineering (BEng).
Four years from senior matriculation. Specialization possible in chemical, chemical (nuclear option), civil, electrical, and mechanical engineering, engineering and management, and engineering physics.

(Graduate studies and research division)

Master of engineering (MEng).
Minimum one year from first degree with second-class honors. Available in chemical, civil, electrical, and mechanical engineering, and engineering physics.

Science, applied

Bachelor of science (applied) (BSc).
Four years from senior matriculation. A unique course of study containing requirements of courses in the humanities and applied science in addition to science requirements.

Science, pure

Bachelor of science (BSc).
Honors and general course, four years from senior matriculation; mathematics and physics.

(Graduate studies and research division)

Master of science (MSc).
Minimum one year from honors BSc. Available in chemistry, mathematics, and physics.

Special programs

Interdisciplinary programs – war studies. An interdepartmental program is available leading to the degree of master of arts in war studies.

Admission requirements

For a general statement regarding admission to university study, see article *Admission to university in Canada.*

For information regarding admission to undergraduate study, consult *Requirements for admission to Canadian colleges and universities* available from Service for Admission to College and University, 151 Slater St., Ottawa, Ont., K1P 5N1, $1.50 prepaid.

An applicant must be a male Canadian citizen and must be between the ages of 16 and 21.

For admission to the first year of the course: senior matriculation. In addition to the general and academic admission standards, service enrolment standards must also be met.

Students who have completed two years of study beyond senior matriculation at Royal Roads Military College, or three years of study beyond junior matriculation level at the Collège militaire royal de Saint-Jean will be admitted to the third year of the course.

Academic year

The college year is divided into three terms. The fall and winter terms together provide a period of 31 weeks' instruction including examination periods.

From September to May inclusive, approximately 85% of the instruction is in academic subjects and the remainder in military subjects.

The summer term, extending from June to mid-August, is spent in practical military training with the armed forces.

Grading system

Standing is graded as A: 75-100%; B: 66-74%; C: 60-65%; D: 50-59%; E: 35-49% (failure); F: below 35% (serious failure).

Fees and costs

The scale of fees is $550 for the first year and $300 in each subsequent year in respect of tuition, clothing, books, instruments, drawing materials, dry cleaning, laundry, and incidental expenses; an annual fee of $585 for accommodation and meals; recreation club fee of $40 plus a deposit of $100 to cover incidental expenses, of which the unexpended balance is refundable. Cadets attending under the regular officer training plan (ROTP) have their fees paid and those holding Dominion cadetships have their first-year fees paid.

Financial awards and assistance

Regular officer training plan.
Scholarships awarded in recognition of academic merit may be retained under the regular officer training plan.

Reserve entry plan.
Applicants under the reserve entry plan are eligible to apply for a number of scholarships and bursaries that are available to students at Canadian universities. Further information may be obtained from the registrar.

Royal Military College Club of Canada foundation scholarship.
Three scholarships annually are open to competition among all reserve entry applicants for admission to the Canadian military colleges. Each scholarship has a value of $1,000 for the first year and a further increment of $400 for each subsequent year up to the time of graduation from the Royal Military College of Canada. An applicant, to be awarded a scholarship, must be an accepted reserve entry candidate for Royal Military College of Canada, Kingston, Ontario; Royal Roads, Victoria, B.C.; or Collège militaire royal de Saint-Jean, Saint-Jean (Québec). Further information may be obtained from the secretary-treasurer, R.M.C. Club of Canada, Royal Military College of Canada, Kingston, Ontario.

Dominion cadetships.
The following cadetships are offered to candidates admitted to their first year at the Canadian services colleges:
a) the value of a cadetship is $580 and shall be applied against the recipient's initial year fees;
b) not more than 15 cadetships may be awarded in a college year, of which five may be awarded to candidates of each service;
c) a candidate, to be eligible for a cadetship, shall satisfy the requirement for entrance and be the son of a person who was killed, died, or is severely incapacitated as a result of service in:
1) the Canadian Forces; or
2) the Canadian Merchant Marine during hostilities;
d) applications for cadetships shall be made in writing giving full particulars of the candidate's eligibility under (c) of this article and shall be forwarded by the first day of July, to: the director of recruiting, Canadian Forces Headquarters, Ottawa, Ontario;
e) the final board of selection shall submit to the minister for approval a list of candidates recommended for cadetships, in the order of selection.

Affiliated colleges

Collège militaire royal de Saint-Jean, Saint-Jean (Québec).
Le commandant, le Colonel J.P. Cadieux, CD, BSc, BEng. Directeur des études: M.A. Benoit, MSc, PhD. Secrétaire général: Denys Dion, BA, LLB, MScsoc, FRSA. Pour hommes. Fondé en 1952. Bilingue. Les deux premières années du cours à RMC peuvent être faites à CMR après une année

préparatoire et les deux dernières années sont faites à RMC.

Royal Roads, Military College, Victoria, British Columbia.
Commandant: Colonel R.C.K. Peers.
Director of studies: E.S. Graham, MSc, PhD.
Registrar: J.M.C. Meiklejohn, BSc. Men only. Founded in 1942. Offers first two years of degree course in arts, science, or engineering; final two years are taken at the Royal Military College of Canada.

Military leadership and management
Lieutenant-Colonel G.J. Carpenter, CD, BA, MA

Physics
M.H. Edwards, BA, MA, PhD, FAPS

Physical education and athletics
Major D.J.F. Hill, CD

Political and economic science
J.P. Cairns, BA, MA, PhD

Deans and chairmen

Arts
J.P. Cairns, BA, MA, PhD

Engineering
J.W. Dolphin, BASc, MSc

Graduate studies and research
T.S. Hutchison, BSc, PhD, FInstP, FAPS, FRSE

Science
J.R. Dacey, MBE, BSc, MSc, PhD, FCIC

Department heads

Electrical engineering
Commander J.B. Plant, CD, PhD

English and philosophy
R.E. Watters, BA, MA, PhD

Chemistry and chemical engineering
S.N. Naldrett, BSc, PhD

Civil engineering
J.S. Ellis, BSc, MEng, PhD

French
G.P.R. Stutzer-Lau Hansen, LèsL, DipPhon, PhD

History
F.F. Thompson, BA, MA, DPhil, DipE

Mathematics
N.K. Pope, BSc, MSc, PhD

Mechanical engineering
W.C. Moffatt, RMC, BSc, MSc, ScD

St. Francis Xavier University *

Antigonish, Nova Scotia

Telephone: 902-863-3303
Direct general correspondence to the registrar
Direct applications to admissions and awards officer

Total full-time student enrolment 3,087; see also separate section *Statistics on Canadian universities and colleges*

Executive and administrative officers

Chancellor
Most Rev. William Power, DD

President
Rev. Malcolm MacDonell, MA

Academic vice-president
J.J. MacDonald, PhD

Vice-president for student services
Rt. Rev. C.H. Bauer, DP, BA

Registrar
J.M. Bauer

Admissions and awards officer
J.A. MacLellan, MA

Dean of men
J.K. MacDonald, BA

Dean of women
Sr. J.M. Ryan, CND

Director, public relations
Brian O'Connell, BA, CPRS

Librarian
Rev. C. Brewer, MLS

University chaplain
Rev. M.J. Gillis, MA

Constituent college

Xavier College, Sydney, Nova Scotia.
Principal: Rev. D.F. Campbell, PhD.
Registrar: Donald Fewer, MEd. Roman Catholic. Established 1951. Co-educational. A non-residential junior college, offering two years of university studies beyond junior matriculation in arts, and business administration, and beyond senior matriculation in science.

Background

Founded in 1853 at Arichat, Nova Scotia, as a diocesan college, St. Francis Xavier College was transferred to Antigonish two years later. In 1866, an act of the provincial legislature of Nova Scotia conferred upon the college full university powers. In 1882 a provincial statute created a board of governors to hold and administer the property of the university. Teaching began in 1853 and the first degrees were awarded in 1868.

St. Francis Xavier University is widely known for its work in adult education. Community activities were sponsored by individual teachers early in the history of the university and the extension department was formally organized in 1928.

The university is a Roman Catholic, co-educational institution.

Facilities and services

The university is located in Antigonish. There are eight teaching buildings, a library (110,000 volumes), a chapel, a gymnasium, a rink, 12 men's residences accommodating 950 students, and residences for women accommodating 575 students at Mount St. Bernard College, an academic centre with classroom accommodations for 2,000 students and an office building containing the

*Ordinary member, AUCC.

offices of the registrar, deans and 70 professors.

Student services include a medical service, an infirmary, a bookstore, a canteen and barber shop, a university counselling centre, and the Canada Manpower Placement offices are on campus.

Campus organizations serving students from abroad include the International co-operative club, the International discussion club, and the Caribbean circle.

Calendars and brochures

Calendar issued in April; "Contemporary" issued quarterly by alumni office; student publications: Xaverian weekly and Xaverian annual.

Courses and degrees

Arts
(Faculty of arts)

Bachelor of arts (BA).
General major and honors courses, four years from junior matriculation. Major courses available in classics, economics, English, history, mathematics, modern foreign languages, music, philosophy, political science, psychology, sociology, and theology. Honors courses available in economics, English, history, mathematics and philosophy. Joint honors available in most fields.

Master of arts (MA).
Two years from bachelor's degree. Available in Celtic studies.

Master of arts in guidance (MAGuid).
One year and summer school from bachelor's degree.

Master of arts in adult education.
One calendar year from bachelor's degree.

Business
(Faculty of arts)

Bachelor of business administration (BBA).
Joint honors, four years from junior matriculation in joint business administration

and economics. General and major, four years from junior matriculation. Majors in accounting, economics, and management.

Education
(Faculty of arts)

Junior diploma in education.
One year after two years in arts, science or commerce from junior matriculation.

Senior diploma in education.
One year after three years in arts, science or commerce from junior matriculation.

Bachelor of education (BEd).
One year after graduation in arts, commerce, or science.

Master of arts in teaching (MA in teaching).
One year from BEd degree and two years of teaching. Specialization in chemistry, English, history, and mathematics. May be taken by attendance at four summer schools.

Master of arts in guidance (MA in Guidance).
One academic year and one summer session from the BEd.

Master of education (MEd).
Equivalent of one year of study from BEd and two years of teaching. Available only at summer school sessions (four sessions).

Engineering
(Faculty of science)

Certificate in engineering.
First three years of engineering course from senior matriculation. Arrangements have been made with other Canadian universities to permit holders of this certificate to attain their engineering degree in an additional two years. After two years (beyond senior matriculation) students may enter the architecture course at Nova Scotia Technical College.

Home economics
(Faculty of science)

Bachelor of science in home economics (BScHEc).
Four years from senior matriculation.

Nursing
(St. Martha's School of Nursing and faculty
of science)

Bachelor of science (BScN).
Four years from senior matriculation, in
affiliation with St. Martha's Hospital.

Science, applied, see engineering above

Science, pure
(Faculty of science)

Bachelor of science (BSc).
General, major and honors courses, four
years from senior matriculation. Major and
honors courses available in biology,
chemistry, geology, mathematics and physics.

*Bachelor of science in physical education
(BScPhysEd).*
Four years from senior matriculation.

Bachelor of science in education (BScEd).
Four years from senior matriculation.

Master of science (MSc).
Two years from bachelor's degree. Available
in biology, chemistry, geology, and physics.

Secretarial arts
(Faculty of arts)

Bachelor of secretarial arts (BSectA).
Four years from junior matriculation.

Secretarial diploma (general or medical).
May be awarded after two years from junior
matriculation; Mount St. Bernard College.

Social leadership
(Coady International Institute)

Diploma in social leadership.
Eight weeks' regular attendance at the Coady
International Institute of the university and in
field work. Designated for men and women
who desire to become community leaders.
Junior matriculation necessary for admission.

Special program

Coady International Institute.
Social leadership course leading to the
diploma in social leadership. Designed for
men and women who are actively engaged in
community development work and allied
fields, or who desire to become community
leaders. Eight weeks' duration at summer
school.

Extension programs

For university credit:

Summer school.
Undergraduate courses in arts for degree
credit and graduate courses leading to MA in
teaching English, history or mathematics and
to MEd.

Admission requirements

For a general statement regarding admission
to university study, see article *Admission to
university in Canada.*

For information regarding admission to
undergraduate study, consult *Requirements
for admission to Canadian colleges and
universities* available from Service for
Admission to College and University, 151
Slater St., Ottawa, Ont., K1P 5N1, $1.50
prepaid.

For admission to the program leading to the
bachelor of science in nursing, credit is
required in each of the following subjects, in
grade XII: chemistry; English; history;
mathematics; one of biology, or physics;
another science or a modern language.

Academic year

Winter session: mid-September to mid-May.

Summer school: early July to mid-August.

Grading system

In all undergraduate degree programs; 50, with an average in general degree program, 55%; major, 60%; honors, 70%. Honors degree distinctions: class I , 80-100%; class II, below 80%.

In master's degree programs: pass — 60% with an average of 70%.

Fees and costs

Full-time tuition fees per year: arts and science, $648. Summer school fees per course: graduate, $130; undergraduate, $130.

Double room and board (3 meals), $850; single room and board (3 meals), $925; subject to change.

Financial awards and assistance

Scholarships and bursaries must be applied for on the form provided by the university. The purpose of university scholarships is to recognize high scholastic achievement, and to assist students of high academic standing who for financial reasons might be unable to attend.

Five $2,000 scholarships are awarded each year to students with the best matriculation record and who show promise of outstanding scholastic achievement.

Many awards in various amounts are available on application. Check university calendar for full data.

Affiliated institutions

Mount St. Bernard College, Antigonish, Nova Scotia.
Principal: Sister Catherine MacNeil, CND, PhD. Roman Catholic. Residential ladies' college. Established 1882. Offers courses in home economics, music, and secretarial arts leading to degrees of the university.

St. Martha's School of Nursing, Antigonish, Nova Scotia.
Dean: Sister Simone Roach, PhD. Roman Catholic. Established 1933. Students in nursing take a four-year degree program at the school and university leading to a degree of the university.

Deans of faculties

Arts
J.T. Sears, BA, MBA, PhD

Science
S. Ajl, PhD

Directors of schools

Coady International Institute
D.H. Gillis, PhD

Extension
Rev. G. Topshee

Summer school
Rev. G. MacKinnon, PhD

Department heads

Art
Sr. Jean Grant, MA

Biology
L.P. Chiasson, PhD

Business administration
J.T. Sears, DBA

Celtic studies
Major C.I.N. MacLeod, MA

Chemistry
W.T. Foley, DSc

Classics
Gerald Power, PhD

Economics
W. Woodfine, PhD

Education and guidance
To be appointed

Engineering
J.H. MacDougall, BE

English
Rev. R.J. MacSween, BA

Geology
W.S. Shaw, PhD

History
R. MacLean, PhD

Home economics
Sr. Margaret Delorey, MA

Mathematics
F.J. Ginivan, PhD

Modern language
C. MacLean, DUP

Music
J. O'Donnell, MMus

Nursing
Sr. M.S. Roach, PhD

Philosophy
C.R. MacDonald, PhD

Physics
D. Pink, PhD

Physical education
A.J. MacAdam, MPE

Political science
Walter Kontak, MA

Psychology
Rev. J.H. MacDonald, MA

Sociology
Rev. D. Campbell, PhD

Secretarial arts
To be appointed

Theology
G.A. MacKinnon, STD, PhD

The University of St. Jerome's College*

(Federated with the University of Waterloo)†
Waterloo, Ontario

Telephone: 519-744-4407
Direct general correspondence to the registrar

Total full-time student enrolment 445; see
also separate section *Statistics on Canadian
universities and colleges*

Executive and administrative officers

Chancellor
Most Rev. J.F. Ryan, DD, JCD, LLD

President
Rev. J.R. Finn, CR, MA, PhD

Registrar
Brian Eby, BA

Treasurer
Rev. N.E. Lavigne, CR, BComm, MBA

Librarian
B.F. Flood, BA, BLS

Director of residence
E.E. Brown, AB

Director of public relations
J.E. Fehrenbach

*Ordinary member, AUCC.

†Holds in abeyance its degree-granting
powers except in theology, during the term of
federation.

Background

St. Jerome's College was founded in 1864 by
the Reverend Dr. Louis Funcken, of the
Congregation of the Resurrection, in a log-
house near St. Agatha, approximately six
miles west of the city of Waterloo. The
college was incorporated on August 15, 1866,
and in that year new and larger quarters were
established in Berlin, the original name of
Kitchener. As enrolment increased, new
buildings were added in 1889 and 1908.

Since 1938 the high school department has
been inspected and approved by the Ontario
Department of Education. In 1947, the
college department became affiliated with the
University of Ottawa. The two departments
were separated in 1953 when the college was
transferred to a new campus near the eastern
limits of Kitchener. The high school now
occupies the old campus in the centre of the
city. New classroom buildings were added to
the facilities there in 1958 and 1964.

In March of 1959, a new charter was
obtained for St. Jerome's through a private
bill passed by the legislature of the province
of Ontario. The name of the college was
changed to The University of St. Jerome's
College in recognition of the university
powers embodied in the new charter,
including the power to grant degrees.

At the same session of the legislature, a
private bill established the University of
Waterloo as a non-denominational
institution, and The University of St.
Jerome's College entered federation with it in
July 1960.

Three buildings, a classroom and
administration building, a men's residence,
and a women's residence (conducted by the
School Sisters of Notre Dame), were erected
on the campus of the University of Waterloo,
in September 1962.

Under the terms of The University of St.
Jerome's College act, the college is governed
by a board of governors, and the senate of
the University of Waterloo.

Facilities and services

The buildings of The University of St. Jerome's College are located on the campus of the University of Waterloo (population of the city of Waterloo 34,000), adjacent to the arts complex and library. The college operates a teaching and administration building including a service library, a men's residence with accommodation for 112 and a women's residence with accommodation for 120 under the supervision of the School Sisters of Notre Dame. St. Jerome's students also have full use of the academic, social, sports and cultural facilities of the University of Waterloo.

Calendars and brochures

The University of St. Jerome's College annual academic calendar (8-month term).
Summer session listings are to be found in the University of Waterloo summer session brochure.

Courses and degrees

Arts
(Faculty of arts)

Bachelor of arts (BA).
General course, three years from senior matriculation. Honors, four years from senior matriculation. Courses are offered in the following subject areas: anthropology, economics, English**, French, history*, Italian, philosophy*, political science, psychology*, religious studies*, sociology. An asterisk indicates subjects in which are offered, at the college itself, a sufficient number of courses for a major; a double asterisk, a sufficient number for an honors program. All other regular arts programs are available to St. Jerome's students through the University of Waterloo.

Environmental studies

Bachelor of environmental studies (BES).
General course, three years from senior matriculation. Honors, four years from senior matriculation. St. Jerome's enrols students in the following programs: man-environment

studies, geography, and urban and regional planning.

Mathematics

Bachelor of mathematics (BMath).
Pass degree program, three years from senior matriculation. Four-year general program, four years from senior matriculation. Honors, four years from senior matriculation. St. Jerome's enrols students in the regular mathematics programs.

All faculties:
By agreement with the University of Waterloo, the college holds its degree granting powers, except in theology, in abeyance. Its students, therefore, are granted degrees by the University of Waterloo.

Extension programs

For university credit:

Undergraduate courses
are offered Saturday mornings and weekday evenings during the fall and winter sessions for the convenience of part-time students.

Summer session
Courses are offered for undergraduates proceeding to a degree and for teachers who may wish to up-grade their professional qualifications.

Admission requirements and grading system

For a general statement regarding admission to university study, see article *Admission to university in Canada.*

For information regarding admission to undergraduate study, consult *Requirements for admission to Canadian colleges and universities* available from Service for Admission to College and University, 151 Slater St., Ottawa, Ont., K1P 5N1, $1.50 prepaid.

The college follows the University of Waterloo as regards admission policy and grading systems. See separate entry.

Academic year

Fall session: early September to end of December.

Winter session: early January to end of April.

Summer session: early July to mid-August.

Fees and costs

Tuition fees per year: full-time $510.
Incidental compulsory fees per year: $61.80.
Tuition fees: part-time students $100 per course.

Residence rates per year: private room, $1,075; semi-private room, $975.

Dean of faculty

Arts
Rev. J.A. Wahl, CR, MA, PhD

317

St. John's College*

(Affiliated with The University of Manitoba)
The University of Manitoba Campus,
Winnipeg 19, Manitoba

Telephone: 204-474-8531
Direct general correspondence to the registrar

Total full-time student enrolment 310; see
also separate section *Statistics on Canadian
universities and colleges*

Executive and administrative officers

Chancellor
Right Reverend Barry Valentine, MA, BD,
DD, Bishop of Rupert's Land

Warden and vice-chancellor
Reverend James Brown, MA, DD

Registrar
Marjorie Ward (Mrs)

Dean of studies
R.C. Bellan, MA, PhD

Bursar and executive assistant to warden
C.E. Kent, MBE, CD, FCIS

Librarian
Rev. A.E. Millward, MA, LTh

Alumni president
Arthur Sutton, BA

Senior don, men's residence
J.M. Wells, MSc

Senior don, women's residence
M.K. Master (Miss), MA, LLM

Chaplain
Rev. Peter Flynn, BA, BTh

Background

St. John's College, after a beginning in 1849, was refounded in 1866. It received its charter of incorporation in 1871, one year after Manitoba was constituted a province. The college, however, can trace its teaching history back to the log school house erected in 1820 by the Reverend John West, first Protestant missionary to the Red River settlement.

St. John's College is a co-educational liberal arts and theological college in connection with the Anglican Church of Canada and affiliated to The University of Manitoba. It has a continuous record of more than 100 years in the field of higher learning and is one of the three colleges which, in 1877, affiliated to bring into being The University of Manitoba. From 1877 until 1914, all university instruction in arts and science was given by the affiliated colleges, the students of these colleges being examined by and receiving degrees from The University of Manitoba, which at first was an examining and degree-granting body only. The act of 1877 empowered the colleges to confer degrees in theology, reserving to the university the right to confer all other degrees. The right of St. John's College to grant degrees in theology is preserved up to the present time.

St. John's College operates under the authority of the university senate in all strictly academic matters in the faculty of arts and science, and is represented on all committees concerned with arts and science studies. It is governed by a corporation and a council.

Facilities and services

St. John's College comprises almost three acres on the 663-acre campus of The University of Manitoba at Fort Garry. There are three principal buildings, including the academic and administration, the residence, and the chapel. The library contains approximately 29,600 volumes, but students of St. John's College use, on equal terms with the students of the university and other colleges, the university libraries and St. Paul's library. The residence accommodation is for 47 women and 52 men.

*Ordinary member, AUCC.

Student services include an accident insurance service, guidance and counselling, and participation in other university services. St. John's College provides cafeteria service, and dining hall, and students use the facilities of the university gymnasia, etc. Regular chapel services are provided not only for St. John's College students but for all university students and personnel who wish to attend. Provision of chaplaincy services is made for St. John's College students and the chapel is also used for an ecumenical service each Sunday.

Calendars and brochures

The college calendar contains all information concerning the college's offerings, residence, fees, etc. Additional information concerning admission requirements and academic regulations may be found in the calendars and brochures of The University of Manitoba.

Courses and degrees

Arts
(Faculty of arts and science)

Bachelor of arts (BA).
(a) General course, three years from senior matriculation. See The University of Manitoba listing.

St. John's offers instruction in: anthropology, classics, economics, English, French, geography, history, mathematics, philosophy, political science, psychology, religion, sociology, and inter-disciplinary courses. (b) Honors course, four years from senior matriculation. St. John's offers instruction in some of the aforementioned subjects.

Master of arts (MA).
At least two years from the general (pass) BA or at least one year from the honors BA. Some courses offered, in conjunction with The University of Manitoba.

Science
(Faculty of arts and science)

Bachelor of science (BSc).
General course, three years from senior matriculation. Instruction given in chemistry, computer studies, and mathematics. Other science courses completed elsewhere in the university.

Theology
(Faculty of theology)

Teaching suspended, since September 1968.

Special programs

Inter-disciplinary course in English-Canadian and French-Canadian poetry. A Canadian studies program is presently being developed.

Extension programs

For university credit:

A program is presently being developed. Summer session courses offered in co-operation with The University of Manitoba.

Admission requirements

For a general statement regarding admission to university study, see article *Admission to university in Canada.*

For information regarding admission to undergraduate study, consult *Requirements for admission to Canadian colleges and universities* available from Service for Admission to College and University, 151 Slater St., Ottawa, Ont., K1P 5N1, $1.50 prepaid.

Academic year

Winter session: mid-September to end of April.

Summer session: July and August.

Grading system

As for The University of Manitoba.

Fees and costs

Full-time tuition fees per year: undergraduate — arts and science, $425; part-time — per subject on pro rata basis. Students' organization, $30.50. Miscellaneous, $10.

Residence rates, single room and board, $811 ($26 per week).

Financial awards and assistance

Scholarships and prizes for achievement in arts and science. Entrance scholarship. A small number of bursaries, chiefly for children of clergy. Students also eligible for bursaries, scholarships, and prizes offered by The University of Manitoba, the government of Manitoba, and private concerns.

Saint Mary's University*

Halifax, Nova Scotia

Telephone: 902-422-7331
Direct general correspondence to the registrar

Total full-time student enrolment 2,296; see also separate section *Statistics on Canadian universities and colleges*

Executive and administrative officers

Chancellor
Most Rev. J.M. Hayes, JCD, DD

Vice-chancellor
Rt. Rev. Colin Campbell, VG, DP, PP, MSW

President
D.O. Carrigan, BA, MA, PhD

Academic vice-president
Rev. G.W. Tait, SJ, BA, PhL, MA, STL

Vice-president, finance and development
E. Morris, BA

Registrar
K.J. Cleary, BA, BEd, MA

Comptroller
R.G. Deegan, BA, BComm, CA, RIA

Librarian
R.A. Hafter (Mrs), BA, MS

Head, counselling services
L.W. Smith, BA, MA

Treasurer
C.S. Bathurst, SJ

Director, adult studies
M.J. Belair, SJ, BA, MA

*Ordinary member, AUCC.

Director, evening division and summer school
J.B. Ternan, BE, PEng

Director, admissions
L.R. MacDonald, BA

Director, personnel and physical services
Richard Ratcliffe

Dean of residence for women students
E.A. Chard (Mrs), BA, BEd, MA

Dean of students
K.P. Bendelier, BComm, MSW

Alumni moderator
M.J. O'Donnell, SJ, BA, STL

Information officer
K. Fredrick, BS

Background

Saint Mary's University was founded in Halifax, Nova Scotia in 1802. Originally a college, an act of the Nova Scotia legislature in 1841 gave it full university powers. From its beginning the university was a church-related institution under the auspices of the Roman Catholic diocese of Halifax. In July, 1970, it was re-incorporated under a new act as a public, non-denominational university. However, a basic Christian philosophy is still very much a part of its educational foundation.

Throughout most of its history the university was an all-male institution but in 1968 became fully co-educational. Although it has been one of the region's fastest growing university-level institutions, the primary emphasis at Saint Mary's is still personalized student-centred education.

The university is incorporated under an act of the Nova Scotia legislature, placing administrative control of the university in a board of governors consisting of 30 members. Membership of the board is drawn from within the university and the community at large.

Facilities and services

Saint Mary's University is situated in south Halifax, on the former Collins estate. The

campus comprises 30 acres. The library contains approximately 100,000 volumes. The residence accommodates 1,450 students in single and double rooms, married student apartments and single student apartments. On campus there is a students' union building, a winter arena and sports stadium, a placement service, a chemistry-biology building, academic and main administration buildings, full counselling services, a resident multi-denominational chaplains' service, a health unit, a swimming pool, an art gallery, a bookstore, a beauty salon, a barber shop, a mini-market and a commercial branch bank. There is on staff an advisor to foreign students. Campus organizations which serve students from abroad include World University Service of Canada.

Courses and degrees

Arts
(Faculty of arts)

Bachelor of arts (BA).
(a) Pass course, four years from junior matriculation. Areas of major concentration: Asian studies, history, languages and literature, philosophy, psychology, religious studies, and social sciences. (b) Honors course, five years from junior matriculation; additional prescribed courses in final two years. Available in economics, English, French, history, mathematics, philosophy, and political science.

Commerce
(Faculty of commerce)

Bachelor of commerce (BComm).
(a) Four years from junior matriculation. Areas of major concentration: accounting, business administration, and economics. (b) Honors course, five years from junior matriculation; additional prescribed courses in final two years. Available in economics.

Education
(School of education)

Bachelor of education (BEd).
One year from bachelor's degree in arts, commerce, engineering, or science.

Master of arts in education (MA).
Two years from bachelor's degree in arts, commerce, engineering, or science; one year from bachelor of education, full-time, by course of instruction, examination, and thesis.

Master of arts in history (MA).
Two years from bachelor's degree, full-time after general BA, 1 year full-time after honors BA; by course of instruction and examination.

Master of arts in philosophy (MA).
Two years, full-time after general BA, 1 year full-time after honors BA; by course of instruction, examination, and thesis.

Engineering
(Faculty of engineering)

Diploma in engineering (DipEng).
First three years of engineering course from junior matriculation. Arrangements have been made with other Canadian universities to permit holders of this diploma to attain their engineering degree in an additional two years. After two years (beyond junior matriculation) students may enter the architecture course at Nova Scotia Technical College.

Science, applied, see engineering above

Science, pure
(Faculty of science)

Bachelor of science (BSc).
(a) Pass course, four years from junior matriculation. Areas of major concentration: biology, chemistry, mathematics, physics. (b) Bachelor of science with major, four years from junior matriculation; may be taken in biology, chemistry, geology, mathematics, physics, and psychology. (c) Honors course, five years from junior matriculation; additional prescribed course in final two years. Available in chemistry, mathematics, and physics. The obtaining of the diploma in engineering at the end of the third year may be combined with the science program.

Theology

Courses offered by affiliated colleges (see below).

Special program

Atlantic Summer School for Advanced Business Administration.

Extension programs

For university credit:

Evening credit program.
Undergraduate courses leading to a degree in arts, commerce, or science.

Summer session.
Undergraduate course leading to a degree in arts, commerce, or science.

For no university credit:

The adult studies program offers courses on a variety of subjects to the general public, including general introductory courses in the use and operation of the university's digital computer.

Admission requirements

For a general statement regarding admission to university study, see article *Admission to university in Canada.*

For information regarding admission to undergraduate study, consult *Requirements for admission to Canadian colleges and universities* available from Service for Admission to College and University, 151 Slater St., Ottawa, Ont., K1P 5N1, $1.50 prepaid.

For admission to graduate study a student must have obtained a first degree with specified grades in appropriate subjects.

Academic year

Winter session: early September to early May.

Summer session: mid-May — end of June, early July — mid-August.

Student may take one full course each session.

Grading system

Transcripts show letter-grades obtained. One course credit equals six semester hours. No course credit is shown for the faculty of engineering. Pass mark, D.

Fees and costs

Full-time tuition fees per year: (a) first degree — arts, commerce, engineering, science, $655; (b) for graduate courses — $655. Special courses, evening, and summer school courses, $130.

Residence rates: *High rise 1* — room only, $540; low rise and high rise 2, single rooms and board only, $975 on 15 meals a week. $1,030 on 21 meals a week.

Double rooms and board only, $900 on 15 meals a week. $955 on 21 meals a week.

High rise 2 — one-bedroom apartments on 12-month lease, $140 a month; two-bedroom apartments, 660 square feet, on 12-month lease, $180 a month. Two-bedroom apartments, 930 square feet, on 12-month lease, $205 a month.

Financial awards and assistance

The scholarship program provides funds of varying amounts up to full tuition for students who have demonstrated scholarship ability. All scholarships are continuing depending on maintenance of scholarship average.

Some bursaries are available for needy students who have demonstrated ability to succeed in university work. Applications are made to chairman, scholarship committee.

Affiliated colleges

Ignatius College, Guelph, Ontario.
Rector: Very Rev. Michael G. Shields, SJ.
Registrar: Rev. W.D. Connor, SJ. Roman
Catholic. Men only. Founded 1913 for the
training of members of the Society of Jesus in
English-speaking Canada. Affiliated to the
university 1957. Offers courses towards
university degree.

Regis College, Toronto, Ontario.
Rector: Very Rev. Rémi Limoges, SJ.
Registrar: Rev. Donald Brown, SJ. Roman
Catholic. Men only. Founded 1930. Affiliated
to the university 1957. Offers courses leading
to the bachelor of divinity (BDiv) and the
master of divinity (MDiv), awarded by the
university.

Deans of faculties

Arts
G.B. Hallett, BA, MA

Commerce
H.G. Beazley, BComm, RIA

Education
D.J. Weeren, BA, MS, PhD

Engineering
J.L. Ryan, BSc, BE

Science
W.A. Bridgeo, BSc, PhD

Departmental chairmen

Accounting and business administration
D.A. Hope, BComm, MBA, CA

Anthropology
J. Lowenstein (subject representative), PhD

Biology
M. Wiles, BSc, PhD

Chemistry
E.R. Hayes, BSc, MSc, PhD

Classics and Latin
V. Tobin (subject representative), BA, MA

Economics
R.L. Ruth, BA, MSc, PhD

English
R. Crowther, BA, MA

French
G. LePierres, BA, LèsL, CAPES

Geology
C.A.R. de Albuquerque (subject
representative), PhD

German
R. Nahrebeckyj (subject representative), MA,
LLD

History
Elizabeth Chard, BA, BEd, MA

Mathematics
K. Singh, BA, MA, MSc, PhD

Philosophy
R. Gruner, DrPhil, PhD

Physics
D.S. Murty, BSc, MSc, MA, DSc, CEng,
MIEE, AMBritIRE

Political science
T.B. Ciuciura, CertifinLaw, MA, DRJur,
Habil

Psychology
G. Gordon, BSc, PhD

Religious studies
S. Armstrong, AB, BD, MA

Sociology
R.L. Cosper, BA, MA

Spanish
A.M. Edwards (Mrs), (subject
representative), BA

University of St. Michael's College*

(Federated with the University of Toronto)†
Toronto 181, Ontario

Telephone: 416-921-3151
Direct general correspondence to the registrar

Total full-time student enrolment 136; see also separate section *Statistics on Canadian universities and colleges*

Executive and administrative officers

Chancellor
Most Rev. Philip Pocock, DD

President
Rev. J.M. Kelly, CSB, MA, PhD

Vice-president and registrar
Rev. H.V. Mallon, CSB, MA

Associate registrar
Rev. H.B. Gardner, CSB, BA, MSinLS

Librarian
Rev. J.B. Black, CSB, BA, MLS

Treasurer
Rev. N. Iversen, CSB, MA

Director, financial aid
Rev. H.P. Coughlin, CSB, MA, STD

Director, student affairs
R.H. Hayward, BA

*Ordinary member, AUCC.
†Holds in abeyance its degree-granting powers in arts and science during the term of federation with the University of Toronto.

Constituent colleges

Loretto College, 70 St. Mary Street, Toronto 181, Ontario.
Dean: Sister Caroline Dawson, IBVM, BA. Roman Catholic. Founded 1912. A foundation of the Institute of the Blessed Virgin Mary, provides accommodation for women students registered in the University of St. Michael's College, and for a limited number of women students registered in other faculties of the University of Toronto.

St. Joseph's College, 90 Wellesley Street West, Toronto 181, Ontario.
Dean: Sister Janet Fraser, CSJ, BA. Roman Catholic. Founded 1911. A foundation of the Sisters of St. Joseph, provides accommodation for women students registered in the University of St. Michael's College, and for a limited number of women students registered in other faculties of the University of Toronto.

Background

St. Michael's College was established in 1852 by the Right Reverend Armand François, Comte de Charbonnel, second bishop of Toronto, and placed under the direction of the Basilian Fathers. It was incorporated as an institution of higher learning by the statutes of the province of Canada in 1855. In 1891, St. Michael's was affiliated, by statute of the university senate, to the University of Toronto. When the University of Toronto was reorganized in 1906, St. Michael's entered the new university federation as an arts college preparing students for university degrees. In 1954, St. Michael's obtained independent civil establishment for its theological school and in 1958 was constituted by the legislature of the province of Ontario as a university in federation with the University of Toronto. See separate entry.

St. Michael's, in conjunction with the University of Toronto, offers full programs in arts, science, and commerce, at the undergraduate level, and independently, in theology and related studies at the graduate level. The Pontifical Institute of Mediaeval Studies is located on the same campus and provides special facilities for research in the middle ages.

Degrees in arts are awarded by the University of Toronto; degrees in mediaeval studies by the Pontifical Institute of Mediaeval Studies; and degrees in theology by the University of St. Michael's College.

Facilities and services

The university is situated on Queen's Park Crescent with a site of 13 acres adjoining the campus of the University of Toronto. There are three teaching buildings, a library (140,000 volumes), student residences for men accommodating 275, and two women's residences, St. Joseph's College and Loretto College, accommodating 350.

Student services include a collegiate church and chapel, a dining-hall, a student cafeteria, and a faculty-student centre.

Courses and degrees

Arts
(Faculty of arts and science, University of Toronto)

Bachelor of arts (BA).
As offered by the University of Toronto; see separate entry.

Business, see commerce below

Commerce
(Faculty of arts and science, University of Toronto)

Bachelor of commerce (BCom).
As offered by the University of Toronto.

Mediaeval studies
(Pontifical Institute of Mediaeval Studies)

Licentiate in mediaeval studies (MSL).
Three years from bachelor of arts.
Specialization offered in history of canon law, histroy of Christian worship, Latin literature, mediaeval history, philosophy, theology, vernacular literature

Doctorate in mediaeval studies (MSD).
Two years from licentiate. Specialization offered in history of canon law, history of Christian worship, Latin literature, mediaeval history, philosophy, theology, vernacular literature

Science
(Faculty of arts and science, University of Toronto)

Bachelor of science (BSc).
As offered by the University of Toronto.

Theology
(Faculty of theology)

Master in divinity (MDiv).
Three years from bachelor of arts.

Master in theology (MTh).
One year from MDiv or equivalent.

Master of religious education (MRE).
Two years from bachelor of arts plus two years' teaching experience or equivalent.

Doctor in theology (DTh).
Two years from master in theology.

(Institute of Christian Thought)

Master of arts in theology (MA).
Two years from bachelor of arts.

Doctor of philosophy in theology (PhD).
Two years from master of arts in theology.

Special program

The Pontifical Institute of Mediaeval Studies.

Admission requirements

For a general statement regarding admission to university study, see article *Admission to university in Canada.*

For information regarding admission to undergraduate study, consult *Requirements for admission to Canadian colleges and universities* available from Service for

Admission to College and University, 151
Slater St., Ottawa, Ont., K1P 5N1, $1.50
prepaid.

For admission to courses leading to degrees
in theology, students must have obtained a
first degree.

Academic year

Winter session: mid-September to early May.

Summer session: early July to mid-August.

Grading system

See the University of Toronto.

Fees and costs

Tuition fees: as outlined by the University of
Toronto.

Residence: $15 per week. Board: by student
arrangement.

Dean of faculty

Theology
Rev. E.B. Allen, csb, MA, PhD, MSL

Directors of institutes

Christian Thought, Institute of
Rev. J.E. Bruns, MA, STD, SSL

Praeses, Pontifical Institute of Mediaeval
Studies
Rev. L.K. Shook, CSB, MA, PhD

Université Saint-Paul*

Saint Paul University*

(Fédérée avec l'Université d'Ottawa)
223, rue Main, Ottawa (Ont.) K1S 1C4

(Federated with the University of Ottawa)
223 Main Street, Ottawa, Ontario, K1S 1C4

Téléphone: 613-235-1421
Prière d'adresser la correspondance d'ordre général au secrétaire général de l'université

Telephone 613-235-1421
Please direct general correspondence to the secretary general of the university

Total des inscriptions des étudiants à plein temps 494; voir aussi la section distincte, intitulée *Statistiques sur les universités et collèges du Canada*

Total full-time student enrolment 494; see also separate section *Statistics on Canadian universities and colleges*

Dirigeants

Executive and administrative officers

Grand Chancelier
S.E.R. Mgr J.-Aurèle Plourde, LScSoc, Archevêque d'Ottawa

Chancellor
S.E.R. Mgr J.-Aurèle Plourde, LScSoc, Archevêque d'Ottawa

Recteur
Marcel Patry, OMI, MA, LPh, PhD, LTh, DPh

Rector
Marcel Patry, OMI, MA, LPh, PhD, LTh, DPh

Vice-recteur à l'enseignement et directeur, extension de l'enseignement
Martin Roberge, OMI, BA, LPh, SSL, DTh

Vice-rector (academic) and director, university extension
Martin Roberge, OMI, BA, LPh, SSL, DTh

Vice-recteur à l'administration
Lucien Pépin, OMI, BA, LPh, LTh, BEd

Vice-rector, administration
Lucien Pépin, OMI, BA, LPh, LTh, BEd

Secrétaire général et registraire
Rodrigue Normandin, OMI, DPh, LTh, LLD

Secretary general and registrar
Rodrigue Normandin, OMI, DPh, LTh, LLD

Historique

Background

Du 26 septembre 1848 au 1er juillet 1965, l'histoire de l'Université Saint-Paul est celle de l'Université d'Ottawa. Le 1er juillet 1965, en vertu d'une loi de la province d'Ontario, l'institution jusqu'alors désignée comme Université d'Ottawa prenait le nom

From 1848 to 1965, Saint Paul University and the University of Ottawa have a common history. On July 1, 1965, through an act of the Ontario provincial legislature, the institution formerly known as the University of Ottawa was given the name of Saint Paul University, while retaining the two charters,

*Membre ordinaire de l'AUCC.

*Ordinary member, AUCC.

d'Université Saint-Paul tout en conservant les deux chartes, civile et canonique, qui la régissaient jusqu'à ce moment. En même temps était créée une nouvelle corporation autonome sous le nom d'Université d'Ottawa.

L'Université Saint-Paul, fédérée avec l'Université d'Ottawa, s'engage envers celle-ci à ne dispenser l'enseignement que dans ses facultés de théologie et de droit canonique, ainsi que dans les instituts annexes, en se réservant le droit de présenter ses étudiants au sénat de l'Université d'Ottawa en vue des grades civils, en plus de son propre pouvoir de conférer des grades canoniques.

Les deux universités se considèrent comme des institutions complémentaires, l'une particulièrement responsable des facultés civiles, l'autre des facultés à caractère religieux. L'Université Saint-Paul nomme huit membres au bureau des gouverneurs de l'Université d'Ottawa. Le recteur de l'Université Saint-Paul est membre du sénat de l'Université d'Ottawa et les facultés de l'Université Saint-Paul y sont représentées. En outre, il y a échange mutuel de professeurs et reconnaissance réciproque des cours.

Installations et services

L'université est située à proximité du centre de la ville d'Ottawa (population, 399,000), et, de ce fait, près des différentes activités culturelles et éducatives de la capitale du Canada: Centre national des arts, Galerie nationale, Musée national, Bibliothèque nationale et autres bibliothèques universitaires.

Sur le campus même, les étudiants et professeurs trouvent les différents services requis pour la marche interne de la vie universitaire: bibliothèque spécialisée (160,000 volumes), librairie, cafétéria, salons d'étudiants et de professeurs, chapelle, service de logement hors-campus.

Annuaire

Annuaire général.

civil and pontifical, which were conferred in 1866 and 1889 respectively. At the same time a new and independent corporation was created to be designated as the University of Ottawa.

Saint Paul University, federated with the University of Ottawa, has agreed with the latter to limit its teaching to the faculties of theology and canon law, including the related institutes. In addition to its own power to grant canonical degrees, the university reserves the right to present its students to the senate of the University of Ottawa for civil degrees in theology and canon law.

Both universities consider themselves as complementary institutions, one being chiefly responsible for the civil faculties, the other for the faculties with religious character. They are in close relationship. Saint Paul University appoints eight members to the board of governors of the University of Ottawa. The rector of Saint Paul University is a member of the senate of the University of Ottawa and the faculties of Saint Paul University are represented in the University of Ottawa academic senate. Moreover, the two universities benefit from a mutual exchange of professors and they mutually recognize their courses.

Facilities and services

The university is located in the vicinity of the capital's downtown area (Ottawa population 399,000), and thereby close to cultural and educational activities, such as, the National Arts Centre, the National Gallery, the National Museum, the National Library and other university libraries.

In order to maintain an internal progressive academic life, various facilities are offered to students and professors. On the campus one can find lounges, a specialized library containing 160,000 volumes, a bookstore, a chapel, a cafeteria, and a service for off-campus living accommodation.

Calendar

General calendar.

Cours et grades	Courses and degrees

L'université emploie le français et l'anglais comme langues d'enseignement.

The university uses both French and English as languages of instruction.

Communications sociales
(Institut des communications sociales)

Diplôme en communications sociales.
Une année d'études et de cours.

Droit canonique
(Faculté de droit canonique)

Grades civils:*

Baccalauréat en droit canonique (BDC).
Deux ans après un baccalauréat ou l'équivalent.

Maîtrise en droit canonique (MDC).
Un an après le BDC. Sans thèse.

Maîtrise ès arts en droit canonique [MA(DC)].
Un an après le BDC. Thèse.

Doctorat en philosophie en droit canonique. [PhD(DC)].
Un an après la MDC.

Grades canoniques:**

Baccalauréat en droit canonique (JCB).
Deux ans après un baccalauréat ou l'équivalent.

Licence en droit canonique (JCL).
Un an après le JCB.

Doctorat en droit canonique (JCD).
Un an après le JCL.

Pastorale
(Institut de pastorale)

*Maîtrise en pastorale.***
Un an après le baccalauréat spécialisé (théologie ou sciences religieuses).

Canon law
(Faculty of canon law)

Civil degrees:*

Bachelor of canon Law (JCB).
Two years after a baccalaureate degree or the equivalent.

Master of canon law (MDC).
One year after the JCB. No thesis.

Master of arts in canon law [MA(CL)].
One year after the JCB. Thesis.

Doctor of philosophy in canon law [PhD(CL)].
One year after the MDC.

Canonical degrees:**

Bachelor of canon law (JCB).
Two years after a baccalaureate degree or the equivalent.

Licentiate in canon law (JCL).
One year after the JCB.

Doctor in canon law (JCD).
One year after the JCL.

Mission studies
(Institute of mission studies)

*Master of arts in mission studies [MA(Miss)].**
Two years after the BA. Thesis. Three years after the BA. No thesis.

*Doctor in theology in mission studies [DTh(Miss)].***
At least one year after the LTh.

Pastoral studies
(Institute of pastoral studies)

---

*Conférés par l'Université d'Ottawa.

**Conférés par l'Université Saint-Paul.

*Conferred by the University of Ottawa.

**Conferred by Saint Paul University.

Philosophie
(Faculté de philosophie)

*Baccalauréat en philosophie (BPh).***
Deux ans après la première année d'une
faculté des arts ou l'équivalent, ou un an
après un BA général comportant un minimum
de 24 crédits en philosophie.

*Licence en philosophie (LPh).***
Au moins deux ans après le BPh.

*Docteur en philosphie (DPh).***
Au moins deux ans après la LPh.

Sciences missionnaires
(Institut des sciences missionnaires)

*Maîtrise ès arts en sciences missionnaires
[MA(Miss)].**
Deux ans après le BA. Thèse. Trois ans après
le BA. Sans thèse.

*Doctorat en théologie en sciences missionnaires
[DTh(Miss)].***
Au moins un an après la licence en théologie.

Théologie
(Faculté de théologie)

Grades civils:*

Baccalauréat en théologie (BTh).
Trois ans après le DEC ou après au moins une
année des arts.

Maîtrise en théologie (MTh).
Un an après le BTh. Sans thèse.

Maîtrise ès arts en théologie [MA(Th)].
Un an après le BTh. Thèse.

*Doctorat en philosophie en théologie
[PhD(Th)].*
Quatre trimestres après la maîtrise.

Grades canoniques:**

Baccalauréat en théologie (BTh).
Trois ans après le BA ou l'équivalent.

*Master of pastoral studies.***
One year after BA (with major in theology or
religious studies).

Philosophy
(Faculty of philosophy)

*Bachelor of philosophy (BPh).***
Two years after the first year in a faculty of
arts, or the equivalent. Or one year after a
general BA comprising a minimum of 24
credits in philosophy.

*Licentiate in philosophy (LPh).***
At least two years after the BPh.

*Doctor of philosophy (DPh).***
At least two years after the LPh.

Social communications
(Institute of social communications)

Diploma in social communications.
One year of courses and research.

Theology
(Faculty of theology)

Civil degrees:*

Bachelor of theology (BTh).
Three years after the DEC or at least one year
of arts.

Master of theology (MTh).
One year after the BTh. No thesis.

Master of arts in theology [MA(Th)].
One year after the BTh. Thesis.

Doctor of philosophy in theology [PhD(Th)].
Four trimesters after the master's degree.

Canonical degrees:**

Bachelor of theology (BTh).
Three years after the BA or the equivalent.

Licentiate in theology (LTh).
Two years after the BTh.

---

*Conférés par l'Université d'Ottawa.

**Conférés par l'Université Saint-Paul.

---

*Conferred by the University of Ottawa.

**Conferred by Saint Paul University.

Licence en théologie (LTh).
Deux ans après le BTh.

Doctorat en théologie (DTh).
Quatre trimestres après la LTh.

Education permanente

Cours de l'année.
Cours de théologie pour religieux et laïcs.

Cours d'été.
Sessions de pastorale. Sessions de l'Institut des sciences missionnaires. Séminaires et cours en psychiatrie pastorale.

Conditions d'admission

On trouvera un exposé général sur l'admission aux études universitaires dans l'article *Admission aux universités canadiennes.*

Afin d'obtenir des renseignements sur l'admission aux études du niveau pré-grade, consultez *Conditions d'admission dans les collèges et universités du Canada* que l'on peut obtenir du Service d'admission au collège et à l'université, 151, rue Slater, Ottawa (Ontario), K1P 5N1, $1.50 port payé.

Année universitaire

Session régulière: du 8 septembre au début de mai.

Cours d'été: du 2 juillet à la mi-août.

Système de mentions

A+ — 95-100%; A — 90-94%; B — 80-89%; C — 70-79%; D — 60-69%; F — moins de 60%.

Droits d'inscription

Etudiant à temps complet, $465; étudiant à temps partiel — baccalauréat (par crédit), $20, baccalauréat (six crédits), $100; candidat au

Doctor of theology (DTh).
Four trimesters after the LTh.

Extension programs

Regular sessions.
Courses in theology for the religious and laity.

Summer sessions.
Sessions in pastoral theology. Sessions by the Institute of mission studies. Seminars and courses in pastoral psychiatry.

Admission requirements

For a general statement regarding admission to university study, see article *Admission to university in Canada.*

For information regarding admission to undergraduate study, consult *Requirements for admission to Canadian colleges and universities* available from Service for Admission to College and University, 151 Slater St., Ottawa, Ont., K1P 5N1, $1.50 prepaid.

Academic year

Regular session: from September 8 to the beginning of May.

Summer session: from July 2 to the middle of August.

Grading system

A+ — 95-100%; A — 90-94%; B — 80-89%; C — 70-79%; D — 60-69%; F — less than 60%.

Fees and costs

Full-time, $465; part-time, baccalaureate (per credit), $20, baccalaureate (six credits), $100; doctoral candidate, (per trimester) $200; total minimum $800.

doctorat, (par trimestre) $200; minimum total $800.

Aide financière

L'université dispose d'un nombre limité de bourses d'études renouvelables annuellement sur demande faite au Service de l'aide financière aux étudiants.

Centres de recherches

Centre canadien de recherches en anthropologie.
Le centre s'occupe de recherches et de publications dans les domaines de l'anthropologie et du développement communautaire (développement et changement socio-économique).

Centre de psychiatrie pastorale.
Le centre a pour but de promouvoir l'information, la recherche et l'entraînement pratique en psychiatrie pastorale; il offre ses services aux prêtres, religieux, médecins, travailleurs sociaux, psychologues, etc.

Centre de recherche en histoire religieuse du Canada.
Le centre cherche à promouvoir les études sur l'histoire religieuse générale du Canada, en devenant un centre de documentation et en favorisant la recherche, l'édition, les colloques entre diverses confessions.

Centre d'études en liturgie.
Créé par l'université à la demande de l'Episcopat canadien, le centre à pour but de favoriser la recherche scientifique et pastorale dans le domaine de la liturgie.

Institutions affiliées

Séminaire St. Augustine's, 2661, chemin Kingston, Scarborough (Ontario).
Recteur: Very Rev. J.A. O'Mara, PC, JCL. Doyen des études: Rev. N.H. Cooper, BA, STL, SSL. Cours en anglais seulement. Cours de baccalauréat en théologie. Grades canoniques conférés par l'Université Saint-Paul. Grades civils conférés par l'Université d'Ottawa. Membre de l'Ecole de théologie de Toronto. Séminaire catholique. Cours du jour. Affilié en 1964.

Financial awards and assistance

The university offers a limited number of bursaries which can be renewed annually by sending a completed request form to the student financial aid service.

Research centres

Canadian Research Centre for Anthropology.
The centre carries out research and publishes material in the fields of anthropology and community development (socio-economic development and change).

Centre of Pastoral Psychiatry.
The centre promotes and offers information, research, and practical training in pastoral psychiatry for priests, religious, doctors, social workers, psychologists, etc.

Research Centre in Religious History of Canada.
The centre promotes studies in general Canadian history by collecting historical documents, by sponsoring research and publications, and organizing inter-denominational seminars.

Research Centre in Liturgy.
The centre, organized by the university, at the request of the Canadian Hierarchy, aims at promoting scientific and pastoral research in the field of liturgy.

Affiliated institutions

St. Augustine's Seminary, 2661 Kingston Road, Scarborough, Ontario.
Rector: Very Rev. J.A. O'Mara, PC, JCL. Dean of studies: Rev. N.H. Cooper, BA, STL, SSL. Courses given in English only. Courses leading to a BTh degree. Canonical degrees conferred by Saint Paul University. Civil degrees conferred by the University of Ottawa. Member of the Toronto school of theology. Catholic seminary. Day students. Affiliated in 1964.

St. Thomas College, North Battleford, Saskatchewan.
Superior: Rev. Adam Exner, OMI. Registrar: Rev. Martin Moser, OMI. Courses given in English only. Courses leading to a BA degree. Degrees conferred by the University of

Collège St. Thomas, North Battleford
(Saskatchewan).
Supérieur: Rev. Adam Exner, OMI.
Registraire: Rev. Martin Moser, OMI. Cours
en anglais seulement. Cours de baccalauréat
ès arts. Grades conférés par l'Université
d'Ottawa. Collège catholique. Cours du jour.
Fondé et affilié en 1939.

Ottawa. Catholic college. Day students.
Founded and affiliated in 1939.

Deans and directors

Anthropology, Canadian Research Centre for
Martin Roberge, OMI, BA, LPh, SSL, DTh

Doyens et directeurs

Anthropologie, Centre canadien de
recherches en
Martin Roberge, OMI, BA, LPh, SSL, DTh

Communications sociales, Institut des
André Ruszkowski, LLM, LLD

Droit canonique
André Guay, OMI, LPh, LTh, DDC

Histoire religieuse du Canada, Centre de
recherche en
Jean-Claude Dubé, OMI, MA, LPh, LTh,
DUP

Liturgie, Centre d'étude en
Germain Hudon, OMI, BA, DiplPh, DTh,
PSL

Pastorale, Institut de
Martin Roberge, OMI, BA, LPh, SSL, DTh

Psychiatrie pastorale, Centre de
Victor Szyrynski, MD, PhD, FRCP(Can),
FBPS, FACP, FAPA

Sciences missionnaires, Institut des
Henri Goudreault, OMI, BA, LPh, DTh, SSL

Théologie
Eugène Marcotte, OMI, MA, LPh, DTh

Canon law
André Guay, OMI, LPh, LTh, DDC

Liturgy, Research Centre in
Germain Hudon, OMI, BA, DiplPh, DTh,
PSL

Mission Studies, Institute of
Henri Goudreault, OMI, BA, LPh, DTh, SSL

Pastoral Psychiatry, Centre of
Victor Szyrynski, MD, PhD, FRCP(Can),
FBPS, FACP, FAPA

Pastoral Studies, Institute of
Martin Roberge, OMI, BA, LPh, SSL, DTh

Social Communications, Institute of
André Ruszkowski, LLM, LLD

Religious History of Canada, Research
Centre in
Jean-Claude Dubé, OMI, MA, LPh, LTh,
DUP

Theology
Eugène Marcotte, OMI, MA, LPh, DTh

St. Paul's College*

(Affiliated to The University of Manitoba)
Winnipeg 19, Manitoba

Telephone: 204-269-1400
Direct general correspondence to the dean

Total full-time student enrolment 570; see
also separate section *Statistics on Canadian
universities and colleges*

Executive and administrative officers

Rector
Very Rev. Vincent Jensen, SJ, BA, MA

Dean of studies
Adam Giesinger, BA, BEd, MSc, PhD

Chairman, board of management
Chief Justice G.E. Tritschler

Secretary-treasurer
D.G. Edmond, AACI

Background

St. Paul's College, under Jesuit direction, was
established in 1926 and was affiliated to The
University of Manitoba in 1931. The
university act provides for the autonomy of
the college in matters of internal discipline.

For 27 years, the college operated on a
downtown site, but in 1958 it moved into
new buildings on the campus adjacent to the
other faculties and schools of The University
of Manitoba. St. Paul's College is co-
educational.

Facilities and services

St. Paul's College has five buildings on the
campus of The University of Manitoba. The
library (32,000 volumes) serves the
immediate needs of the staff and students
who also have access to the general library of
The University of Manitoba.

Student services include college chapel
services, student counselling and a cafeteria.
In addition, the students use the facilities of
The University of Manitoba students' union
building. A student employment service is
provided by the university.

Campus organizations serving students from
abroad include the International students
organization, World University Service of
Canada, the Chinese students' association,
and the African students' association. There
is on staff an advisor to Chinese students.

Calendars and brochures

General calendar available from the dean's
office, St. Paul's College.

Courses and degrees

Arts

Bachelor of arts (BA).
(a) General course, three years from senior
matriculation, specialization in the humanities
and social sciences. (b) Honors courses, four
years from senior matriculation, in
conjunction with the university.

Master of arts (MA).
At least two years from the general (pass)
BA, or at least one year from the honors BA,
in conjunction with The University of
Manitoba.

Science, pure

Bachelor of science (BSc).
General course, three years from senior
matriculation.

---

*Ordinary member, AUCC.

Extension programs	Deans of faculties and department heads

For university credit:

See The University of Manitoba.

Summer school courses in conjunction with
The University of Manitoba.

Admission requirements

For a general statement regarding admission
to university study, see article *Admission to
university in Canada.*

For information regarding admission to
undergraduate study, consult *Requirements
for admission to Canadian colleges and
universities* available from Service for
Admission to College and University, 151
Slater St., Ottawa, Ont., K1P 5N1, $1.50
prepaid.

Academic year

Winter session: mid-September to early May.

Summer session: early July to mid-August.

Grading system

As for The University of Manitoba.

Fees and costs

Tuition fees per year: arts and science $85 for
each course. Student's organization fees $36.

Financial awards and assistance

St. Paul's students are eligible for the
scholarships and bursaries available to
students of The University of Manitoba.

St. Thomas More College*

representative of each of the six Catholic dioceses of Saskatchewan. Its professors teach in the university classrooms, and are deemed to be members of the staff of both college and university. They belong to the faculty of arts and science and to the university council (Saskatoon). Their classes are open to any qualified university students, so far as space permits.

(Federated with the University of Saskatchewan, Saskatoon campus)
1437 College Drive, Saskatoon, Saskatchewan

Telephone: 306-343-4561
Direct general correspondence to the registrar

Total full-time student enrolment 778; see also separate section *Statistics on Canadian universities and colleges*

Executive and administrative officers

Principal
Rev. P.J.M. Swan, CSB, PhD

Registrar
Rev. W.O. Regan, CSB, BA, MEd

Advisor to women students
Margaret Dutil, MA

Librarian
Madeleine Bayet, BA, BLS

Treasurer
Rev. T.G. Mallon, CSB, MA

Background

St. Thomas More College was established and federated with the University of Saskatchewan in 1936. In 1943, the college was incorporated by an act of the provincial legislature. It is governed by a corporation consisting of the Basilian Fathers stationed at the college, tenured members of the faculty, alumni representatives and one lay

Facilities and services

The college is located on the university campus in Saskatoon (population 130,000). It has a library (19,000 volumes), an art gallery, a music room, staff offices, seminar rooms, staff and student lounges, and an auditorium. Student services include chapel services, student counselling, housing service and a cafeteria.

Calendars and brochures

Classes given by St. Thomas More professors are described in the calendar of the college of arts and science, University of Saskatchewan, (Saskatoon campus). General information concerning St. Thomas More College is contained in a brochure published annually and obtainable from the registrar.

Courses and degrees

Arts
(Faculty of arts and science, University of Saskatchewan)

Bachelor of arts (BA).
As offered by the University of Saskatchewan, Saskatoon campus.

Science, pure
(Faculty of arts and science, University of Saskatchewan)

Bachelor of science (BSc).
As offered by the University of Saskatchewan, Saskatoon campus.

*Ordinary member, AUCC.

Combined courses

Combined courses in arts and science and agriculture, or commerce, or education, or engineering, or home economics, or law, or pharmacy, as offered by the University of Saskatchewan, Saskatoon.

Extension programs

For university credit:

Evening classes, intersession classes, summer school classes and correspondence classes, in conjunction with the University of Saskatchewan, Saskatoon.

For no university credit:

Adult education programs in theology and allied fields.

Admission requirements

For a general statement regarding admission to university study, see article *Admission to university in Canada.*

For information regarding admission to undergraduate study, consult *Requirements for admission to Canadian colleges and universities* available from Service for Admission to College and University, 151 Slater St., Ottawa, Ont., K1P 5N1, $1.50 prepaid.

Academic year

Winter session: early September to early May.

Intersession: mid-May to late June.

Summer session: early July to mid-August.

Grading system and fees and costs

As for the University of Saskatchewan, Saskatoon campus.

Financial awards and assistance

Students of St. Thomas More College are eligible to receive scholarships, bursaries, prizes, and loans available to arts and science students of the University of Saskatchewan, Saskatoon .

The college itself offers undergraduate scholarships ($350) to its own second- and third-year students, and honors scholarships ($500) and honors fee awards (up to $425), to its fourth-year honors students.

Department heads

Economics and political science
Stewart Farnell, PhD

English
Jean Seaton, BS, MA, PhD

French
Rev. W.H. O'Brien, CSB, MA

History
T.G. Heath, MA, DPhil

Philosophy
P.J.M. Swan, CSB, MA, PhD

(Members of the departments of biblical literature, psychology and sociology report directly to the principal.)

University of Saskatchewan*

Regina, Saskatchewan

Telephone: 306-584-4111
Direct general correspondence to the secretary of the campus

Total full-time student enrolment 4,245; see also separate section *Statistics on Canadian universities and colleges*

Officers of the university

Chancellor
The Rt. Hon. John Diefenbaker, PC, QC, BA, MA, LLB, DCL, LLD, DLitt, DSL, DH, FRSC, FRSA, MP

President and vice-chancellor
J.W.T. Spinks, MBE, PhD, DSc, LLD, FRSC, CC

Vice-presidents, university
R.W. Begg, BSc, MSc, MD, CN, DPhil, FRCP(C)
John Archer, BA, MA, BLS, PhD
L.I. Barber, BA, BComm, MBA, DBA

Vice-president, research
B.W. Currie, BSc, MSc, PhD, FRSC

University secretary and assistant to the president
J.A.E. Bardwell, BA, MSc, PhD, DPhil

Assistant to the president Regina
W.A. Riddell, BA, BSc, MSc, PhD

Dean of University college of graduate studies
A.B. Van Cleave, BSc, MSc, PhD, FRSC

Controller and treasurer
J.A. Pringle, BAcc

---

*Ordinary member, AUCC.

Assistants to the controller
M.G. Sheppard, BComm
Amy Meredith
J.W. Joyce, BA

Director of planning
J.A. Wedgwood, BE

Director of development
F. Lovell, BComm, BA

Director of alumni affairs, university
G.A. Saunders, BA

Executive and administrative officers
— Regina campus

Principal
J.H. Archer, BA, MA, BLS, PhD

Vice-principal
R.F.E. Harvey, BA, BEd, PhD

Director, academic services
E. Stanley, BSc, PhD

Director, extension services
G.H. Beatty, BA, BComm

Co-ordinator of liberal studies in extension
R.M. Sherdahl

Director, conservatory of music (Regina campus), and director, program of Western Board of Music
H. Leyton-Drown, DFC, DipMus, FGSM

Director, Norman Mackenzie art gallery
H.C. Dillow (Mrs), BA

Supervisor, matriculation program
L.G. Crossman, BA, BEd, MA, PhD

Director of counselling services
Ann Gustin, BA, MS, PhD

Director, AV/TV centre
C.E.G. Bates, BSA, PAg

Librarian
S. Harland, BA, MA, FLA

Director, publicity and public relations
Lyn Goldman

News and information officer
Lynn Redekopp

Business manager
S.G. Mann, BA, BComm

Chief accountant
R.R.F. Carter

Purchasing officer
J.S. Neudorf

Personnel officer
J.M. Blake (Miss)

Director of ancillary enterprises
R. Duck

Bookstore manager
A.G. Whitaker (Mrs)

Food services manager
To be appointed

Duplicating services manager
W. Quan

Secretary
W.C. Blight, BSc, MS

Registrar
N.A. Stables, BComm, CA

Admissions officer
I. Louis (Mrs)

Awards officer
N.A. Beirnes, BA, MA

Director of physical plant
D.A. Larmour, BE

Director of maintenance and operation
T.E. Tribe

Director of computer centre
L.R. Symes, BA, MS, PhD

Institutional services officer
R. Borrowman

Budget officer
J. Ayre

Background

The University of Saskatchewan was
established by an act of the legislative
assembly of Saskatchewan in 1907. Teaching
began in 1909 and the first degrees were
awarded in 1912.

Regina College, which was established in
1911, was taken over by the university as a
constituent college in 1934. In 1961, the name
of the college was changed to the University

of Saskatchewan, Regina campus. On July 1,
1964, the two teachers colleges at Saskatoon
and Regina became part of the university and
all teacher-training programs are now
integrated within the university. The Regina
campus issued its first degree in May 1965.

The University of Saskatchewan is provincial,
non-denominational and co-educational. It is
governed by a board of governors, a senate, a
general university council and two campus
councils (Saskatoon and Regina). The board
of governors is responsible for the business
management of the university, while the
senate and the councils are responsible for
academic policy.

Facilities and services

The University of Saskatchewan has two
campuses, one in Saskatoon (population
129,000), the other at Regina (population
143,000).

Unlike many other universities whose growth
has been haphazard, Regina campus, with its
distinctive architecture, has developed from a
master plan. The campus is a part of the
Wascana centre development, a government
education and cultural centre designed by an
internationally known architect Minoru
Yamasaki. All buildings on the new campus
are built on a common base or podium, so
that it will be possible to go from one
building to another without going outside. At
present the classroom, laboratory and library
buildings have a common podium with
enclosed connecting passageways and
common courtyards.

The physical education centre, Campion
College (a federated Roman Catholic arts
college), the education building and the
student services centre will eventually be
joined to future buildings such as the
administration/humanities building, Luther
College (a federated Lutheran arts college)
and College west, an academic and
residential complex. This campus also
includes the original Regina College campus
located on College Avenue with the Norman
Mackenzie art gallery and Darke hall. The
division of fine arts, the department of
extension programs and the conservatory of
music are located on this campus.

Luther College, which was ready for
occupancy in the fall of 1971, provided the
first residence accommodation on campus and
has facilities for 200 students. College west,

scheduled for completion in 1972 will provide residence accommodation for 600 students.

The Regina campus offers the following services to students:

(a) a student service centre complete with lounging areas, cafeteria services, banking services and students' representative council office;
(b) a general non-academic student counselling office;
(c) a nursing service which is available to students Monday through Friday;
(d) temporary insurance coverage for students who have not established their eligibility under the Saskatchewan hospitalization and medical care acts. There is a charge for this coverage;
(e) housing – the students' representative council has listings of residence accommodation in the city. In addition, there is a housing co-op and Luther College will have accommodation for 200 students;
(f) cafeterias – there are cafeterias and vending machines placed in convenient areas around the campus;
(g) library – the university library collection includes 200,000 book volumes, 3,300 serials and 100,000 other items;
(h) bookstore – the Regina campus operates a bookstore which is located in the podium of the classroom building;
(i) parking – the university has parking facilities on the College Avenue and Main campuses. Students require parking permits;
(j) student placement service – the Department of Manpower and Immigration, manpower service, maintains an office at the campus.

See separate entry for details of the Saskatoon campus.

Calendars and brochures

Faculty, spring/summer and evening class calendars may be obtained free-of-charge from the registrar's office.

General calendars cost $2 each and may be obtained by writing to or visiting the campus bookstore.

Calendars and brochures describing non-credit and certificate classes may be obtained from the department of extension.

Courses and degrees

Administration
(Faculty of administration)

Bachelor of administration (BAdmin).
Four years from senior matriculation. Three areas of concentration: behavioral, quantitative and economics.

Arts
(Faculty of arts and science)

Bachelor of arts (BA).
(a) Ordinary course, three years from senior matriculation. Areas of emphasis: humanities, fine arts, and social sciences. (b) Honors courses, four years from senior matriculation, available in economics, English, French, geography, history, philosophy, political science, psychology, sociology or social sciences and Canadian plains areas study.

Bachelor of fine arts (BFA).
Ordinary course four years from senior matriculation. Areas of emphasis, visual arts or drama. Honors course not available.

(Faculty of graduate studies and research)

Master of arts (MA).
At least two years from ordinary BA, or at least one year from honors BA. Available in communications, economics, English, French, history, philosophy, political science, psychology, social studies and Canadian plains area study.

Doctor of philosophy (PhD).
At least two years from MA. Available in psychology only.

Education
(Faculty of education)

Bachelor of education (BEd).
Four years from senior matriculation. Specialization offered in elementary school teaching and secondary school teaching.

Bachelor of education (BEAD).
Two-year program following an approved bachelor's degree.

Bachelor of music education (BMusEd).
Four-year program for preparation of music teachers for secondary schools. May be taken through faculty of arts and science if preferred.

(Faculty of graduate studies and research)

Postgraduate diploma in education administration (DipEdAdmin).
At least one year from BEAD.

Master of education administration (MEdAdmin).
At least one year from BEAD, plus thesis.

Postgraduate diploma in guidance and counselling.
At least one year from BEAD.

Master of guidance and counselling.
At least one year from BEAD plus thesis.

Engineering
(Faculty of engineering)

Bachelor of science in engineering (BE).
Four years from senior matriculation. Specialization offered in chemical, civil, electrical and mechancial engineering.

(Faculty of graduate studies and research)

Master of science in engineering (MSc).
At least one year from a baccalaureate degree. Specialization offered in chemical, civil, electrical and mechanical engineering.

Laboratory technology
(Faculty of arts and science)

Bachelor of laboratory technology (BL).
Three years from senior matriculation. Areas of emphasis; microbiology and biochemistry.

Certificate in hospital laboratory technology (HLT).
Two years from senior matriculation. For hospital laboratory work, 12 months of apprenticeship must follow.

Music
(Faculty of arts and science)

Associate in music (AMUS).

Licentiate in music (LMUS).

Bachelor of music (BMus).
Four years from senior matriculation. Areas of emphasis; performers, music teachers, school music teachers, and composition.

Science, applied, see engineering above

Science, pure
(Faculty of arts and science)

Bachelor of arts (BA).
(a) Ordinary course, three years from senior matriculation. Areas of emphasis; biology, chemistry, geology, mathematics and physics.
(b) Honors course, four years from senior matriculation; available in biology, chemistry, mathematics, and physics.

Bachelor of science (BSc).
(a) Ordinary course, four years from senior matriculation. Areas of emphasis; biology, chemistry, geology, geophysics, mathematics and physics. (b) Honors course, four years from senior matriculation; additional classes in major subject.

(Faculty of graduate studies and research)

Master of science (MSc).
At least two years from ordinary bachelor's degree in science or at least one year from honors bachelor's degree in science. Available in biology, chemistry, mathematics, and physics.

Doctor of philosophy (PhD).
At least two years from MSc. Available in biology, chemistry, mathematics and physics.

Pre-professional program

The faculty of arts and science offers preparatory courses for students intending to enter certain professional colleges such as agriculture, home economics, law, medicine, veterinary medicine, nursing and dentistry. Before registering at the Regina campus, students intending to enter any of these professional programs should acquaint themselves thoroughly with the requirements and the courses of the college they intend to enter.

Extension programs

For university credit:

Evening classes.
Undergraduate classes (on- and off-campus) in a wide range of subjects in arts and science, administration and education.

Spring and summer sessions.
A complete range of undergraduate classes in arts and science, administration, education and engineering, together with a few graduate classes in education.

For no university credit:

Certificate courses.
Certificate in business administration and public administration; four years of evening study from senior matriculation. Certificate in data processing, three years of evening study from senior matriculation.

Programs such as the fellows program in banking and the Federation of Canadian Personnel Association. Personnel administration program leads to certification by the organization involved.

A number of individual classes in administration and in the liberal arts are offered as well.

Extension services for urban and rural communities and organizations include specially designed short courses, seminars and conferences in general adult education: community development, human relations and communication, current issues in public policy.

Pre-matriculation courses

Preparatory courses.
The Regina campus offers junior matriculants and adult students a one-year program of studies in preparation for university (senior) matriculation. Some senior matriculation subjects are taught in the university summer school.

Special programs

Bilingual program.
A three-year program leading to the BA degree has been offered since September 1968. The program is based essentially on the regular degree program of the university and differs substantially only in the matter of the language of instruction which will be French. To qualify under the bilingual program, a student must complete at least 40% and not more than 60% of his classes in French.

Canadian plains area study program.
This program provides interdisciplinary major and honors studies focused on the Canadian plains region. Its aim, as a liberal undergraduate program, is an understanding of a regional society in its many aspects and in its broad context. It has been designed in such a way as to fulfil the requirements of the college of arts and science.

Co-operative program in engineering.
This program enables students to combine full-time employment opportunities with full semester of study in engineering.

Admission requirements

For a general statement regarding admission to university study, see article *Admission to university in Canada.*

For information regarding admission to undergraduate study, consult *Requirements for admission to Canadian colleges and universities* available from Service for Admission to College and University, 151 Slater St., Ottawa, Ont., K1P 5N1, $1.50 prepaid.

For admission to law, or veterinary medicine, a student must have completed two years beyond senior matriculation, with appropriate selection of subjects, in arts or science.

For admission to dentistry and medicine, one year in arts and science beyond senior matriculation.

For admission to graduate study, a student must have obtained a first degree at the honors level or equivalent with specified grades in appropriate subjects.

Academic year

Fall semester: September 8 to December 21.

Winter semester: January 10 - April 26.

Spring session: early May to mid-June.

Summer session: early July to mid-August.

Campus operates on a modified tri-semester system.

Grading system

Standing is graded in each subject as follows: 5 — outstanding; 4 — very good; 3 — good; 2 — satisfactory; 1 — passing grade; 0 — failing grade; IN — incomplete, EX — exempt; C — credit for hours shown.

AU — audit, no credit; W — withdrew from class; WF — withdrew, failing grade; DE — deferred examination; S — supplemental granted; P — pass standing; AG — aegrotat standing; N — no credit for hours shown.

If grades are converted to percentages, the University of Saskatchewan, Regina campus considers the grades at mid-point, e.g., grade 1 — 55%; grade 2 — 65%; grade 3 — 75%; grade 4 — 85%; grade 5 — 95%.

A student may take twelve hours of pass/fail or non-contributory classes in the faculty of arts and science.

Fees and costs

Fees per year (excluding books, art fees, etc): full-time (a) for first degee — first year, $410; upper years — arts and science, education, administration, engineering, music, $425-$505; (b) master's degree, $425; (c) doctor's degree, each year, $425; (d) part-time (per subject), $64, music, $76. Students fees, per year, approximately $35. Semester fees are approximately one-half of the full-year fees.

In September 1971, there will be on-campus residence accommodation for approximately 200 students. In September 1972 there will be space for 800 resident students. Cost for board and room, approximately $120 per month.

Financial awards and assistance

Assistance for students is available in three principal forms: scholarships, bursaries and loans. Scholarships are awarded on the basis of academic ability and financial need, with the emphasis on academic ability; bursaries are awarded on the basis of academic ability and financial need, with the emphasis on financial need. Educational loans are also obtainable when financial assistance is required with the only academic qualification being that the applicant has been accepted at a post-secondary educational institution.

The government of Saskatchewan has provided entrance scholarships to enable students of superior ability to attend first-year programs in institutions of higher learning. These scholarships are tenable at the following institutions:

1. The University of Saskatchewan;
2. Campion College, Regina;
3. Luther College, Regina;
4. St. Joseph's College, Yorkton;
5. St. Peter's College at Muenster;
6. Saskatchewan schools of nursing for students enroled in the first year of a two-year program (maximum $300);
7. The school of agriculture for students enroled in the first year of a two-year program (maximum $300);
8. The Saskatchewan Technical Institutes, Moose Jaw and Saskatoon, for students enroled in the first year of a two-year program (maximum $300);
9. Any approved institution of higher learning outside the province if the course being pursued is of the first-year level and is not offered in Saskatchewan.

The scholarships, under points 1 to 5 and 9, are valued at $300 or $500, depending upon whether or not the student is a resident of the city or town where the institution is located. Application forms may be obtained from the Department of Education, Avord Tower, Regina, Saskatchewan, and must be completed and returned before June 15th.

The University of Saskatchewan offers for competition a number of entrance scholarships as well as scholarships leading to a degree. These scholarships, valued at $1,250 per year, are awarded to students completing grade XII. They are renewable up to a maximum of four years, provided the student maintains a sufficiently high grade point average. Special application forms for this type of scholarship are available at the registrar's office and must be completed and returned before March 15th. The University of Saskatchewan Regina campus offers one conservatory entrance scholarship valued at $250 and three bachelor of music entrance scholarships valued at $350. Special

application forms are available at the registrar's office and must be completed and returned before September 1st.

General proficiency scholarships, valued at $175 per semester, are also available to students after they have completed at least one semester's work. These scholarships are awarded on the basis of grade point averages. No application is required. A student having a grade point average of 4 or better can be almost certain of receiving one of these scholarships.

A number of other scholarships and bursaries have been established at both campuses of the university. These are described in the scholarship calendar, a copy of which may be obtained from the registrar's office or by writing directly to the awards officer.

The Canada Student Loans Plan was instituted by the federal government to provide loans to supplement the resources of a student, and of his immediate family, who, without this aid, would be unable to pursue a post-secondary education. In most cases, to be eligible a student must have completed his grade XII and be accepted into a post-secondary educational institute. Application forms can be obtained from the Student aid office, Department of Education, Avord Tower, Regina, Saskatchewan.

The maximum loan a student can obtain in any one year is $1,000 and under no circumstances may the total loan exceed $5,000. Repayment begins six months after the student has finished his course. There are also a number of university administered loan funds available. These are used primarily for short-term loans.

Research institute

Canadian plains area centre.
The centre fosters a community of research and discourse which facilitates the interdisciplinary training of graduate students in studies pertaining to the Canadian plains.

Federated colleges

Campion College, Regina, Saskatchewan. Principal: Very Rev. Peter Nash, SJ, MA, PhD. Dean: Rev. Desmond Burke-Gaffney, SJ, MA, PhD. Bursar: E.J. Noonan. Co-educational. Established 1918. Undergraduate arts college, offering in co-operation with the university's faculty of arts and science, Regina campus, all courses leading to the degrees offered by the faculty of arts and science. Serves as student centre for Roman Catholic students. No residential accommodation.

Luther College, Regina, Saskatchewan. Principal: M.A. Anderson, BA, BEd, MA. Academic dean: R.O. Ostrem, MA, PhD. Dean of students: J. Dale, BA. Development director: Rev. D.A. King, BA, BD. Business manager: R.E. Sommerfeld. Lutheran and co-educational. Established 1921. Undergraduate arts college, offering in co-operation with the university's faculty of arts and science, Regina campus, all courses leading to the degrees offered by the faculty of arts and science. Serves as a student centre for Lutheran students. Residential accommodation for 200 students.

Deans of faculties

Administration
W.G. Bolstad (acting), BA, BComm, MPA

Arts and science
Sir G.E. Vaughan, KBE, MA, FRHistS

Campion College
Rev. Desmond Burke-Gaffney, SJ, MA, PhD

Education
A. Kratzmann, BEd, MEd, PhD

Engineering
J.B. Mantle, BE, MS

Graduate studies and research
A.B. Van Cleave, BSc, MSc, PhD, FRSC

Luther College
R.O. Ostrem, MA, PhD

Associate deans

Fine arts
F.A. Nulf, BA, MA, PhD

Education
W.N. Toombs, BA, BEd, MEd, PhD

Humanities
R.C. Cosbey, BA, MA, PhD

Natural sciences and mathematics
J.R. Wolfson, BSc, MSc, PhD

Social sciences
F.W. Anderson, BA, MA

Directors of centres and institutes

Bilingual program centre
B.J. Wilhelm, DèsL

Canadian plains area centre
D. de Vlieger, BA, MA

Physical education
P. Ventre, DipPhysEd, MEd

Department heads

Anthropology
D. McNickle (acting)

Biology
G.F. Ledingham, BSc, MSc, PhD

Chemistry
W.B. McConnell, BSc, MSc, PhD

Drama
E. Salmon, BA

Economics
J.A. Boan, BA, PhD

English
K. Costain, BA, DipEd, MA, PhD

Geography
E.H. Dale, BSc, MSc, PhD

Geology
W.A. Gordon, BSc, PhD

History
R.W. Swales (acting), BA, PhD

Mathematics
I. McDonald, BA, MA, PhD

Modern languages
M. Belcher [*acting (Miss)*], BA, MA

Music
H.B. Lobaugh, BS, MM, PhD

Philosophy and classics
W.A. Berriman (acting), BA, MA

Physics
G.A. Papini, DinF

Political science
J.K. Roberts, BA, PhD

Psychology
C.K. Knapper, BA, PhD

Sociology
J.N. McCrorie, BA, MA, PhD

Social studies
D.W. Smythe, AB, PhD

Visual arts
J. Nugent

University of Saskatchewan*

Saskatoon, Saskatchewan

Telephone: 306-343-2100
Direct general correspondence to the
secretary of the campus

Total full-time student enrolment 9,464; see
also separate section *Statistics on Canadian
universities and colleges*

Officers of the university

Chancellor
The Rt. Hon. John G. Diefenbaker, PC, QC,
BA, MA, LLB, DCL, LLD, DLitt, DSL, DH,
FRSC, FRSA, MP

President and vice-chancellor
J.W.T. Spinks, MBE, PhD, DSc, LLD, FRSC,
CC

Vice-presidents, university
R.W. Begg, BSc, MSc, MD, CN, DPhil,
FRCP(C)
John Archer, BA, MA, BLS, PhD
L.I. Barber, BA, BComm, MBA, DBA

Vice-president, research
B.W. Currie, BSc, MSc, PhD, FRSC

University secretary and assistant to the
president
J.A.E. Bardwell, BA, MSc, PhD, DPhil

Assistant to the president, Regina
W.A. Riddell, BA, BSc, MSc, PhD

Dean of university college of graduate studies
A.B. Van Cleave, BSc, MSc, PhD, FRSC

Controller and treasurer
J.A. Pringle, BAcc

Assistants to the controller
M.G. Sheppard, BComm
Amy Meredith
J.W. Joyce, BA

Director of planning
J.A. Wedgwood, BE

Director of development
F. Lovell, BComm, BA

Director of alumni affairs, university
G.A. Saunders, BA

Executive and administrative officers
— Saskatoon campus

Vice-principals, Saskatoon campus
R.N. Haslam, MA, PhD, FRSC
C.A. King, MA, PhD

Campus secretary
N.K. Cram, BA, BEd

Registrar
J.A. Dorgan, BSA

Dean of academic services
C.A. King, MA, PhD

Dean of students
R.A. Rennie, BA, BEd

Foreign students advisor
W.G. Feuder, BComm

Librarian
D.C. Appelt, MA, ABLS

Director of counselling and student affairs
M.E. Hacking, BA, BComm

Director of division of audio-visual services
P.R. Greenough, DVM, RVC, FRCVS

News and information secretary
J.P. Campbell

Background

The University of Saskatchewan was
established by an act of the legislative
assembly of Saskatchewan in 1907. Teaching
began in 1909 and the first degree was
awarded in 1912.

*Ordinary member, AUCC.

Regina College, which was established in 1911, was taken over by the university as a constituent college in 1934. In 1961, the name of the college was changed to the University of Saskatchewan, Regina Campus. On July 1, 1964, the two teachers' colleges at Saskatoon and Regina became part of the university and all teacher-training programs are now integrated within the university.

The University of Saskatchewan is provincial, non-denominational and co-educational. It is governed by a board of governors, a senate, a general university council and two campus councils (Saskatoon and Regina). The board of governors is responsible for the business management of the university, while the senate and the councils are responsible for academic policy.

Facilities and services

The University of Saskatchewan has two campuses, one in Saskatoon (population, 129,000), the other in Regina (population, 143,000).

The university in Saskatoon is situated on the South Saskatchewan River with a site of 3,200 acres of which 300 acres comprise the campus and 2,900 acres the university farm and experimental plots. There are 14 major teaching buildings, a linear accelerator laboratory, a library, a physical education centre, farm buildings, facilities for administration and student activities, student residences accommodating 600 men and women, Kirk hall which includes extension services and the school of agriculture offices. Federated and affiliated colleges with buildings on the campus are St. Thomas More, College of Emmanuel and St. Chad, and St. Andrew's, and the Lutheran Theological Seminary. Also located on the campus are the university hospital, the Prairie regional laboratory of the National Research Council, the Canada Department of Agriculture research laboratory, the Saskatchewan research council building, a PFRA building, the Cancer and medical research institute building, and St. Pius X seminary.

Student services include a health service, guidance and counselling, a housing registry, a food service building, a students' union and an employment service.

There is on staff an advisor to foreign students. Campus organizations serving students from abroad include the International students' club, World University Service of Canada, and the Chinese students' club.

See separate entry for details on the Regina campus.

Calendars and brochures

A general information bulletin, individual calendars for all colleges and schools, and for the BFA and BMus programs, and a scholarships and awards bulletin are obtainable from the registrar's office. A brochure of information for prospective students from outside of Canada is also available from the registrar's office.

Courses and degrees

Agriculture
(College of agriculture)

Bachelor of science in agriculture (BSA).
Four years from senior matriculation. Specialization offered in agricultural chemistry, agricultural economics, agricultural mechanics, agricultural microbiology, animal science, biology, crop science, dairy and food sciences, economics, horticulture, plant ecology, poultry science, and soil science.

(College of graduate studies)

Master of science (MSc).
At least one year from a bachelor's degree in agriculture. Specialization offered in agricultural economics, animal science, crop science, dairy science, horticulture, plant ecology, poultry science, and soil science.

Doctor of philosophy (PhD).
At least two years from MSc. Ordinarily available in those branches of agriculture listed for MSc.

Post-graduate diploma course.
At least one year from BSA degree.

Arts
(College of arts and science)

Associate in arts (AA).
One year from senior matriculation.

Bachelor of arts (BA).
(a) General course, three years from senior matriculation. Areas of emphasis: humanities and social sciences. (b) Honors courses, four years from senior matriculation. Available in anthropology, art, drama, economics, English, far eastern studies, French, geography, German, Greek, history, Latin, music, North American literature in English, philosophy, political science, psychology, Russian, sociology and Ukrainian. (c) Advanced level, four years from senior matriculation in areas listed above.

(College of graduate studies)

Master of arts (MA).
At least two years from general BA or at least one year from honors BA. Available in anthropology, classics, drama, economics, English, French, geography, German, history, philosophy, political science, and psychology.

Doctor of philosophy (PhD).
At least two years from MA. Available in economics, English, history, political science, psychology, and sociology.

Doctor of letters (DLitt).
Research requirements and calibre of scholarly work in advance of those accepted for PhD.

Business, see commerce below

Commerce
(College of commerce)

Bachelor of commerce (BComm).
(a) General course, four years from senior matriculation. Specialization possible in accounting, business administration (including administration and management of co-operatives), computational science and quantitative analysis, economics, and marketing. (b) Honors course, at least four years from senior matriculation.

(College of graduate studies)

Master of science in commerce (MSc).
At least one year from BComm.

Master of business administration (MBA).
One year from BComm or two years from other degrees.

Dentistry
(College of arts and science)

Pre-dental.
One year.

Doctor of dentistry (DMD).
Five years following at least one year of pre-dental university education beyond senior matriculation. Fifth year will take the form of internship (unique in Canada).

Education
(College of education)

Bachelor of education (BEd).
Four years from senior matriculation or two years for students with a bachelor's degree, or one year for students with a bachelor's degree and a teacher's certificate or three years for graduates of a teachers' college. Specialization offered in elementary school teaching, industrial arts education, secondary school teaching, and technical-vocational education.

(College of graduate studies)

Post-graduate diploma course in education and continuing education.
At least one year from bachelor's degree.

Master of continuing education (MCEd).
At least one year from an approved degree.

Master of education (MEd).
At least one year from BEd degree.

Engineering
(College of engineering)

Bachelor of science in engineering (BE).
Four years from senior matriculation. Specialization offered in agricultural, chemical, civil, electrical, geological (including a geophysics option), mechanical and mining engineering, and engineering physics.

(College of graduate studies)

Post-graduate diploma.
In some branches, at least one year from BE degree.

Master of science (MSc).
At least two years from BE degree. Available in agricultural, biomedical, chemical, civil, electrical, geological, and mechanical engineering, and engineering physics.

Doctor of philosophy (PhD).
At least two years from MSc. Available in agricultural, chemical, civil, electrical, geological, and mechanical engineering, and engineering physics.

Fine arts
(College of arts and science)

Bachelor of fine arts (BFA).
Four years from senior matriculation. Specialization offered in studio art or art history.

Home economics
(College of home economics)

Bachelor of science in home economics (BSHEc).
Four years from senior matriculation. Specialization offered for teaching and extension work, food and nutrition, other fields.

Law
(College of law)

Bachelor of laws (LLB).
Three years from the second year of arts beyond senior matriculation.

Master of laws (LLM).
At least one year from LLB degree.

Medicine
(College of medicine)

Diploma in physiotherapy.
Two and one-half years from senior matriculation.

Bachelor of science in medicine [BSc(Med)].
At least one year from the second year of medicine.

Degree in medical laboratory technology [BSc(MLT)].
Two years from one year in science.

Doctor of medicine (MD).
Five years from one year of science beyond senior matriculation.

(College of graduate studies)

Master of science (MSc).
At least one year from an MD degree. Available in anatomy, biochemistry, biomedical engineering, cancer research, pathology, physiology and pharmacology, psychiatry.

Doctor of philosophy (PhD).
At least two years from an MSc degree. Ordinarily available in same departments as MSc.

Music
(College of arts and science and college of education)

Bachelor of music and *bachelor of music education (BMus and BMusEd).*
Four years from senior matriculation. BMus available in theory and composition; history and literature, performance; BMusEd in instrumental, choral, elementary and junior high school.

Nursing
(School of nursing, college of medicine)

Diploma in public health nursing, diploma in nursing service administration, diploma in advanced psychiatric nursing.
One year from diploma in nursing, with interval of at least one year's experience.

Bachelor of science in nursing (BSN).
Four years from senior matriculation or three years from graduation from an approved school of nursing.

Pharmacy
(College of pharmacy)

Bachelor of science in pharmacy (BSP).
Four years from senior matriculation.

Specialization offered in retail pharmacy, hospital pharmacy, manufacturing, or preparation for graduate study in biochemistry, pharmaceutics, pharmaceutical chemistry, pharmacognosy, physiology, pharmacology.

(College of graduate studies)

Master of science (MSc).
At least one year from BSP. Available in biochemistry, pharmaceutics, pharmaceutical chemistry, physiology, pharmacology, pharmacognosy.

Physical education
(School of physical education, college of arts and science)

Bachelor of arts in physical education [BA(PE)].
Four years from senior matriculation.

(College of graduate studies)

Master of arts or master of science (MA or MSc).
At least one year from BA(PE) or its equivalent.

Science, applied, see engineering above

Science, pure
(College of arts and science)

Bachelor of science (BSc).
(a) General course, three years from senior matriculation. (b) Honors course, four years from senior matriculation. Available in anatomy, bacteriology (microbiology), biochemistry, biology, biophysics, chemistry, computational science, geology, histology, mathematics, physics, physiology and pharmacology. (c) Advanced level, four years from senior matriculation in areas listed above.

(College of graduate studies)

Master of science (MSc).
At least two years from general bachelor's degree in science or at least one year from honors bachelor's degree in science. Available in anatomy, bacteriology (microbiology), biochemistry, biology, chemistry, geology, mathematics, physics, physiology and pharmacology.

Doctor of philosophy (PhD).
At least two years from MSc. Available in most departments as MSc.

Doctor of science (DSc).
Research requirements and calibre of scholarly work in advance of those accepted for PhD. Only graduates of the University of Saskatchewan through examination or by admission *ad eudem gradum* are eligible.

Theology

Courses offered by affiliated colleges.

Veterinary medicine
(College of veterinary medicine)

Doctor of veterinary medicine (DVM).
Four years from the second year of science beyond senior matriculation.

(College of graduate studies)

Diploma in diagnostic pathology.
One year (12 months) beyond DVM degree.

Master of science (MSc).
At least one year from DVM degree.

Doctor of philosophy (PhD).
Minimum three-year course offered in anatomy, pathology, microbiology and physiology.

Combined courses

Combined courses in arts or science and certain professional fields enable a student to obtain two degrees in less time than if the two courses were taken separately.

Special programs

The college of education offers a four-year BEd degree program for teachers in Indian and northern communities.

The college of arts and science offers a general three-year program in international studies.

Extension programs

For university credit:

Correspondence courses.
Courses offered in a number of first-year arts subjects.

Evening classes.
Limited number of undergraduate classes in arts, commerce, and education.

Saturday morning off-campus classes
in arts and science and education offered during the winter at a limited number of centres.

Summer school and intersession.
Courses are offered for undergraduates proceeding to a degree and for teachers who may wish to improve their professional qualifications, chiefly subjects in arts, commerce, science, and education; also a limited number in other areas, and a fee at the graduate level.

For no university credit:

Pre-matriculation courses.

Diploma in agriculture;
two years.

Admission requirements

For a general statement regarding admission to university study, see article *Admission to university in Canada.*

For information regarding admission to undergraduate study, consult *Requirements for admission to Canadian colleges and universities* available from Service for Admission to College and University, 151 Slater St., Ottawa, Ont., K1P 5N1, $1.50 prepaid.

For admission to law, or veterinary medicine, a student must have completed two years beyond senior matriculation, with appropriate selection of subjects, in arts or science.

For admission to dentistry and medicine, one year in appropriate subjects in arts and science beyond senior matriculation.

For admission to graduate study a student must have obtained a first degree at the honors level or equivalent with specified grades in appropriate subjects.

Academic year

Winter session: mid-September to early May.

Intersession: May and June.

Summer session: early July to mid-August.

Grading system

Standing is graded in each subject as division 1: 80-100%; division 11: 70-79%; division 111: 60-69%; division 1V: 50-59%; or failed: below 50%. Merit points are assigned as follows: division 1 — 3 points; division 11 — 2 points; division 111 — 1 point.

Fees and costs

All inclusive fees per year: full-time (a) for first degree — first year, $410; upper years — agriculture, arts and science, education, administration, commerce, nursing, pharmacy, engineering, home economics, music, $425-$505; law, $450; medicine and veterinary medicine, $635; (b) master's degree, $425; (c) doctor's degree, each year, $425; (d) part-time (per subject), $100.

Student fees, per year, approximately $40.

Residence rates, room and board. First term $383-$413; second term $344-$470. Apartment accommodation is provided in McEown park located on university property about five blocks south of the campus. Unfurnished accommodation (except for stove and refrigerator) is available for married students with children, married students without children and single students on a "sharing basis" from $95 to $125 per month.

Furnished units for six students per unit on a "sharing basis" are available at $390 per month ($65 per occupant).

Research institutes

Institute for Northern Studies.
The two fundamental aims of the institute are research on problems of northern Canada and the training of personnel to work in that region.

Institute of Space and Atmospheric Studies.
Research in consistency, photochemistry, morphology, particle flux, electric and magnetic fields, radio wave — plasma interaction of upper atmosphere near the aurora. Study of telluric currents and micropulsations and dynamics of lower atmosphere.

Space Engineering Division.
Instrumentation and launching of research rockets. Development and construction of rocket and satellite experiment on housekeeping equipment.

Matador Project, International Biological Program.
The Matador project is an integrated ecosystem study of grasslands. It is a Canadian contribution to the international biological program financed by the National Research Council, with the co-operation of the University of Saskatchewan. During 1969, 123 persons contributed 37 man-years of study to the interaction of soil-plants-animals-atmosphere in a natural system, with comparison of an artificial (wheat) system. The Matador project is the international centre for IBP grasslands studies.

Institute for Child Guidance.
Principal areas of speciality: (1) children with learning and related disabilities; (2) early childhood education. Educationally based, but interdisciplinary. A teaching facility with developing research in areas of psycholinguistic and perceptual aspects of communication.

Institute of Pedology.
Principal fields of research: basic soil surveys, classification and utilization of Saskatchewan soils; fundamental, physical, chemical, biological and mineralogical research. Studies of soil-water-nutrients-plant interrelationships.

Federated college

St. Thomas More College, Saskatoon, Saskatchewan.
Principal: Rev. P.J.M. Swan, CSB, MA, PhD. Registrar: Rev. W.O. Regan, BA, MEd. Roman Catholic (Basilian). Co-educational. Established 1936. Undergraduate arts and science, Saskatoon, all courses leading to the BA and BSc degree of the university. Serves as student centre for Roman Catholic students.

Affiliated colleges

College of Emmanuel and St. Chad, Saskatoon, Saskatchewan.
Principal: Rev. J.D.F. Beattie, MA, BD. Registrar: Rev. J.R. Fife, MA, CdeG, CdeL'OdeLeopold 11. Anglican. Co-educational. Emmanuel College established in 1879. St. Chad's College established 1907. In 1964 the two colleges amalgamated. Offers courses in theology leading to the testamur, the licentiate in theology, and the degree of bachelor of divinity (BD), which are awarded by the college. Teaches certain courses which may be offered for credit toward a BA degree of the university.

Lutheran Theological Seminary, Saskatoon, Saskatchewan.
President: W.E. Hordern, BA, BD, ThD, DD. Lutheran. Men only. Established in 1965, the faculty is successor to the Lutheran faculty of theology and the two institutions, Lutheran College and Seminary and Luther Theological Seminary. Offers courses in theology leading to graduation diploma and degree of bachelor of divinity (BD) which are awarded by the faculty. Teaches certain courses which may be offered for credit toward a BA degree of the university.

St. Andrew's College, Saskatoon, Saskatchewan.
Principal: Rev. R.F. Schnell, MA, PhD. Registrar: Rev. B.R. Bater, MA, BD. United Church. Co-educational. Established 1912. Offers courses in theology leading to degree in bachelor of divinity (BD), which is awarded by the college. Teaches certain courses which may be offered for credit toward a BA degree of the university.

St. Joseph's College, Yorkton, Saskatchewan.
Ukrainian diocese of Saskatchewan. Brothers of the Christian Schools. Director: Brother

Justin. Junior college, offering evening classes in arts and science and in education. Also operates a high school.

St. Peter's College, Muenster, Saskatchewan. Rector: Rev. Vincent Morrison, OSB. Roman Catholic (Benedictine). Established 1926. Junior college, offering one year of university studies beyond senior matriculation in arts and science. Also operates a high school (grades 9 to 12).

Deans of faculties

Agriculture
W.J. White, BSA, MSc, PhD

Arts and science
D.R. Cherry, BA, MA, PhD

Commerce
S. Laimon, BComm, MBA, RIA

Dentistry
K.J. Paynter, DDS, PhD

Education
J.B. Kirkpatrick, BA, MEd, EdD

Engineering
A.D. Booth, BSc, PhD, DSc

Graduate studies
K.J. McCallum, BSc, MSc, PhD, FRSC

Home economics
Edith C. Rowles Simpson, BHSc, MSc, EdD

Law
R.C. Carter, QC, BA, LLB, LLM

Medicine
J.R. Guteluis, BA, MDCM, FRCS(Can)

Pharmacy
W.C. MacAulay, BSP, MS, DPharm

Veterinary medicine
D.L.T. Smith, DVM, PhD

Directors of schools

Agriculture
A.A. Stilborn, BA, BEd, BSA

Nursing
Lucy D. Willis, BS, MA, EdD

Physical education
H.R. Nixon, BPE, MS

Department heads

Accounting
M.L. Dasgupta, BComm, MA, DPhil, AIC, WAI

Administration and marketing
H.B. Tennant, BBA, MBA

Agricultural economics
P.J. Thair, BSA, MSc, PhD

Agricultural engineering
O.L. Symes, BA, BE

Anaesthesia
G.M. Wyant, MD, FFARCS, FACA, FRCP(C)

Anatomy
S. Fedoroff, BA, MA, PhD

Animal science
J.M. Bell, BSc, MSc, PhD

Anthropology and archaeology
J.F.V. Millar, BASc, PhD

Art
To be appointed

Bacteriology
G. Dempster, MB, ChB, BSc, MD

Biochemistry
J.D. Wood, BSc, PhD

Biology
J.M. Naylor

Cancer research
J.F. Morgan, BA, MSA, PhD, FRSC

Chemistry and chemical engineering
J.M. Pepper, BA, MA, PhD

Civil engineering
A.H. Douglas, BE

Computational science
B.A. Holmlund, BE, MSc

Continuing education
Jane Abramson, AB, MA

Crop science
D.R. Knott, BSA, MS, PhD

Curriculum studies
J.R. Bryner, BS, MA, EdD

Dairy and food sciences
D.L. Gibson, MBE, BSA, MS, PhD

Diagnostic radiology
H.P. Kent, BA, MA, MB, BChir, DMRD

Drama
D.F. Nalbach, PhD

Economics and political science
L.F. Kristjanson, BA, MA, PhD

Education administration
J.G. Egnatoff, BA, BPaed, EdD

Educational psychology
H.W. Savage, BA, MEd, EdD

Education foundations
Doris J. Dyke, BA, BEd, MEd, MA, EdD

Electrical engineering
R.E. Ludwig, BScEE, MS

English
J.K. Johnstone, BA, MA, PhD, FRSL

Far eastern studies
H.V. Guenther, PhD

Finance and quantitative methods
M.L. Dasgupta (acting), BComm, DPhil

French and Spanish
R.S. Ridgeway, BA, MA, Ddel'Univ

Geography
J.H. Richards, BSc, MA, PhD

Geological sciences
A.R. Byers, BSc, MSc, PhD, FRSC

Germanic languages
K.M. Gunvaldsen, BA, MA, PhD

Greek and Roman studies
C.D. Pritchet, BA, MA, PhD

History
I.N. Lambi, BA, MA, PhD

Horticultural science
S.H. Nelson, BSA, MS, PhD

Mathematics
G.H.M. Thomas, BSc, MS, PhD

Mechanical engineering
P.N. Nikiforuk, BSc, PhD

Medicine
L. Horlick, BSc, MD, CM, MSc, FRCP(C)

Music
D.L. Kaplan, BM, MM

Obstetrics and gynecology
T.B. MacLachlan, MD, FRCS(C)

Ophthalmology
R.G. Murray, BA, MD, FRCS(C)

Oral diagnoses
J.H. Sinclair, BDS, MDS, FDS(Eng)

Oral surgery
B.K. Arard, BSc, BDS, MS, FRCD(C)

Paediatrics
J.W. Gerrard, BA, BM, BCh, DM, MRCP,
FRCP(C)

Pathology
D.F. Moore, MD, BSc(Med), FRCP(C)

Philosophy
L.G. Miller, BA, MA, PhD

Physics
L. Katz, BSc, MSc, PhD, FRSC

Physiology and pharmacology
L.B. Jaques, MA, PhD, FRSC

Plant ecology
R.T. Coupland, BSA, PhD

Poultry science
J.B. O'Neil, BSA, MSA

Psychiatry
I.M. McDonald, MD

Psychology
R.G.A. Stretch, BA, PhD

Rehabilitation medicine
T.E. Hunt, BA, MD, FRCP(C)

Slavic studies
C.H. Andrusyshen, BA, MA, PhD, FRSC

Social and preventive dentistry
C.W.B. McPhail, BSc, DDS, MSD, MScD, FI

Social and preventive medicine
V.L. Matthews, BA, MD, DPH

Sociology
E.J. Abramson, BA, MA

Soil science
D.A. Rennie, BSA, PhD

Special education
J. McLeod, BSc, EdB, PhD

Surgery
J.R. Gutelius, BA, MD, FRCS(C), FACS

Therapeutic radiology
C.C. Burkell, BSc, MD, DMRT(Eng)

Veterinary anatomy
A. Horowitz, DVM, PhD

Veterinary clinical studies
C.M. Fraser, BSA, DVM, MVSc

Veterinary microbiology
C.H. Bigland, DVM, DVPH, MSc

Veterinary pathology
N.O. Neilson, BSA, DVM, MSc

Veterinary physiology
R.H. Dunlop, DVM, PhD

Université de Sherbrooke*

Cité universitaire, boulevard de l'Université
Sherbrooke (Québec)

Téléphone: 819-565-5970
Prière d'adresser la correspondance d'ordre
général au secrétaire général

Total des inscriptions des étudiants à plein
temps 4,165; voir aussi la section distincte,
intitulée "*Statistiques sur les universités et
collèges du Canada*"

Dirigeants

Grand chancelier
S.E. Mgr Jean-Marie Fortier,
Archevêque de Sherbrooke

Recteur
Mgr Roger Maltais, PD, LPh

Vice-recteur, affaires universitaires
Roger Bernier, BA, BScS, LPh, DPh

Vice-recteur, affaires administratives
Jean-Jacques St-Pierre, BA, LScCom, CA

Vice-recteur à la recherche
Louis-Paul Dugal, BA, LSc, MSc, PhD, LLD

Vice-recteur, disciplines de la santé
Gérald LaSalle, MD, DAH

Secrétaire général et directeur du service des
relations publiques
Daniel Croteau, BA, DiplBibl

Registraire
Pierre Mercier, BA, BPh, LPh

Adjoint au recteur, informatique
Gérald Gosselin

Adjoint au recteur, vie étudiante
J.-Aurèle Gagnon, MA

Directeur des bibliothèques
Trefflé Michaud

Directeur de l'admission
Jean-Robert Langlois, BA, BTh, LPéd

Directeur de l'inscription
Guy Langevin, BA

Directeur de la coordination
Gilles Joncas, BScA, MScA

Directeur des finances
Jean-Claude Poulin, MScCom, MScCompt,
CA

Historique

L'Université de Sherbrooke a été érigée
civilement le 4 mai 1954 et fut érigée
canoniquement par le décret de la sacrée
congrégation des séminaires et des universités
le 21 novembre 1957. Sa charte civile lui
reconnaît tous les pouvoirs d'ordre
universitaire. Issue du Séminaire de
Sherbrooke, elle en est totalement séparée
depuis 1960. A l'exception de sa Faculté de
médecine située sur le campus de l'est, au sein
du centre hospitalier universitaire,
l'Université de Sherbrooke occupe un vaste
terrain de 850 acres aux limites sud-ouest de
la ville de Sherbrooke. Une vaste cité
universitaire s'y déploie maintenant selon les
plans fonctionnels d'un urbaniste de renom.
Près de 500 professeurs de carrière et chargés
de cours dispensent l'enseignement dans les
huit facultés existantes.

Installations et services

L'université peut offrir à ses étudiants les
avantages d'une cité universitaire bien
organisée avec tous les services requis: six
pavillons d'enseignement avec laboratoires
des mieux outillés, un centre social, deux
cafétérias, des résidences pouvant accueillir
près de 1,500 étudiants et étudiantes et
comportant des salles de jeux et de détente,
une vaste bibliothèque générale climatisée
d'une capacité de 300,000 volumes et trois
bibliothèques particulières, un auditorium de
1,600 places pour collations de grades et
manifestations artistiques, un gymnase pour

*Membre ordinaire de l'AUCC.

la pratique des sports intérieurs et des terrains d'athlétisme.

La cité universitaire est le foyer de nombreuses activités contribuant à la culture ou à la détente des étudiants: concerts, conférences, théâtre, cinéma et autres. De plus, reconnaissant l'importance du secteur de la vie étudiante, l'université a voulu lui donner des cadres qui favorisent son développement. Ces cadres comprennent une commission consultative, une direction et les services suivants: service d'orientation, logement, service des sports, emploi, service de santé, aide financière aux étudiants, la FEUS.

Annuaires et brochures

Annuaire général; annuaires de faculté; brochure "Renseignements généraux".

L'annuaire général ainsi que les annuaires de faculté font l'objet d'une diffusion contrôlée. On peut se procurer la brochure "Renseignements généraux" en s'adressant au bureau du registraire.

On peut également se procurer le bulletin d'information de l'Université de Sherbrooke, "Liaison", en s'adressant au service des relations publiques.

Cours et grades

Administration
(Faculté d'administration)

Baccalauréat en administration (BAdm).
Trois années ou 90 crédits après le DEC ou l'équivalent. Spécialisation en comptabilité, finance, marketing ou gestion des ressources humaines.

Maîtrise en administration des affaires (MBA).
Programme coopératif: quatre sessions d'études et trois stages pratiques après le baccalauréat ou un diplôme universitaire reconnu dans quelle que discipline que ce soit.

Maîtrise ès arts (MA).
Un an après le baccalauréat en administration spécialisé avec options en comptabilité, finance, marketing ou analyse de systèmes. Mémoire.

Arts
(Faculté des arts)

Baccalauréat ès arts,
dans les disciplines: anglais, français, géographie et histoire; également dans les options: économique et général. Trois ans après le DEC ou l'équivalent.

Baccalauréat en service social (BServSoc).
Programme coopératif: cinq sessions d'études et trois stages pratiques après le DEC ou l'équivalent.

Baccalauréat en philosophie (BPh).
Trois ans après le DEC ou l'équivalent.

Baccalauréat en psychologie (BPs).
Trois ans après le DEC ou l'équivalent.

Maîtrise en service social (MServSoc).
Programme coopératif: de trois à six sessions ou plus, selon le titre d'admission, après le BServSoc ou l'équivalent.

Certificat d'études avancées en service social (CEAServSoc).
Quatre ans à temps partiel (6cr./année) après la MServSoc.

Maîtrise ès arts (MA).
Un an après le baccalauréat spécialisé ou la licence dans les disciplines: économique, français, géographie, histoire, littérature canadienne comparée et philosophie. Mémoire.

Doctorat ès lettres (DèsL).
Deux ans après la MA (ou l'équivalent). Connaissance approfondie d'une langue moderne. Thèse.

Droit
(Faculté de droit)

Licence en droit (LLL).
Trois ans après le DEC ou un diplôme équivalent.

Maîtrise en droit (LLM).
Un an après la LLL dans l'option droit des affaires.

Génie
(Faculté des sciences appliquées)

Baccalauréat ès sciences appliquées (BScA),
avec spécialisation en génie chimique, civil, électrique ou mécanique. Programme

coopératif: sept sessions d'études et cinq stages pratiques après le DEC ou l'équivalent.

Maîtrise ès sciences appliquées (MScA), avec spécialisation en génie chimique, civil, électrique, mécanique, aérospatial ou médical. Un an après le BScA. Mémoire.

Doctorat ès sciences appliquées (PhD), avec spécialisation en génie chimique, civil, électrique, mécanique ou aérospatial. Deux ans après la MScA. Thèse.

Lettres, voir arts

Médecine
(Faculté de médecine)

MD.
Quatre ans après un DEC ou l'équivalent.

Maîtrise ès sciences (MSc).
Un an après le MD ou BSc spécialisé. Dans les disciplines: anatomie, biochimie, biologie cellulaire, biophysique, microbiologie, pathologie, pharmacologie, physiologie, sciences cliniques et science épidémiologique. Mémoire.

Doctorat (PhD).
Deux ans après la MSc. Dans les disciplines: anatomie, biochimie, biologie cellulaire, biophysique, microbiologie, pathologie, pharmacologie, physiologie, sciences cliniques et science épidémiologique. Thèse.

Notariat
(Faculté de droit)

Un an d'entraînement professionnel à la faculté après la LLL.

Pédagogie
(Faculté des sciences de l'éducation)

(1) Sciences de l'éducation

Baccalauréat ès sciences de l'éducation (BScEd).
Trois ans après le DEC ou l'équivalent dans les disciplines: éducation physique, information scolaire et professionnelle, orthopédagogie et psycho-éducation.

Maîtrise ès sciences de l'éducation (MScEd).
Un an après le BScEd, dans les options orthopédagogie et psycho-éducation. Mémoire.

Maîtrise en éducation option administration scolaire (MEdAdmScol).
Trois à quatre ans à temps partiel après seize (16) années de scolarité. Formation pédagogique et titulaire d'un poste d'administrateur scolaire.

(2) Formation des maîtres

Licence d'enseignement élémentaire (Ld'ensél).
Trois ans après le DEC ou l'équivalent, soit au premier cycle ou deuxième cycle de l'enseignement élémentaire.

Licence d'enseignement secondaire (Ld'enssec).
Trois ans après le DEC ou l'équivalent. Diverses options offertes aux facultés des arts, sciences ou théologie.

CAPES (Certificat d'aptitudes pédagogiques à l'enseignement secondaire).
Un an après un premier diplôme universitaire dans une discipline enseignée au niveau secondaire.

Sciences appliquées, voir génie

Sciences économiques, voir arts

Sciences pures
(Faculté des sciences)

Baccalauréat ès sciences (BSc).
Trois ans après le DEC ou l'équivalent avec spécialisation en mathématiques, physique, chimie ou biologie.

Maîtrise ès sciences (MSc).
Un an après le BSc, (mathématiques, physique, chimie, biologie ou psychomathématiques). Mémoire.

Doctorat (PhD).
Deux ans après la MSc (biologie, chimie, mathématiques, physique ou psychomathématiques). Thèse.

Sciences religieuses, voir théologie

Théologie
(Faculté de théologie)

Baccalauréat en théologie (BTh).
Trois ans après le DEC ou l'équivalent (grade canonique et civil).

Maîtrise en théologie (MTh).
Un an après le BTh. Dans les options: théologie, pastorale scolaire. Mémoire.

Maîtrise ès arts (MA).
Un an ou 3 sessions après le BTh, dans l'option: sciences humaines de la religion. Mémoire.

Maîtrise en pastorale.
Un an ou 3 sessions après le BTh, dans les options: pastorale scolaire ou pastorale fondamentale. Un stage.

Programmes spéciaux

Prière de se référer à la rubrique "cours et grades".

Education permanente

Cours réguliers à temps partiel. Désireuse de répondre à une attente du monde adulte, et particulièrement des enseignants, l'Université de Sherbrooke offre à temps partiel la plupart de ses programmes réguliers dans les domaines des lettres, des sciences, des sciences de l'éducation et des sciences religieuses ainsi qu'un programme spécial conduisant à un diplôme en administration des affaires.

On peut obtenir des informations complètes sur ces différents cours en s'adressant à la direction des cours à temps partiel.

Conditions d'admission

On trouvera un exposé général sur l'admission aux études universitaires dans l'article *Admission aux universités canadiennes.*

Afin d'obtenir des renseignements sur l'admission aux études du niveau pré-grade, consultez *Conditions d'admission dans les collèges et universités du Canada* que l'on peut

obtenir du Service d'admission au collège et à l'université, 151, rue Slater, Ottawa (Ontario), K1P 5N1, $1.50 port payé.

Pour être admis à suivre les cours du premier cycle des études universitaires, il faut, en plus de connaître suffisamment le français pour suivre les cours donnés en cette langue, avoir obtenu soit le diplôme de bachelier ès arts de l'Université de Sherbrooke ou d'une autre université reconnue, soit le diplôme d'études collégiales (DEC) d'un collège d'enseignement général et professionnel (CEGEP) du ministère de l'Education dont le choix d'options préalables répondra aux profils d'entrée exigés par les différentes facultés. Dans certains cas, l'université exige un examen spécial d'admission. Un brevet d'admission à l'étude est aussi exigé par certaines associations professionnelles. Pour être admis à des études de deuxième et de troisième cycles, un étudiant doit, en plus de manifester de nettes aptitudes pour les études supérieures, détenir le grade préalablement requis ou l'équivalent.

Année universitaire

Session régulière:
début de septembre, environ, à la mi-avril. Les étudiants des cours de génie (BScA), de la maîtrise en administration des affaires (MBA), du baccalauréat et de la maîtrise en service social participent à un programme coopératif, formé alternativement de stages pratiques et de sessions d'études à l'université. Chacun de ces stages est d'une durée de quatre mois. Il permet à l'étudiant d'ajouter à sa formation scolaire et scientifique un entraînement pratique plus poussé.

Cours d'été:
(deux sessions) mai-juin et juillet-août.

Système de mentions

L'université a adopté officiellement, au cours de la présente année, le système des cinq lettres: A: excellent; B: très bien; C: bien; D: passable; E: échec. Ce système qui est assorti d'un mode de contrôle par la moyenne cumulative, s'implante graduellement dans les facultés.

Droits d'inscription

Faculté de médecine, $708. Autres facultés, $523, comprenant scolarité, sports, service de santé, fédération des étudiants (FEUS) et frais d'inscription.

Etudiants à temps partiel: $20 du crédit.

Maison des étudiants, logement: $33 par mois; repas, environ: $2.50 par jour.

Aide financière

On peut obtenir des informations à ce chapître en adressant sa demande comme suit: a) pour les études du 1er cycle — Service de l'aide financière à l'étudiant, Université de Sherbrooke; b) pour les études de 2ième et 3ième cycles — Service des bourses et subventions aux étudiants de 2ième et 3ième cycles, Université de Sherbrooke.

Instituts de recherche

Le Centre d'étude des littératures d'expression française (CELEF).
Par la publication de thèses, de guides bibliographiques, de dossiers d'oeuvres de création d'écrivains francophones, le CELEF a comme objectifs d'étudier et d'encourager la création et la recherche, de faire connaître les auteurs, de recueillir et communiquer une documentation riche et variée sur les plans culturels et littéraires au sein de la francophonie. Directeur: Antoine Naaman, DèsL.

Le Centre d'études de la Renaissance.
Le centre, qui est conçu comme un organisme interdisciplinaire, rassemble des professeurs qui ont des projets de recherche sur l'époque de la Renaissance et les étudiants, aux niveaux de la maîtrise et du doctorat, qui ont choisi cette période comme spécialisation. Depuis sa fondation, le centre a réussi à rassembler une solide documentation de base qui permet d'effectuer les recherches pour divers travaux en cours. Directeur: J. Martinez De Bujanda, $D3^e$ cycle.

Le Centre de recherches en aménagement régional (CRAR).
Il se veut un exemple concret non seulement de l'intégration de l'université dans son milieu mais de collaboration entre plusieurs disciplines. De création récente, ce centre se propose de contribuer au développement régional des Cantons de l'Est (sans pour cela exclure les études économiques qui se font tant au niveau provincial qu'au niveau fédéral) et pour ce, les directeurs des projets de recherches mettent en commun les subventions qui leur sont accordées. Directeur: Serge Racine, BA, MA.

Le Centre de recherche en psychomathématique.
Le Centre de recherche en psychomathématique a été le premier du genre à être formé au sein d'une université. Ce centre s'intéresse avant tout à l'étude de l'apprentissage des structures en général, et des structures mathématiques en particulier. Cette étude se fait sur trois plans: au niveau de la psychologie expérimentale, au niveau de la mathématique et à celui de la pédagogie. Le centre compte déjà plusieurs réalisations importantes. Directeur: Zoltan Dienes, PhD.

L'Institut de recherche et de perfectionnement en administration (IRPA).
L'IRPA est un organisme de caractère départemental composé de professeurs de la Faculté d'administration et constitué dans le but de diriger certains travaux de recherches commandités et d'offrir des cours de perfectionnement en administration. Directeur: André Gingras, BSc, MBA.

Institutions affiliées

Institutions affiliées à la Faculté des arts:

Séminaire de Sherbrooke, c.p. 790, Sherbrooke (Qué.). Fondé en 1875. Recteur: Georges Cloutier, ptre. Registraire: Victor Audet, ptre. Institution d'enseignement secondaire et collégial, (pour garçons) dirigée par le clergé diocésain. Décerne le diplôme d'enseignement collégial. Programme d'enseignement général. Résidence.

Ecole de musique Vincent-D'Indy, 200, chemin Bellingham, Outremont 153. Directrice: Soeur Stella Plante, snjm. Registraire: Soeur Claire Landry, snjm. Fondée 1932. Institution d'enseignement général, concentration: musique. Mixte. Dirigée par les Soeurs des Saints Noms de Jésus et de Marie. Egalement divers cours de niveau universitaire en musique. Résidence pour filles.

Collège militaire royal de Saint-Jean, Saint-Jean (Qué.). Commandant: Colonel J.-P. Cadieux. Directeur des études: M.A. Benoît. Secrétaire général: Denys Dion. Fondé en 1952. Bilingue. Pour hommes. Les études sont poursuivies à l'institution même, cependant à la suite d'une entente récente, les diplômes sont délivrés par l'Université de Sherbrooke.

Doyens des facultés

Administration
Marcel-P. Lafrenière, BScA, MSc

Arts
Jean Houpert, BA, MA, DèsL

Droit
Jean Melanson, BA, LLL, DES

Formation des maîtres
Normand LaRochelle (directeur général), BA, BSc, MA

Médecine
Jean de L. Mignault, MD, CSPQ

Sciences
Jean-Marc Lalancette, BSc, MSc, PhD

Sciences appliquées
Pierre Bourgault, BSc, MA

Sciences de l'éducation
Richard Joly, BA, BTh, MA, LPh

Théologie
Lucien Vachon, ptre, BA, LTh, DTh

Directeurs des départements

Anatomie
Théodore Lévêque, MSc, PhD

Anesthésie-réanimation
George F. Brindle, MD, CM, CSPQ, DABA, FRCP(C)

Anglais
Ronald Sutherland, BA, MA, PhD

Biologie
Louis-C. O'Neil, BA, BScA, MSc, PhD

Biophysique
Otto Schanne, MD

Chimie
Gérard-E. Pelletier, BA, BSc, MèsSc, DSc

Chirurgie générale
Bernard Perey, BSc, MD, CM, MSc, CSPQ, FRCS(C), FACS

Chirurgie cardio-vasculaire et thoracique
Claude Labrosse, MD, CSPQ, FRCP(C)

Economique
Jean-Guy Latulippe, BA, BScSoc, MScSoc

Education physique
Roch Roy, BA(EdPhys), MPhysEd, PhD

Epidémiologie
Louis Munan, AB, MSc, FAPHA

Finance
Carl Prezeau, LLL, MS, MBA

Français
Antoine Sirois, BA, BTh, BPéd, LèsL, Dd'U

Génie civil
Paul-Edouard Brunelle, Ing, BScA, DrIng

Génie électrique
Jules Delisle, PEng, BA, LPh, BScA, MScA,D

Génie mécanique
Gilles Faucher, Ing, BA, BScA, MScA, PhD

Géographie
Romain Paquette, BA, LPhetTh, MA, PhD

Gynécologie-obstétrique
Réal Lafond, MD, CSPQ

Histoire
André Lachance, BA, BPéd, LèsL, DES

Management
Jean Robidoux, BA, MBA

Marketing
Gaétan Couture, BA, MCom

Mathématiques
Jean-Pierre Samson, BA, BSc, MSc

Médecine
Jean-Marc Pépin, MD, CSPQ, FRCP(C)

Médecine communautaire
Léonard Langlois, MD, MPH, CSPQ,
FRCP(C), FAAP

Médecine nucléaire et radiobiologie
Etienne Lebel, MD, BSc, CSPQ

Méthode quantitative de gestion
Normand Roy, BA, BScA, IngMS

Microbiologie
Pierre Bourgaux, MD

Neurochirurgie
Maurice Héon, MD, CSPQ, FRCS(C), FACS,
DABNS

Ophtalmologie
Jean de Margerie, MD, PhD, CSPQ,
FRCS(C), FACS

Orthopédie
Antoni Trias, MD, CSPQ, FRCS(C), FICS,
DABOS

Pathologie
Roger Côté, MD, MSc, DABCP, CSPQ

Pédagogie et didactique
René Hivon, BA, BPéd, LPéd, D3^e cycle

Pédiatrie
Victor Marchessault, MD, CSPQ, FRCP(C),
FAAP

Pharmacologie
Domenico Regoli, MD

Philosophie
Jacques Plamondon, BA, BPh, LPh, D3^e
cycle

Physiologie
Guy Lamarche, MD, CSPQ

Physique
Jean Lefaivre, BA, BScA(Phys), MSc(Phys)

Psychiatrie
Pierre Martel, MD, CSPQ, CRCP(C)

Psycho-éducation
Michel Rheault, BA, MA(Ps)

Psychologie
Yves St-Arnaud, BA, LPh, BPs, LPs, PhD

Radiologie diagnostique
Domenico Dilenge, MD, MSc, LDoc, CSPQ

Sciences comptables
Claude Bégin, BA, BCom, MCom,
MScCompt, CA

Sciences du comportement
Richard Béland, BSc(écon), MA(écon)

Service social
Jules Perron, MA

Urologie
Jacques Susset, MD, MSc, CSPQ, FRCS(C),
FACS

Simon Fraser University*

Burnaby 2, British Columbia

Telephone: 604-291-3111
Direct general correspondence to the registrar

Total full-time student enrolment 4,377; see
also separate section *Statistics on Canadian
universities and colleges*

Executive and administrative officers

Chancellor
Kenneth Caple, BSA, MSA

President
Kenneth Strand, BA, MS, PhD

Vice-president development
S.C. Robert, BSc

Vice-president administration
George Suart, BSc, BSc, MBA

Vice-president academic
Brian Wilson, BSc, PhD

Registrar
Harry Evans, BA

University librarian
D.A. Baird, BA, MS

Director, ancillary services
C.A. Buchanan

Academic planner
J. Chase, BBA, MA, PhD

Director, athletics
W.L. Davies, BA, MS

Director, physical plant and planning
W. DeVries, MSc

Director, recreation
M. Hendy, MA

Director, computing centre
T.R. Jewell, BSc, MS

Director, secretariat services
I.B. Kelsey, MPE, PhD

Director, records, scheduling, and systems
A. Kuiper, BA

Director, university counselling service
B.G. Lipinski, BA, MA, PhD

Director, continuing education
M. McClaren (acting), BEd, PhD

Director, admissions
D. Meakin, MA, PhD

Director, personnel
H. Murr, BA

Bursar
D.H.M. Ross, BA, BCom, CA

Director, university services
S.T. Stratton, BPE, BEd, MS, EdD

Director, purchasing
J.H. Wyman

Background

Simon Fraser University was established in
1963 by an act of the legislative assembly of
British Columbia, following a report by Dr.
J.B. Macdonald which cited the need for
another university in the province. The
university was planned to complement the
existing universities - to provide additional
facilities in the areas in which they are most
urgently needed without necessary
duplication of existing facilities. Two special
features of the university are the trimester
system and lecture-tutorial method of
instruction.

Simon Fraser University is provincial, non-
denominational, and co-educational. The first
students were enrolled in 1965.

The university is governed by a board of
governors, responsible for the management
of the business affairs of the university, and a
senate, responsible for the academic policy.

*Ordinary member, AUCC.

Facilities and services

The university is situated on a 1,200-acre site atop Burnaby Mountain, municipality of Burnaby (population 129,700). Buildings now in operation include the academic quadrangle, the library, the science complex, the gymnasium, and the theatre. The library currently has a collection of 400,000 monographs and over 15,000 serials. Special arrangements exist for graduate students and faculty members to make use of the one-million-volume library at The University of British Columbia. The audio-visual centre provides services in the areas of resources, technical services, and graphics.

Madge Hogarth house provides single-room accommodation for 65 women while Shell house accommodates 160 men in 20 double and 120 single rooms. The married students' residence has 62 two-bedroom and 148 one-bedroom suites. In addition, the university has a listing service for various types of accommodation within commuting distance.

Student services include a health service, a counselling service, chaplains, cafeterias, athletic and recreational facilities, and an employment service.

Calendars and brochures

Undergraduate and graduate calendars are issued each spring to cover fall semester of current year and spring and summer semesters of following year.

Undergraduate admissions bulletin, outlining admission procedure and listing university services for new applicants, available upon request. Student newspaper "The Peak" published weekly.

Courses and degrees

Since Simon Fraser University operates on a trimester system, programs specify the number of semesters (each 16 weeks long) rather than the number of years.

Arts
(Faculty of arts)

Bachelor of arts (BA).
(a) General degree, a minimum of 120 semester hours, usually taking eight semesters; (b) honors degree, a minimum of 132 semester hours, usually taking eight semesters. Available in anthropology, archaeology, commerce, economics, English, French, geography, German, history, philosophy, political science, psychology, Russian, sociology, and Spanish.

Master of arts (MA).
Minimum of 30 semester hours with bachelor's degree with high second-class standing or equivalent. Available in anthropology, economics, English, French linguistics, geography, German linguistics, history, linguistics (general, applied, area, and contrastive), philosophy, political science, psychology, Russian linguistics, sociology, and Spanish linguistics.

Doctor of philosophy (PhD).
Number of courses and semester hours vary subject to the department. Available in anthropology, economics, French linguistics, geography, German linguistics, history, linguistics (general, applied, area, and contrastive), political science, psychology, Russian linguistics, sociology, and Spanish linguistics.

Business administration
(Faculty of arts)

Master of business administration (MBA).
A six-semester program in commerce, involving 10 courses and a research project. (Evening program: see extension programs.)

Education
(Faculty of education)

Bachelor of education (BEd).
(a) General degree: a minimum of 150 semester hours usually taking 10 semesters, including the three-semester professional development program. (b) Honors degree: a minimum of 162 semester hours usually taking ten semesters, including the professional development program. Available in all fields of study offered by the faculties of arts and science as specified by the faculty of education. Minor specialization required in programs offered by the faculty of education.

Master of arts (education) [*MA(Education)*]
and *master of science (education)*
[*MSc(Education)*].
Minimum of three semesters (30 semester
hours) with BA or BSc degree with high
second-class standing or equivalent, or BEd;
additional requirements dependent upon
special admission requirements of
department in which applicant wishes to
pursue studies.

General studies program

Bachelor of general studies (BGS).
A non-specialist degree program in the
faculties of arts, science, and education.
Students are not required to specialize in any
subject but must complete a minimum of 15
semester hours in each of the general areas of
humanities, social sciences, and natural
sciences. A minimum of 120 semester hours is
required, usually taking eight semesters.

Minor specialization in Canadian studies,
Latin American Studies, and African/Middle
East Studies can be undertaken for credit
toward any of the undergraduate degree
programs.

Kinesiology - interdisciplinary studies
(Interdisciplinary program offered by the
faculties of arts, science, and education)

Bachelor of science (kinesiology)
[*BSc(Kinesiology)*].
A general and an honors degree are
available; requirements are as for the BSc.

Master of science (kinesiology)
[*MSc(Kinesiology)*].
Minimum of 18 semester hours of courses
plus a thesis with a bachelor's degree with
major in biology, pre-medicine, physical
education, kinesiology or allied areas, with a
high second-class standing including at least
24 semester hours of appropriate
undergraduate science preparation.

Science
(Faculty of science)

Bachelor of science (BSc).
(a) General degree: a minimum of 120
semester hours, usually taking eight
semesters; (b) honors degree: a minimum of
132 semester hours, usually taking eight

semesters. Available in biochemistry,
biological sciences, chemical physics,
chemistry, mathematics, and physics.

Master of science (MSc).
Requires bachelor's degree with high second-
class standing or equivalent. Number of
courses and semester hours vary, depending
on department. Available in biological
sciences, chemistry, mathematics, and
physics.

Doctor of philosophy (PhD).
Number of courses and semester hours vary,
depending on department. Available in all
departments listed for MSc.

Extension programs

Summer session:
eight-week program (maximum credit 10
semester hours) directed toward completion
of degree requirements or up-grading of
teaching certificates for teachers, or graduates
of the professional development program at
Simon Fraser University.

Evening classes:
opportunities for students to complete certain
graduate degree requirements while
employed full-time. Applicants must
normally have an undergraduate degree with
at least good, second-class standing.

An expanded program of extension studies,
including both credit and non-credit course
offerings, is currently under development.

Admission requirements

For a general statement regarding admission
to university study, see article *Admission to
university in Canada.*

For information regarding admission to
undergraduate study, consult *Requirements
for admission to Canadian colleges and
universities* available from Service for
Admission to College and University, 151
Slater St., Ottawa, Ont., K1P 5N1, $1.50
prepaid.

For admission to graduate studies, a student
must normally have obtained a bachelor's
degree with high second-class standing or its

equivalent. Applications and enquiries should be directed to the chairman of the department concerned.

Academic years (trimester)

Spring semester: January to April.

Summer semester: May to August.

Fall semester: September to December.

Grading system

A, B, C, and D: passing grades; F: failure; N: did not write; DEF: deferred examination granted.

Fees and costs

Undergraduates:
registered for 12 or more semester hours of credit, $214 per semester; registered for 11 or less semester hours of credit, $15 per semester hour.

Graduates:
MA, MSc, MSc(kinesiology) and PhD following an MA or MSc from another university, $400 total for first three semesters, and $20 for each subsequent semester on campus; PhD after obtaining from Simon Fraser University an MA or MSc, $190 for first semester, and $20 for each subsequent semester on campus.

For all students: $11 student activity fee per semester.

Residence (including meals): $402 to $420 for men, $384 for women. Apartments (including all utilities): one and two bedrooms, $106 to $131 per month.

Financial awards and assistance

Undergraduate:
all scholarships, bursaries, and awards are made on the recommendation of the senate committee on scholarships, bursaries, and awards and administered by the university financial aid officer.

Eligibility for scholarship: applicant must normally be registered in a program of 15 semester hours or more, with high academic standing in previous work.

Eligibility for bursary: applicant must be registered in a program of 12 semester hours or more with a satisfactory academic standing.

Eligibility for university awards: applicant must have good academic standing and have made substantial contributions to university, high school, and/or community life.

Eligibility for athletic awards: based on good academic records and excellence in athletic activity.

Loans: Canada student loans plan, PEO Sisterhood education loan fund, student emergency loan fund.

Graduate:
scholarships awarded by this university, scholarships and fellowships awarded by other institutions and associations, graduate assistantships (teaching and research) available; details from financial aid officer. Canada student loans also available for eligible applicants.

Research institute

Pestology Centre,
biological sciences department; research and professional training in the principles and practice of pest management. The centre has a faculty of 12.

Deans of faculties

Arts
D.H. Sullivan, BA, MSc, MFA

Education
To be appointed

General studies
R.C. Brown (interim), BS, MS, PhD

Graduate studies
J. Wheatley, BA, MA, PhD

Science
S. Aronoff, BA, PhD

Department heads

Archaeology
R.L. Carlson, BA, MA, PhD

Biological sciences
G.H. Geen, BA, MA, PhD

Chemistry
T.N. Bell, BSc, PhD

Economics and commerce
J.P. Herzog, BS, PhD

Educational foundations centre
T.J. Mallinson, BA, MA, PhD

English
G.M. Newman, BA

Geography
R.B. Sagar, BSc, MSc

History
I. Mugridge, MA, MA, PhD

Mathematics
E.M. Shoemaker, BA, MS, PhD

Modern languages
N.J. Lincoln, BA, MA, PhD

Philosophy
N.M. Swartz, BA, MA

Physical development studies
E.W. Banister, BSc, MPE, PhD, FACSM

Physics
R.R. Haering, BA, MA, PhD, FRSC

Political science, sociology and anthropology
H. Adam, DipSoc, PhD

Professional development centre
D.R. Birch, BA, MA, PhD

Psychology
A.L. Diamond, BA, MA, PhD

Sir George Williams University*

Montreal 107, Quebec

Telephone: 514-879-5995
Direct general correspondence to the registrar

Total full-time student enrolment 5,766; see also separate section *Statistics on Canadian universities and colleges*

Executive and administrative officers

Chancellor
C.F. Carsley, BA

Chairman, board of governors
C. A. Duff, BSc

Principal
John O'Brien, MA, PhD

Vice-principal (academic)
Jack Bordan, BEng, MSc(Eng), MEIC

Vice-principal (administration and finance)
John Smola, BCom, BA, MA, PhD

Registrar
Kenneth Adams, BSc, LMus

Director, guidance services
J.A. Sproule, BA, MPsSc

Dean of students
Magnus Flynn, BComm

Librarian
Helen Howard, MLS

Background

Sir George Williams University was developed from the formal educational work of the Montreal YMCA inaugurated in 1873. The first classes at the university level were offered in 1929 in the evening division, and day courses in arts, science, and commerce were inaugurated in 1932. The members of the first class graduated in 1936 and by 1969 some 12,811 degrees had been presented.

In March 1948, the university was granted a specific charter by the provincial legislature, establishing it a body corporate and politic, for the purpose of conducting a college or university in the province of Quebec.

The university charter is held by the corporation of Sir George Williams University, which exercises ultimate financial control of the university. Appointments and policy and actual financial management are the responsibility of the board of governors. The academic policy and program are the responsibility of the university council, which is made up of all faculty deans, senior officers of administration and members elected from the rank of full professors. Students are represented on the board of governors, each faculty council, and the university council. The university council is responsible to the board of governors. Each of the four faculties is headed by a dean, under the general supervision of the academic vice-principal of the university.

Facilities and services

Sir George Williams University is a university without a campus. Located in central Montreal, the university is housed in two large buildings. The newer building, opened in 1966, houses engineering and science libraries; 57 class and seminar rooms; 10 auditoria; faculty offices; 84 laboratories for natural sciences and engineering; psychology, sociology and language laboratories; computer terminals; a theatre; a cafeteria; a student activities centre, art galleries, etc. The older building houses the main libraries (350,000 volumes; 32,000 periodicals), the faculty of commerce and administration, 14 classrooms and administration offices.

*Ordinary member, AUCC.

The university also owns a number of domestic houses located in the vicinity of the main building. After renovation, these houses are used to provide additional faculty offices and for special departments and programs. The computer centre is located in nearby rented quarters.

Calendars and brochures

Collegial program; undergraduate announcement; graduate studies announcement; brochures for the special summer sessions — day division; information on admission for foreign students (may be obtained from registrar); student handbook (dean of student's office); the paper; the Georgian; commerce perspective.

Courses and degrees

Collegial program

As a contribution to the establishment of the new structure of higher education in the province of Quebec, pending the creation of the new general and vocational colleges, the university is offering, during this period of transition, a two-year collegial program. Entry is from grade XI, and successful completion of the two-year program will admit the students to the new three-year undergraduate curriculum which came into effect in 1971.

Courses in the collegial program are of the same standard as those offered in the first year, and in several cases, the second year of the former four-year undergraduate curriculum. The emphasis, however, is on breadth, and premature specialization is avoided.

As the collegial program is not operational for evening studies at this time the length of the university course, from junior matriculation, continues to be equivalent to four years BA, BA honors, BFA, BSc honors, BCom, BCom honors. Five years — BEng.

Arts
(Faculty of arts)

Bachelor of arts (BA, BA honors).
Three years from collegial level (see above).

Areas of emphasis: applied social science, Canadian politics, Canadian studies, comparative political studies, early childhood education, economics, education, English, fine arts, French, geography, German, Greek, history, humanities of science, international affairs, Judaic studies, Latin, mathematics, philosophy, political philosophy, political science, psychology, religion, Russian studies, social welfare, sociology, Spanish, and combinations of these. Honors courses are available in economics, English, French, geography, history, mathematics, philosophy, political science, psychology, religion, sociology, and urban studies.

Bachelor of fine arts (BFA).
Three years from collegial level (see above). Areas of emphasis: design, drama, graphics, painting, and sculpture.

Master of arts (MA).
One year from honors BA, BFA. Areas of study: art education, economics, educational technology, English literature, history, philosophy, psychology, and religion.

Doctor of philosophy (PhD).
Available in economics and history.

Business, see commerce below

Commerce
(Faculty of commerce and administration)

Bachelor of commerce (BCom, BCom honors).
Three years from collegial level (see above). Areas of emphasis: accounting, economics, finance, management, marketing, and quantitative methods.

Master of business administration (MBA).
Two years from a bachelor's degree in any field.

Engineering
(Faculty of engineering)

Certificate in engineering.
Three years from junior matriculation, evening division only.

Bachelor of engineering (BEng).
Four years from collegial level (see above), however, it is expected that about 20% of the students will be able to complete an accelerated program in three years.

Specialization in civil, electrical, and mechanical engineering.

Master of engineering (MEng).
Two years from a bachelor's degree in engineering, or equivalent, and must be currently employed in engineering.

Doctor of engineering (DEng).
At least two calendar years of full-time graduate study beyond the master's degree, or three calendar years of full-time graduate study beyond the bachelor's degree. At least two years must be spent in full-time residence; available in research areas of structures, fluid controls, networks and systems.

Science, applied, see engineering above

Science, pure
(Faculty of science)

Bachelor of science (BSc, BSc honors).
Three years from collegial level (see above). Areas of emphasis: biochemistry, biological sciences, chemistry, geology, mathematics, physics, and psychology. Honors courses available in cell and molecular biology, chemistry, ecology, mathematics, physics, physiology and developmental biology, and statistics.

Master of science (MSc).
One year from honors BSc. Areas of study: biological sciences, chemistry, physics and teaching of mathematics (MTM).

Doctor of philosophy (PhD).
At least two calendar years of full-time graduate study beyond the master's degree, or three calendar years beyond the bachelor's degree available in biological science, chemistry, and physics.

Special programs

Centre for Human Relations and Community Studies; computer centre.

Extension programs

For university credit:

Evening classes.
Undergraduate classes in arts, science, commerce, and engineering. All of the courses which are offered in the day division of the university are also available to students who may obtain the necessary credits to complete the requirements for the degree of the university through evening studies. Most graduate degrees may be pursued in evening classes.

Summer school.
Evening courses are offered for undergraduates during the summer in all fields except engineering. Graduate level courses are offered in engineering and in other areas. The university also conducts summer day programs in applied social science; education; English; English as a second language; French; geography; history; philosophy, and religion; and sociology.

Admission requirements

For a general statement regarding admission to university study, see article *Admission to university in Canada.*

For information regarding admission to undergraduate study, consult *Requirements for admission to Canadian colleges and universities* available from Service for Admission to College and University, 151 Slater St., Ottawa, Ont., K1P 5N1, $1.50 prepaid.

Academic year

Winter session: mid-September to end of April

Summer session: late May to end of July (evening division); six week sessions scheduled during period early June to end of July (day division).

Grading system

Undergraduate level — passing grades: A — excellent; B — very good; C — acceptable; D — marginal. Failing grades: F, absent, incomplete, repeat.

Graduate level — grades designated for use in reporting graduate courses are honors, satisfactory, unsatisfactory, audit, in progress, or late.

Fees and costs

Annually for tuition: day division — collegial studies, $375; arts and commerce, $450; fine arts and science, $475; engineering, $525; plus $40 laboratory fee for each course involving laboratory work, and $61 student activities and services fee; evening division — $90 for each 8-month subject, $45 for each 4-month subject, plus $40 laboratory fee for each course involving laboratory work and student activities and services fee — undergraduate student $8, partial student $14.

Graduate fee: MA in art education, education, economics, English, history, psychology, religion, PhD, DEng, MSc in biology, chemistry and physics, $400 full-time, $250 half-time. MBA $65 per half course — maximum $650 per academic year, full-time; MEng $50 per half course — maximum fee per graduate course work and dissertation $700; MTM $100 per course.

Financial awards and assistance

There are a limited number of university bursaries available to students. Application forms must be submitted prior to June 30. These awards are based on financial need plus academic standing. In addition, government assistance is available through the student aid service, Department of Education, Province of Quebec. Application deadline — September 30.

The office of the dean of students operates a small "emergency loan fund", maximum amount to any one student is $200 repayable within 90 days.

Research institutes

SGWU houses or takes part in five specialized institutes.

Le Centre d'étude du Québec is housed at SGWU. Its staff is working at present on a reconstruction of the debates of the legislative assembly of the united Canadas, 1841-67.

Le Centre de recherches en histoire économique du Canada français is sponsored jointly with the Ecole des hautes études commerciales. It has accumulated one of the most important collections of documents on the economic and social history of French Canada, and has published several volumes.

The Canadian International Centre of Research and Information on Public and Co-operative Economy was established by the department of economics in conjunction with the Conseil de la coopération du Québec and the Co-operative Union of Canada. Courses on the theory and practice of co-operation are given by the department in both English and French. The centre organizes seminars recently on labor relations in the quasi-public sector — and publishes the Canadian CIRIEC review.

The Centre of Human Relations and Community Studies is a research, consultation, and training service of the department of applied social science, functioning on an interdisciplinary basis. In seven years of operation it has worked with 50 clients — professional groups and organizations, industry and government — from British Columbia to Newfoundland.

The International Institute of Quantitative Economics was established jointly with the Ecole des hautes études commerciales. Its main objective is to initiate and carry out quantitative research projects in the field of applied economics, particularly those that have a bearing on the problems of developing countries. Chairman of its international council of advisors is Professor Jan Tinbergen, Nobel prize winner from the Netherlands school of economics.

Deans of faculties

Arts
Ian Campbell, MSc

Commerce and administration
Gunther Brink, BComm, MBA

Engineering
J.C. Callaghan, MS

Graduate studies
Stanley French, PhD

Science
John Ufford, PhD

Department heads

Accountancy
James Finnie, BSc(Com), CA

Applied social science
Hedley Dimock, EdD

Biological sciences
Gérard Leduc, PhD

Chemistry
Roger Verschingel, PhD

Civil engineering
Matthew Douglass, PhD

Classics, modern languages, and linguistics
Paul Widdows, PhD

Economics
Arthur Lermer, MA

Education
Jitendra Bhatnagar, LLB, MA, PhD

Electrical engineering
M.N.S. Swamy, PhD

English
Sidney Lamb, BA

Finance
Calvin Potter, PhD

Fine arts
Edwy Cooke, MFA

French
Paul d'Hollander, LèsL, Agregation

Geography
D.A. Fraser, PhD

Geology
André Deland, PhD

History
John Hill, PhD

Management
Joseph Kelly, PhD

Marketing
Vishnu Kirpalani, DèsCCom

Mathematics
Victor Byers, PhD

Mechanical engineering
Morne du Plessis, PhD

Philosophy
Stanley French, PhD

Physics
Walter Raudorf, PhD

Political science
Harold Angell, MA

Psychology
Jane Stewart, PhD

Quantitative methods
Zoltan Popp, MBA

Religion
Charles Davis, STL

Sociology
John Jackson, PhD

University of Toronto*

Toronto 181, Ontario

Telephone: 416-928-2011
Direct general correspondence to the vice-president and registrar

Total full-time student enrolment 26,568; see also separate section *Statistics on Canadian universities and colleges*

Executive and administrative officers

Chancellor
D.W. McGibbon (Mrs), BA, LLD

President
J.H. Sword (acting), MA, LLD

Chairman of the board of governors
W.B. Harris, MA

Executive vice-president (academic) and provost
D.F. Forster (acting), BA, AM

Executive vice-president (non-academic)
A.G. Rankin, BCom, FCA

Vice-president (administration)
F.R. Stone, BCom, FCA

Vice-president (health sciences)
J.D. Hamilton, MD, FRCP(C)

Vice-president and registrar, and secretary of the senate
R. Ross, MBE, MA

Chief librarian
R.H. Blackburn, MA, BLS, MS, LLD

Vice-provost (research administration)
S. Dymond (Miss), BA, QC

Assistant to the president
N.S.C. Dickinson, CD, BA

Executive assistant to the executive vice-president (non-academic)
J.F. Brook

Secretary, board of governors
D.S. Claringbold

Director of administrative services
M.A. Malcolm, BA

Director of physical plant
F.J. Hastie, BSc, PEng

Director, division of university extension
E.M. Gruetzner (acting), BA

Assistant registrar and director of admissions
W. Kent, MA

Assistant registrar
H.L. Reimer (Miss), BA, BPed

Director, student awards
P.S. Phillips, BA, CA

Secondary school liaison officer
W.A. Hill

Director, statistics and records
J.M. Tusiewicz, BSc(Eng), MASc, MBA

Director, university health service
G.E. Wodehouse, MC, MD, FRCP(C), MRCP

Assistant director of university health service – women
F.H. Stewart (Miss), BA, MD

Director of career counselling and placement centre
David Currey, BASc

Director, international student centre
E.A. McKee (acting), MA

Director, advisory bureau
D.J. McCulloch, BA, MD, DPsych, FRCP(C)

Director, housing service
M.G. Jaffary (Mrs), BA

Director, University of Toronto Press
M. Jeanneret, BA, LLD

Director of university news bureau
K.S. Edey

*Ordinary member, AUCC.

Director, alumni affairs
John Duncanson, BA

Director of development
R.L. Jones

Warden, Hart house
E.A. Wilkinson, BA

Director, athletics and recreation – men
A.D. White, BA, MEd

Director, athletics and physical education
– women
A. Hewett (Miss), BEd, PE

Constituent colleges

University College, University of Toronto,
Toronto 181, Ontario.
Principal: A.C.H. Hallett, BA, PhD.
Registrar: L.W. Forguson, BA, MA, PhD.
Established 1853. Co-educational. Non-
denominational. Courses offered lead to the
degrees of BA, BSc and BCom. Residence
accommodation is available in the Sir Daniel
Wilson residence and in Whitney hall.

New College, University of Toronto, Toronto
181, Ontario.
Principal: D.G. Ivey, MA, PhD. Registrar:
F.A. Hare, MA. Established 1962. Co-
educational. Non-denominational. Provides
residence accommodation, tutorial
arrangements, instruction in some subjects,
common rooms and dining facilities.
Enrolment is drawn from all undergraduate
divisions of the university.

Innis College, University of Toronto, Toronto
181, Ontario.
Principal: P.H. Russell, MA. Registrar: D.B.
King, BA, MA. Established 1964. Non-
denominational. Co-educational. A college
for full-time students of all undergraduate
divisions of the university. Instruction in
some arts subjects is taken with classes in
University College. Interdisciplinary courses
are conducted on an experimental basis
within Innis College. Accommodation is
offered in university and student-operated
residences and houses. The college also
conducts a writing laboratory and tutorial
program.

Scarborough College, University of Toronto,
1265 Military Trail, West Hill, Ontario.
Principal: A.F.W. Plumptre, CBE, MA.

Dean: S.J. Colman, MA. Associate dean and
registrar: J.D. King, BA, PhD. Established
1964; classes began 1965. Co-educational.
Non-denominational. Courses offered lead to
the BA and BSc degrees (three and four
years). Located 20 miles to the east of the St.
George campus of the university.

Erindale College, University of Toronto, 3359
Mississauga Road, Clarkson, Ontario.
Principal: J.T. Wilson, SM, OBE, BA, MA,
PhD, ScD, LLD, DSc, FRSCan, FRS.
Registrar: J.J. Rae, BA, MA, PhD, FCIC.
Established 1964; classes began 1966. Non-
denominational. Co-educational. Provides
courses leading to BA and BSc degrees.

Background

The University of Toronto was founded in
1827 by royal charter as King's College at
York, the state university of the province of
Upper Canada, in close connection with the
Church of England. It was not until 1843 that
the work of instruction began at King's
College. The first degrees were granted in
1844. In 1849 King's College was secularized,
removed entirely from its connection with the
Church of England, and its name changed to
the University of Toronto.

The Church of England in 1851 founded its
own University of Trinity College. Some
other denominations had already established
colleges; Victoria had been founded by the
Methodists in 1841. In 1852 the Basilian
order established St. Michael's College.

In 1853 a further change was made in the
University of Toronto through the creation of
University College, to which was given the
entire work of instruction, the university itself
becoming merely a legislative and examining
body.

In the early eighties representatives of the
other colleges entered into negotiations for a
scheme of federation, which was embodied
in an act of the Ontario legislature in 1887. In
1905 the Ontario government appointed a
commission to investigate and recommend
action in regard to the university. The
University of Toronto Act of 1906 laid the
foundation of the present constitution of the
university. The present authority is that given
by the University of Toronto Act 1947 (as
amended up to 1964). The university is the

provincial university of Ontario. It is co-educational and, except through its three federated universities, non-denominational. Federation is confined to the faculty of arts and science.

The overall administration of the university rests in the board of governors which appoints the president, controls the finances, administers the property and buildings. It makes all appointments (on the nomination of the president) to positions on the staff of the university and all constituent colleges of the university. The senate directs the academic policy of the university.

Other bodies which play a prominent part in the government of the university are the Caput and the councils of the faculties and schools of the university. The Caput has a general oversight over discipline, and supplements the authority of individual divisions of the university where the university as a whole is concerned. The councils deal with academic questions under the general supervision of the senate.

For the last two years the entire governmental structure of the university has been under careful examination. The initial examination was conducted by the Commission on the Government of the University of Toronto and resulted in the fall of 1969 in the release of a report entitled "Toward community in university government". The report contains proposals for wide-ranging changes in the governing structure of the university. These changes were recently discussed by the entire university community.

A new University of Toronto Act has been passed by the legislature of the province of Ontario. The act, when it is proclaimed, will provide for a single governing council whose memberships will be drawn from the faculty, students, staff and alumni of the university as well as persons appointed by the lieutenant-governor in council.

Facilities and services

Geographically, the university is in the heart of Toronto (population 2,050,000). Four of the city's principal north-south arteries bound or cut through university properties. Queen's Park is ringed by university buildings. The park itself, including the land on which the Ontario parliament buildings stand, belongs to the university. Elsewhere are many other university properties including the faculty of dentistry building in the hospital district, one-time country estates on the city's periphery, the university forest of 20,000 acres far to the north of the city, the university survey camp, and the David Dunlap Observatory.

The library collections of the university exceed three million volumes; 6,000 manuscript titles, 551,340 microtexts, 77,000 maps, 22,900 current serials, and 53,000 other non-book items. These figures include the holdings of the central university library, more than 45 libraries in colleges, faculties and departments of the university, and the libraries of federated, affiliated, and related institutions. The central library has special collections in Anglo-Irish literature from the 1890s to the present (especially W.B. Yeats); a Darwin collection; the library of Rev. James Forbes, English non-conformist; a French-Canadian literature collection; a Hobbes collection; more than 3,000 17th-19th century Italian libretti; more than 700 16th and 17th century Italian plays; a Petronius collection; a Spanish literature collection including more than 700 comedias sueltas; and a growing collection of manuscripts of Canadian authors including Earle Birney, A.J.M. Smith, and Leonard Cohen. Construction has begun on a large humanities and social sciences research library which is expected to be completed by 1972. The fourteen-storey triangular structure will have an ultimate stack capacity of 4.7 million volumes and will have more than 4,000 study-places, including nearly 1,000 private carrels.

Special research facilities include the Banting Institute and the Charles H. Best Institute for teaching, clinical investigation and medical research; the Connaught Medical Research Laboratories for research in preventive medicine and related fields; the David Dunlap Observatory for research in astronomy; the Institute for Aerospace Studies for conducting research in the mechanisms of gases and plasmas, design and analysis of flight structures, etc.; the Institute of Computer Science which maintains an IBM 7094 (Mod. II) computer facility and systems 360/65 and 360/50 for research in numerical analysis, programming theory, computing, and data processing; the Institute of Environmental Sciences and Engineering for a multi-disciplinary approach to environmental studies; the Wallberg memorial building for chemistry and chemical engineering for research in nuclear engineering.

Other inter-disciplinary research units include the Centre of Criminology, the Centre for Culture and Technology, the Centre for Industrial Relations, the Centre for Linguistic Studies, the Centre for Mediaeval Studies, the Centre for Renaissance Studies, the Centre for Research in the Social and Health Services, the Centre for Russian and East European Studies, the Centre for the Study of the Drama, the Centre for Urban and Community Studies, the Institute of Applied Statistics, the Institute of Bio-Medical Electronics, the Institute of Computer Science, the Institute of Immunology, the Institute for the History and Philosophy of Science and Technology, the Institute of Medical Science, the Institute for the Quantitative Analysis of Social and Economic Policy, and the Pontifical Institute of Mediaeval Studies.

Student facilities in the university, in addition to those provided by the federated universities and colleges, include seven residences including a graduate students' residence, accommodating 827 men and 770 women. A married students' housing complex, consisting of two apartment towers, provides accommodation for 713 families, and is located within walking distance of the campus. The complex is owned and operated by the Ontario Student Housing Corporation for the university. Other services provided for students are a health service, a career counselling and placement service, a housing service, an advisory bureau, and indoor and outdoor athletic facilities. Hart house provides a variety of food services, as well as facilities for recreation, reading, debate, music, and art.

Special services for overseas students are co-ordinated by the international student centre which serves as headquarters for the centre staff, the overseas student adviser and working committees. National groups on campus include the African students union; the Arab students association, the Chinese overseas students association, the friends of India association, the Malaysian Singaporean students association, the Pakistan students association, the Filipino students association and the West Indian students association. Student groups work closely with overseas students in many information and orientation programs. Student groups particularly interested in overseas students include the Canadian University Service Overseas, the Students' Administrative Council and World University Service of Canada.

Calendars and brochures

The following schools, faculties, colleges, and institutes publish calendars.

Undergraduate: faculty of arts and science; faculty of applied science and engineering; faculty of architecture, urban and regional planning and landscape architecture; faculty of dentistry; division of dental hygiene; college of education; division of university extension; faculty of food sciences; faculty of forestry; faculty of law; faculty of medicine; division of rehabilitation medicine; faculty of music; school of nursing; faculty of pharmacy; school of physical and health education.

Graduate: school of business; institute of child study; postgraduate dental education; school of hygiene; school of library science; school of social work; school of graduate studies.

Brochures:

Undergraduate admission handbook (to be obtained from the office of admissions); admission awards (to be obtained from the office of student awards).

Colleges: Emmanuel College; Erindale College; Innis College; Knox College; Massey College; New College; St. Michael's College; Scarborough College; Trinity College; University College; Victoria College; Wycliffe College.

Courses and degrees

Architecture, urban and regional planning and landscape architecture
(Faculty of architecture, urban and regional planning and landscape architecture)

Bachelor of landscape architecture (BLArch).
Four years from senior matriculation.

Bachelor of architecture (BArch).
Five years from senior matriculation.

Diploma in urban and regional planning (DipUandRP).
One year after a first degree.

(School of graduate studies)

Master of science in urban and regional planning [MSc(Pl)].
Two years from a bachelor's degree in appropriate disciplines in the humanities or social sciences, or professional disciplines.

Master of architecture (MArch).
At least one year after BArch or BASc.

Arts
(Faculty of arts and science)

Bachelor of arts (BA).
Three or four years after obtaining Ontario grade 13, or equivalent senior matriculation standing. The program enables each student in full-time attendance in one of the eight colleges of the faculty of arts and science to devise his or her own program by combining together each year five full courses chosen to fit the student's interests. Certain programs are suggested for those who desire a degree of specialization, but one could not list all the variants that are possible within a given program to achieve special emphasis in a particular aspect of the subject. Subjects offered include anthropology, cinema, classics (Greek, Latin, Greek and Roman history, Greek and Latin literature in translation), east Asian studies (Chinese, Japanese), economics, English, ethics, fine art, French, geography, German, history, inter-disciplinary courses, Islamic studies (Arabic, Persian, Turkish), Italian and Hispanic studies (Italian, Spanish, Portuguese), linguistics, literature, mathematics, music, near eastern studies (Hebrew, Akkadian, Syriac, Egyptian, Hellenistic, Greek), philosophy, political science, psychology, religious studies, Sanskrit and Indian studies, Slavic languages and literatures (Russian, Czech, Polish, Serbo-Croatian, Ukranian), and sociology.

(School of graduate studies)

Diploma in development studies.
One-year program in economics and public administration.

Master of arts (MA).
At least two years from three-year BA, at least one year from four-year BA. Available in anthropology, classical studies, comparative literature, criminology, drama, east Asian studies, educational theory, economics, English, French language and literature, geography, Germanic languages and literature, history, history and philosophy of science and technology, history of art, Islamic studies, Italian and Hispanic languages and literatures, linguistics, mediaeval studies, music, near eastern studies, philosophy, political science, psychology, public administration, Slavic languages and literatures, and sociology.

Conjunct *master of arts and diploma in Russian and east European studies.*
At least two years from four-year BA. Available in economics, geography, history, political science, and Slavic languages and literatures.

Master of philosophy (PhilM).
Open to graduates in arts of this or another recognized university by pursuing an advanced course of study for at least two years under the direction of one department. Applicants holding an MA from another university may apply for a program of 12 months of continuous residence. Available in anthropology, classical studies, drama, east Asian studies, economics, educational theory, English, French language and literature, geography, Germanic languages and literature, history of art, Islamic studies, Italian and Hispanic languages and literatures, near eastern studies, philosophy, political science, Slavic languages and literatures, and sociology.

Doctor of philosophy (PhD).
At least two years from MA. Available in almost any subject in which a master's degree is available.

Business, see commerce below

Child study
(Institute of child study of the college of education)

Diploma in child study (DipCS).
Two years from a bachelor's degree.

Commerce
(Faculty of arts and science)

Bachelor of commerce (BCom).
Four years from Ontario grade 13 or equivalent standing. Available in commerce and finance.

(School of business)

Diploma in business administration (DipBusAdmin).
One year from a first degree.

(School of graduate studies)

Master of business administration (MBA).
Two years from bachelor's degree, of which one year may be credited for appropriate fourth year work.

Doctor of philosophy (PhD).
A minimum of two years beyond the MBA or its equivalent.

Computing and data processing
(School of graduate studies)

Master of science (MSc).
Graduates of degree courses with substantial mathematics will be admitted to a one-year program.

Doctor of philosophy (PhD).
At least two years from MSc.

Dentistry
(Faculty of dentistry)

Diploma in dental hygiene (DipDentHyg).
Two years from senior matriculation.

Bachelor of science in dentistry (BScD).
At least one year from the second dental year, i.e. at least four years from senior matriculation.

Doctor of dental surgery (DDS).
Four years from the one pre-professional year beyond senior matriculation, i.e. five years from senior matriculation.

Diploma in dental public health (DDPH).
At least one year from DDS degree.

Diploma in oral surgery and anaesthesia (DipOralSurg).
At least 32 months from DDS degree.

Diplomas in orthodontics, paedodontics, periodontics (DipOrthodont, DipPaedodont, DipPeriodont).
Twenty-two months (in a period of two calendar years) from DDS degree.

(School of graduate studies)

Master of science in dentistry (MScD).
At least two years from a DDS degree.

Doctor of philosophy (PhD).
At least three years from DDS degree.

Education
(The college of education)

A one-year teacher training program (after an acceptable undergraduate academic degree) leading to a *bachelor of education* degree *(BEd)* awarded by the university and an interim high school assistant's certificate, type B, granted by the Ontario Department of Education. A number of additional and special certificate programs are offered, generally in the summer, for teachers holding a type B certificate.

(School of graduate studies)

Master of arts (MA).
At least one year from BA degree. Available in educational theory.

Master of education (MEd).
At least one year from bachelor's degree, one year teacher training and one year teaching experience required.

Master of philosophy (PhilM).
At least two years from four-year BA. Available in educational theory.

Doctor of philosophy (PhD).
At least two years from MA. Available in educational theory.

Engineering, applied science
(Faculty of applied science and engineering)

Bachelor of applied science (BASc).
Four years from senior matriculation. Courses offered: chemical engineering and applied chemistry, civil, electrical, geological, industrial and mechanical, engineering science, and metallurgy and materials science.

(School of graduate studies)

Master of applied science (MASc).
At least one year from BASc or BSc in science or applied mathematics. Available in aerospace studies, chemical (including nuclear) engineering, civil, electrical, industrial, and mechanical engineering,

geology, and metallurgy and materials science.

Master of engineering (MEng).
No general residence requirement. Available in the same departments as MASc (except geology).

Doctor of philosophy (PhD).
At least two years from MSc or MASc. Available in the same departments as MASc.

Food sciences
(Faculty of food sciences)

Bachelor of science (food sciences) [BSc(FoodSci)].
Four years from senior matriculation. After a first common year, students may specialize in nutrition, textiles or food chemistry, or by choosing options from each area, in a general professional program.

(School of graduate studies)

Master of science (MSc).
At least one year from BSc(FoodSci) or equivalent.

Forestry
(Faculty of forestry)

Bachelor of science in forestry (BScF).
Four years from senior matriculation.

(School of graduate studies)

Master of science in forestry (MScF).
At least one year from BScF degree or a bachelor's degree in a related field. Available in forest and resource policy, forest biology, forest ecology, forest management and resources economics, forest pathology, harvesting and production, silviculture, urban forestry, and wood science and forest products.

Doctor of philosophy (PhD).
In certain areas in collaboration with other departments.

Hygiene
(School of hygiene)

Diploma in nutrition (DipNutrit).
One year from an undergraduate degree.

Certificate in public health (CPH).
One year from an arts or science degree.

Diploma in hospital administration (DipHA).
Two years from an undergraduate degree.

Diploma in public health (DPH).
One year from MD degree.

Diploma in epidemiology and community health (DipEandCH).
One year from MD degree, or acceptable equivalent degree.

Diploma in veterinary public health (DVPH).
One year from veterinary medicine degree.

Diploma in industrial health (DIH).
One year from MD degree.

Diploma in bacteriology (DipBact).
One year from a degree in agriculture, arts or science, dentistry, medicine, pharmacy, or veterinary medicine.

(School of graduate studies)

Master of science (MSc).
At least two years from general BSc or one year from honors BSc. Available in biometrics, epidemiology, health administration, microbiology, nutrition, parasitology and physiological hygiene.

Doctor of philosophy (PhD).
At least two years from MSc degree. Available in same fields as MSc.

Law
(Faculty of law)

Bachelor of laws (LLB).
Three years from at least two years' academic study beyond senior matriculation, i.e. at least five years from senior matriculation.

(School of graduate studies)

Master of laws (LLM).
At least one year from LLB degree.

Doctor juris (DJur).
At least one year from LLM degree.

Library science
(School of graduate studies)

Master of library science (MLS).
Two years from bachelor's degree.

Doctor of philosophy (PhD).
At least two years from MLS degree.
Available in library science.

Medicine
(Faculty of medicine)

*Diploma in physical and occupational therapy
(DipPandOT).*
This course is being replaced over the next
two years by the following courses.

*Bachelor of science (occupational therapy)
[BSc(OT)].*
Four years following Ontario grade XIII.
Requirements: first year of arts and science,
U of T or equivalent.

*Bachelor of science (physical therapy)
[BSc(PT)].*
Four years following Ontario grade XIII.
Requirements: first year of arts and science,
U of T or equivalent.

*Certificate as a teacher of physical or
occupational therapy (TchrCertPhysTher),
(TchrCertOccTher).*
Two-year course open to graduates in
physical or occupational therapy, who have
spent at least three years in practice.

*Bachelor of science (art as applied to medicine)
[BSc(AAMed)].*
Three years from senior matriculation plus
two and a half years of formal training in art.

Doctor of medicine (MD).
Four years from second year in arts and
science, University of Toronto, or from BA or
BSc degree.

*Diploma in speech pathology and audiology
(DipSpeechPathandAud).*
Two years from a bachelor's degree.

Diploma in medical radiology (DMR).
Two years from at least one year's internship,
i.e. three years from MD degree.

Diploma in psychiatry (DPsych).
Three years from at least one year's
internship, or three years including a straight
internship in psychiatry at a teaching hospital,
i.e. three years from an MD degree.

Diploma in anaesthesia (DipAnaes).
Three years from at least one year's
internship, i.e. four years from MD degree.

Diploma in ophthalmic science (DipOphthSc).
Three years following two years'
postgraduate education after MD degree.

Diploma in clinical chemistry (DCC).
Two years from PhD, or MD with adequate
science background.

(School of graduate studies)

Master of science (MSc).
At least one year from MD degree or from
four-year BSc. Available in anatomy,
biochemistry, medical biophysics, medical
science, pathological chemistry, pathology,
pharmacology, physiology, and Banting and
Best research.

Doctor of philosophy (PhD).
At least three years from MD degree.
Available in same departments as MSc.

Museology
(School of graduate studies)

Master of museology (MMuseol).
Fifteen-month program from the four-year
BA. This program consists of two summers
plus one academic session. It is a joint
program offered by the university and the
Royal Ontario Museum.

Music
(Faculty of arts and science)

Bachelor of arts (BA).
Four years from senior matriculation.

(Faculty of music)

Artist diploma (ArtDipMus).
Three years from four-year high school
course and examination in performance.

Licentiate diploma (LicDipMus).
Three years from four-year high school
course and examination in performance.

Bachelor of music in performance (MusBac).
Four years from four-year high school course.

Diploma in operatic performance.
Two years from ArtDipMus or equivalent,
and examination in performance.

Bachelor of music (MusBac).
Four years from senior matriculation.
Candidates must also hold certificates of the
Royal Conservatory of Music or pass a

musical entrance test. Available in the major areas of history and literature of music, composition, music education (instrumental), and music education (vocal).

(School of graduate studies)

Master of music (MusM).
One year from honors MusBac; two years from general MusBac. Available in composition, music education, and in performance and literature.

Master of arts (MA).
At least one year from a four-year BA specialist program in music or bachelor of music program with major concentration in history and literature. Available in musicology

Doctor of music (MusDoc).
Two years from MusM degree.

Doctor of philosophy (PhD).
At least two years from master's degree. Available in musicology.

Nursing
(School of nursing)

Certificate in public health nursing, general (CertPHN).
One year from senior matriculation plus qualification as a professional nurse.

Bachelor of science in nursing (BScN).
Basic degree course, four years from senior matriculation. Degree course for graduate nurses, three years from senior matriculation plus qualification as a professional nurse.

(School of graduate studies)

Master of science in nursing (MScN).
At least sixteen months from BScN degree. Available in community health nursing, medical-surgical nursing and psychiatric nursing.

Pharmacy
(Faculty of pharmacy)

Bachelor of science in pharmacy (BScPhm).
Four years from senior matriculation.

(School of graduate studies)

Master of science in pharmacy (MScPhm).
At least one year from BScPhm degree. A

program of studies in the general field of medicinal chemistry for the degree of doctor of philosophy may be followed in co-operation with other appropriate departments in the university. The department of pharmacy should be consulted for details.

Physical and health education
(School of physical and health education)

Bachelor of physical and health education (BPHE).
Four years from senior matriculation.

Science, applied, see engineering, applied science

Science, pure
(Faculty of arts and science)

Bachelor of science (BSc).
Three or four years after obtaining Ontario grade 13, or equivalent senior matriculation standing. The program enables each student in full-time attendance in one of the eight colleges of the faculty of arts and science to devise his or her own program by combining together each year five full courses chosen to fit the student's interests. Certain programs are suggested for those who desire a degree of specialization, but one could not list all the variants that are possible within a given program to achieve special emphasis in a particular aspect of the subject.

Subjects offered include anatomy, astronomy, biochemistry, biology, botany, chemistry, chemical engineering, computer science, electrical engineering, geography, geology, industrial engineering, mathematics (actuarial science, applied mathematics, statistics), microbiology, parasitology, physics, physiology, psychology, and zoology.

(School of graduate studies)

Master of science (MSc).
At least two years from three-year BA or BSc, at least one year from four-year BA or BSc. Available in anatomy, applied mathematics, astronomy, biochemistry, botany, chemistry, computer science, food sciences, geology, hygiene, mathematics and mathematical statistics, medical biophysics, medical science, pathological chemistry, pathology, pharmacology, physics, physiology, and zoology.

Doctor of philosophy (PhD).
At least two years from MSc. Available in the same departments as MSc.

Social work
(School of graduate studies)

Master of social work (MSW).
At least two years from bachelor's degree.

Diploma in advanced social work (AdvDipSW).
At least one year from MSW.

Doctor of social work (DSW).
At least three years from MSW.

Extension programs

For credit towards degrees, certificates, and diplomas:

(a) Evening classes, fall and winter session.
Undergraduate courses for students proceeding to a degree in the faculty of arts and science are available at the St. George, Erindale, and Scarborough campuses. Full programs offered. Undergraduate courses for graduates of diploma schools of nursing for nurses proceeding to a degree. The final year must be taken in residence. Undergraduate courses for students proceeding to a degree in the faculty of applied science and engineering. The first year only is available by part-time study; the second, third, and fourth years must be taken in residence. Undergraduate courses for students proceeding to a degree in the school of physical and health education. The first year only is available by part-time studies; the second, third, and fourth years must be taken in residence. Bachelor of education degree offered on a part-time basis.

(b) Summer evening classes, summer day classes.
Undergraduate courses for students proceeding to a degree in the faculty of arts and science are available at the St. George and Scarborough campuses. Full programs offered. Undergraduate courses for students proceeding to a degree in the faculty of applied science and engineering. Only courses in the first year are available on a part-time basis. Bachelor of education degree offered on a part-time basis (summer day only).

For credit towards certificates:

Diploma program in translation.
This program provides instruction for both French- and English-speaking students who desire formal training as translators. Applicants must hold a BA from a North American university or have equivalent academic qualifications. Proficiency in French and English and professional experience in translation is desirable. Candidates for admission will be required to pass an entrance examination which will admit them to the three-year course.

Certificate program in business.
This program provides instruction in the basic principles of modern business. The program is designed for students who are capable of undertaking courses at university undergraduate level. A certificate is awarded on successful completion of six courses. Admission requirements are those for normal university entrance.

Certificate program in public administration.
This program is intended primarily for those with considerable experience in public service who wish to acquire a broader background in the political and social sciences. A certificate is awarded on successful completion of six courses. Admission requirements are those for normal university entrance.

Certificate program in criminology.
This program is designed to deepen the knowledge and understanding of criminology in its various aspects. It proposes to examine some of the basic problems of criminal justice, and the treatment of offenders. It is intended primarily for those interested in, or practising in, fields concerned with the prevention of crime in our society. A certificate is awarded on successful completion of six courses. Admission requirements are those for normal entrance to the university.

Certificate program in personnel and industrial relations.
This program is designed for labor, management, and government representatives who have an interest in personnel and industrial relations. This program combines both theoretical and practical material and is so structured to permit specialization in either personnel or industrial relations. A certificate is awarded on successful completion of seven courses. Admission requirements are those for normal university entrance.

Non-degree courses:

Non-degree courses in business, engineering, and special programs are offered on the St. George, Scarborough, and Erindale campuses. Many of the courses are at a post-degree level; and some are offered at the places of business for major corporations and institutions.

Correspondence courses.
Correspondence courses in business subjects, social sciences, and the liberal arts are given in co-operation with national organizations and institutes, and are available also to individual applicants.

Courses for the preparation of teachers in pre-school education.
A three-part course leading to certification by the Nursery Education Association of Ontario, after a year in the field.

English-language summer school.
For students in Canadian universities. The courses are for students whose first language is not English. Applicants must be in attendance at a university or accepted by a Canadian university.

Pre-university courses in chemistry, English, history, mathematics, and physics are offered regularly throughout the year.

St. Pierre et Miquelon summer school of French.
Courses in oral French, French literature, drama and art are given in two four-week sessions, the first in July and the second in August.

Admission requirements

For a general statement regarding admission to university study, see article *Admission to university in Canada.*

For information regarding admission to undergraduate study, consult *Requirements for admission to Canadian colleges and universities* available from Service for Admission to College and University, 151 Slater St., Ottawa, Ont., K1P 5N1, $1.50 prepaid.

Students wishing to enrol in the school of graduate studies must normally have a four-year University of Toronto bachelor's degree with at least B standing or its equivalent from this or another approved university.

Students with normal university entrance requirements from grade XIII are eligible for admission to the following professional faculties and schools: faculty of applied science and engineering; faculty of architecture, urban and regional planning and landscape architecture; faculty of food sciences; faculty of forestry; division of dental hygiene; faculty of music; school of nursing; faculty of pharmacy; and the school of physical and health education.

Students who have completed successfully a minimum of one academic year in an acceptable program at a level beyond grade XIII will be considered for admission to the doctor of dental surgery program and the degree programs in physical and occupational therapy in the faculty of medicine.

Both the faculty of law and the faculty of medicine require a minimum of two years in an academic program beyond the grade XIII level.

The college of education, the schools of business, hygiene, library science, and social work require a bachelor's degree before admission can be considered.

Academic year

Winter session: mid-September to early May.

Summer day session: early July to mid-August.

Summer evening session: early May to end of July.

Grading system

Faculty of arts and science — new program A: 80-100%; B: 70-79%; C: 60-69%; D: 50-59%; fail: below 50%.

Generally speaking a candidate requires 50% in a subject to pass.

The grading systems used by other faculties and schools vary; the individual calendars may be consulted.

Fees and costs

The following include academic and compulsory incidental fees for male students in their first year. Women pay slightly less. Applied science and engineering, $719; architecture, $719; arts and science, $522-$539; child study, $464; college of education, $539; dentistry, $1,154; food sciences, $536; forestry, $561; graduate school, $525; law, $569; medicine, $529-$774; music, $495-$555; nursing, $492-$537; pharmacy, $562; physical and health education, $561; rehabilitation medicine, $464-$555; social work, $549.

Diploma course in applied science, $529; architecture, $505; business administration, $529; dentistry, $485; forestry, $550; hygiene, $625-$790; postgraduate medicine, $135-$290; social work, $529.

Special and part-time – arts, $95; architecture, $165; business administration, $55; child study, $89; graduate school, $62.50-$150; law, $100; pharmacy, $55; social work, $55.

Residence fees – Devonshire, $611 + $245 (meals); Innis College, single room, $1,002; double room, $952; New College, plan A, $1,075, plan B, $855; University College, plan A, $1,091, plan B, $809.

Incidental fees (included in above fees): (a) undergraduate courses – men $10-$70; women $10-$47; (b) graduate courses – graduate studies, men $40, women $20.

Residence dues: the total cost of residence accommodation, including meals, varies from $855-$1,075 per session.

(All fees and costs are subject to change.)

Financial awards and assistance

Awards and financial assistance are available from the university, government, and many "outside" agencies. The university and its colleges provide scholarships at admission (only a very small number of which are open to students from outside the province), in-course scholarships and bursaries in the higher years, and fellowships for graduates. Some loans are also available under special circumstances.

The provincial government offers scholarships to students entering from grade 13, graduate fellowships, and, in co-operation with the federal government, a loan/grant scheme (based on need alone) for Ontario residents. For further information consult "admission awards", an annual publication available at all secondary schools in the province or on request from the office of student awards, and the various college, faculty and school calendars, or contact the office of student awards (admission and undergraduate awards) or the school of graduate studies (graduate awards).

Research institutes

The Banting and Best Department of Medical Research.
Director: I.B. Fritz, DDS, PhD.
The staff of the Banting and Best Department of Medical Research are involved primarily in research on various aspects of metabolic control. Emphasis continues to be directed towards an analysis of the sites and mechanisms of hormone action, particularly insulin.

Centre for Culture and Technology.
Director: H.M. McLuhan, MA, PhD, FRSC, LLD, DLitt.
The centre is concerned with the impact of media (extensions of man) on psyche and society, i.e. man caught up in his own feed-back loop, ever creating new service/disservice environments.

Centre for Industrial Relations.
Director: J.H.G. Crispo, BCom, PhD.
The centre is a non-degree-granting and non-teaching institute of the university, facilitating faculty and student research primarily through its comprehensive information service.

Centre for Linguistic Studies.
Director: J. Wevers, BA, ThB, ThD.
Research and graduate teaching after four-year BA, in linguistics; staff of 18 give 25 year-courses to 60 candidates for MA or PhD in linguistics.

Centre for Mediaeval Studies.
Director: J.F. Leyerle, BA, MA, PhD.
The centre offers interdisciplinary graduate programs in the mediaeval period and encourages specialization in research, particularly in often neglected areas between traditional departments.

Centre for Renaissance Studies.
Chairman: J.H. Parker, MA, PhD, FRSCan.
Interdisciplinary programs will be arranged
for individual students involving more than
one department but leading to a degree in
one of them, in consultation with the officers
of Renaissance studies and of the appropriate
department.

*Centre for Russian and East European
Studies.*
Director: H.G. Skilling, MA, PhD.
The centre promotes the development of
undergraduate and graduate studies and
scholarly research related to Russia and
eastern Europe. The centre acts as a liaison
between the departments and conducts a
diploma program taken conjointly with an
MA in a principal discipline.

Centre for the Study of the Drama.
Director: R.B. Parker, MA, PhD.
The centre offers graduate programs for
higher degrees based on academic graduate
courses and on practical courses and
experimental studio work for those who wish
to obtain qualifications as critics, historians,
and teachers of dramatic literature.

Centre for Urban and Community Studies.
Acting director: L.S. Bourne, BA, MA, PhD.
The centre created in 1964, serves three
functions: 1) responds to staff interests in
formulating interdisciplinary research
projects; 2) assists staff in obtaining support,
administrative assistance, and service
facilities; 3) facilitates graduate student
research experience.

Centre of Criminology.
Director: J.L. Edwards, LLB, MA, PhD,
LLD.
An interdisciplinary research centre
concerned with problems of crime and
criminal justice and staffed by persons trained
in law, sociology, psychology, mathematics,
economics, and statistics. MA degree offered.

Connaught Medical Research Laboratories.
Director: J.K.W. Ferguson, MBE, MA, MD,
FRSCan.
Conducts research in preventive medicine.
Produces insulin, blood fractions, and
vaccines for human and veterinary uses.
Offers postdoctoral fellowships.

David Dunlap Observatory.
Director: D.A. MacRae, BA, AM, PhD.
Established in 1935, a 74-inch reflecting
telescope (largest in Canada), a 19-inch and a
24-inch telescope, all equipped for
spectrography, photography, and
photoelectric studies in astronomy and

astrophysics, including infrared astronomy;
radio telescopes and receivers are also used;
machine shops and major research library.

Institute for Aerospace Studies.
Director: G.N. Patterson, BSc, MA, PhD,
LLD, FRAeS, FRSCan, FCASI, FAIAA,
FAAAS.
The institute provides the only opportunity in
Canada to obtain primary (BASc) and
advanced (MEng, MASc, and PhD) degrees
in the aerospace sciences and engineering. It
has a staff of 15 and 90 graduate students
and postdoctoral fellows.

*Institute for the History and Philosophy of
Science and Technology.*
Director: J.W. Abrams, AB, PhD.
With a staff of 19 members and affiliates,
conducts research in its subject fields and
offers courses leading to the MA and PhD
degrees.

*Institute for the Quantitative Analysis of
Social and Economic Policy.*
Director: T.A. Wilson, BA, AM, PhD.
The general purpose of this institute is to
encourage continuing on-campus quantitative
research on social and economic policy
problems which complements programs of
graduate training in associated teaching
departments.

Institute of Applied Statistics.
Director: J.C. Ogilvie, BSc, MA, PhD.
The purpose of the institute is to bring
together researchers in pure and applied
statistics, to conduct and encourage research
in applied statistics, and to provide a central
location for statistical advice throughout the
university.

Institute of Bio-Medical Electronics.
Director: N.F. Moody, BEng, SMIEE, FIEF,
MEIC, PEng.
The institute was founded in 1962; there is
on staff nine full-time academics; 30 graduate
students. Areas of interdisciplinary research
are: electrical and chemical engineering,
mathematics, pharmacology, physics,
physiology, and surgery.

*Institute of Environmental Sciences and
Engineering.*
Director: P.H. Jones, BASc, MS, PhD.
The institute provides a framework for a
multi-disciplinary approach to environmental
studies, and involves close collaboration of 13
departments, including engineering, health
sciences, law, life sciences, and social sciences.

Institute of Immunology.
Director: B. Cinader, PhD, DSc.
The institute provides a common forum for
investigators in many areas of the university
and an interdisciplinary research experience
in immunology.

Institute of Medical Science.
Director: J.C. Laidlaw, MD, PhD, FRCP(C).
The institute provides an interdisciplinary
research experience in the area of human
biology; thereby it furnishes an opportunity
for students to work towards an MSc or PhD
degree in a wide range of biological fields on
problems which may involve patients and/or
experimental animals.

Pontifical Institute of Mediaeval Studies,
Queen's Park Crescent East, Toronto 5.
Director: Rev. L.K. Shook, MA, PhD.
Conducts research, provides courses, gathers
library and archival materials, publishes texts,
translations, studies and a learned journal
(Mediaeval Studies) in the thought, culture,
writings, and institutions of the middle ages.

University of Toronto Computer Centre.
Director: J.C. Wilson, BASc, MSc, PhD.
The institute's primary purpose is to provide
research and computer facilities for the
various divisions of the university. It is not a
teaching division.

Federated institutions

University of St. Michael's College, Toronto
181, Ontario.
President: Rev. J.M. Kelly, MA, PhD. Vice-
president and registrar: Rev. H.V. Mallon,
MA.
Co-educational; Catholic; 1852; federated
with the University of Toronto; full
undergraduate programs in theology and
related studies; residence for 725. Degrees
awarded by the University of Toronto;
degrees in mediaeval studies by the Pontifical
Institute of Mediaeval Studies; and degrees
in theology by the University of St. Michael's
College.
See also separate entry.

University of Trinity College, Toronto 181,
Ontario.
Provost: D.R.G Owen, MA, PhD, DD, DCL.
Registrar: R.L. Cummins, BA.
Co-educational; Anglican; 1852; constituent
college federated with the University of
Toronto; full undergraduate programs;
residence for 345. Degrees awarded by the

University of Toronto (BA, BCom, BSc) and
degrees in theology: STB, MTh, ThD.
See also separate entry.

Victoria University, 73 Queen's Park, Toronto
181, Ontario.
President: J.E. Hodgetts, MA, PhD, FRSC.
Registrar: A.C.M. Ross, CD, MA, PhD.
Co-educational; United Church; 1836;
federated with the University of Toronto;
full undergraduate programs; residence for
326. Degrees awarded by the University of
Toronto (BA, BCom, BSc) and degrees in
theology: LTh, BRE, BD, ThM, ThD.
See also separate entry.

Knox College, Toronto 181, Ontario.
Principal: Rev. J.S. Glen, PhD, ThD, DD.
Bursar: Mrs. E.F. Kirk, BA.
Presbyterian. Co-educational. Established
1844. Federated with the university in 1890.
Offers courses in theology leading to the
diploma and the degrees of BD, ThM, and
ThD which are awarded by the college.
Residential accommodation for 104 men.

Wycliffe College, Hoskin Avenue, Toronto
181, Ontario.
Principal: Rev. Canon Leslie Hunt, BA, BD,
MTh, DD. Registrar: Mr. Donald Ireland.
Anglican. Established 1877. Federated with
the university 1890. Offers courses in theology
leading to the graduation diploma, the LTh,
and the degree of BTh. In addition the
college has authority to confer the following
degrees in theology: BD, MTh, DTh and the
DD. Residential accommodation for 75 men.

Emmanuel College of Victoria University,
Toronto 181, Ontario.
Acting principal: W.O. Fennell, BA, SGM,
DD. Registrar: Rev. A.G. Reynolds, MA,
DD. United Church.
Victoria University founded 1836. Emmanuel
College one of seven seminaries in Toronto
forming Toronto school of theology. Offers
courses in theology leading to the college
diploma; also the title LTh, and degrees of
BD, BRE, ThM, and ThD, which are
awarded by the senate of Victoria University.
Residential accommodation available for
men and women.

Massey College, University of Toronto,
Toronto 181, Ontario.
Master: Robertson Davies, BLitt, DLitt,
LLD.
Residential college for male students and
senior scholars, engaged in research. Opened
in 1963-64. The college provides living
accommodation, dining and common room
facilities, and a library for research studies.

Deans of faculties

Applied science and engineering
J.M. Ham, BASc, SM, ScD, FIEEE

Architecture, urban and regional planning
and landscape architecture
T. Howarth, PhD, FRIBA, FRAIC

Arts and science
A.D. Allen, BSc, PhD

Dentistry
Gordon Nikiforuk, DDS, MS, FRCD(C)

Education, the college of
D.F. Dadson, BA, BEd

Food sciences
Iva Armstrong (Mrs), (acting), BA, MA

Forestry
V.J. Nordin, BA, BScF, PhD

Graduate studies
A.E. Safarian, BA, PhD

Law
R. St. J. Macdonald, BA, LLB, LLM

Medicine
A.L. Chute, OBE, MA, MD, PhD, FRCP(C)

Music, faculty of
J. Beckwith, MusBac, MusM

Pharmacy
F.N. Hughes, BSc, PhmB, MA, LLD

Directors of schools

Business
J.H.G. Crispo (acting), BCom, PhD

Extension, division of university
E.M. Gruetzner (acting), BA

Hygiene
B. Bucove, MD, DPH

Library science
R.B. Land, BLS, MA, MLS

Nursing
Helen Carpenter, BS, MPH, EdD

Physical and health education
J.H. Ebbs, MD, FRCP(Can), FRCP(Lond),
DCH

Social work
A. Rose, MA, PhD

Department chairmen

Anaesthesia
R.A. Gordon, CD, BSc, MD, FFARCS,
FRCP(C)

Anatomy
J.S. Thompson, BA, MA, PhD

Anthropology
D.R. Hughes, MA, PhD

Architecture
P. Prangnell, AADip, MArch, ARIBA,
MRAIC

Art as applied to medicine
Nancy Joy (Miss)

Astronomy
D.A. MacRae, BA, AM, PhD, FRSCan

Behavioral science
R.F. Badgley, BA, MA, PhD

Biochemistry
G.R. Williams, BSc, PhD, DSc

Botany
J. Dainty, MA, DSc, FRSE

Business administration
J.H.G. Crispo, BCom, PhD

Cell biology
L. Siminovitch, BSc, PhD

Chemical engineering and applied chemistry
W.F. Graydon, MASc, PhD

Chemistry
A.G. Brook, BA, PhD

Civil engineering
T.C. Kenney, MSc(Eng), PhD

Classical studies
J.M. Rist, MA

Classics
Rev. J.J. Sheridan, MA, PhD

Computer science
T.E. Hull, MA, PhD

Dental anaesthesia
R.S. Locke, MS, DDS

Dental hygiene, division of
Marjorie Jackson (director), DDS

Dental materials
W.D. MacKay, DDS

Dental public health
D.W. Lewis, DDS, DDPH, MScD

Dental radiology
H.G. Poyton, LDS, FDS, HDD

Dentistry
A.M. Hunt, DDS, DDPH, MScD

East Asian studies
W.G. Saywell, MA, PhD

Educational theory
G.E. Flower

Electrical engineering
G.R. Slemon, MASc, DIC, PhD, DSc

Engineering science
B. Etkin, MASc, FRSCan

English
B.S. Hayne, AM, PhD

English (graduate studies)
M. MacLure, MA, PhD

Environmental health
A.M. Fisher, MA, PhD

Epidemiology and biometrics
W.H. LeRiche, BSc, MD, MPH, FAPHA

Family and community medicine
F.B. Fallis, MD, CCFP, FCFP

Fine art
F.E. Winter, BA, PhD

Food sciences
I.L. Armstrong (acting), BA, MA

Forestry
V.J. Nordin, BA, BScF, PhD

French
P. Mathews, AM, PhD

French (graduate studies)
E.A. Joliat, BA, DU

Geography
P.D. Kerr, BA, MA, PhD

Geology and geological engineering
E.W. Nuffield, BA, PhD, FRSCan

German
C.N. Genno, MA, PhD

German (graduate studies)
H. Eichner, MA, PhD

Health administration
F.B. Roth, MD, FACHA

Histology
A.A. Axelrad, BSc, MD, PhD

History
A.P. Thornton, MA, DPhil, FRHisS

History of art
F.E. Winter, BA, PhD

History and literature of music
H.J. Olnick, BS, MA

Hygiene
B. Bucove, MD, DPH

Industrial engineering
B. Bernholtz, MA, PhD

Islamic studies
R.M. Savory, MA, PhD

Italian and Hispanic studies
G.L. Stagg, MBE, MA, AM

Landscape architecture
R. Strong, BLA, MLA, CSLA, ASLA, OALA

Law
R. St. J. Macdonald, BA, LLB, LLM

Library science
R.B. Land, MA, MLS

Mathematics
G.F.D. Duff, MA, PhD, FRSCan

Mechanical engineering
W.D. Baines, BSc, MS, PhD

Medical biophysics
H.E. Johns, BA, LLD, MA, PhD, FRSCan

Medical biophysics (graduate studies)
G.F. Whitmore, MA, PhD

Medical microbiology
A.E. Franklin, BSc, PhD

Medical research (Banting and Best medical research department)
I.B. Fritz, DDS, PhD

Medicine
C.H. Hollenberg, MD, FRCP(C)

Metallurgy and materials science
C.B. Alcock, ARCS, DSc, PhD, FRIC

Microbiology
L.W. MacPherson (acting), MRCUS, DVSM, PhD

Music
L. Klein, BA, MS, PhD

Musical theory and composition
G. Ciamaga, MFA

Music education
R.A. Rosevear, AB, BM, MM

Near Eastern studies
J. van Seters, MA, BD, PhD

Near Eastern studies (graduate studies)
R.J. Williams, MA, BD, PhD

Nursing
H. Carpenter, BS, MPH, EdD

Nutrition
G.H. Beaton, MA, PhD

Obstetrics and gynaecology
J.L. Harkins, MD, FRCS(C), FACOG

Opera
G. Philipp

Ophthalmology
J.C. McCulloch, MD

Oral diagnosis
J.A. Pedler, BDS, MRCS, LRCP, MDS, FDS, RCS

Oral surgery
P.T. Smylski, DDS, DiplOralSurg, FRCD

Orthodontics
D.G. Woodside, BSc, DDS, MScD, FRCD(C)

Otolaryngology
D.P. Bryce, MD, FRCS(C)

Paediatrics
H.W. Bain, MD, FRCP(C)

Paedodontics
K.W. Davey, DDS, MScD, FRCD(C)

Parasitology
R.S. Freeman (acting), BS, MA, PhD

Pathological chemistry
A.G. Gornall, BA, PhD

Pathology
A.C. Ritchie, MB, ChB, DPhil, FRCP(C), FRCPath, FCAP

Performance (music)
E. Schabas, BS, MA

Periodontics
C.H.M. Williams, DDS, BScD, FRCD(C)

Pharmacology
W. Kalow, MD

Pharmacy
G.R. Duncan, DPhil, MScPhm

Philosophy
J.G. Slater, MA, PhD

Philosophy (St. Michael's)
L.E.M. Lynch, MA, MSL, PhD

Physics
J.M. Daniels, MA, DPhil, FRSCan

Physiology
R.E. Haist, BA, MA, PhD, MD

Political economy
J.S. Dupré, AM, PhD

Preventive dentistry
J. Kreutzer, DDS, BScD

Preventive medicine
H.S. Gear, BSc, MD, DPH, DTMT&H

Prosthodontics
G.A. Zarb, BChD, MS, DDS

Psychiatry
R.C.A. Hunter, MD, DPsych

Psychology
G.E. Macdonald, BEd, MA, PhD

Radiology
R.B. Holmes, MD, MSc, FRCP(C), FACR

Rehabilitation and physical medicine
A.T. Jousse, BA, LLD, MD, FRCP(C)

Religious studies
J. Meagher, MA, PhD

Restorative dentistry
J.H. Hibberd, BDS, DDS, MDSc, FACDS

Sanskrit and Indian studies
A.K. Warder, BA, PhD

Slavic languages and literatures
C.H. Bedford, MA, PhD

Social work
A. Rose, BA, MA, PhD

Sociology
P.J. Giffen, MA

Surgery
W.R. Drucker, BSc, MD, FACS, FRCS(C)

Urban and regional planning
A.J. Dakin, BA, PhD, MRAIC, ARIBA,
MTPIC, MTPI

Zoology
D.A. Chant, MA, PhD

Trent University*

Peterborough, Ontario

Telephone: 705-748-1011
Direct general correspondence to the registrar

Total full-time student enrolment 1,653; see also separate section *Statistics on Canadian universities and colleges*

Executive and administrative officers

Chancellor
The Honorable Leslie Frost, PC, QC, LLD, DCL

President and vice-chancellor
T.H.B. Symons, MA

Vice-president
R.H. Sadleir, MA

Vice-president (academic) and dean of arts and science
T.E.W. Nind, MA

Vice-president (finance), comptroller, and secretary to the board of governors
J.E. Leishman, BCom, CA

Registrar
A.O.C. Cole, MA

Director, admissions
G.D. Pollock, MA

Director, student aid and placement
R.J. Bowman, BA

Director, part-time studies
H.G. Hooke, BScF

Director, health services
M.F. Clarkson, MD

Librarian
J.D.P. Martin, BA, BLS

Director of information
J.G. English, BA

Director of athletics
P.S.B. Wilson, BA

Constituent colleges

Peter Robinson College, Peterborough, Ontario.
Master: I.D. Chapman, BSc, MA. Men and women. Opened 1964.

Catharine Parr Traill College, Peterborough, Ontario.
Principal: Mrs. Nancy Sherouse, BA. Men and women. Opened 1964.

Champlain College, Peterborough, Ontario.
Master: W.B.D. Heeney, BA, BD, DPhil. Men. Opened 1966.

Lady Eaton College, Peterborough, Ontario.
Principal: Mrs. Marjorie Seeley, AM. Women. Opened 1968.

Each college offers to its members in addition to residential accommodation for members of the academic staff and students, the use of a dining room, common rooms, library, seminar rooms and tutorial offices. Every student and every member of the faculty is a member of a college in which they have the opportunity to live and work together in a relatively small academic community within the large body of the university.

Background

Trent University was formally created with degree-granting powers by an act of the Ontario legislature in 1960. In that same year, a nucleus of faculty members and administrative staff was formed and the first undergraduate class was accepted in 1964. The university was officially opened in October 1964 by Governor-General Georges Vanier.

During the early years, the academic planning committee initiated the broad academic preparation for the university while a campus planning committee planned the university

*Ordinary member, AUCC.

site and architecture. The proposals of the two were accepted as the basic policies of the university.

The university operates under a board of governors and a senate. It is non-denominational and co-educational.

Facilities and services

The main campus of the university is located on both sides of the Otonabee River at the northern edge of Peterborough (population, 58,000), but functions of the university are also carried on at three locations in the downtown area. The core of the main campus was a gift of the Canadian General Electric Company, and additional land totalling over 1,400 acres has been acquired to meet the needs of the university.

In the first five years of the university's operation, an administration, teaching and laboratory complex and two residential and teaching colleges were developed in the city. On the main campus the master plan has been implemented to the completion of the first phase of construction. This includes two residential teaching colleges, the main library with a capacity of some 350,000 volumes, two science buildings and athletic facilities.

The city colleges — Peter Robinson and Catharine Parr Traill — are both co-educational and provide residential accommodation for 280 students in addition to non-resident members. The campus colleges — Champlain for men and Lady Eaton for women - provide accommodation for 450 students. For the academic year 1971-72 half of the student body will have a place in residence.

Calendars and brochures

University calendar; graduate studies calendar; part-time studies - summer session; part-time studies - winter session; high school information brochure; Arthur; available from the director of research.

Courses and degrees

Arts

Bachelor of arts (BA).
(a) General course, 15 course credits from senior matriculation. Available in classical studies, economics, English literature, French studies, German, Hispanic studies, history, Indian-Eskimo studies, mathematics, philosophy, politics, psychology, sociology.
(b) Honors course, 20 course credits from senior matriculation. Available in classical studies, English literature, French studies, German, Hispanic studies, history, mathematics, philosophy, politics, sociology.

Master of arts (MA).
At least two years from general BA, or at least one year from honors BA. Available in history.

Science, pure

Bachelor of science (BSc).
(a) General course three years from senior matriculation. (b) Honors course, four years from senior matriculation. Available in anthropology, biology, chemistry, economics, geography, mathematics, physics, and psychology.

Master of science (MSc).
At least two years from general BSc, or at least one year from honors BSc. Available in chemistry and physics.

Extension programs

For university credit:

Winter academic session.
Courses leading to a BA and BSc are offered concurrent with the regular undergraduate program during the day and evening.

Summer session.
Courses are offered in arts and in science for undergraduates proceeding to a degree.

For no university credit:

A number of non-credit courses in the
humanities and social and physical sciences
are offered in the evening during the regular
academic session.

During the summer, an intensive non-credit
course in French is offered which enables
students to improve their working knowledge
of the French language to the university level.

Admission requirements

For a general statement regarding admission
to university study, see article *Admission to
university in Canada.*

For information regarding admission to
undergraduate study, consult *Requirements
for admission to Canadian colleges and
universities* available from Service for
Admission to College and University, 151
Slater St., Ottawa, Ont., K1P 5N1, $1.50
prepaid.

Academic year

Autumn term: mid-September to early
December.

Winter term: early January to late February.

Spring term: mid-March to mid-May.

Summer session: early July to mid-August.

Grading system

There are four passing grades: A, B, C, D,
and one failing grade: F. There are no
supplemental examinations.

Overall standing is granted in major subjects
only and includes all courses taken in that
subject. Grades are A, B, C.

Introduction of a course-credit system
replaced year promotion in 1970-71.

Aeg. (aegrotat), following a grade, indicates
that the student was absent with reason from
the final examination, but that standing was
granted on the basis of the year's work.

Fees and costs

The total annual fee for full-time
undergraduates is $555. This amount includes
registration, tuition fees, and incidental fees.

Part-time students pay $115 per full course,
$60 per half course, or $115 for two half
courses.

Residential fees, including room and board
for the academic year (excluding vacation
periods), are $1,200 in a single room, $1,130
in a double room, payable in three
instalments. For students in lodgings or living
at home, there is a non-resident fee of $75.

Financial awards and assistance

Trent University has a generous scholarship
program designed to reflect its insistence on
high standards and to reward and encourage
its leading students.

Through the generosity of private donors,
scholarships have been endowed; these
scholarships will be awarded to students
entering the university and during the course
of their studies. In addition, the university
awards a generous number of scholarships to
students entering the university with high
standing.

Since all students with high standing will
automatically be considered, no separate
application for scholarships awarded by the
university is necessary.

All university scholarships may be held in
conjunction with other scholarships awarded
by external agencies when their conditions
permit, up to a normal maximum of $1,755 in
1971-72. In order to be considered for
scholarships, a student entering first year
normally must have undertaken at least five
of the seven credits required for admission
during the current academic year. No student
applying for admission to the university after
August 1 will normally be considered for a
scholarship.

The university endeavours to guarantee all
scholarship holders, including those from the
Peterborough area, places in residence if they
wish them.

Students attending Trent University will be eligible for assistance under the Ontario student awards program.

Deans of faculties

Arts and science
T.E.W. Nind, MA

Graduate studies
B.R. Blishen, MA

Department chairmen

Anthropology
R.K. Vastokas, MA, PhD

Biology
D.B. Carlisle, MA, DPhil, DSc, FLS, FZS, FIBiol

Chemistry
G.O. Aspinall, BSc, PhD, DSc, FRIC, FRSE

Classical studies
B.P. Reardon, MA, DU

Economics
M.J. Boote, BA, PhD

English literature
B.E. Rooke (Miss), MA, PhD

French studies
F.K. Harper, MA

Geography
W.P. Adams, BA, MSc, PhD

German
D.D. Stewart, MA, PhD

Hispanic studies
J.M. Valverde, LicFilyLet, DrFilyLet, ex-Catedratico

History
Alan Wilson, MA, PhD

Indian-Eskimo studies program
Walter Currie, BA

Mathematics
A.P. Guinand, BSc, DPhil

Philosophy
W.H. Dray, MA, DPhil, FRSC

Physics
J.I. Lodge, MA, PhD

Politics
D.R. Cameron, BA, MSc, PhD

Psychology
A.G. Worthington, BCom, PhD, MAPS

Sociology
R.F. White, BA, BASc, MCom, PhD

University of Trinity College*

(Federated with the University of Toronto)†
Toronto 181, Ontario

Telephone: 416-928-2522
Direct general correspondence to the registrar

Total full-time student enrolment 36; see
also separate section *Statistics on Canadian
universities and colleges*

Executive and administrative officers

Chancellor
The Most Reverend H.H. Clark, BA, BD,
DCL, LLD

Provost and vice-chancellor
Rev. D.R.G. Owen, MA, PhD, DD, DCL

Registrar
R.L. Cummins, BA

Bursar
G.O. Shepherd, BComm

Dean of men students
G.A.B. Watson, MA, STB

Dean of women students
M.H. Seaman (Miss), MA

Director of development
P.C.B. Richardson

Librarian
B.L. Saunders (Miss), BA, BLS

Constituent college

St. Hilda's College, University of Trinity
College, Toronto 181, Ontario.
Principal: Miss M.H. Seaman, MA. Founded
in 1888. The residence for women students of
Trinity College.

Background

The University of Trinity College was
founded in 1852 by the Honorable and Right
Reverend John Strachan, first Bishop of
Toronto, to be the Church of England
University of Upper Canada. The occasion
for its founding was the secularization, in
1850, of King's College of which the bishop
had been a founder and at one time
president, and which became the original
foundation of the provincial University of
Toronto.

Under the powers obtained by royal charter
in 1852, the University of Trinity College
conferred degrees in seven faculties, until
1904. In that year in response to the
movement for the federation of the various
universities in the province, Trinity College
federated with the University of Toronto and
ceased to give instruction in all the faculties
except arts and divinity. It also placed in
abeyance its degree-granting power in the
faculty of arts.

St. Hilda's College was founded in 1888 by
the Reverend Dr. Body, the second provost of
Trinity College, to provide a residence for the
women students of Trinity College, together
with some separate instruction. At a later date
all instruction became fully co-educational
and St. Hilda's continued to be the residence
for women students of Trinity College and to
provide a centre for their social life at
university.

At the present time the college's connection
with the Anglican Church of Canada is
chiefly traditional and historical. It
acknowledges no ecclesiastical control and
places no religious or denominational tests or
other restrictions upon its students or staff.

---

*Ordinary member, AUCC.

†Holds in abeyance its degree-granting
powers in arts and science during term of
federation with the University of Toronto.

Facilities and services

The college is situated on Hoskin Avenue within the University of Toronto campus (Toronto population, 2,316,000). The main quadrangle presently includes a chapel, a library (82,500 volumes), administrative offices, a dining hall, and residence accommodation for 220 men. A separate building for classrooms, staff offices and student activities was completed in 1961.

St. Hilda's College, on Devonshire Place, provides residence accommodation for 125 women and additional facilities for women students registered in Trinity College.

Student services of the University of Toronto, as well as those of the college, are available to all Trinity students.

Calendars and brochures

This is Trinity College, Toronto. A descriptive brochure providing information about the college, intended mainly for prospective students from Canada and overseas.

The calendar of the faculty of arts and science of the University of Toronto describes undergraduate programs in arts, science and commerce.

The calendar of the faculty of divinity of Trinity College and bulletin of the Toronto school of theology describe basic and advanced degree programs in theology.

Copies of the above-named publications may be obtained from the registrar.

Courses and degrees

Arts
(Faculty of arts and science, University of Toronto)

Bachelor of arts (BA).
As offered by the University of Toronto. See separate entry.

Business, see commerce

Commerce
(Faculty of arts and science, University of Toronto)

Bachelor of commerce (BCom).
As offered by the University of Toronto.

Science, pure
(Faculty of arts and science, University of Toronto)

Bachelor of science (BSc).
As offered by the University of Toronto.

Theology
(Faculty of divinity in federation with the Toronto school of theology)

Bachelor of sacred theology (STB).
Three years from first degree.

Master of theology (MTh).
At least one year from STB.

Doctor of theology (ThD).
At least two years from STB.

Admission requirements

For a general statment regarding admission to university study, see article *Admission to university in Canada.*

For information regarding admission to undergraduate study, consult *Requirements for admission to Canadian colleges and universities* available from Service for Admission to College and University, 151 Slater St., Ottawa, Ont., K1P 5N1, $1.50 prepaid.

For admission to courses leading to degrees in theology, students must have obtained a first degree.

Academic year

Mid-September to early May.

Grading system

Arts, science and commerce: as for University of Toronto. Divinity: A — 80 + %; B + — 76-79%; B — 70-75%; C — 60-69%; D — 50-59%; F — below 50%. An overall C average is required with no subject under D in the basic degree course.

Fees and costs

University and college tuition and incidental fees per year: arts, science and commerce — $648.50 (men); $622 (women). Divinity, $475 plus $37 miscellaneous fees.

Residence rates, room and board, per year: men, $1,020; women, $1,010.

Financial awards and assistance

The college offers admission and in-course scholarships. Trinity students in arts, science and commerce are also eligible for University of Toronto admission and in-course scholarships. Both University of Toronto and Trinity College admission scholarships in arts, science and commerce are described in the admission awards calendar of the University of Toronto, obtainable from the office of student awards, University of Toronto. Awards in the faculty of divinity are described in the calendar of that faculty.

The college maintains a substantial bursary and loan fund.

The college also offers six graduate fellowships providing free room and board in residence for one year, for men and women pursuing graduate studies at the University of Toronto or in the Toronto school of theology. Application must be made to the registrar before February 1.

Deans of faculties

Arts
A. Dalzell, BLitt, MA

Divinity
Rev. Canon H.W. Buchner, BA, LTh, STM, DD

Department heads

Classics
D.J. Conacher, MA, PhD

English
M.T. Wilson, MA, PhD

French
W.S. Rogers, MA

German
D.A. Joyce, MA, PhD

Philosophy
G. Edison, MA, PhD

Religious studies
G.A.B. Watson, MA, STB

University of Victoria*

Victoria, British Columbia

Telephone: 604-477-6911
Direct general correpondence to the registrar

Total full-time student enrolment 5,119; see also separate section *Statistics on Canadian universities and colleges*

Executive and administrative officers

Chancellor
R.L. Haig-Brown, LLD

President
B.J. Partridge, AB, LLB, JD

Vice-president for administration
J.T. Kyle, BSc, MSc

Bursar
R.W. McQueen, BCom, CA

Librarian
D.W. Halliwell, MA, BLS

Registrar
R.J. Ferry, BA

Director of admissions
R.R. Jeffels, CD, BA, BEd, MA

Assistant dean of arts and science
W.R. Gordon, BA, MA, PhD

Director of buildings and grounds
G.E. Apps, BASc, PEng

Director, personnel services
W.G. Bender, BA

Director, counselling centre
R.S. Martin (acting), CD, BA, PhD

Director of campus planning
I.W. Campbell (acting), BSc, PEng

Executive assistant to the president
J.E. Currie, BCom, MBA

Director, continuing education
L.E. Devlin, BEd, MA, PhD

Director of academic advising, faculty of arts and science
E.N. Foord, BA, MA, EdD

Assistant to the president; secretary, board of governors
J.T. Matthews, BA, MBA

Director, advising centre, faculty of education
Anne McLaughlin, BCom

Director, general university services
T.J. Sawchuk, BEd, MSc, MEd

Background

The University of Victoria came into being on July 1, 1963, but as Victoria College, it had enjoyed a prior tradition of sixty years' distinguished teaching at the university level. These sixty years of history may be viewed conveniently in three distinct stages.

Between the years 1903 and 1914, Victoria College was affiliated to McGill University, offering first- and second-year McGill courses in arts and science. Administered locally by the Victoria school board, the college was an adjunct to Victoria High School and shared its facilities. The opening in 1915 of The University of British Columbia obliged college to suspend operations in higher education in Victoria.

In 1920, Victoria College began the second stage of its development, reborn in affiliation to The University of British Columbia. Though still administered by the Victoria school board, the college was now completely separated from Victoria High School, moving in 1921 into the magnificent Dunsmuir mansion known as Craigdarroch. Instruction in first- and second-year arts and science was offered.

*Ordinary member, AUCC.

The final stage, between the years 1954 and 1963, saw the transition from a two-year college to a university. During this period, the college was governed by the Victoria College council, representative of the parent University of British Columbia, the greater Victoria school board, and the provincial department of education. In 1946 the college was forced by post-war enrolment to move from Craigdarroch to the Lansdowne campus of the provincial normal school. The normal school joined Victoria College in 1956 as its faculty of education. Late in this transitional period (through the co-operation of the Department of National Defence and the Hudson's Bay Company), the 284-acre campus at Gordon Head was acquired. Academic expansion was rapid after 1956, until in 1961 the college still in affiliation with The University of British Columbia, awarded its first bachelor's degrees.

The University of Victoria was granted autonomy in 1963. It is governed by a board of governors, a senate, and the faculty council.

The Alma Mater Society of the university makes special arrangements to assist students coming from abroad. More specifically, they help foreign students to find accommodation, introduce them to members of the faculty and administration, and assist them with the many problems of living in a new country. The population of the Victoria area approximates 200,000.

Facilities and services

Apart from ancillary teaching and research installations, the university has six permanent buildings for academic purposes together with a students' union building, a campus services building, two colleges with residences accommodating 290 women and 320 men, a stadium, a gymnasium, playing fields, a restaurant, etc. The library contains approximately 475,000 volumes.

The university is in close proximity to the Pacific Naval Laboratories, the Provincial Archives, the Dominion Astrophysical Observatory and a federal research laboratory for forest products. The federal biological station is located 70 miles to the north in the city of Nanaimo.

The university also possesses an astrodome and a computing centre.

Full-time counsellors are available to confer with students regarding academic problems, course selection, vocational guidance and personal problems. The student placement office, operated by the federal Department of Manpower and Immigration, is also located on the campus.

Calendars and brochures

Annual calendar (available from the registrar's office). Summer session calendar (available from the summer session office). Graduate studies brochure (available from the faculty of graduate studies). High school brochure (available from information services office).

Courses and degrees

Arts
(Faculty of arts and science)

Bachelor of arts (BA).
Four years from grade 12 (B.C.). Honors courses available in anthropology, classics, economics, English, French, geography, German, Greek, history, Latin, linguistics, mathematics, philosophy, political science, psychology, Russian, sociology, Spanish.

(Faculty of graduate studies)

Master of arts (MA).
Minimum requirement: 15 units or one full winter session of study. Available in anthropology, English, geography, history, linguistics, mathematics, philosophy, political science, psychology, sociology.

Doctor or philosophy (PhD).
Minimum requirement: two full winter sessions of study beyond the MA or three full winter sessions of study beyond the BA. Thesis. Available in English, geography, psychology.

Education
(Faculty of education)

Bachelor of education (BEd).
Preparing elementary and secondary teachers.
Five years from grade 12 (B.C.).

Master of arts (MA).
Minimum requirement: 18 units or one full
winter session of study. Available in areas of
educational psychology, educational
administration, curriculum and instruction.

Doctor of philosophy (PhD).
Educational psychology only.

Fine arts
(Faculty of fine arts)

Bachelor of arts (BA),
in history in art. Four years from grade 12
(B.C.).

Bachelor of fine arts (BFA).
Four years from grade 12 (B.C.). Programs
available in art and in theatre.

Bachelor of Music (BMus).
Four years from grade 12 (B.C.).

(Faculty of graduate studies)

Master of arts (MA).
Minimum requirement: 15 units or one full
winter session of study. Available in music
and theatre.

Master of fine arts (MFA).
Minimum requirement: 15 units or one full
winter session of study. Available in theatre.

Master of music (MMus).
Minimum requirement: 15 units or one full
winter session of study. Available in areas of
composition and performance.

Doctor of philosophy (PhD).
Minimum requirement: two full winter
sessions of study beyond the MA or three full
winter sessions of study beyond the BA.
Thesis. Available in music.

Nursing
School of nursing approved but postponed.

Science, pure
(Faculty of arts and science)

Bachelor of science (BSc).
Four years from grade 12 (B.C.). Honors
courses available in astronomy, bacteriology,
biochemistry, biology, chemistry, geography,
mathematics, physics, psychology.

(Faculty of graduate studies)

Master of science (MSc).
Minimum requirement: 15 units or one full
winter session of study. Available in biology,
chemistry, mathematics, nutritional
biochemistry, physics, psychology.

Doctor of philosophy (PhD).
Minimum requirement: two full winter
sessions of study beyond the MSc or three
full winter sessions beyond the BSc. Thesis.
Available in biology, chemistry, physics,
psychology.

Extension programs

For university credit:

Evening courses.
The university provides a substantial offering
of courses scheduled in the late afternoon
and evening to accommodate adult students,
particularly teachers.

Summer session.
A summer session, lasting approximately
seven weeks, is held during July and August.

For no university credit:

Evening and summer sessions.
The university offers a limited number of
non-credit courses.

La maison française.
A course in practical studies in the French
language is offered annually in July and
August.

Admission requirements

For a general statement regarding admission
to university study, see article *Admission to
university in Canada.*

For information regarding admission to undergraduate study, consult *Requirements for admission to Canadian colleges and universities* available from Service for Admission to College and University, 151 Slater St., Ottawa, Ont., K1P 5N1, $1.50 prepaid.

For admission to courses leading to a first degree in education; graduation on the academic-technical program, B.C. residents; others, matriculation.

For admission to the faculty of graduate studies, an academic standing acceptable to the department or school or faculty concerned. In general, this will be a baccalaureate degree from a recognized university, or its equivalent with a "B" average (70%) in the work of the last two years.

Academic year

Winter session: mid-September to end of April.

Summer session: early July to mid-August.

Grading system

Students' marks are classified as follows: first class, A+, A, A-; second class, B+, B, B-; pass, C+, C, D; E (conditional supplemental); F (no supplemental).

Fees and costs

Undergraduate tuition fees per year, $428. Part-time students, $30 per unit. Alma Mater society fees, $32.

Graduate tuition fees: master's program (first year), $450; (second year), $150. Doctoral program (first year), $450; (second year), $450. Part-time, special and qualifying students, $30 per unit. Graduate students' society fee, $15.

Room and board in university residences: double room, $728; single room, $790.

Financial awards and assistance

The government of British Columbia provides scholarships and bursaries.

The University of Victoria itself distributes scholarships and other awards totalling more than $160,000 each year to its leading scholars. Included are the president's scholarships to a value of $20,000, awarded to outstanding students, including those who are about to enter their first year.

In addition to the outright grants that have been described, loans with a deferred payment plan are available in case of need. Under the Canada Student Loans Plan of the federal government, the student need not begin repayment until he has left the university.

Special financial needs, particularly when they are unexpected and urgent, can be met through the university's rotating loan fund.

Affiliated institution

The Victoria Conservatory of Music is affiliated with the University of Victoria.

Students in the bachelor of music program and in the music teaching area in the bachelor of education program receive their solo performance tuition from the faculty of the conservatory.

Deans of faculties

Arts and science
J.L. Climenhaga, MA, PhD

Education
H.E. Farquhar (pro tem), MA, PhD

Fine arts
Peter Garvie, MA

Graduate studies
A.R. Fontaine (pro tem), BSc, DPhil

Department heads

Anthropology and sociology
Margaret Cumming, MA, PhD

Bacteriology and biochemistry
A.J. Wood, BSA, MSA, PhD

Biology
G.O. Mackie, MA, DPhil

Chemistry
S.A. Ryce, BA, PhD

Classics
H.H. Huxley, MA, FIAL

Economics
L.I. Bakony, BA, PhD

English
R.F. Leslie, MA, PhD

French language and literature
O.M. Abrioux, DES, PhD

Geography
C.N. Forward, BA, MA, PhD

Germanic languages and literature
J.B. MacLean, BA, MA, PhD

Hispanic and Italian studies
P. Cabanas, licenciado,
doctorenfilsofiayletras, Lic, DFL

History
J.E. Hendrickson, BA, BEd, MA, PhD

History in art
A. Gowans, MA, MFA, PhD

Linguistics
J.-P. Vinay, LèsL, DES, MA, FRCS

Mathematics
O.P. Noble, BA

Music
P.T. Young, BA, MusM

Philosophy
K.W. Rankin, MA, PhD

Physics
H.W. Dosso, BA, MSc, PhD

Political science
N.A. Swainson, BA, BEd, MA

Psychology
G.A. Milton, BA, MS, PhD

Slavonic and oriental studies
T.M. Rickwood, BA, PhD

Theatre
R.G. Allen, BA, DFA

Visual arts
Norman Toynton

Victoria University*

(Federated with the University of Toronto)†
73 Queen's Park, Toronto 181, Ontario

Telephone: 416-928-3801
Direct general correspondence to the registrar

Total full-time student enrolment 77; see also separate section *Statistics on Canadian universities and colleges*

Executive and administrative officers

President and vice-chancellor
J.E. Hodgetts, MA, PhD, FRSC

Registrar
A.C.M. Ross, CD, MA, PhD

Bursar and alumni secretary
F.C. Stokes, MA

Dean of men
M.S. Cross, BA, MA, PhD

Dean of women
E.A. Bindon, BA

Director of student aid
R.H. Macdonald, AM, PhD

Librarian
L.D. Fraser (Miss), MA, BLS

Constituent colleges

*Victoria College,*Toronto 5, Ontario.
President: J.E. Hodgetts, MA, PhD, FRSC.
Principal: J.M. Robson, MA, PhD. Registrar:
A.C.M. Ross, CD, MA, PhD. United Church

*Ordinary member, AUCC.

†Holds in abeyance its degree-granting powers in arts and science during the term of federation with the University of Toronto.

affiliation. Co-educational. Established 1836. One of the eight arts colleges within the faculty of arts and science of the University of Toronto. Courses offered leading to the bachelor of arts, bachelor of science, and the bachelor of commerce degrees of the University of Toronto. Residence accommodation is available for out-of-town students.

*Emmanuel College,*Toronto 5, Ontario.
Acting principal: Rev. W.O. Fennel, BA, STM, DD. Acting registrar: Rev. A.G. Reynolds, MA, DD. United Church. Co-educational. Established 1928. Courses offered leading to the title of licentiate in theology and to the degrees of bachelor of divinity, bachelor of religious education, master of theology, and doctor of theology which are awarded by Victoria University. Residence accommodation is available for out-of-town students.

Background

Originally established as the Upper Canada Academy at Cobourg, Ontario, in 1836, degree-conferring powers were granted, under the charter, by the provincial legislature in 1841 and the name of the institution was changed to Victoria College. When the faculties of medicine, law, and theology were added to the original faculty of arts, Victoria College became Victoria University.

In 1892, having entered into federation with the University of Toronto, Victoria moved to Toronto and agreed to hold in abeyance its power to grant degrees except in theology; arts students at Victoria receive their degrees from the University of Toronto.

In 1928, by act of the legislature of the province, Victoria University received an amended charter by which it continues in federation with the University of Toronto and in connection with the United Church of Canada.

The two colleges, Victoria College in arts and Emmanuel College in theology (formed by the union of the Victoria University faculty of theology with Union Theological College), are under the control of one board of regents and one senate.

Facilities and services

The university is situated on a 15-acre site in the north-east corner of Queen's Park. There are three classroom buildings, a library (156,892 volumes), staff houses, a gymnasium, students' union and cafeteria, and students residences accommodating 258 men and 268 women.

Courses and degrees

Arts
(Victoria College, faculty of arts and science, University of Toronto)

Bachelor of arts (BA).
As offered by the University of Toronto; see separate entry.

Business, see commerce below

Commerce
(Victoria College, faculty of arts and science, University of Toronto)

Bachelor of commerce (BCom).
As offered by the University of Toronto; see separate entry.

Science
(Victoria College, faculty of arts and science, University of Toronto)

Bachelor of science (BSc).
As offered by the University of Toronto; see separate entry.

Theology
(Emmanuel College)

Licentiate in theology (LTh).
One year arts plus three years' theology.

Master of religious education (MRE).
Two years from BA.

Master of divinity (MDiv).
Three years from BA.

Master of theology (ThM).
One year from BD.

Doctor of theology (ThD).
Two years from BD.

Admission requirements

For a general statement regarding admission to university study, see article *Admission to university in Canada.*

For information regarding admission to undergraduate study, consult *Requirements for admission to Canadian colleges and universities* available from Service for Admission to College and University, 151 Slater St., Ottawa, Ont., K1P 5N1, $1.50 prepaid.

For admission to MDiv course at Emmanuel College, a student must have obtained a first degree from a recognized university.

Academic year

Mid-September to early May.

Grading system

See the University of Toronto.

Fees and costs

Tuition fees — as outlined by the University of Toronto. Room and board, $122-$127 a month.

Emmanuel College: tuition fees, full-time, $450; incidental fees, $102; degree fees, $35.

Candidates for the ministry of the United Church of Canada pay no tuition fees.

Residence rates, room and board, $123-$127 a month.

Department heads

Classics
G.L. Keyes, MA, PhD

English
F.J.D. Hoeniger, MA, PhD

French
A.R. Harden, MA, PhD

German
G.W. Field, ED, MA, PhD

Near eastern studies
Rev. E.G. Clarke, MA, BD, DLitt

Philosophy
J.A. Graff, AM, PhD

Religious studies
Rev. D.V. Wade, MA, PhD

University of Waterloo*

Waterloo, Ontario

Telephone: 519-885-1211
Direct general correspondence to the registrar

Total full-time student enrolment 11,716; see also separate section *Statistics on Canadian universities and colleges*

Executive and administrative officers

Chancellor
I.G. Needles, AB, LLD

Chairman of the board of governors
C.A. Pollock, BASc, BS

President emeritus
J.G. Hagey, BA, LLD

President and vice-chancellor
B.C. Matthews, BSA, AM, PhD

Academic vice-president
H.E. Petch, BSc, MSc, PhD, FRSC

Vice-president, finance and operations
A.B. Gellatly, BA, CGA

Registrar
C.T. Boyes, BA

President, St. Jerome's College
J.R. Finn, CR, MA, PhD

Academic dean, St. Jerome's College
J.A. Wahl, CR, BA, MA, PhD

President, Conrad Grebel College
J.W. Fretz, BA, MA, BD, PhD

Principal, St. Paul's College
A.M. McLachlin, MA, BD, ThD

Principal, Renison College
D.G.S. M'Timkulu (acting), MA, MA, PhD

Dean of women
H. Marsden (Mrs), BA, MA

Director, audio-visual centre
G. Downie

Director, academic services
D.P. Robertson, BComm

Comptroller
A.H. Headlam, CA

Director, Centre for continuing studies in marketing
D.V. Deverall, BA

Director, department of career planning and placement
A.S. Barber, BIE, PEng

Director, department of co-ordination
R.J. Weiser, BEng, PEng

Director, counselling services
W.W. Dick, BA, BD, MA, PhD

Medical director, health services
D.E. Andrew, BA, MD, CRCP(C)

Director, information services
J.D. Adams, BA

University librarian
W.J. Watson, BA, MA, BLS

Warden (village 1, village 2), Minota Hagey residences
H.R.N. Eydt, MSc, PhD

Director of housing and residence operations
H.C. Vinnicombe, BSc(Eng)

Director, university extension
A.A. Beveridge, BA, MSc

Associate registrar (admissions)
B.A. Lumsden, BA

Associate registrar (records and scheduling)
To be appointed

Associate registrar (graduate studies)
B. Ingram, BA

*Ordinary member, AUCC.

Background

The University of Waterloo is incorporated as a non-denominational institution of higher learning offering courses, both at the undergraduate and the graduate levels in: architecture, arts, engineering, environmental studies, mathematics, optometry, physical education and recreation, and science. Classes commenced in July 1957, with the introduction of the co-operative engineering program.

In March 1959, a private bill was approved by the legislative assembly of the province of Ontario incorporating the University of Waterloo as a degree-granting institution. The university is a member of the Association of Universities and Colleges of Canada and of the Association of Commonwealth Universities.

Under the terms of the University of Waterloo Act (1959), the university is governed by a board of governors and the senate. The board of governors has jurisdiction over the business affairs of the university. The senate is responsible for academic policy.

Facilities and services

The picturesque 1,000-acre campus is located in the city of Waterloo, in the hub of mid-western Ontario. Waterloo, together with its twin city Kitchener, has a combined population of approximately 140,661 and is a thriving industrial centre.

There are 25 buildings on the University of Waterloo campus including engineering buildings, science buildings, a mathematics and computer building, a physical education centre, humanities and social science buildings, an arts lecture hall, an arts library building, two theatres, a student campus centre, a health services building, sports and food services facilities, a book-store, and a faculty club. Additions to the engineering buildings and the science buildings are now under construction, as well as a new student services building, an administration building, and a psychology building. Residence accommodation for both men and women is provided on campus by the four church colleges associated with the university, the two non-denominational university residence villages, and the Minota Hagey residence for graduate women. Residence accommodation for married students became available in the fall of 1970.

The university computing centre has six computers, an IBM system 360/75, an IBM system 360/44, an IBM 1710, and three 1620's. Interfaced with the IBM 360/75 are two IBM 360/20's and a PDP 9 both belonging to the faculty of engineering. The PDP 9 functions separately most of the time. As well, there is an IBM 360/50 belonging to the faculty of mathematics.

The two centres for library service and study on campus, the Dana Porter arts library and the engineering and science library, provide immediate accommodation for more than 440,000 volumes of books and periodicals, with a growing collection of pamphlets, phonorecords, microfilms, and microcards.

Calendars and brochures

The University of Waterloo publications include: the University of Waterloo academic calendar; the admissions brochure; the extramural brochure (degree courses available to part-time students); summer session calendar; post degree brochure; correspondence program brochure; department of university extension brochure.

In addition the various faculties, departments, and church colleges provide several brochures and pamphlets.

Courses and degrees

Architecture
(School of architecture – division of environmental studies)

Bachelor of environmental studies (BES).

Bachelor of architecture (BArch).
Available in pre-professional program in architecture (three years' co-operative work/study program – BES). Professional

architecture (two years following completion of the BES pre-professional program in architecture. Co-operative program — see "Special programs" section).

Arts
(Faculty of arts)

Bachelor of arts (BA).
(a) General program — three years. (b) Honors program — four years. Programs are available in: anthropology, applied social sciences (Renison College only), art, Canadian studies, economics, English, English (drama), fine arts, French, geography, German, history, Latin, Latin and Greek, medieval studies, philosophy, political science, psychology, religious studies, Russian, sociology, and Spanish.

Various combinations of the above programs are also available.

Engineering
(Faculty of engineering)

Bachelor of applied sciences (BASc).
Honors program — four and two-thirds years. Co-operative system of study only (see "Special programs" section). Programs are available in: chemical, civil, electrical, mechanical engineering, and systems design.

Environmental studies
(Division of environmental studies)

Bachelor of environmental studies (BES).
Programs are available in: geography (major in geography — three years, honors geography — four years); man-environment studies (honors program — four years).

(Graduate studies)

Master of arts (MA).
Program is available in: economics, English, French, geography, German, history, philosophy, political science, psychology, regional planning and resource development, Russian, and sociology.

Master of applied science(MASc).
Program is available in: applied psychology (co-operative — see "Special programs" section), chemical, civil, electrical, and mechanical engineering, management science, and systems design.

Master of mathematics (MMath).
Program available in applied analysis and computer science, applied mathematics, combinatorics and optimization, pure mathematics, and statistics.

Master of science (MSc).
Program is available in: biology, chemistry, earth sciences, and physics. The minimum period of registration for the master's degree is one academic year from an honors bachelor's degree or equivalent, except in certain clearly identified two-year master's programs.

Master of philosophy (MPhil).
Program is available in: English, German, history, mathematics, and philosophy. The MPhil is a scholarly degree intermediate between the MA and the PhD. Candidates are normally admitted to the MPhil program after having completed an honors bachelor's degree. The minimum requirements for the MPhil are satisfied when the candidate has: 1) successfully completed six two-term courses (or twelve-term courses); 2) presented and defended a thesis embodying the results of his study on an approved topic.

Doctor of philosophy (PhD).
Program is available in: biology, chemical engineering, chemistry, civil engineering, electrical engineering, geography, German, management science, mathematics, mechanical engineering, philosophy, physics, psychology, regional planning and resource development, Russian, sociology, and systems design.
The minimum period of registration for the PhD is two years from the completion of a master's degree, or three years from the completion of the honors bachelor's degree.

Integrated studies
(Program of integrated studies)

Bachelor of independent studies (BIS).
Integrated studies is a new unstructured
program wherein the curriculum is developed
by both students and faculty. Students are
not required to enrol in regular classes or
write regular examinations but will engage in
individual studies under the direction of a
qualified faculty member. After two years of
study a student may petition for a degree.
The integrated studies program seeks to
attract students highly motivated in the
direction of self-education. There are no pre-
determined admission criteria. Students are
considered on the basis of a personal
interview and, possibly, a written essay.

Mathematics
(Faculty of mathematics)

Bachelor of mathematics (BMath).
(a) Pass degree program — three years; (b)
general program — four years; (c) honors
program — four years. Programs are
available in: actuarial science, applied
analysis and computer science, applied
mathematics, combinatorics and
optimization, mathematics and economics,
mathematics and philosophy, pure
mathematics, statistics, statistics and
psychology, and teaching.

Honors co-operative program,
four and two-thirds years — see "Special
programs" section. Co-operative program is
available with specialization in the following
areas: actuarial science, business
administration, chartered accounting,
computer science, optimization, statistics, and
teaching.

Optometry
(School of optometry — faculty of science)

Doctor of optometry (OD).
Honors program — five years. The first year is
a pre-optometrical year preparatory to four
years of the professional optometrical
program. The courses are designed to qualify
men and women for the practice of
optometry and also to provide the student
with sufficient general and specialized
knowledge in science to enable him to follow
a career in research or teaching.

Physical education and recreation
(School of physical education and recreation)

*Bachelor of science (kinesiology)
[BSc(kinesiology)].
Bachelor of arts (recreation) [BA(recreation)].*
Program is available in kinesiology and
recreation and may be studied under either
the regular or the co-operative system of
study.

Science
(Faculty of science)

Bachelor of science (BSc).
(a) General program — three years and four
years; (b) honors program — four years.
Programs are available in: biology, biology
and chemistry, chemistry, chemistry
(mathematics or physics option), earth
sciences, and physics.

Honors co-operative program,
four and two-thirds year — see "Special
programs" section. Co-operative program is
available in: applied chemistry, and applied
physics.

Urban and regional planning
(School of urban and regional planning —
division of environmental studies)

Bachelor of environmental studies (BES).
Program available in: honors urban and
regional planning, four years.

Special programs

The co-operative plan

The co-operative program at the University
of Waterloo consists of eight four-month
academic terms and six four-month work
terms in industry, business, and education.
Students enroled in the co-operative program

must perform satisfactorily during their co-operative work assignments as well as during their academic terms at the university.

Co-operative education is based on the principle that during the undergraduate years an academic program combined with integrated work experience in alternating terms, is relevant to, and desirable for, effective professional preparation. The work terms allow the student to acquire experience in the area of his career interest, while the academic terms are devoted to fundamental and theoretical studies.

Various programs in several faculties may be studied under the co-operative plan. See the "Courses and degrees" section for further information.

Inter-faculty program board

The inter-faculty program board originates and sponsors multi-disciplinary courses open as electives to properly qualified students within the university. These courses, some of which will be concerned with crucial problems confronting today's world and approaches to their solutions, are intended specifically for students enroled in existing programs. The board is prepared to sponsor certain non-specialist courses that faculties may request for students in their programs, leading to bachelor's degrees. From time to time the board sponsors guest lecturers, special speakers, and colloquia.

Program of integrated studies, see integrated studies under section "Courses and degrees".

Extension programs

For university credit:

Extramural courses

The majority of undergraduate courses available in the evening during the fall and winter are offered through the faculty of arts. These courses are available to full-time students as well as to part-time students.

At the present time the university does not have a formal program of studies for extramural students that would guarantee a certain sequence of courses leading to a

degree in a specified period of time. However, present and future offerings are planned so as to enable students to complete the requirements of the general BA program in any of the ten departments within the faculty of arts.

Students wishing to pursue a degree program on a part-time basis in one of the other faculties should contact the registrar or the appropriate faculty for further information.

Summer session

The summer session program has been planned to meet the different needs of various kinds of students. These include: 1) current university students, either full- or part-time, who wish to take one or two courses; 2) entering students, from grade 13 or elsewhere, who wish to begin their university studies in the summer with the intention of completing their degree requirements more quickly than usual or to facilitate their adjustment to university; 3) post-degree program students who require honors courses to meet the academic requirements for specialist standing of secondary school teachers; 4) other students who may not be interested in a degree, but who wish to take university level courses. The summer session has been planned to enable students to complete the general BA requirements on a part-time basis.

For no university credit:

The department of university extension offers courses in continuing education that are designed for both personal and professional development. Areas of study include industrial accounting, business, management and supervision, sales and marketing, engineering, education, liberal arts and humanities, languages, the social sciences, and community issues. As well, the International Film Society offers a program consisting of 10 selected foreign and domestic films.

Certificate programs

offered by the department of university extension include courses in: supervision/ management studies, the Canadian Industrial Management Association's four-year

certificate program, the Society of Industrial Accountant's five-year diploma program, and the appraisal of real estate three-year program.

Marketing courses

The Centre for continuing studies in marketing offers marketing and management courses and seminars in the field of continuing education for upper or middle management people at all levels of line and staff responsibility. Courses and seminars include such topics as: field sales management, advertising management, marketing research, product management, and generalized management and labor relations. Special workshops are held in human relations, communications, motivation, managing management time, and leadership.

Admission requirements

For a general statement regarding admission to university study, see article *Admission to university in Canada.*

For information regarding admission to undergraduate study, consult *Requirements for admission to Canadian colleges and universities* available from Service for Admission to College and University, 151 Slater St., Ottawa, Ont., K1P 5N1, $1.50 prepaid.

Students applying for admission to graduate studies should possess an honors bachelor's degree or equivalent from an approved university or college with such standing that they will be acceptable to a faculty graduate committee to study for a higher degree.

Academic year

The University of Waterloo offers programs on the regular and on the co-operative system of study. The regular system follows the conventional eight-month academic year from September until late in April and the student then has a summer vacation. Students in the co-operative system alternate four-month academic terms at the university with four-month work terms in business, industry, or education.

Some faculties at the university offer programs only on the regular system, others only on the co-operative system, and still others offer programs on both the regular and the co-operative systems.

Grading system

The university has a common grading system for all faculties.

Under this system grades for all courses appear on grade reports and transcripts either as one of 15 letter grades from A plus through F minus, or as numeric marks on a 100-point scale. Each faculty (or comparable academic unit) chooses one or the other; all departments within the faculty are then bound by this selection.

The following provides details of grading scales, interpretation of averages, symbols, etc.

Letter grades	Percentage ranges	Weighting factors
A+	90-100	95
A	85-89	89
A-	80-84	83
B+	77-79	78
B	73-76	75
B-	70-72	72
C+	67-69	68
C	63-66	65
C-	60-62	62
D+	57-59	58
D	53-56	55
D-	50-52	52
F	42-49	46
F	35-41	38
F	0-41	32

Interpretation of averages:
80-100%, first-class honors, excellent. 70-79.99%, second-class honors, very good. 60-69.99%, third-class honors, good. 50-59.99%, passing. 0-49%, failure.

Fees and costs

Note: (r) designates regular system of study per year; (co-op), co-operative program per four-month academic term.

Tuition and incidental fees, full-time students.

Arts (r) $571.80. Engineering (co-op) $363.70 per term. Environmental studies (r) $571.80, (co-op) $363.70 per term. Graduate studies $565.00. Integrated studies (r) $571.80. Mathematics (r) $571.80, (co-op) $346.20 per term. Physical education and recreation (r) $571.80, (co-op) $346.20 per term. Science (r) $571.80, (co-op) $346.20 per term.

Residence fees range from approximately $900 to $1,100 depending upon the type of accommodation.

Financial awards and assistance

The University of Waterloo administers the Canada student loans plan and the Ontario student awards program and has a limited number of scholarships and several bursaries. Small loans on a short-term basis are also available for emergency situations.

Research institutes and administrative research

The Office of research administration is responsible for the administration of research, grants, and contracts for the University of Waterloo. The office acts as a centre of communication between granting agencies and members of the university staff. It also administers the university's patent assistance program.

The Waterloo Research Institute, established in 1967, provides a working liaison between the university and all organizations in which contracted research and development offer potential assistance. The WRI stimulates, arranges, and manages the execution of research and development programs sponsored by industry and other organizations. The institute draws upon the resources of all faculties of the university to achieve this purpose.

The Office of Human Research, established in 1971, reviews university research programs involving human subjects, as to ethical acceptability, legal liability, and medical advisability. As the official liaison office between the university and local public and separate school boards, the OHR is responsible for obtaining school-age children for suitable university research programs.

The Planning and Resources Institute, established in 1966, fosters and supports research that will further the understanding of human settlement and its relationship to the natural environment, and contribute to sensitive planning and development, at any level, of regions of settlement. The institute also acts as a bridge between interested elements of the university community and outside agencies concerned with resource use and administration and with the planning, design, servicing and development of man-oriented regions. This bridging may take the form of seminars, conferences, short courses, or publications.

Federated college

St. Jerome's College, a church-related, liberal arts college, entered into federation with the University of Waterloo in July, 1960. St. Jerome's College offers courses in conjunction with the university leading to the BA degree and the BMath degree. In September of 1962 the college opened three new buildings on the university campus; a teaching and administration building, a men's residence with accommodation for 100 students, and a women's residence with accommodation for 55 students under the supervision of the School Sisters of Notre Dame.

Affiliated colleges

Renison College is an Anglican arts college that was founded in 1959 and has been affiliated with the university since 1960. In conjunction with the

university, Renison offers courses in international studies, social work, and general arts leading to a BA degree. The college has residence accommodation for 100 men and 80 women. Co-educational.

St. Paul's College
is a residential and teaching affiliate of the university sponsored by the United Church. The college offers elective courses in religious studies for academic credit towards degrees in arts, mathematics, and science. The residence provides accommodation in 75 semi-private rooms for 100 men and 50 women.

Conrad Grebel College
is a Mennonite church-supported college that affiliated with the university in 1961. Courses are offered in music, religious studies, and sociology. Residence accommodation is available for 66 men and 40 women.

Deans of faculties

Arts
P.G. Cornell, ED, MA, PhD

Engineering
A.N. Sherbourne, BSc, MS, MA, PhD

Environmental studies
P.H. Nash, PhD

Graduate studies
G.E. Cross, MA, PhD

Mathematics
D.A. Sprott, MA, PhD

Physical education and recreation
G.S. Kenyon, BPE, MS, PhD

Science
W.B. Pearson, MA, DSc, DFC, FRSC, FCIC

Directors of schools

Architecture
P.H. Nash (acting), BA, MA, CE, MCP, MPA, PhD, AIP

Optometry
E.J. Fisher, BA, MA, DSc

Urban and regional planning
L.O. Gertler, BA, MA, MTPIC

Department heads

Applied analysis and computer science
D.D. Cowan, BASc, PhD

Applied mathematics
D.G. Wertheim, BA, PhD

Biology
P.S. Corbet, BSc, PhD, DSc

Chemical engineering
K.F. O'Driscoll, BChE, MS, PhD

Chemistry
W.A.E. McBryde, MA, PhD, FCIC

Civil engineering
W.A. McLaughlin, BEng, MS, PhD

Classics and romance languages
R.L. Myers, BA, MA, PhD

Combinatorics and optimization
G. Berman, MA, PhD

Earth sciences
R.N. Farvolden, BSc, MSc, PhD

Economics
S. Weintraub, PhD

Electrical engineering
P.R. Bryant, MSc, MA, PhD

English
J. Gold, BA, PhD

Fine arts
N.L. Patterson (Mrs), (acting), BA

Geography
R.M. Irving, BA, MA, PhD

Germanic and Slavic languages
J.W. Dyck, AB, MA, PhD

History
J.F.H. New, MA, PhD

Kinesiology
N.J. Ashton, BSc, MS

Management sciences
D.J. Clough, BASc, MBA

Mechanical engineering
E. Brundrett, BSA, BASc, MASc, PhD

Philosophy
B.H. Suits, BA, MA, PhD

Physics
J.W. Leech, BSc, PhD, FInstP

Political science
T.H. Qualter, BA, PhD

Psychology
J.A. Dyal, BA, PhD

Pure mathematics
W. Benz, PhD

Recreation
C.A. Griffith, BA, MS, ReD

Religious studies
J.R. Horne (acting), MA, BTh, PhD

Sociology and anthropology
G.L. De Gre, BSS, MA, PhD

Statistics
D.A. Sprott, PhD

Systems design
H.K. Kesavan, BSc, BE, MS, PhD

Waterloo Lutheran University*

Waterloo, Ontario

Telephone: 519-744-8141
Direct general correspondence to the registrar

Total full-time student enrolment 2,826; see also separate section *Statistics on Canadian universities and colleges*

Executive and administrative officers

Chancellor
Honorable W.R. MacDonald, PC, LLD

Pro chancellor
To be appointed

President and vice-chancellor
F.C. Peters, BA, BD, MSc, PhD, ThD

Vice-president (academic)
P.B. Healey, MBA, MA, PhD

Vice-president (controller)
Tamara Giesbrecht (Miss)

Registrar
H.H. Dueck, BSc, MA

Librarian and archivist
Rev. Erich Schultz, BA, BD, MTh, BLS

Director of alumni relations and university resources
H.C. Mecredy, CD, BA

Director of educational services
Colin McKay, BA

Director, summer session and extension
J.M. Clark, CD, MA

Director of personnel and business manager
C.G. Bilyea, BA, MBA

Dean of students
F.L. Nichols, BA, MA

Associate registrar (records)
H.E. Forler (Miss), BA

Assistant registrar (admissions)
K.A. Rae, BA

Dean of women
E.J. Brandon (Miss), MA

Director of information
R.K. Tayler, BA

Background

On July 11, 1910, as a result of a mutual agreement between the Canada synod and the synod of central Canada, a board of management was organized to establish a Lutheran theological seminary in Canada. The town of Waterloo was selected as the location and the Evangelical Lutheran Seminary of Canada was formally opened on October 30, 1911, and incorporated under the laws of the province of Ontario in 1913.

Facilities for pre-theological education were established in 1914. For 15 years, courses leading to senior matriculation were given in the Waterloo College School. In 1923 the school offered a one-year arts course beyond senior matriculation. In 1924 this venture was expanded into the third of Waterloo's education units, the Waterloo College of Arts, offering a four-year arts course. Emphasis having been shifted to higher education, the preparatory courses of the college school were reduced and finally abandoned in 1929.

In 1925 the faculty of arts under the name of Waterloo College became affiliated to The University of Western Ontario. Five years later Waterloo College was granted the right to offer courses leading to the BA honors degree.

With the purpose of expanding the program of higher education at Waterloo, particularly in science, a non-denominational board of governors was organized and in June 1956 this board established the associate faculties offering courses in science and engineering. In this way science facilities were developed

* Ordinary member, AUCC.

with the assistance of provincial grants not available to denominationally controlled universities in Ontario. The associate faculties pioneered the first co-operative engineering program in Canada and continued its development with Waterloo College until 1959 when it severed its connection and received a provincial charter, becoming the University of Waterloo.

Also in 1959, the Evangelical Lutheran Seminary of Canada applied for a revision of its charter changing the corporate title to Waterloo Lutheran University and giving the institution university powers and degree-granting rights. By mutual agreement, the affiliation of Waterloo College to The University of Western Ontario was terminated when the new charter became effective on July 1, 1960. There are five distinctive units controlled by the university: (i) Waterloo University College, the faculty of arts and science, for men and women of all faiths; (ii) school of business and economics; (iii) Waterloo Lutheran Seminary which educates men for the ministry; (iv) the graduate school of social work; (v) graduate council in arts. In August 1961, the Mennonite Brethren College of Arts in Winnipeg, Manitoba, affiliated to the university and provided two years of the BA (general) program. This affiliation was terminated June 30, 1971.

The board of governors is responsible for all university matters but has delegated academic responsibilities to the senate. The senate reports to the board of governors.

Facilities and services

In addition to college and seminary teaching buildings, there is a library, (225,000 items, which include 125,000 volumes, 40,000 government documents, 45,000 microfilms and other library materials), a theatre auditorium, a dining hall, a new student union building and 11 residence units (accommodating 225 women and 475 men) on campus. A new teaching building was completed in September 1969. A new physical education complex is presently under construction.

Student services include a housing registry for off-campus accommodation, a part-time and full-time job placement service for undergraduates and graduates, counselling, and health service.

Calendars and brochures

The university prepares the following publications annually, which may be obtained from the offices listed below:
Office of the registrar:
university calendar; admissions bulletin and brochures; intersession and summer session calendar; extension session calendar; introducing W.L.U.
Director of graduate studies:
graduate studies calendar.

Courses and degrees

Arts
(Faculty of arts and science)

Bachelor of arts (BA).
(a) General program, three years from senior matriculation. Available in anthropology, classics, economics, English, French, geography, German, Greek, history, Latin, mathematics, near eastern studies, philosophy, political science, psychology, religious studies, romance languages, Russian, sociology, Spanish, and combinations of these. (b) Honors program, four years from senior matriculation. Available in classics, English language and literature, English and French, English and German, English and Greek, English and history, English and Latin, English and philosophy, English and Spanish, French and Latin, French and Spanish or German (modern languages and literatures), geography, history, history and philosophy, history and political science, philosophy and Greek, Latin, Latin and Greek, philosophy, philosophy and French, philosophy and German, philosophy and Latin, philosophy and psychology, philosophy and sociology, political science, psychology, psychology and sociology, religion and culture (Asian studies, pretheology, near eastern studies).

(Council of graduate studies)

Master of arts (MA).
At least two years from ordinary BA or at least one year from honors BA. Offered in history, geography, political science, psychology, religion and culture and romance languages.

Business and economics
(School of business and economics)

Bachelor of arts (BA).
Honors program, four years from senior matriculation. Available in business administration and economics.

Divinity
(Waterloo Lutheran Seminary)

Master of divinity (MDiv).
Three years from an undergraduate degree.

Music
(Faculty of arts and science)

Bachelor of music (BMus).
General program, three years from senior matriculation. Available in general music and church music options.

Science
(Faculty of arts and science)

Bachelor of science (BSc).
General program, three years from senior matriculation. Available in biology, chemistry, mathematics, physical geography and physics.

Social work
(Graduate school of social work)

Master of social work (MSW).
Two years from an undergraduate degree. The program is based on a combination of on-campus and field practice terms.

Combined courses

Combined courses in social work and theology are also available.

Extension programs

For university credit:

Extension and evening credit programs.
Undergraduate courses are offered on Saturdays in Waterloo, Brampton and Orillia leading to the general BA degree. Courses are available in the humanities, social sciences and business administration.

Evening credit courses are also offered by the school of business and economics on the Waterloo campus.

Summer session.
Courses are offered for undergraduates proceeding to a BA degree and for teachers who may wish to improve their professional qualifications towards graduate degrees. Subjects offered are chiefly arts, science and business administration. Special courses are also taught in England and Palestine.

Admission requirements

For a general statement regarding admission to university study, see article *Admission to university in Canada.*

For information regarding admission to undergraduate study, consult *Requirements for admission to Canadian colleges and universities* available from Service for Admission to College and University, 151 Slater St., Ottawa, Ont., K1P 5N1, $1.50 prepaid.

Graduate studies.
Admission requirements for social work are a BA degree or an equivalent accepted degree.

For admission to graduate study a student must have obtained a first degree with specified grades in appropriate studies. Apply to the director of graduate studies for details.

Academic year

Winter session: early September to end of April.

Summer session: part I, early May to end of June; part II, early July to mid-August.

Grading system

Grade A+ − 12 points; A − 11; A- − 10;
B+ − 9; B − 8; B- − 7; C+ − 6; C − 5; C-
− 4; D+ − 3; D − 2; D- − 1; F − 0.

Fees and costs

Tuition fees per year; full-time: (a)
undergraduate − arts, business
administration, economics, science, $520. (b)
Graduate − arts, $485; social work, $740;
theology, $150. Miscellaneous compulsory
fees per year: undergraduate, $69.50,
graduate, $25.

Residence rates, board and room $1,000 per
academic year based on a 7-day meal ticket.

Financial awards and assistance

Matriculation scholarships:

Centennial scholarships valued at $1,500
annually for senior matriculation students
who achieve a minimum of 90%.

Faculty board scholarships valued at $400
annually for senior matriculation students
who achieve a minimum of 80%.

Proficiency scholarships valued at $250
annually for senior matriculation students
who achieve a minimum of 75%.

W.L.U. student-aid bursaries ranging in
value from $50 to $100 are available to
students who attain a minimum of 60% and
are in financial need.

Ontario student awards program. Awards
under this program will be made available to
all full-time students who demonstrate need
of financial assistance. Financial aid involves
both loans and grants.

Deans of faculties

Arts, and graduate studies in arts
N.H. Tayler, BA, MA, PhD

Business and economics
J.R. Jenkins, BA, MBA, PhD

Divinity
D.J. Glebe, BA, MA, BD, ThD

Graduate studies
N.E. Wagner, BA, BD, MA, PhD

Social work
F.J. Turner, BA, MSW, DSW

Department heads

Biology
D.A. MacLulich, BScF, PhD

Business administration
D.J. Dengler, BA, MBA

Chemistry
R.A. Heller, BSc, PhD

Classics
H.A. MacLean, BA, MA, PhD

Economics
J.A. Weir, BCom, MBA, PhD

English
F. Roy, BA, MA, PhD

Geography, geology and planning
J.H. McMurry, BS, MPA, PhD

German
H. Cheyne, BA, MA, PhD

History
W.H. Heick, BA, MA, PhD

International business program
B. Bonner, PhB, PhD

Mathematics
H.B. Secord, BSc, MSc

Music
W.H. Kemp, MusBac, MusM, AM, FRCCO,
ARCT

Philosophy
J.F. Little, BA, BD, ThM, MA, PhD

Physics
H. Bezner, BA, BSc, PhD

Political science
T. Miljan, BA, MA

Psychology
V.H. Schaefer, BA, PhD

Religion and culture
R.W. Fisher, AB, BD, PhD

Romance languages
T. Scully, BA, MA, PhD

Sociology and anthropology
T.R. Maxwell, BA, MTh, MA

The University of Western Ontario*

London 72, Ontario

Telephone: 519-679-2311
Direct general correspondence to the registrar

Total full-time student enrolment 12,219; see also separate section *Statistics on Canadian universities and colleges*

Executive and administrative officers

President and vice-chancellor
D.C. Williams, BA, MA, PhD, LLD

Chairman of the board of governors
Capt. J. Jeffery, OBE, QC

Chancellor
A.W. Trueman, BA, MA, DLitt, LLD, FRSC

Vice-president (academic) and provost
R.J. Rossiter, BSc, DM, MA, DPhil, BMBCh, FRIC, FCIC, FRSc

Vice-president (health sciences)
O.H. Warwick, MA, MD, CM, MRCP, FRCP(C), FACP, LLD

Vice-president (administration and finance)
A.K. Adlington, BA

Executive assistant to the president
R.N. Shervill, BA, MA, PhD

Assistant to the vice-president (academic)
W.S. Turner, BA, LLD

*Ordinary member, AUCC.

Secretary of the board of governors
C.F. Way, BA

Registrar and secretary of the senate
J.K. Watson, MA, PhD

Deputy registrar
W.G. Nediger, BA

Chief librarian
R.E. Lee, BA, BSLS, MFA, PhD

Comptroller
R.R. Glover, BA

Associate registrar
Margaret May (Miss), BA

Assistant registrar
D.G. Henderson, BA

Registrar, Althouse College
G.L. Hartsell, BA

Secondary school liaison officer
W.A. Barill, BA

Assistant to the secretary of senate
A.G.R. Sweeny, BA, PhD

Director, summer school and extension
Angela Armitt (Miss), BA, MA

Director, French/English summer school at Trois-Pistoles
Gilles Gagnon, BA, LèsL, MA, CREDIF

Dean of men
T.L. Hoskin, MA

Dean of women
Leola Neal, MA, PhD

Director, alumni affairs, information services, and university publications
Campbell McDonald, BA

Director, athletics
J.P. Metras

Director, computing centre
G.T. Lake, BSc

Director, health services
R.J. Bowen, BA, MD

Director, information analysis and systems
B.G. Hartwick, BComm

Director, office of international education
D.G. Simpson, MA, PhD

Director, physical plant
R.M. Yeo, BSc, PEng

Director, space analysis and planning
H.J. Schulz, DiplIng(Arch), MRAIC

Director, student financial aid
E.J. McLeod, BA

Director, student placement and off-campus
housing services
D.W. Klinger, BA, MA

Executive director, university community
centre
Philip Ranke, MA

Foreign student advisor
R.W. McGraw, BA

Assistant director, libraries/library operations
J.F. Macpherson, BA, MA

Assistant director of libraries/technical
services
R.E. Stierwalt, BA, MLS

Assistant director of libraries/public services
Donna Berg, BA, BLS

Residences and housing business manager
R.A. Virtue, psc

Warden of men's residences
W.C. Henry, PhD

Warden of women's residences
To be appointed

Manager, married students' apartments
E.M. Laing

Manager, bookstore
D. Mason

Constituent college

Althouse College of Education,
1137 Western Road, London, Ontario.
Dean: E. Stabler, BA, MA, PhD. Registrar:
G.L. Hartsell. Established in 1965. Co-
educational, non-denominational. Offers a
program of studies of at least one year from a
bachelor's degree; leading to high school
teachers certificates granted by the minister
of education of Ontario.

Background

"The Western University of London,
Ontario" received its charter from the
legislature of the province of Ontario in 1878.
Teaching began in 1881 and the first classes
graduated in arts and in medicine in 1883. In
1923 by act of the provincial legislature, the
name of the university was changed to The
University of Western Ontario.

Western is composed of the faculties of arts,
dentistry, engineering science, graduate
studies, law, medicine, music, nursing science,
social science; the schools of business
administration, library and information
science; Althouse College of Education; and
the following arts colleges affiliated with the
university: Huron College (see separate
entry), Brescia College (see separate entry),
and King's College (see separate entry).

Present authority is given by the university
act of 1878 as amended in 1967. The
university's government is under provincial
and municipal control. Western has been co-
educational from the start and non-
denominational since 1908, except in some of
its affiliated colleges.

The university act provides for a board of
governors, responsible for the business
management of the university, and a senate
responsible for academic policy.

Facilities and services

In 1968 Western became 90 years old.
Officially known as "The University of
Western Ontario", the move to the present
500-acre campus along the River Thames in
North London was made in 1924.

Today there are more than 45 buildings,
including a health sciences centre,
observatories, a wind tunnel, and a bio-
engineering building. The health sciences
centre, when the university hospital is
completed, will have 22 acres of floor space
devoted to study and research in the health
sciences. An observatory with a 48-inch
reflector telescope is located some 15 miles
north of the campus. Other special facilities
include faculties and school for business
administration, law, engineering, music,
library and information science, and a college
of education.

A co-educational, non-denominational institution, Western has three affiliated denominational colleges (each has its own campus close to the North London campus): Brescia College for women (Roman Catholic); Huron College (Anglican) and King's College (Roman Catholic) are both co-educational.

Special research facilites in: cancer research laboratory; agricultural research institute; centre for radio science; photochemistry laboratory; wind tunnel; university observatories; computing centre. Current research papers are listed in the annual *Report of the president.*

The general library is housed in the Lawson memorial building. Libraries and reading rooms are also located in the Josephine Spencer Niblett faculty of law building, Alexander Charles Spencer faculty of engineering building, medical sciences building, Kresge school of nursing building, natural sciences centre, University College, Middlesex College, Talbot College, Richard Ivey school of business administration building, A.E. Silverwood faculty of music building, Althouse College of Education and the school of library and information science. The affiliated colleges (Huron College, Brescia College and King's College) each provide good undergraduate libraries with collections meant to complement holdings of the other libraries. The book collections of the university total over 600,000 volumes and 400,000 microforms. Currently the university receives annually about 7,500 periodicals in all subjects and in many languages.

Spencer hall has accommodation for 86 students, Delaware hall — 452 students, and Maitland hall — 306 students. Application forms for admission to women's residences may be obtained from the dean of women.

Medway hall, Sydenham hall, and Saugeen hall are Western's three men's residences. Medway hall accommodates 300 students, Sydenham hall — 292 students, and Saugeen hall — 901 students. Application forms and further details may be obtained from the residence admissions office, Saugeen hall.

Married students' apartments include 300 one-bedroom and 100 two-bedroom apartments. For information and application forms write to: the business manager, married students' apartments, The University of Western Ontario, London 72, Ontario.

Brescia College has accommodation for 128 students, Huron College — 200 men and 100 women, King's College — 310 students (men and women). Westminister College is a co-educational residence for students at The University of Western Ontario. It has accommodation for 230 men and women.

Foreign students information bureau. Counselling for foreign students is available through the Foreign students information bureau. A handbook entitled: *Information for prospective students from countries outside Canada* may be requested. Visa information must be obtained from the Department of Manpower and Immigration, Government of Canada, Ottawa, Ont., or from your nearest Canadian embassy or consulate.

The population of London is approximately 216,000.

Calendars and brochures

A composite calendar of the university is available as are individual faculty calendars. Also of interest are the booklets "general information" and "information for prospective students from countries outside Canada".

Courses and degrees

Arts

Bachelor of arts (BA).
(a) General program, three years from senior matriculation. (b) Honors program, four years from senior matriculation in classics, comparative literature, English, fine art, French, German, Latin, linguistics, philosophy, Spanish, Russian, and combinations of these subjects.

Master of arts (MA).
Minimum one year full-time, or two years full-time from general BA; by thesis and examination. Offered in classics, English, French, German, philosophy, and Spanish.

Doctor of philosphy (PhD).
At least two years from MA. Ordinarily available in English, French, German, and philosophy.

Business administration

Bachelor of arts (BA).
Honors business administration with liberal arts options, four years from senior matriculation.

Diploma in business administration (DipBusAdmin).
One year from a bachelor's degree in any field, with grade B standing or better in the final year.

Master of business administration (MBA).
Two years from a bachelor's degree in any field, or one year from an honors bachelor's degree in business administration or commerce, with grade B standing or better in the final year.

Doctor of philosphy (PhD).
At least two years from MBA.

Commerce, see business administration above

Dentistry

Doctor of dental surgery (DDS).
Four years from two years of arts and science beyond senior matriculation.

Engineering, see science, applied

Journalism

Bachelor of arts (BA).
Honors program, four years from senior matriculation.

Diploma in journalism.
One year from a bachelor's degree in another field.

Law

Bachelor of laws (LLB).
Three years following the second year beyond senior matriculation or, preferably, three years from a bachelor's degree.

Library and information science

Master of library science (MLS).
One year beyond honors degree or two years from a general degree.

A PhD program in bibliography and bibliographic control is planned for the academic year 1972-73.

Medicine

Doctor of medicine (MD).
Four years from two years of arts and science beyond senior matriculation or from graduation in arts with science options.

Master of clinical science (MClSc).
Applicants must hold MD degree or equivalent and have completed one year of internship. Available in anaesthesia, obstetrics and gynaecology, paediatrics, surgery, and therapeutic radiology. The course of training is directed by the head of the clinical department in which the candidate is taking his work.

Doctor of philosphy (PhD).
Minimum three years full-time, which may be reduced to two years for applicants possessing master's degree; by thesis and examination; offered in epidemiology and preventive medicine.

Medical rehabilitation

Bachelor of science in medical rehabilitation (BScMR).
Three years from one-year arts and science beyond senior matriculation, four years for occupational therapy. Available in communication disorders, occupational therapy, and physical therapy.

Medical sciences

Bachelor of science (BSc).
Honors program, four years from senior matriculation; in anatomy, bacteriology and immunology, biochemistry, biophysics, and physiology.

Master of science (MSc).
At least one year from MD degree. Available in anatomy, bacteriology and immunology, biochemistry, biophysics, epidemiology and

preventive medicine, pathology, pathological chemistry, pharmacology, and physiology.

Doctor of philosophy (PhD).
Minimum three years full-time, which may be reduced to two years for applicants possessing master's degree; by thesis and examination; offered in anatomy, bacteriology and immunology, biochemistry, biophysics, epidemiology and preventive medicine, pathology, pathological chemistry, pharmacology, and physiology.

Music

Bachelor of arts (BA).
(a) General program, three years from senior matriculation. (b) Honors program, four years from senior matriculation.

Bachelor of musical arts (BMusA).
Three years from senior matriculation.

Bachelor of music (MusB).
Honors program. Four years from senior matriculation in music education, performance, theory and composition, and music history.

Master of arts in musicology (MA), master of music (MusM).
At least one year beyond honors degree studies.

Nursing

Bachelor of science in nursing (BScN).
Four years from senior matriculation. Specialization is offered in nursing service administration, nursing education, or public health nursing.

Master of science in nursing (MScN).
At least two years from a bachelor's degree in nursing.

Science, applied

Bachelor of engineering science (BESc).
Four years beyond senior matriculation. Specialization is possible in the two final years in chemical, civil, electrical, mechanical engineering, and materials science.

Master of engineering science (MESc).
One year beyond BESc or comparable standing. Available in chemical, civil,

electrical, mechanical engineering and materials science.

Master of engineering (MEng).
Minimum one year full-time; by course of instruction offered in environmental engineering.

Doctor of philosophy (PhD).
At least two years from MESc degree. Available in the same areas as the MESc.

Science, pure

Bachelor of arts (BA).
(a) General program, three years from senior matriculation in botany, computer science, mathematics, physics, and zoology. (b) Honors program, four years from senior matriculation in mathematics.

Bachelor of science (BSc).
(a) General program, three years from senior matriculation in: applied mathematics, chemistry, computer science, geophysics, mathematics, and physics. (b) Honors program, four years from senior matriculation in: applied mathematics, astronomy, botany, chemistry, computer science, geography, geology, geophysics, physics, and zoology.

(Faculty of graduate studies)

Master of science (MSc).
At least one year from an honors bachelor's degree in science. Available in applied mathematics, astronomy, chemistry, computer science, geography, geology, geophysics, physics, plant sciences, and zoology.

Doctor of philosophy (PhD).
At least two years from MSc. Available in the same departments as MSc.

Social sciences

Bachelor of arts (BA).
(a) General program, three years from senior matriculation in economics, geography, history, home economics, political science, psychology, secretarial science, and sociology. (b) Honors program, four years from senior matriculation in economics, geography, history, physical and health education, political science, psychology, secretarial science and business administration, sociology, and combinations of these subjects.

Master of arts (MA).
Minimum one year full-time, or two years
full-time from general BA; by thesis and
examination. Offered in economics,
geography, history, physical education,
political science, psychology, and sociology.

Doctor of philosophy (PhD).
At least two years from MA. Ordinarily
available in economics, geography, history,
political science, and psychology.

Social welfare

Bachelor of social welfare (BSW).
A four-year honors program after senior
matriculation (offered at King's College
only).

Theology

Courses in theology offered by the affiliated
colleges.

Special program

Summer school of Indian archaeology
at Penetanguishene, Ontario, under the
direction of the curator of the Museum of
Indian Archaeology of the university.

Extension programs

For university credit:

Correspondence courses.
Courses are offered in a limited number of
arts subjects only.

Evening and weekend classes.
Undergraduate classes in arts only, offered
during the winter session in London and in
ten other centres in western Ontario.

Summer school.
Arts, science, music, and physical education
courses are offered in London and Owen
Sound for undergraduates proceeding to a
degree and for teachers who wish to improve
their academic qualifications.

Evening summer extension classes
offered in London only from mid-May to
mid-August.

For no university credit:

Adult education services.
Non-credit evening classes where and when
there is sufficient demand.

Summer school in French Canada.
Courses are offered at Trois-Pistoles in the
province of Quebec, in English for French-
speaking students, mainly teachers, and in
French for English-speaking students, mainly
university undergraduates. Occasionally the
latter courses are studied for university credit.

Admission requirements

For a general statement regarding admission
to university study, see article *Admission to
university in Canada.*

For information regarding admission to
undergraduate study, consult *Requirements
for admission to Canadian colleges and
universities* available from Service for
Admission to College and University, 151
Slater St., Ottawa, Ont., K1P 5N1, $1.50
prepaid.

For admission to business administration,
dentistry, law, and medicine, at least two
years must have been completed, with
appropriate selection of subjects in arts, arts
and science combined, beyond senior
matriculation.

For admission to graduate study, a student
must have obtained a first degree with
specified grades in appropriate subjects.

Academic year

Winter session: mid-September to mid-May.

Summer session: early July to mid-August.

Faculty of graduate studies: fall term (mid-
September); winter term (mid-January);
summer term (mid-May).

Grading system

MBA: 4, distinction; 3, high pass; 2, pass; 1, low pass; 0, unsatisfactory. In law, grade A: 75-100%; B: 67-74%; C: 60-66%; D: 50-59%; F: below 50%. In all other programs, grade A: 80-100%; B: 70-79%; C: 60-69%; D: 50-59%; F: below 50%.

Fees and costs

Tuition and incidental fees per year: full-time (a) undergraduate — medicine, $727.50; dentistry, $727.50; engineering, $602.50; law, $552.50; arts, science, and social science, $542.50; music, $552.50; (b) graduate studies — MBA, $536; qualifying year, $541. All other graduate programs are on a trimester system with consecutive payments of $260, $260, and $17.50. Part-time (per course), $105 (laboratory courses $115).

Residence rates, room and board $1,160 for the academic year.

Financial awards and assistance

A full list of awards and admission scholarships offered by the university is available in the booklet "general information". Ontario students also have access to the province of Ontario student awards plan. Students from outside Ontario should not anticipate financial assistance and should approach the government of their home province or country.

Research facilities and institutes

Cancer Research Laboratory.
The Cancer Research Laboratory was established by a grant from the Ontario division of the Canadian Cancer Society, and is maintained chiefly by annual grants from the National Cancer Institute of Canada. It is housed in its own building on the main campus of the university. Activities are centred on a variety of problems in basic cancer research. Senior members of the laboratory hold joint appointments in appropriate departments of the faculty of medicine, and participate in the teaching of undergraduate and graduate students.
Director: J.A. McCarter, PhD

Centre for Radio Science.
The University of Western Ontario has developed a particular competence in the scientific aspects of the generation, propagation and detection of radio waves. The Centre for Radio Science is not an instructional unit in the university, but does provide facilites for graduate research in many areas of radio science. Facilities are now available for a variety of researches, including the generation and detection of radio waves ranging down to submillimeter wavelengths, quantum electronics, quasi-optical techniques, interaction of radio waves with solids, gases, plasmas and beams of charged particles, the exploration of all levels of the earth's atmosphere, the sun's atmosphere and the interplanetary medium, using groundbased, rocket-borne and satellite-borne instruments. Co-operative research arrangements exist with several universities in Ontario.
Director: P.A. Forsyth, MA, PhD, FRSC.

Inter-American Studies Group.
The purpose of this group is to encourage and facilitate a cross-disciplinary and sometimes a cross-faculty approach to inter-American studies in a close co-operation with existing faculties and departments. It does so by such means as promoting closer liaison between departments and faculties, assisting in building up the resources of the library and in general by any other method approved from time to time by the graduate dean and faculty. The university has long been concerned with Canadian-American studies. Since 1936 the university has extended the scope of its interest in Canadian-American affairs to include Latin America.
Director: N.L. Nicholson, MSc, PhD.
Secretary: J.C.M. Ogelsby, PhD.

Inter-University Consortium for Political Research.
The purpose of the consortium is to promote the conduct of research on selected phases of the political process. It is expected that both partners will contribute to the success of the consortium and that each will benefit from the association. In order to realize its aims, the ICPR offers summer seminars in research design, data analysis, mathematical politics, and special selected topics of general interest serve as a repository for a wide variety of data and technical services. Seminars, data, and technical services are available at little or no charge to faculty and students of member universities. Official representative: T.G. Harvey, MA, PhD.

Urban and Regional Development Studies.
The university provides facilities for
interdisciplinary research by its faculty and
students in the field of urban and regional
development. Through the Urban and
Regional Development Studies group, a unit
of the faculty of graduate studies, it enables
the student seeking a master's or doctor's
degree to undertake a program of courses and
research projects in a number of departments
and/or faculties. While each student is
expected to take his degree in his basic
discipline, arrangements are made with the
approval of the academic units concerned, for
a program that includes work in other
disciplines. The interests and proposals of
each student are considered in defining his
program. Such interdisciplinary programs are
intended for students desiring to prepare for
research, teaching, administration, or
planning in the field of urban and regional
development.
Director: E.A. Beecroft, MA, PhD.

Affiliated colleges

Brescia College, Western Road, London 72,
Ontario.
Dean: Sister Arleene Walker, BA, MA.
Registrar: Mrs. E.M. Arnold. Roman
Catholic. Women only. Established and
affiliated in 1919. Undergraduate arts college,
offering in co-operation with the university's
faculties of arts and social science, all the
general and some of the honors arts
programs of the university, especially the
general program with home economics
options.
See separate entry.

Huron College, 1349 Western Road, London
72, Ontario.
Principal: J.G. Morden, BA, LTh, DD, STM,
DTh. See separate entry.

King's College, 266 Epworth Avenue,
London 11, Ontario.
Principal: A.F. McKee, BA, MA, MSc, PUP.
See separate entry.

Deans of faculties or schools

Arts
J.G. Rowe, AB, BD, MA, PhD

Business administration, school of
J.J. Wettlaufer, MBA, LLD

Dentistry
W.J. Dunn, DDS, FACD

Education, college of
E. Stabler, BA, MA, EdD

Engineering science
A.I. Johnson, BASc, MChe

Graduate studies
W.S. Turner (acting), BA, LLD

Law
R.S. Mackay, QC, BA, LLM

Library and information science, school of
W.J. Cameron, MA, PhD

Medicine
D. Bocking, MD, DTM, FRCP(C), FACP

Music
C. vonKuster, MusBac, LRCT

Nursing
Catherine Aikin, BA, BN, MA

Science
A.E. Scott, DSc, PhD

Social science
G.L. Reuber, BA, AM, PhD

Director of centres, councils, and study
groups

Executive secretary, Council on University
Theatres and Art
Wesanne McKellar (Mrs), MusBac, LRSM,
ARCT, AMusA

Executive secretary, University Research
Council
H.W. Baldwin, BA, MA, PhD

Director, Centre for Radio Science
P.A. Forsyth, MA, PhD, FRSC

Director, Inter-American Studies Group
N.L. Nicholson, MSc, PhD

Official representative, Inter-University
Consortium for Political Research
T.G. Harvey, MA, PhD

Director, Urban and Regional Development
Studies Group
A.E. Beecroft, MA, PhD

Resident artist
G. Lorcini, ARCA

University art curator
M. Stubbs, AOCA

Manager, Talbot theatre
Marion Wood (Miss)

Curator, Museum of Indian Archaeology and
Pioneer Life
W. Jury, DèsL, LLD

Division and departmental chairmen

Anaesthesia
W.E. Spoerel, MD, FRCP(C)

Anatomy
R.C. Buck, MD, MSc, PhD

Applied mathematics
J.H. Blackwell, Ed, BSc, MSc, PhD

Art (education)
A.D. Logan

Astronomy
W.H. Wehlau, AB, PhD

Bacteriology and immunology
R.G. Murray, BA, MA, MD, CM, FRSC

Biochemistry
K.P. Strickland (acting), BSc, MSc, PhD

Biophysics
M.R. Roach, BSc, MDCM, PhD, FRCP(C)

Business and commerce (education)
H.J. Kaluza

Cancer research
J.A. McCarter, BA, MA, PhD, FRSC

Cardiovascular and thoracic surgery
J.C.G. Coles

Chemical group (engineering science)
J.E. Zajic, BA, MS, PhD, JD

Chemistry
H.C. Clark, MSc, PhD

Civil group (engineering science)
M.P. Poucher, DIC, MSc

Classical studies
D.E. Gerber, MA, PhD

Classics (education)
G.R. Lambert

Clinical neurological sciences
C.G. Drake, MD, MSc, MS, FRCS(C)

Communication disorders
F.J. Rounthwrite (acting)

Community medicine (division of
epidemiology and preventive medicine)
C. Buck, MD, PhD, DPh

Community medicine (division of family
medicine)
I.R. McWhinney, MB, BCh, MD

Computer science
J.F. Hart, MA, PhD

Core studies group (engineering science)
G.S. Emmerson, BSc, MSc

Dental clinics
K.M. Baird

Diagnostic radiology
L.S. Carey, MD, CM, MSc, MS

Economics
R.J. Wonnacott, BA, AM, PhD

Electrical group (engineering science)
I.I. Inculet, DipIng, MSc

Elementary education
K.W. Kenney

English
P. Fleck (on leave), MA, PhD

English (education)
J. Smallbridge

Epidemiology and preventive medicine
C.W. Buck, MD, PhD, DPh

Family medicine
I.R. McWhinney, MB, BCh, MD

Fine art
W.S.A. Dale, MA, PhD

French
C.P. Barbier, MA

Geography
Wm. Warntz, BS, AM, PhD

Geography (education)
R.C. Langman

Geology
A.E. Beck (acting), BSc, PhD

Geophysics
A.E. Beck, BSc, PhD

German
R.M. Immerwahr, BA, MA, PhD

Guidance (education)
P.K. Schmidt, BA, MEd

History
C.A. Ruud, BA, AM, PhD

History (education)
G. Milburn

History of education
W.B. Hamilton

History of medicine and science
R.A. Richardson (acting), BA, MA, PhD

Home economics (education)
Grace Porterfield (Miss)

Journalism
J.L. Wild, BA, MA

Materials science group (engineering science)
J.D. Brown, BSc, McM, PhD

Mathematics
D. Borwein, DSc, PhD

Mathematics (education)
A.W. Harris

Mechanical group (engineering science)
J.E.K. Foreman, BASc, MME

Medicine
R.W. Gunton, MD, DPhil, FRCP(C), FACP

Modern languages (education)
W.E. Kieser

Music (education)
D. Woodburn

Neurology
H.J.M. Barnett

Neurosurgery
C.G. Drake

Obstetrics and gynaecology
E.R. Plunkett, MD, PhD

Occupational therapy
M. Trider (Mrs)

Ophthalmology
C. Dyson, MD, DO, CRCS(C)

Oral medicine
D.S. Moore, DDS, DipPerio, FRCD(C)

Oral surgery
A.G. Parnell, LDS, FDS, RCS

Orthopaedic surgery
J.C. Kennedy

Otolaryngology
F.J. Rounthwaite, BSc, MDCM, FRCS(C), FACS

Paediatric dentistry
W.H. Feasby, DDS, DipPaed, FRCD(C)

Paediatrics
J.C. Rathbun, MD

Pathological chemistry
A.H. Neufeld, BSc, MSc, PhD, MDCM, FCIC

Pathology
A.C. Wallace, BA, MD, FACP, CRCP(C)

Pharmacology
C.W. Gowdey, BA, MSc, DPhil

Philosophy
R.W. Binkley (acting), BA, PhD

Philosophy (education)
V.A. Howard

Physical and health education
W.J. L'Heureux, MA, LLD

Physical and health education (education)
W.I. Paterson (acting)

Physical medicine and rehabilitation
M.G. Cameron, MD, FRCP(C)

Physical therapy
S.M. Morgan (Miss)

Physics
J.W. McGowan, MS, DSc, FAPS

Physiology
V.B. Brooks, BA, MS, PhD

Plant sciences
D.B. Walden (acting), MSc, PhD

Plastic and reconstructive surgery
R.M. McFarlane

Political science
S.J. Noël, BA, MA, DPhil

Professional practice and administration
(education)
G.F. Allison

Psychiatry
G.F.D. Hesdtine, BA, LMSA, DipPsych,
CRPC

Psychology
W.J. McClelland, MA, PhD

Psychology (education)
J.G. McMurray

Restorative dentistry
R.E. Jordan, BA, DDS, MSD, FICD

Russian studies
R. Neuhauser, MA, PhD

School librarianship (education)
E.M. Gordon (Miss)

Science (education)
J.S. Wright

Secretarial science
E.M. Chapman (Mrs), BA

Social dentistry
B.P. Martinello, DDS, DDPH

Sociology
J.H. Kunkel, MA, PhD

Spanish and Italian
W. Flint, MA, PhD

Surgery
A.D. McLachlin, MD, MSc, DPhil

Teaching aids (education)
P.J. McKeon

Technical education (education)
H.W. Beatty

Therapeutic radiology
T.A. Watson, MB, ChB, MD, DMR, FACR,
FRCP(C)

Urology
L.N. McAninch

Zoology
M. Locke, MA, PhD

University of Windsor*

Windsor, Ontario

Telephone: (Windsor) 519-253-4232
(Detroit) 313-963-6113
Direct general correspondence to the registrar

Total full-time student enrolment 5,940; see also separate section *Statistics on Canadian universities and colleges*

Executive and administrative officers

Chancellor
The Hon. Lucien Lamoureux, QC, BA, LPh, MA, LLD

Vice-chancellor and president
J.F. Leddy, DPhil, DLitt, DèsL, LLD, DCL

Vice-president
F.A. DeMarco, PhD, FCIC

Vice-president administration, and treasurer
W.R. Mitchell, BScCE

Registrar
Rev. P.T. Holliday, BA, BD, MTh, MA

Librarian
W.F. Dollar, MA, AMLS

Secretary of the university and board of governors
J.W. Whiteside, BA

Secretary of the senate
Barbara Birch, BA, MA

Dean of students
G.A. McMahon, MA

Dean of men
G.L. DeLuca, BA

Dean of women
Evelyn McLean, BA, MA

Assistant registrar, admissions
Rosary Carney, BA, MSW

Assistant registrar, data processing
Graham Hobbs

Assistant registrar, records
James Morrison

Assistant registrar (academic programs)
F.L. Smith, BA

Awards officer
D.L. Kasta, BA, MA

Director of extension and summer school
Rev. E.C. Pappert, CSB, PhD

Alumni director and secondary school liaison officer
R.J. Scott, BComm

Assistant vice-president, administration
Douglas Brombal, BA

Director, administrative services
Dennis Drew

Director of public relations
G.A. MacGibbon, BA

Director of media centre
Esio Marzotto, BASc

Director, planning and construction
C.W. Morgan, BSc, PEng

Director, computer centre
L.F. Miernicke, BBA

Director of finance
J.E. Schiller, BA

Director, personnel services
G.D.T. Wintermute, BComm

Director of institutional research
A.M. Marshall, BSc

Director, physical facility
T.D. Ray, BSc

Director, university centre
C.M. Tolmie, BComm

---

*Ordinary member, AUCC.

Background

Assumption College was founded in 1857 and incorporated in 1858 by a public act of the legislature of the province of Canada. From 1919 to 1953, the college was affiliated to The University of Western Ontario. In 1953, the Ontario legislature established a new government for the college and granted it university powers.

Teaching began in 1857 and the first degrees were awarded in 1954. In 1956, the Ontario legislature passed an act which changed the name of Assumption College to Assumption University of Windsor. On July 1, 1963, the University of Windsor was incorporated as a non-denominational and co-educational university, and Assumption University became a federated college.

The affiliated colleges are legally and financially distinct, but subject in academic matters to the senate.

The board of governors, the supreme governing body, is responsible for the conduct, management, and control of the university, and deals with financial matters. The senate has responsibility for academic matters.

Facilities and services

The university is situated on a 100-acre campus south of the Detroit River and east of the Ambassador Bridge, which forms a physical link between Canada and the United States (the city of Windsor has a population of approximately 221,000). There are seven teaching buildings, a library (500,000 volumes) and administration building, a university centre, a large new physical and health education complex, including a gymnasium and a swimming pool, a dining and recreation centre (Vanier hall), men's residences (St. Michael's hall, Cody hall, Huron hall, and Sir John A. Macdonald hall) and women's residences (Electa hall and Sir Wilfred Laurier hall), accommodating 700 men and 250 women respectively, and a residence for married students (Geoffrey Fisher hall).

Holy Redeemer College is located about five miles from the university and Canterbury and Iona Colleges are located in the vicinity of the university.

Student services include a placement bureau, a guidance and counselling centre, a housing registry, and an infirmary.

Calendars and brochures (on request from the registrar)

General calendar.

Calendars of the following faculties of: arts and science; applied science; business administration; education; graduate studies; law; and physical and health education.

Calendars of the division of: extension (intersession and summer session); extension (evening division).

Undergraduate awards and financial aid; admission brochure.

Courses and degrees

Arts
(Faculty of arts and science)

Bachelor of arts (BA).
(a) General program, four years from junior matriculation or three years from senior matriculation. Majors are offered in anthropology, art history, Asian studies, classical civilization, communication arts, comparative literature, drama, economics, English, fine arts, French, geography, German, Greek, history, home economics, Italian, Latin, linguistics, mathematics, music, philosophy, political science, psychology, Russian, sociology, Spanish and theology. (b) Honors program, five years from junior matriculation or four years from senior matriculation. Available in anthropology, art history, Asian studies, drama, economics, English, French, geography, German, Greek, history, international relations, Latin, Latin-American studies, mathematics, philosophy, political science, psychology, Russian, sociology, Spanish, theology, and combinations of these.

(Faculty of graduate studies)

Master of arts (MA).
At least two years from general BA or at least one year from honors BA. Available in creative writing, economics, English, geography, history, philosophy, political science, psychology, romance languages, sociology, and theology.

Doctor of philosophy (PhD).
At least two years beyond the master's or its equivalent. Available in psychology.

Commerce
(Faculty of business administration)

Bachelor of commerce (BComm).
Honors program, five years from junior matriculation or four years from senior matriculation.

(Faculty of graduate studies)

Master of business administration (MBA).
At least two years from general bachelor's degree or at least one year from honors BComm.

Computer science
(School of computer science)

Bachelor of computer science (BCS).
(a) General program, four years from junior matriculation or three years from senior matriculation. (b) Honors program, five years from junior matriculation or four years from senior matriculation, with options in mathematics, computer design, or business.

Engineering
(Faculty of applied science)

Bachelor of applied science (BASc).
Five years from junior matriculation or four years from senior matriculation. Specialization offered in chemical, civil, electrical, geological, industrial and mechanical engineering, and engineering materials.

(Faculty of graduate studies)

Master of applied science (MASc).
At least one year from BASc or equivalent degree. Available in chemical, civil, electrical, industrial, and mechanical engineering, and engineering materials.

Doctor of philosophy (PhD).
At least three years from BASc or equivalent degree or at least two calendar years from the master's degree. Available in chemical, civil, electrical, industrial, and mechanical engineering, and engineering materials.

Fine arts
(Faculty of arts and science)

Bachelor of fine arts (BFA).
Honors program, five years from junior matriculation or four years from senior matriculation. Available in fine arts or in dramatic art.

Law
(Faculty of law)

Bachelor of laws (LLB).
Three years from bachelor's degree. Some students may be admitted after two years of university work beyond grade 13.

Music
(Faculty of arts and science)

Bachelor of music (BMus).
Honors program, five years from junior matriculation or four years from senior matriculation. Available in history and theory, and in school music.

Nursing
(School of nursing, faculty of arts and science)

Diploma in public health nursing (DiplPHN).
One year from senior matriculation (preferred) or junior matriculation plus qualification as a professional nurse.

Bachelor of science in nursing (BScN).
Five years from junior matriculation or four years from senior matriculation; three years for a professional nurse with senior matriculation, or four years for a professional nurse with junior matriculation.

Physical and health education
(Faculty of physical and health education)

Bachelor of physical and health education (BPHE).
Five years from junior matriculation, or four years from senior matriculation.

(Faculty of graduate studies)

Master of physical education (MPE).
At least one year from honors BPHE degree.

Science, applied, see engineering above

Science, pure
(Faculty of arts and science)

Bachelor of science (BSc).
(a) General program, four years from junior matriculation or three years from senior matriculation. Majors in biology, chemistry, geology, mathematics, physics. (b) Honors program, five years from junior matriculation or four years from senior matriculation. Available in biology, chemistry, geology, mathematics, physics, and combinations of these.

(Faculty of graduate studies)

Master of science (MSc).
At least two years from general BSc, or at least one year from honors BSc. Available in biology, chemistry, mathematics, and physics.

Doctor of philosophy (PhD).
At least three years from honors BSc or equivalent or two years from MSc. Available in biology, chemistry, mathematics, and physics.

Social work
(School of social work, faculty of arts and science)

Bachelor of social work (BSW).
Honors program, five years from junior matriculation or four years from senior matriculation.

(Faculty of graduate studies)

Master of social work (MSW).
At least two years from general bachelor's degree, or one year from honors BSW degree.

Extension programs

For university credit:

Evening school.
Courses leading to BA degree; science, business administration and nursing subjects; courses for teachers who wish to improve their professional qualifications (arts and science). Certificate in business administration (designed primarily for businessmen with experience). Certificate in public administration. Certificate in theology. Courses leading to the degrees of MBA and MASc.

Intersession and summer school.
Courses leading to BA degree; science subjects; courses for teachers who wish to improve their professional qualifications (arts and science).

For no university credit:

Evening school.
The extension department co-operates with certain groups in the offering of non-credit courses. The groups are: Certified General Accountants, Industrial and Cost Accountants of Ontario (RIA) and Industrial Foremen's Club of Windsor. The extension department also provides space for courses of instruction offered by and for other vocational and professional groups. All courses offered for credit are open to auditors who may attend them for no credit.

The division of continuing education of the University of Windsor also offers non-credit courses of advanced education.

Admission requirements

For a general statement regarding admission to university study, see article *Admission to university in Canada.*

For information regarding admission to undergraduate study, consult *Requirements for admission to Canadian colleges and universities* available from Service for Admission to College and University, 151 Slater St., Ottawa, Ont., K1P 5N1, $1.50 prepaid.

For admission to graduate study, a bachelor's degree is required with specified grades in appropriate subjects.

Academic year

Winter session: mid-September to early May.

Intersession: May 15 to July 1.

Summer session: early July to mid-August.

Grading system

A-, A, A +, 80-100% (excellent); B, B +, 70-79% (good); C, C +, 60-69% (fair); D, D +, 50-59% (pass); F-, F, below 50% (failure). A supplemental examination may be allowed at the discretion of the academic standing committee. Certain options may be taken on a pass non-pass basis; the grades are not released for such courses, and are not included in the year's average.

Fees and costs

Tuition and incidental fees per year: (a) full-time — preliminary year, $580; undergraduate arts, science, $540; music, fine arts, nursing, $550; dramatic art, $550 (plus first year audition fee of $10); social work, commerce, $545; physical education, $555; engineering, $620 (plus fourth year civil engineering camp fee of $40); law, $560; education, $527.50; make-up and first-year masters, $527.50; graduate studies, $475; plus $100 non-resident fee for students outside Canada; (b) part-time (undergraduate, day or evening) — full course of three or more hours a week, $142.50; full course of two hours a week, $100; plus appropriate laboratory fees.

Residence rates vary with plan selected.

Financial awards and assistance

Several university entrance scholarships are available, each of the total possible value of up to $2,000; some are allocated to residents of Essex county, some to residents of Ontario outside the county, and others to residents of Canada outside Ontario. United States students may apply for the Friends of Assumption Foundation scholarship (total value $2,000) or Assumption alumni award ($3,200). Five University of Windsor alumni scholarships (total value $2,000 each) are available on entrance. Many in-course scholarships and bursaries are awarded. Postgraduate fellowships and assistantships, to a total maximum value of $4,500, are offered for study towards master's or doctorate degrees.

Research institute

The Industrial Research Institute, the first in Canada, promotes active co-operation between science and industry, by offering extensive laboratory facilities and advanced skills of staff to industry on contract basis.

Federated university

Assumption University, Windsor, Ontario. President: Rev. E.R. Malley, CSB, MA, STL, STD. Registrar: Rev. N.J. Ruth, CSB, MA. By the provisions of the University of Windsor Act, 1962-63, Assumption University of Windsor became a federated university of the University of Windsor. By the federation agreement, its degree-granting power is held in abeyance during the term of federation except for degrees in the faculty of theology. By act of the Ontario legislature in April 1964, the name of Assumption University of Windsor was shortened to Assumption University in order to avoid confusion with the University of Windsor.

Affiliated colleges

Canterbury College, Windsor, Ontario.
Principal: Rev. F.T. Kingston, MA, LTh, BD,
DPhil. Anglican. Co-educational. Established
1957. The college co-operates in the
interdenominational department of theology
in the university and provides a social and
religious centre for Anglican students.

Holy Redeemer College, Windsor, Ontario.
Principal: Rev. D.L. Egan, CSsR, STL.
Roman Catholic (Redemptorist). Men only.
Established 1956. Seminary of the
Redemptorist Fathers, affiliated to the
faculties of arts and science and theology,
and authorized to give instruction leading to
bachelor of arts degree of the University of
Windsor and bachelor of theology degree of
Assumption University.

Iona College, Windsor, Ontario.
Principal: Rev. J.C. Hoffman, BA, BD, STM,
PhD, ThD. While Iona College has not yet
acquired physical facilities on campus, it has
undertaken to co-operate with the university
in the provision of academic courses of
United Church theology.

Note: all students are registered for academic
purposes in the University of Windsor; the
federated university (Assumption University)
and affiliated colleges (Canterbury, Holy
Redeemer and Iona) provide residence
facilities and social and religious centres.

Deans of faculties

Applied science
J.G. Parr, BSc, PhD

Arts and science
W.G. Phillips, PhD

Business administration
G.R. Horne, PhD

Education
To be appointed

Graduate studies
Rev. C.P.J. Crowley, CSB, PhD

Law
W.S. Tarnopolsky, AM, LLB, LLM

Physical and health education
P.J. Galasso, BA, BPhysED, MA, DPhil

Directors of schools

Computer science
E.W. Channen, BA, PhD

Dramatic art
D.P. Kelly, BA, MAy

Nursing
Florence Roach, RRC, RegN, BSc, RRL

Social work
H.B. Morrow, MSW

Department heads

Asian studies
J.W. Spellman, BA, PhD

Biology
R.J. Doyle, MA, MS, PhD

Chemical engineering
Maurice Adelman, MASc, PhD

Chemistry
E.J. Bounsall, BASc, MA, PhD

Civil engineering
J.B. Kennedy, BSc, PhD

Classics
Charles Fantazzi, MA, PhD

Communication arts
Walter Romanow, BA, MA

Economics
Z.M. Fallenbuchl, PhD

Electrical engineering
Edmund Kuffel, BSc, MSc, PhD, DSc

Engineering materials
R.G. Billinghurst, MASc

English
J.F. Sullivan, BS, MA, PhD

Fine arts
J.N. DeLauro, BFA, MFA

French language and literature
J.P. Andreoli-deVillers, LèsL, PhD

Geography
J.C. Ransome, MA, PhD

Geology
Peter Sonnenfeld, BA, PhD

Germanic and Slavic studies
Fritz Wieden, BA, MA, PhD

Hispanic and Italian studies
Rev. R.S. Pazik, CSB, BA, MA,
CertEstdelDoct

History
M.N. Vuckovic, MA, PhD

Home economics
Phyllis McDermott, BSc, MS

Mathematics
Rev. D.T. Faught, BA, MA

Mechanical engineering
W.G. Colborne, MSc

Music
Paul McIntyre, MusDoc

Philosophy
P.F. Wilkinson, BA, MA, LTh

Physics
Lucjan Krause, BSc, MA, PhD, FIP

Political science
R.H. Wagenberg, BA, MA, PhD

Psychology
Miriam Bunt, BA, BS, MEd, PhD

Sociology
Vito Signorile, BA, MA, PhD

Theology
J.C. Hoffman, BA, BD, STM, PhD, ThD

The University of Winnipeg*

515 Portage Avenue, Winnipeg 2, Manitoba

Telephone: 204-786-7811
Direct general correspondence to the registrar

Total full-time student enrolment 2,408; see also separate section *Statistics on Canadian universities and colleges*

Executive and administrative officers

Chancellor
P.H.T. Thorlakson, CC, MD, CM, DSc, FRCS(C), FACS

President and vice-chancellor
H.E. Duckworth, BA, BSc, PhD, DSc, FRSC

Assistant to the president (administration)
R.J. Riddell, BSc, BPaed

Assistant to the president (development and planning)
J.G. Pincock, MD, LMCC, CRCP(C), FACP

Comptroller
J.K.A. Brown, CA

Registrar
R.M. Bellhouse, BSc

Director, summer and evening sessions
J.A. Dowsett, BSc, MSc

Director, student counselling services
N.W. Phillips, BA, MA, PhD

Librarian
R.C. Wright, BA, BLS

Academic awards officer
H.L. Mak, BA

Director of alumni affairs
Joy McDiarmid, BA

Background

Higher education began in Manitoba with the creation of church colleges and The University of Manitoba was founded in 1877, largely on the initiative of these colleges, as an examining and degree-conferring body only. However, commencing in 1904, and continuing until the present, instruction in arts and science has been given at both the university and the colleges.

Two of the aforementioned colleges were Manitoba College, founded by the Presbyterian Church in 1871, and Wesley College, founded in 1877 by the Methodist Church. In 1926, following the union of these two Churches, Manitoba and Wesley Colleges were united. From 1931 to 1938, they functioned as "united colleges"; they were incorporated as "United College" in 1938. United College operated as an affiliated college of The University of Manitoba until it was granted university status in 1967; on July 1, 1967, the college became The University of Winnipeg.

The University of Winnipeg represents a partnership between Church and state and it operates under the authority of a board of regents. The senate has charge of all academic matters and the courses of instruction given. The name "United College" is retained to designate the arts and science faculty of the university.

The university is an autonomous, independent body with power to grant degrees in arts and science, as well as in theology.

Facilities and services

The University of Winnipeg is located in the heart of downtown Winnipeg (population 553,000). It is comprised of eight buildings: Wesley hall, George Bryce hall, Manitoba hall, Ashdown hall, Graham hall, the university men's residence accommodating

*Ordinary member, AUCC.

120 students; Sparling hall, the university women's residence accommodating 69 students; Riddell hall comprising the dining hall, cafeteria, and gymnasium. The library, in George Bryce hall, contains over 170,000 volumes; approximately 20,000 volumes are added annually.

A new building, Lockhart hall, completed in January, 1970, added further lecture-room, laboratory, and cafeteria space.

Student services include an accident insurance service, guidance and counselling, an employment service, a cafeteria and a gymnasium.

Calendars and brochures

General calendar for arts and science, theology, collegiate division; summer session calendar, evening session calendar; admissions bulletin; mature student booklet; theology bulletin; annual report; collegiate brochure.
Available from registrar's office.

"The Uniter" — student newspaper available from The University of Winnipeg students' association.

Courses and degrees

Arts
(Faculty of arts and science)

Bachelor of arts (BA).
(a) General course, three years from senior matriculation. Five-course major subjects: anthropology, economics, English, French, geography, German, history, Latin, mathematics, philosophy, political science, psychology, religious studies, and sociology. Courses available also in botany, classical civilization, Greek, Hebrew, and statistics. Distributed majors also available in administrative studies, Canadian studies, dramatic studies, environmental studies, urban studies, and molecular biology. (b) Honors courses, four years from senior matriculation. Available in economics, English, French, geography, German, history, Latin, philosophy, political science, psychology, and sociology.

Science, pure
(Faculty of arts and science)

Bachelor of science (BSc).
General course, three years from senior matriculation. Five-course major subjects: biology, chemistry, geography, and physics.

Theology
(Faculty of theology)

Due to a commitment to the Division of Ministry and Education of the United Church of Canada, the faculty of theology will no longer accept students beginning their work for either the BTh or the BD degrees. All such work for the Prairie provinces is to be continued at Saskatoon. This does not apply to those clergy who, having received a diploma (or testamur) when they graduated in theology, wish to engage in extra work to qualify for the BD or the BD(Hons) degree.

Master of sacred theology (STM).
Two years from BD. Historical, pastoral, and practical theology.

Extension programs

For university credit:

Evening classes.
September to April. Normally one night each week, three hours each night. Undergraduate classes in arts and science for credit towards BA and BSc degrees and for credit on teaching certificates.

Summer session.
(1) Mid-May to end of July. Normally two nights each week, three hours each night. (2) Early July to mid-August. Normally two hours each day. Undergraduate classes in arts and science for credit towards BA and BSc degrees and for credit towards teaching certificates.

For no university credit:

Evening classes.
As above but for department of education credit on teaching certificates only.

Collegiate.
The collegiate division of the University College offers the complete program of studies of grades XI (junior matriculation) and XII (senior matriculation).

Summer school.
Courses are held in August for three weeks in grade XII subjects to assist students who have previously had instruction in the courses for which they register to prepare for the examination. Grade XII courses are held in July and August for six weeks for those students who are studying subjects for the first time in preparation for writing August examinations.

Admission requirements

For a general statement regarding admission to university study, see article *Admission to university in Canada.*

For information regarding admission to undergraduate study, consult *Requirements for admission to Canadian colleges and universities* available from Service for Admission to College and University, 151 Slater St., Ottawa, Ont., K1P 5N1, $1.50 prepaid.

Theology: for admission to STM course, a student must have obtained a BD degree.

Academic year

Winter session: mid-September to end of April.

Summer session: (1) mid-May to end of July; (2) early July to mid-August.

Grading system

Standing is graded in each subject as: excellent: A+, A, A-; superior: B+, B; slightly above average: C+; average achievement: C; marginal pass: D; failure: F.

Fees and costs

Tuition fees per year: $85 per course in arts and science, full- or part-time. Students' organization fee, $30. Residence rates, double room, $225.

Research institute

Institute of Urban Studies
established in 1969 to develop a university-based centre for research, community action, and education in the area of urban issues and involving students, faculty, and interested community people.

Associated institutions

Mennonite Brethren College of Arts, 77 Henderson Highway, Winnipeg 5, Manitoba. President: Rev. V. Adrian, BA, BD, MTh. Registrar: Rev. P.M. Hamm, MA, BD. Founded 1944; associated 1970. A co-educational institution supported and controlled by the Canadian Mennonite Brethren Conference. In addition to two years of a liberal arts program, the college offers extensive preparation for theology and Christian education, granting degress in theology — bachelor of theology and religious education (ThB) — bachelor of religious education (BRE). A three-year course in sacred music is also offered.

The college has residential accommodation for single men and women in addition to quarters for married couples and families. Students transfer to the university for the final year of the arts degree program.

Deans of faculties

Arts and science
J. Clake, BA, PhD

Collegiate
W. Rutherford, BA, BEd

Theology
G.E. Taylor, BA, MA, BD, PhD

Director of institute

Institute of Urban Studies
N.L. Axworthy, BA, MA

Department chairmen

Anthropology
J.H. Steinbring, BA, MA

Biology
J.C. Conroy, BSc, MSc

Chemistry
L.A. Swyers, BSc

Classics
E.D. Eagle, BA, MA, PhD

Economics
G. Blake, BA, MA, PhD

English
W.E. Swayze, BA, MA, PhD

French
J.E. Dixon, Dipd'etFr, MA, PhD

Geography
B.M. Evans, BA, MA, PhD

German
J. Thiessen, BA, PhD

History
H.V. Rutherford, BA, PhD

Mathematics and statistics
W.C. Campbell, BA

Philosophy
V.Y. Shimizu, BA, MA

Physics
J.F.K. Duff, BSc, MSc

Political science
S.R. Veatch, BA, MA

Psychology
J.J. Coté, BSc, MA, PhD

Religious studies
J.C. Ridd, BA, MA, BD

Sociology
J. Hofley, BA, MA, PhD

York University*

4700 Keele Street, Downsview, Ontario

Telephone: 416-635-2100
Direct general correspondence to the registrar

Total full-time student enrolment 9,787; see also separate section *Statistics on Canadian universities and colleges*

Executive and administrative officers

Chancellor
F.S. Chalmers, SM, LLD, LittD, FIAL

President
D.W. Slater, BComm, BA, MA, PhD

Vice-president (academic)
To be appointed

Vice-president (administration)
W.W. Small, BCom, MA

Vice-president (finance)
H.B. Parkes, BA, CA

Vice-president (academic services)
A.C. Johnson, BA, MA, PhD

Registrar
M.A. Bider, BA, MA

Principal, Glendon College
A.V. Tucker, BA, MA, PhD

Secretary of the university
W.D. Farr, BA, MA

Director of libraries
T.F. O'Connell, AB, MS

Comptroller
K. Clements, BComm, MBA, CA

Director, department of information
W. Sanders, BA

*Ordinary member, AUCC.

Director of admissions
J.A.S. McNeil, BA

Assistant registrar (student awards)
G. Fontaine, BA

Associate registrar (student records)
P. Kelly, BA

Constituent colleges

Joseph E. Atkinson College, Toronto, Ontario. Established 1962. Dean: Harry Crowe, MA. The college has instituted evening and part-time courses leading to the BA degree. At present, ordinary programs, requiring 15 courses are offered in computer science*, economics*, English*, geography*, history*, mathematics*, philosophy*, political science*, psychology*, science, sociology*, and urban studies. Honors programs, requiring 20 courses, in subjects marked *, also administration.

The college also offers a program of liberal studies of related courses which offers greater flexibility than the usual major program.

Glendon College, Toronto, Ontario. Established in 1966 on the Glendon campus of the university. Principal: Albert Tucker, PhD. Glendon College offers degree courses in economics, English, French, history, philosophy, political science, psychology, and sociology; all students take a second language (French for English speaking students) for their first two years, and some subject courses in the higher years are offered in French. The environment in the college is designed to foster discussion of, and an interest in, public affairs, especially affairs of Canada.

Founders College, opened in 1965, *Vanier College,* opened in 1966, *Winters College,* opened in 1967, *McLaughlin College,* opened in 1968, *Stong College,* opened in September 1969, *Calumet College* opened in 1970, and *College "G"* opened in 1971 are the first seven of twelve planned colleges on the York campus, each of which will accommodate about 250 resident and 750 non-resident students.

York University has been developed on the college system. Every freshman enroled in the university is assigned to a college with which he will be associated during his undergraduate years. Each college, with its own master, dons, and tutors, is a distinctive

unit with seminar, lecture, and recreation areas, a dining hall, and residence building. Students have the combined advantage of being members of a small college while exposed to the facilities and intellectual vigor of a large university.

Background

York University was founded by an act of the Ontario legislature in 1959. It began operation in 1960 as an affiliate of the University of Toronto — the affiliation agreement was terminated in 1965.

York moved to the Glendon campus in 1961. In 1962 the Joseph E. Atkinson College first offered degree courses for evening and part-time students. The university accepted its first post-graduate students in 1964. The York campus, which became the principal seat of the university, was opened at Keele Street and Steeles Avenue in 1965. In the next year, the faculty of administrative studies was established and Glendon College officially was opened. In 1967, the faculty of fine arts and in 1968, the faculty of environmental studies, were established. The Osgoode Hall Law School, established in 1872, became a constituent of the university in July 1968 and moved from its location in Osgoode Hall on Queen Street to its new building on the York campus in 1969.

York is composed of the faculties of arts, science, fine arts, administrative studies, graduate studies, environmental studies, Osgoode Hall Law School, the Joseph E. Atkinson College, and Glendon College.

The governing bodies of the university are the board of governors and the senate, both of which were established by the act of incorporation. The university is co-educational and non-denominational.

Facilities and services

York campus consists of 600 acres of rolling land on the northern boundary of Metropolitan Toronto, and is the main campus of the university. It is being developed to accommodate 20,000 full-time

students by 1980. The campus contains six colleges and their associated residences, four science and social science buildings, two libraries, an auditorium, a physical education centre, a skating rink, Atkinson College, the law school, a lecture hall building and three graduate student residences.

Glendon campus situated on the 84-acre estate of Glendon Hall at Bayview and Lawrence Avenues in Toronto, provides a parkland setting for a small, residential liberal arts college able to accommodate approximately 1,200 students. Buildings on the campus include York hall with its lecture and seminar rooms, laboratories, administrative offices, and two dining halls; the Leslie Frost library; the Wood residence capable of accommodating 188 male students, the Hilliard residence capable of accommodating 248 female students, and the Proctor Field house with swimming pool, gymnasia, squash courts and an adjoining outdoor artificial ice rink.

Calendars and brochures

Calendars are available for the faculties of arts, science, fine arts, administrative studies, graduate studies, Osgoode Hall Law School, Atkinson College and Glendon College.

Brochures have been printed concerning Glendon College, the faculty of science, the faculty of environmental studies, admission requirements, the college tutorial, the college system at York University.

The calendars and brochures may be obtained from the office of admissions.

Courses and degrees

Note: The York University curriculum is based on the principle that students should be able to pursue a wide range of interdisciplinary studies before selecting a disciplinary specialty. Students in their first year select a broad range of interdisciplinary courses in the humanities, social sciences, and natural sciences. In higher years of study, when students have chosen a disciplinary specialty, cognate interdisciplinary courses are offered as options.

Administrative studies
(Faculty of administrative studies)

Bachelor of arts (BA).
A four-year specialized honors program leading to the BA (honors in business) degree is offered. This course comprises two years in another undergraduate faculty followed by two years in the faculty of administrative studies.

Arts
(Faculty of arts)

Bachelor of arts (BA).
(a) Ordinary program three years from senior matriculation (b) Specialized honors, combined honors, and general honors programs, four years from senior matriculation. The ordinary program is offered in anthropology*, economics*, English*, French*, geography*, German, Greek, history*, Latin, mathematics*, philosophy*, political science*, psychology*, Russian, sociology*, and Spanish. Specialized honors programs in subjects marked *, also physical education.

Combined honors programs are offered in certain combinations of the above subjects plus computer science, German, Greek, humanities, Latin, Russian, and Spanish. The general honors program has been established as a framework to enable students, with the approval of the faculty, to select a pattern of studies not otherwise available to BA honors candidates. At present, five general honors programs have been mounted formally: East Asian studies, human resources development, philosophy and history of science, social and political thought, urban studies.

Bachelor of arts (BA).
Glendon College. (a) Ordinary program, three years from senior matriculation. (b) General honors, specialized honors, and combined honors programs, four years from senior matriculation. Ordinary and honors programs are available in economics, English, French, history, philosophy, political science, psychology, and sociology.

Fine arts
(Faculty of fine arts)

Bachelor of arts (BA).
Four-year honors program leading to the BA degree is offered in fine arts with honors in art, dance, film, music, and theatre arts.

Science
(Faculty of science)

Bachelor of science (BSc).
(a) Ordinary program, three years from senior matriculation. (b) Honors program, four years from senior matriculation. The ordinary program is offered in biology, chemistry, mathematics, physics, and psychology. Specialized honors program is offered in the same subjects, also physical education. Combined honors programs are offered in certain combinations of these subjects. (c) The liberal science program – a three-year program – is designed to provide a broad education in science with emphasis on the relationship of science to other areas of knowledge (e.g. history, economics, industry, government) and to society in general.

Graduate studies
(Faculty of graduate studies)

Master of arts (MA).
Two years from three-year BA, or one year from four-year BA. This degree is presently offered in the fields of economics, English, geography, history, mathematics, philosophy, political science, psychology, and sociology.

Master of science (MSc).
Two years from three-year BSc or one year from four-year BSc. This degree is presently offered in the fields of biology, chemistry, physics, and in the interdisciplinary Centre for Research in Experimental Space Science.

Master of business administration (MBA) and *master of public administration (MPA).*
Two years from a three-year or four-year degree in courses other than business administration or commerce. One year from a four-year degree in business administration or commerce. This course is also open to part-time students.

Doctor of philosophy (PhD).
At least two years from MA or three years from four-year BA. This degree is available in biology, chemistry, English, history, philosophy, physics, political science, psychology, sociology, and in the interdisciplinary Centre for Research in Experimental Space Science.

Law
(Osgoode Hall Law School)

Bachelor of laws (LLB).
Three years from third year beyond junior
matriculation of an approved university
course; or three years from second year
beyond senior matriculation of an approved
university course; or three years from a
bachelor's degree.

Master of laws (LLM)
At least one year from LLB degree from an
approved law faculty or school.

Doctor of jurisprudence (DJur).
At least one year from LLM degree from an
approved law faculty or college. May be
awarded for published work.

Special programs

Interdisciplinary programs, see note under
courses and degrees.

Extension programs

For university credit:

The Joseph E. Atkinson College offers degree
programs on an evening or part-time basis in
both the summer and winter sessions. The
faculty of administrative studies of the
university offers programs of part-time study
leading to the degree of master of business
administration and master of public
administration.

For no university credit:

The centre for continuing education of York
University offers non-degree courses,
programs, and seminars and has been
established to aid individuals who wish to
continue their education through formal
participation in university-level programs. At
the present time, courses are being offered
within four distinct study areas: the
performing arts, urban studies, studies in
human relations, and special studies in
education.

Admission requirements

For a general statement regarding admission
to university study, see article *Admission to
university in Canada.*

For information regarding admission to
undergraduate study, consult *Requirements
for admission to Canadian colleges and
universities* available from Service for
Admission to College and University, 151
Slater St., Ottawa, Ont., K1P 5N1, $1.50
prepaid.

Osgoode Hall Law School. A candidate for
admission to the first year of the LLB
program at Osgoode Hall Law School must
present proof that following junior
matriculation he has completed three years of
an approved course, leading to a degree, in a
recognized university; or ii) following senior
matriculation he has completed two years of
an approved course, leading to a degree, in a
recognized university; or iii) he has been
awarded a degree in an approved course in a
recognized university. All applicants for
admission to the Osgoode Hall Law School
are required to take the law school
admissions test conducted by Princeton
University.

Academic year

Winter session: mid-September to early May.

Summer session: mid-June to mid-August
(for part-time students only).

Osgoode Hall: early September to mid-May.

Grading system

All courses in the university (except Osgoode
Hall Law School) are graded by the letters A,
B, C, D, together with "plus" modifications;
or by E or F. When numerical assignments
are required the following correspondences
are used. Grade and numerical
correspondence: $F - O$; $E - 1$; $D - 2$; $D+
- 3$; $C - 4$; $C+ - 5$; $B - 6$; $B+ - 7$; $A - 8$;
$A+ - 9$. Osgoode Hall Law School: *Average*
— honors: 75-100%; pass class I: 66-74%;
pass class II: 56-65%; failure: below 56%.
Subject — A: 75-100%; B: 66-74%; C: 56-
65%; D: 50-55%; F: below 50%.

Fees and costs

Full-time students, all-inclusive fee of $560 for the academic year. Graduate students in arts and science, $500; administrative studies, $550. Part-time students, $110 per course registration.

Residence accommodation, including full room and board for all the academic year: single rooms, $1,200; double rooms, $1,125 per person. (These fees refer to the 1971-72 academic session.)

Financial awards and assistance

Admission scholarships for students entering from grade 13 or equivalent.

General Motors scholarship. Gift of General Motors of Canada Limited. The scholarship is valued at $1,000 a year for three or four years, provided that the student maintains a standing acceptable to the senate committee on scholarships and other awards.

William Pearson Scott scholarship. A scholarship of $1,000 to be awarded to an outstanding student in economics or political science who is entering either his fourth year of specialized honors studies, or is in his first year of graduate work in either or both of these fields.

Cape and Company scholarship. Alternately awarded in the faculty of Glendon College and the faculty of arts to a senior student in the humanities. Value $300.

The Lex Mackenzie scholarship. This scholarship is named in honor of Major A.A. Mackenzie, MC, for his long devotion to his constituents over 22 years as the member of York North in the Ontario legislative assembly. The scholarship fund will award $150 annually to an outstanding full-time undergraduate in Canadian historical studies. This scholarship will be awarded in alternate years in the faculty of arts and science and Glendon College. The recipient must reside within the boundaries north of Steeles Avenue of the old provincial riding of York North as it existed until June 1966, comprising the townships of Vaughan, King, East Gwillimbury, Whitchurch, Markham, North Gwillimbury, Georgina, and all municipalities within this area.

It is not necessary for grade 13 students in the province of Ontario to make special application for the admission awards mentioned above. Others should write to the office of student awards, York University, to request application forms.

Research institutes

The chemistry and physics departments are engaged in a co-operative research endeavor in laboratory astrophysics, chemical aeronomy and chemical physics, organized in the *Centre for Research in Experimental Space Science (CRESS)*. All the graduate work and research of the two departments is done in the centre, which is intended to be the first of a number of such co-operative programs.

Other special research programs include: the *Institute for Behavioral Research* which through the services of three subsections — the survey research centre, the data bank, the data analysis section — facilitates and encourages extensive interdisciplinary studies in the behavioral sciences; the York University *Transport Centre* established to promote, support, and co-ordinate programs of study and research in the transportation field.

Deans of faculties

Administrative studies
J.M. Gillies, BA, MA, PhD

Arts
J.T. Saywell, BA, MA, PhD

Environmental studies
G.A.P. Carrothers, BArch, MArch, MCP, PhD

Fine arts
J. Heller, BA, MA, PhD

Graduate studies
M. Collie, MA

Joseph E. Atkinson College
H.S. Crowe, MC, BA, MA

Osgoode Hall Law School
G.E. LeDain, QC, BCL, Ddel'Univ

Science
M.I. Schiff, BA, MA, PhD

Department chairmen

Accounting
J.R.E. Parker

Art
D. Morton

Behavioral sciences
R.C. Joyner

Biology
R.H. Haynes

Chemistry
H.O. Prichard

Computer science
D. Solitar (acting)

Dance
G. Strate

Economics
G.H. McKechnie

Economics (administrative studies)
W.A. Jordan

Economics (Glendon College)
D. McQueen

English
H. Rinehart

English (Glendon College)
M.J. Gregory

Film
J. Beveridge

Finance
S. Friedland

Foreign literature
I. Bar-Lewaw

French (Glendon College)
H.S. Robertson

French literature
C.E. Rathe

Geography
A.M. Blair (acting)

History
S. Eisen

History (Glendon College)
A. Tucker

Humanities
M. Creal

Humanities (Glendon College)
W. Beringer

Linguistics and language training
M.L. Kay

Management science
J.D. Fleck

Marketing
G.A. Edwards

Mathematics
D. Solitar

Music
R.S. Beckwith

Natural science
C.B. Cragg

Natural science (Glendon College)
A.G. Sangster

Philosophy
J.W. Yolton

Philosophy (Glendon College)
H.S. Harris

Physical education
B.M. Taylor

Physics
R.M. Hobson

Political science
H. Kaplan

Political science (Glendon College)
T.K. Olson

Psychology
M. Westcott

Social science
T.W. Olson (acting)

Sociology
J. O'Neill

Sociology (Glendon College)
J. Burnet (Miss)

Theatre arts
J.G. Green

Degree-granting institutions which are not AUCC members nor federated with or affiliated to members of the association

Institutions conférant des grades qui ne sont pas membres de l'AUCC ni rattachées à un membre de l'association par fédération ou affiliation

Le Collège
Sainte-Anne

Le Collège
Sainte-Anne

Church Point, Nova Scotia

Church Point, Nouvelle-Ecosse

Rector
Raymond LeBlanc, cjm, BA

Recteur
Raymond LeBlanc, cjm, BA

Registrar
Blaise Corrivault, cjm, BA, BEd

Secrétaire général
Blaise Corrivault, cjm, BA, BEd

Collège Sainte-Anne was founded in 1890 by the priests of the Congregation of Jesus and Mary, known as Eudists. The college was incorporated in 1892, by an act of the provincial legislature, and was endowed with the power to confer university degrees. The first degrees were awarded in 1903. The college is bilingual, co-educational, and Catholic.

Collège Sainte-Anne offers:
1. Courses leading to a *BA* degree in the following fields as majors: French; English; history; social sciences; sociology.
2. A general *bachelor of arts* (humanities-science major) program of three years for future students of medicine or dentistry, or future science teachers. This program is open to students with a Nova Scotia grade XII or the equivalent, and having taken the following grade XII subjects: mathematics (2) and two courses from chemistry, biology, physics.
3. *Bachelor of commerce* (first two years).
4. *Bachelor of science* (first two years).

Le Collège Sainte-Anne a été fondé en 1890 par des Pères Eudistes venus de la France. Le 30 avril 1892, en vertu d'un acte de la législature provinciale, il a été incorporé et il a reçu le titre d'université avec tous les pouvoirs et tous les privilèges afférents à ce titre. Les premiers grades furent conférés en 1903. L'institution est bilingue, catholique et mixte. Elle est sous la direction des Pères Eudistes.

Le Collège Sainte-Anne dispense les cours suivants:
1. Cours conduisant au *baccalauréat ès arts* avec mention dans les matières suivantes: français, anglais, histoire, sciences sociales et sociologie.
2. Cours de *baccalauréat ès arts* (mention humanités-science) de trois ans pour futurs étudiants en médecine ou en art dentaire, et pour les futurs professeurs de sciences. Ce programme s'adresse aux étudiants qui ont terminé la XIIe année de la Nouvelle-Ecosse ou l'équivalent, et qui ont suivi les cours de mathématiques (2 cours) et deux cours dans les matières suivantes: chimie, biologie ou physique au niveau de la XIIe année.
3. Cours de *baccalauréat en commerce* (les deux premières années).
4. Cours de *baccalauréat ès sciences* avec spécialisation (les deux premières années).

Seminary of
Christ the King

Mission City, British Columbia

Rector
Augustine Kalberer, osb

Registrar
Lawrence Bilesky, osb

Established in 1931, the seminary in 1966
received a charter from the provincial
legislature to grant the bachelor of arts
degree and degrees in theology. The
seminary is staffed by Benedictines and
offers four years of tuition in the faculty
of arts and four years in the faculty of
theology to students preparing for the
priesthood.

Bachelor of arts (BA).
Degree granted on a general program and
on a major program.

Bachelor of theology (BTh).
Degree granted after three years of
theological studies for which the BA or its
equivalent is prerequisite. A fourth year of
theological studies is required to complete
the professional training for the
priesthood.

Statistics on Canadian universities and colleges

Statistics on Canadian universities and colleges includes full- and part-time enrolment, foreign student full-time enrolment, teaching staff and earned degrees conferred

Statistiques sur les universités et collèges du Canada

Statistiques sur les universités et collèges du Canada comprenant les inscriptions à temps plein ou partiel, le nombre d'étudiants étrangers à plein temps, le corps enseignant et les diplômes ou grades conférés

Table 1. Full-time student enrolment at Canadian universities and colleges, 1970–71
Tableau 1. Etudiants à plein temps inscrits aux universités et collèges du Canada, 1970–71

Institution	Non-university level courses / Cours du niveau non universitaire		Students not studying for a degree, diploma or certificate / Etudiants non inscrits en vue d'un grade, diplôme ou certificat		Undergraduates / 1er cycle		Graduates / 2e et 3e cycles		Full-time totals / Total des étudiants à plein temps	
	Total	Females Femmes	Total	Females Femmes	Total	Females Femmes	Total	Females Femmes	Total	Females Femmes
Acadia University	—	—	—	—	2,284	984	66	12	2,350	996
Alberta, The University of	—	—	829	551	15,584	6,363	2,329	467	18,742	7,381
Bishop's University	—	—	2	—	1,140	447	17	3	1,159	450
Brandon University	—	—	—	—	1,150	507	—	—	1,150	507
Brescia College	—	—	—	—	275	274	—	—	275	274
British Columbia, The University of	—	—	123	27	17,280	6,839	2,754	703	20,157	7,569
Brock University	—	—	—	—	2,138	673	25	2	2,163	675
Calgary, The University of	—	—	249	67	8,126	3,083	881	209	9,256	3,359
Carleton University	—	—	97	28	7,457	2,737	716	180	8,270	2,945
Christ the King, Seminary of	—	—	—	—	2	—	—	—	2	—
Dalhousie University	—	—	—	—	4,574	1,655	971	248	5,545	1,903
Guelph, University of	202	5	—	—	5,455	2,171	560	67	6,217	2,243
Huron College	—	—	—	—	543	228	—	—	543	228
Jean-de-Brébeuf, Collège	—	—	—	—	184	65	—	—	184	65
King's College, University of (Halifax)	—	—	—	—	282	139	3	1	285	140

Full-time students/Etudiants à plein temps

Institution	Non-university level courses/ Cours du niveau non universitaire		Students not studying for a degree, diploma or certificate/ Etudiants non inscrits en vue d'un grade, diplôme ou certificat		Undergraduates/ 1er cycle		Graduates/ 2e et 3e cycles		Full-time totals/ Total des étudiants à plein temps	
	Total	Females Femmes	Total	Females Femmes	Total	Females Femmes	Total	Females Femmes	Total	Females Femmes
King's College (London)	—	—	—	—	751	287	—	—	751	287
Lakehead University	313	51	118	118	2,419	754	81	8	2,931	931
Laurentian University of Sudbury/ Laurentienne de Sudbury, Université	—	—	—	—	2,092	721	16	—	2,108	721
Laval, Université	—	—	—	—	9,222	2,515	1,106	206	10,328	2,721
Lethbridge, The University of	—	—	—	—	1,409	603	—	—	1,409	603
Loyola College	167	—	53	17	3,812	1,270	—	—	3,865	1,287
Manitoba, The University of	—	—	83	21	11,232	4,499	1,410	289	12,892	4,809
Marianopolis College	—	—	—	—	114	114	—	—	114	114
McGill University	—	—	663	87	11,455	4,695	3,060	891	15,178	5,673
McMaster University	—	—	327	30	6,398	2,495	1,203	153	7,928	2,678
Memorial University of Newfoundland	—	—	—	—	6,045	2,216	333	81	6,378	2,297
Moncton, Université de	—	—	20	8	2,999	1,241	130	30	3,149	1,279
Montréal, Université de	82	74	—	—	11,076	3,563	1,974	557	13,132	4,194
Mount Allison University	—	—	—	—	1,342	598	5	—	1,347	598
Mount Saint Vincent University	—	—	2	2	942	913	—	—	944	915

New Brunswick, University of	1,553	5,102	81	459	1,472	4,643	—	—
Notre Dame University of Nelson	253	646	—	—	253	646	—	—
Nova Scotia Agricultural College	26	194	—	—	26	194	—	—
Nova Scotia College of Art and Design	198	388	—	—	196	383	2	5
Nova Scotia Technical College	8	567	3	41	5	526	—	—
Ontario Institute for Studies in Education[1]	..	377	..	377	—	—	—	—
Ottawa, Université d'/ Ottawa, University of	2,921	8,243	400	1,420	2,471	6,572	50	251
Prince Edward Island, University of	737	1,755	—	—	737	1,755	—	—
Québec, Université du								
à Chicoutimi	188	864	10	29	178	835	—	—
à Montréal	1,593	4,035	12	40	1,520	3,882	61	113
à Rimouski	89	241	—	—	89	241	—	—
à Trois-Rivières	529	1,698	26	106	503	1,591	—	1
Ecole Nationale d'administration publique	2	25	2	25	—	—	—	—
Institut nationale de la recherche scientifique	1	10	1	10	—	—	—	—
Queen's University at Kingston	2,780	8,087	134	999	2,603	6,856	43	232
Royal Military College of Canada	—	542	—	14	—	528	—	—
Sainte-Anne, Le Collège	47	134	—	—	47	134	—	—
St. Francis Xavier University	1,340	3,087	14	34	1,312	2,973	14	80
St. Jerome's College	142	445	22	65	120	380	—	—

.. Figures not available.

.. Chiffres non disponibles.

1. The 377 graduate students are also included with the University of Toronto.

1. Les 377 étudiants des 2e et 3e cycles sont aussi compris dans ceux de l'Université de Toronto.

Full-time students/Etudiants à plein temps

Institution	Non-university level courses / Cours du niveau non universitaire		Students not studying for a degree, diploma or certificate / Etudiants non inscrits en vue d'un grade, diplôme ou certificat		Undergraduates / 1er cycle		Graduates / 2e et 3e cycles		Full-time totals / Total des étudiants à plein temps	
	Total	Females Femmes	Total	Females Femmes	Total	Females Femmes	Total	Females Femmes	Total	Females Femmes
St. John's College	—	—	—	—	310	10	—	—	310	10
Saint Mary's University	—	—	—	—	2,280	460	16	2	2,296	462
St. Michael's College[2]	—	—	—	—	58	—	78	20	136	20
Saint-Paul, Université / Saint Paul University (Ottawa)	—	—	63	46	267	53	164	16	494	115
St. Paul's College	—	—	—	—	554	219	16	4	570	223
St. Thomas More College	—	—	—	—	778	357	—	—	778	357
Saskatchewan, University of, Regina Campus	72	19	14	4	3,567	1,442	140	29	3,793	1,494
Saskatchewan, University of, Saskatoon Campus	201	1	—	—	8,660	3,400	603	83	9,464	3,484
Sherbrooke, Université de	—	—	46	9	3,403	766	716	98	4,165	873
Simon Fraser University	—	—	—	—	3,658	1,459	719	99	4,377	1,558
Sir George Williams University	—	—	43	14	5,528	1,811	195	51	5,766	1,876
Toronto, University of[3]	—	—	1,154	231	20,499	8,075	4,915	1,351	26,568	9,657
Trent University	—	—	—	—	1,643	717	10	1	1,653	718
Trinity College, University of[4]	—	—	—	—	31	—	5	—	36	—
Victoria, University of (B.C.)	—	—	213	68	4,723	2,133	183	46	5,119	2,247

Victoria University (Toronto)[5]	9	5	56	6	12	2	77	13
Waterloo, University of	192	29	10,225	2,369	1,299	159	11,716	2,557
Waterloo Lutheran University	—	—	2,638	841	188	63	2,826	904
Western Ontario, The University of	—	—	10,480	3,961	1,739	351	12,219	4,312
Windsor, University of	—	—	5,474	1,924	466	64	5,940	1,988
Winnipeg, The University of	43	16	2,362	828	3	—	2,408	844
York University	—	—	9,002	3,416	785	151	9,787	3,567

2. 2,107 (1,043 male, 1,064 female) undergraduates are included with the University of Toronto.

3. Includes 377 graduate students from the Ontario Institute for Studies in Education, 2,107 (1,043 male, 1,064 female) undergraduates from St. Michael's College, 723 (359 male, 364 female) undergraduates from University of Trinity College, and 2,550 (1,226 male, 1,324 female) undergraduates from Victoria University.

4. 723 (359 male, 364 female) undergraduates are included with the University of Toronto.

5. 2,550 (1,226 male, 1,324 female) undergraduates are included with the University of Toronto.

2. 2,107 étudiants du 1er cycle (1,043 étudiants, 1,064 étudiantes) sont compris dans ceux de l'Université de Toronto.

3. Comprend 377 étudiants des 2e et 3e cycles de l'Ontario Institute for Studies in Education, 2,107 étudiants du 1er cycle (1,043 étudiants, 1,064 étudiantes) du St. Michael's College, 723 étudiants du 1er cycle (359 étudiants, 364 étudiantes) de l'Université du Trinity College et 2,550 étudiants du 1er cycle (1,226 étudiants, 1,324 étudiantes) de l'Université Victoria.

4. 723 étudiants du 1er cycle (359 étudiants, 364 étudiantes) sont compris dans ceux de l'Université de Toronto.

5. 2,550 étudiants du 1er cycle (1,226 étudiants, 1,324 étudiantes) sont compris dans ceux de l'Université de Toronto.

Table 2. Part-time student enrolment at Canadian universities and colleges, 1970–71
Tableau 2. Etudiants à temps partiel inscrits aux universités et collèges du Canada, 1970–71

Institution	Non-university level courses / Cours du niveau non universitaire		Students not studying for a degree, diploma or certificate / Etudiants non inscrits en vue d'un grade, diplôme ou certificat		Undergraduates / 1er cycle		Graduates / 2e et 3e cycles		Part-time totals / Total des étudiants à temps partiel	
	Total	Females Femmes	Total	Females Femmes	Total	Females Femmes	Total	Females Femmes	Total	Females Femmes
Acadia University	—	—	—	—	44	20	—	—	44	20
Alberta, The University of	—	—	661	322	2,338	1,445	678	190	3,677	1,957
Bishop's University	—	—	6	4	190	83	20	8	216	95
Brandon University	—	—	—	—	1,100	624	—	—	1,100	624
Brescia College	—	—	—	—	13	13	—	—	13	13
British Columbia, The University of	—	—	573	309	1,469	1,015	307	87	2,349	1,411
Brock University	—	—	432	17	1,600	739	3	—	2,035	756
Calgary, The University of	—	—	820	420	1,529	198	574	158	2,923	1,529
Carleton University	—	—	3,914	1,584	1,362	586	455	76	5,731	2,246
Dalhousie University	—	—	—	—	512	290	277	87	789	377
Guelph, University of	1	—	—	—	263	142	110	26	374	168
Huron College	—	—	—	—	7	4	—	—	7	4
Jean-de-Brébeuf, Collège	—	—	—	—	6	4	—	—	6	4
King's College, University of (Halifax)	—	—	—	—	12	4	2	—	14	4
King's College (London)	—	—	—	—	34	23	—	—	34	23

Institution										
Lakehead University			—	—	1,395	..	35	..	1,430	..
Laurentian University of Sudbury / Laurentienne de Sudbury, Université			61	32	2,033	1,010	—	—	2,094	1,042
Laval, Université			4,551	1,328	1,648	711	818	137	7,017	2,176
Lethbridge, The University of			130	82	486	319	—	—	486	319
Loyola College					4,510	1,473		—	4,640	1,555
Manitoba, The University of			155	64	3,512	1,788	518	107	4,185	1,959
McGill University	8	3	11,540	4,606	2,989	373	426	189	14,963	5,171
McMaster University			3,623	1,018	2,409	1,209	477	43	6,509	2,270
Memorial University of Newfoundland					2,747	..	115	..	2,862	..
Moncton, Université de			471	221	2,192	1,419	101	33	2,764	1,673
Montréal, Université de			7,903	831	4,154	1,540	2,318	655	14,375	3,026
Mount Allison University					36	26		9	36	26
Mount Saint Vincent University			31	25	233	210	25		289	244
New Brunswick, University of			583	261	1,182	686	62	18	1,827	965
Notre Dame University of Nelson			9	6	49	18			58	24
Nova Scotia College of Art and Design			38	25	5	1		—	43	26
Nova Scotia Technical College						—	58	2	58	2
Ontario Institute for Studies in Education[1]							2,043	..	2,043	..
Ottawa, Université d' / Ottawa, University of					3,626	1,962	1,468	358	5,094	2,320
Prince Edward Island, University of			62	49	1,006	653		—	1,068	702
Québec, Université du										
à Chicoutimi	120	56	158	10	954	468	—	—	1,232	534
à Montréal	1,140	353	—	—	4,346	2,423	—	—	5,480	2,776
à Rimouski	265	145	75	2	719	406	—	—	1,059	553
à Trois-Rivières	152	68	247	..	2,928	1,447	—	—	3,327	1,515

— Figures not available.

.. Chiffres non disponibles.

1. The 2,043 graduate students are also included with the University of Toronto.

1. Les 2,043 étudiants des 2e et 3e cycles sont aussi compris dans ceux de l'Université de Toronto.

Part-time students/Etudiants à temps partiel

Institution	Non-university level courses/ Cours du niveau non universitaire		Students not studying for a degree, diploma or certificate/ Etudiants non inscrits en vue d'un grade, diplôme ou certificat		Undergraduates/ 1er cycle		Graduates/ 2e et 3e cycles		Full-time totals/ Total des étudiants à temps partiel	
	Total	Females Femmes	Total	Females Femmes	Total	Females Femmes	Total	Females Femmes	Total	Females Femmes
Queen's University at Kingston	—	—	10	1	2,313	1,138	273	50	2,596	1,189
Royal Military College of Canada	—	—	—	—	22	—	15	—	37	—
Sainte-Anne, Le Collège	—	—	—	—	8	—	—	—	8	7
St. Francis Xavier University	—	—	6	6	1,057	640	—	—	1,063	646
St. Jerome's College	—	—	—	—	143	70	—	—	143	70
Saint Mary's University	—	—	43	25	487	172	38	7	568	204
St. Michael's College	—	—	—	—	15	6	8	2	23	8
Saint-Paul, Université/ Saint Paul University (Ottawa)	—	—	5	3	29	18	21	2	55	23
St. Paul's College	—	—	—	—	36	9	3	1	39	10
St. Thomas More College	—	—	9	4	32	16	2	2	43	22
Saskatchewan, University of, Regina Campus	465	48	87	49	923	525	138	39	1,613	661
Saskatchewan, University of, Saskatoon Campus	—	—	24	4	1,668	893	276	73	1,968	970
Sherbrooke, Université de	—	—	115	64	1,036	470	—	—	1,151	534
Simon Fraser University	—	—	1	—	461	248	11	4	473	252
Sir George Williams University	—	—	3,453	1,255	8,279	3,174	641	126	12,373	4,553

Toronto, University of[2]	1,372	603	5,845	3,457	2,372	650	9,589	4,710
Trent University	—	—	530	245	2	—	532	245
Trinity College, University of	—	—	7	—	12	—	19	—
Victoria, University of (B.C.)	174	81	480	306	101	22	755	409
Victoria University (Toronto)	—	—	—	—	32	—	32	—
Waterloo, University of	740	184	250	160	331	41	1,321	385
Waterloo Lutheran University	—	—	3,872	1,519	71	12	3,943	1,531
Western Ontario, The University of	—	—	3,118	1,627	130	77	3,248	1,704
Windsor, University of	—	—	2,883	1,435	186	42	3,069	1,477
Winnipeg, The University of	285	127	1,928	1,037	2	—	2,215	1,164
York University	428	122	5,873	1,772	774	53	7,075	1,947

2. Includes 2,043 graduate students from the Ontario Institute for Studies in Education.

2. Comprend 2,043 étudiants des 2e et 3e cycles de l'Ontario Institute for Studies in Education.

Table 3. Full-time foreign student enrolment at Canadian universities and colleges, 1970–71
Tableau 3. Étudiants étrangers inscrits à plein temps dans les universités et collèges du Canada en 1970–71

Institution	Undergraduates (permanently resident outside of Canada)/ 1er cycle (domiciliés à l'extérieur du Canada)		Graduates (non-Canadian citizens)/ 2e et 3e cycles (non-citoyens canadiens)		Total full-time foreign students/ Total des étudiants étrangers à plein temps	
	Total	Females Femmes	Total	Females Femmes	Total	Females Femmes
Acadia University	130	45	17	4	147	49
Alberta, The University of	459	74	900	182	1,359	256
Bishop's University	101	45	1	—	102	45
Brandon University	34	7	—	—	34	7
Brescia College	27	27	—	—	27	27
British Columbia, The University of	295	76	1,032	209	1,327	285
Brock University	35	8	20	2	55	10
Calgary, The University of	131	40	383	63	514	103
Carleton University	232	80	200	32	432	112
Christ the King, Seminary of	1	—	—	—	1	—
Dalhousie University	226	44	250	60	476	310
Guelph, University of	94	15	223	19	317	34
Huron College	12	4	—	—	12	4
Jean-de-Brébeuf, Collège	45	8	—	—	45	8
King's College, University of (Halifax)	2	—	1	1	3	1

King's College (London)	8	3	—	—	8	3
Lakehead University	148	29	22	1	170	30
Laurentian University of Sudbury/ Laurentienne Université de Sudbury, Université	21	4	1	—	22	4
Laval, Université	243	73	290	72	533	145
Lethbridge, The University of	20	7	—	—	20	7
Loyola College	185	42	—	—	185	42
Manitoba, The University of	885	222	430	63	1,315	285
Marianopolis College	26	26	—	—	26	26
McGill University	1,205	360	1,382	317	2,587	677
McMaster University	296	70	635	67	931	137
Memorial University of Newfoundland	44	11	113	27	157	38
Moncton, Université de	14	6	4	1	18	7
Montréal, Université de[1]	1,651	..	—	—	1,651	..
Mount Allison University	50	19	5	—	55	19
Mount Saint Vincent University	36	36	—	—	36	36
New Brunswick, University of	187	33	142	21	329	54
Notre Dame University of Nelson	100	28	—	—	100	28
Nova Scotia Agricultural College	..	..	—	—	..	..
Nova Scotia College of Art and Design	40	20	—	—	40	20
Nova Scotia Technical College	27	1	28	3	55	4
Ontario Institute for Studies in Education	..	..	..	..	..	..
Ottawa, Université d'/Ottawa, University of	655	163	433	98	1,088	261
Prince Edward Island, University of	94	16	—	—	94	16

.. Figures not available.

1. Includes both full-time undergraduates and graduates.

.. Chiffres non disponibles.

1. Comprend les étudiants à plein temps des 1er, 2e et 3e cycles.

Full-time foreign students/Etudiants étrangers à plein temps

Institution	Undergraduates (permanently resident outside of Canada)/ 1er cycle (domiciliés à l'extérieur du Canada)		Graduates (non-Canadian citizens)/ 2e et 3e cycles (non-citoyens canadiens)		Total full-time foreign students/ Total des étudiants étrangers à plein temps	
	Total	Females Femmes	Total	Females Femmes	Total	Females Femmes
Québec, Université du						
à Chicoutimi	:	:	:	:	:	:
à Montréal	:	:	:	:	:	:
à Rimouski	:	:	:	:	:	:
à Trois-Rivières	:	:	:	:	:	:
Ecole Nationale d'administration publique	:	:	:	:	:	:
Institut national de la recherche	:	:	:	:	:	:
Queen's University at Kingston	323	106	369	36	692	142
Royal Military College of Canada	16	1	—	—	16	1
Sainte-Anne, Le Collège	3	1	—	—	3	1
St. Francis Xavier University	180	34	8	3	188	37
St. Jerome's College	:	:	—	—	:	:
St. John's College	:	:	—	—	:	:
Saint Mary's University	93	2	—	—	93	2
St. Michael's College	15	—	56	14	71	14
Saint-Paul, Université/Saint Paul University	75	6	62	1	137	7
St. Thomas More College	2	—	—	—	2	—

Saskatchewan, University of, Regina Campus	142	39	50	13	192	52
Saskatchewan, University of, Saskatoon	67	24	124	12	191	36
Sherbrooke, Université de	51	9	86	8	137	17
Simon Fraser University	86	..	..	..	86	..
Sir George Williams University	504	..	72	14	576	14
Toronto, University of	934	271	1,887	447	2,821	718
Trent University	45	23	2	—	47	23
Trinity College, University of	..	..	..	..	..	..
Victoria, University of (B.C.)	34	14	69	13	103	27
Victoria University (Toronto)	..	..	5	—	5	—
Waterloo, University of	112	24	588	62	700	86
Waterloo Lutheran University	99	10	30	—	129	10
Western Ontario, The University of	326	97	407	78	733	175
Windsor, University of	235	76	155	14	390	90
Winnipeg, The University of	27	9	2	—	29	9
York University	199	87	267	56	466	143

Table 4 (part I). Undergraduate degrees, diplomas and certificates awarded by Canadian universities and colleges, 1969–70
Tableau 4 (partie I). Grades, diplômes et certificats du niveau du premier cycle, décernés par les universités et collèges du Canada, 1969–70

Institution	Bachelor and first professional degrees / Baccalauréats et premiers grades professionnels		Undergraduate diplomas / Diplômes du 1er cycle		Undergraduate certificates / Certificats du 1er cycle		Total undergraduate degrees, diplomas and certificates / Total des grades, diplômes et certificats du 1er cycle	
	Total	Females Femmes	Total	Females Femmes	Total	Females Femmes	Total	Females Femmes
Acadia University	520	248	40	29	32	—	592	277
Alberta, The University of	3,231	1,396	93	93	—	—	3,324	1,489
Bishop's University	173	65	—	—	28	13	201	78
Brandon University	200	65	1	—	235	169	436	234
British Columbia, The University of	3,548	1,481	65	64	—	—	3,613	1,545
Brock University	215	60	—	—	—	—	215	60
Calgary, The University of	1,313	499	—	—	—	—	1,313	499
Carleton University	1,356	504	—	—	15	—	1,371	504
Christ the King, Seminary of	—	—	4	—	—	—	4	—
Dalhousie University	985	405	186	172	—	—	1,171	577

Guelph, University of	1,154	434	128	—	—	—	1,282	434
Huron College	5	—	—	—	—	—	5	—
Lakehead University	429	140	268	141	—	—	697	281
Laurentian University of Sudbury/ Laurentienne de Sudbury, Université	434	130	—	—	—	—	434	130
Laval, Université	4,288	1,596	302	217	432	272	5,022	2,085
Lethbridge, The University of	181	70	—	—	—	—	181	70
Manitoba, The University of	2,630	859	139	70	596	360	3,365	1,289
McGill University	2,440	954	276	209	—	—	2,716	1,163
McMaster University	1,303	514	—	—	—	—	1,303	514
Memorial University of Newfoundland	823	290	66	5	—	—	889	295
Moncton, Université de	415	134	—	—	9	—	424	134
Montréal, Université de	7,653	3,283	327	254	158	100	8,138	3,637
Mount Allison University	326	154	—	—	22	1	348	155
Mount Saint Vincent University	216	216	28	27	—	—	244	243
New Brunswick, University of	953	352	9	—	—	—	962	352
Notre Dame University of Nelson	91	34	6	6	—	—	97	40
Nova Scotia College of Art and Design	9	7	28	9	—	—	37	16
Nova Scotia Technical College	198	—	—	—	—	—	198	—
Ottawa, Université d'/ Ottawa, University of	1,516	587	—	—	167	129	1,683	716
Prince Edward Island, University of	277	101	34	24	—	—	311	125
Québec, Université du	186	52	—	—	—	—	186	52
Queen's University at Kingston	1,736	686	21	21	—	—	1,757	707
Royal Military College of Canada	182	—	—	—	—	—	182	—
Sainte-Anne, Le Collège	20	9	—	—	—	—	20	9
St. Francis Xavier University	669	305	149	59	—	—	818	364

Undergraduate degrees, diplomas and certificates/Grades, diplômes et certificats du niveau du premier cycle

Institution	Bachelor and first professional degrees/ Baccalauréats et premiers grades professionnels		Undergraduate diplomas/ Diplômes du 1er cycle		Undergraduate certificates/ Certificats du 1er cycle		Total undergraduate degrees, diplomas and certificates/ Total des grades, diplômes et certificats du 1er cycle	
	Total	Females Femmes	Total	Females Femmes	Total	Females Femmes	Total	Females Femmes
Saint Mary's University	435	73	23	—	—	—	458	73
St. Michael's College, University of	14	—	—	—	—	—	14	—
Saint-Paul, Université/ Saint Paul, University (Ottawa)	161	21	—	—	—	—	161	21
Saskatchewan, University of, Regina Campus	737	249	13	11	135	33	885	293
Saskatchewan, University of, Saskatoon Campus	2,195	743	150	51	77	20	2,422	814
Sherbrooke, Université de	1,127	396	52	2	182	82	1,361	480
Simon Fraser University	644	161	—	—	—	—	644	161
Sir George Williams University	1,442	500	7	7	6	—	1,455	507
Toronto, University of	5,012	2,261	150	145	119	55	5,281	2,461
Trent University	209	106	—	—	—	—	209	106

Trinity College, University of	14	—	—	—	—	—	14	—
Victoria, University of (B.C.)	597	235	—	—	—	—	597	235
Victoria University (Toronto)	15	2	8	—	—	—	23	2
Waterloo, University of	1,231	244	—	—	—	—	1,231	244
Waterloo Lutheran University	1,030	288	47	2	28	2	1,105	292
Western Ontario, The University of	2,116	916	12	8	—	—	2,128	924
Windsor, University of	1,217	456	33	33	36	6	1,286	495
Winnipeg, The University of	630	247	—	—	—	—	630	247
York University	1,404	525	—	—	—	—	1,404	525

Table 4 (part II).   Graduate degrees, diplomas and certificates awarded by Canadian universities and colleges, 1969–70
Tableau 4 (partie II).   Grades, diplômes et certificats des 2e et 3e cycles, décernés par les universités et collèges du Canada, 1969–70

Institution	Total undergraduate degrees, diplomas and certificates (from table 4, part I)/ Total des grades, diplômes et certificats du 1er cycle (extrait du tableau 4, partie I)		Graduate diplomas/ Diplômes des 2e et 3e cycles		Masters/ Maîtrises et équivalents		Doctorates/ Doctorats		Total undergraduate and graduate degrees, diplomas and certificates/ Total des grades, diplômes et certificats des 2e et 3e cycles	
	Total	Females Femmes	Total	Females Femmes	Total	Females Femmes	Total	Females Femmes	Total	Females Femmes
Acadia University	592	277	—	—	15	1	—	—	607	278
Alberta, The University of	3,324	1,489	143	2	417	73	150	9	4,034	1,573
Brandon University	436	234	4	—	—	—	—	—	440	234
British Columbia, The University of	3,613	1,545	36	23	610	141	138	17	4,397	1,726
Brock University	215	60	—	—	3	—	—	—	218	60
Calgary, The University of	1,313	499	81	31	170	41	18	2	1,582	573
Carleton University	1,371	504	34	3	247	59	10	1	1,662	567
Dalhousie University	1,114	552	2	—	156	48	18	—	1,290	600
Guelph, University of	1,282	434	—	—	152	17	26	1	1,460	452
Lakehead University	697	281	7	—	7	1	—	—	711	282

Laval, Université	5,022	2,085	8	3	329	55	53	8	5,412	2,151
Manitoba, The University of	3,365	1,289	9	—	373	76	50	2	3,797	1,367
McGill University	2,716	1,163	146	9	676	208	137	14	3,675	1,394
McMaster University	1,303	514	—	—	346	35	75	7	1,724	556
Memorial University of Newfoundland	889	295	—	—	41	6	2	2	932	303
Moncton, Université de	424	134	26	4	23	5	—	—	447	139
Montréal, Université de	8,138	3,637	—	—	593	184	68	11	8,825	3,836
Mount Allison University	348	155	—	—	4	1	—	—	352	156
Mount Saint Vincent University	244	243	—	—	4	4	—	—	248	247
New Brunswick, University of	962	352	—	—	120	19	22	1	1,104	372
Nova Scotia Technical College	198	—	1	—	36	—	4	—	234	—
Ottawa, Université d'/Ottawa, University of	1,683	716	—	—	320	75	57	6	2,061	797
Québec, Université du	186	52	10	—	5	—	—	—	191	52
Queen's University at Kingston	1,757	707	—	1	200	23	47	3	2,014	734
Royal Military College of Canada	182	—	—	—	9	—	—	—	191	—
St. Francis Xavier University	818	364	—	—	13	2	—	—	831	366
Saint Mary's University	458	73	—	—	12	3	—	—	470	76
St. Michael's College, University of	14	—	—	—	13	1	3	1	30	2
Saint-Paul, Université/St. Paul University (Ottawa)	161	21	—	—	58	4	2	—	221	25
Saskatchewan, University of, Regina Campus	885	293	—	—	25	6	10	—	920	299
Saskatchewan, University of, Saskatoon Campus	2,422	814	270	112	159	20	49	6	2,900	952
Sherbrooke, Université de	1,361	480	—	—	168	11	2	—	1,531	491
Simon Fraser University	644	161	—	—	67	9	13	—	724	170
Sir George Williams University	1,455	507	—	—	58	17	—	—	1,513	524
Toronto, University of	5,281	2,461	219	56	1,577	454	252	31	7,329	3,002

Graduate degrees, diplomas and certificates/Grades, diplômes et certificats des 2e et 3e cycles

Institution	Total undergraduate degrees, diplomas and certificates (from table 4, part I)/ Total des grades, diplômes et certificats du 1er cycle (extrait du tableau 4, partie I)		Graduate diplomas/ Diplômes des 2e et 3e cycles		Masters/ Maîtrises et équivalents		Doctorates/ Doctorats		Total undergraduate and graduate degrees, diplomas and certificates/ Total des grades, diplômes et certificats des 2e et 3e cycles	
	Total	Females Femmes	Total	Females Femmes	Total	Females Femmes	Total	Females Femmes	Total	Females Femmes
Trent University	209	106	—	—	2	—	—	—	211	106
Trinity College, University of	14	—	—	—	2	—	—	—	16	—
Victoria, University of (B.C.)	597	235	—	—	50	5	1	—	648	240
Victoria University (Toronto)	23	2	—	—	1	—	—	—	24	2
Waterloo, University of	1,231	244	—	—	356	41	74	2	1,661	287
Waterloo Lutheran University	1,105	292	—	—	46	17	—	—	1,151	309
Western Ontario, The University of	2,128	924	6	—	509	91	63	2	2,706	1,017
Windsor, University of	1,286	495	1	—	204	32	20	1	1,511	528
Winnipeg, The University of	630	247	—	—	2	—	—	—	632	247
York University	1,404	525	—	—	253	33	9	1	1,666	559

Table 5.   Full-time university teaching staff in Canadian universities and colleges, 1970–71
Tableau 5.   Professeurs à plein temps dans les universités et collèges du Canada en 1970–71

Institution	Total	Institution	Total
Acadia University	149	Ottawa, Université d' /Ottawa,	
Alberta, The University of	1,268	University of	653
Bishop's University	81	Prince Edward Island,	
Brandon University	95	University of	123
Brescia College	..		
		Québec, Université du	
British Columbia,		à Chicoutimi	99
The University of	1,532	à Montréal	417
Brock University	152	à Rimouski	56
Calgary, The University of	668	à Trois-Rivières	185
Carleton University	480	Ecole Nationale d'administra-	
Christ the King, Seminary of	8	tion publique	5
		Institut national de la recherche	4
Dalhousie University	493		
Guelph, University of	698	Queen's University at Kingston	699
Huron College	25	Royal Military College of Canada	82
Jean-de-Brébeuf, Collège	..	Sainte-Anne, Le Collège	17
King's College, University of		St. Francis Xavier University	192
(Halifax)	15	St. Jerome's College	25
King's College (London)	21	St. John's College	..
Lakehead University	209	Saint Mary's University	146
Laurentian University of Sudbury		St. Michael's College	93
/Laurentienne de Sudbury,		Saint-Paul, Université/Saint Paul	
Université	192	University (Ottawa)	27
Laval, Université	1,265	St. Thomas More College	24
Lethbridge, The University of	139		
		Saskatchewan, University of	
Loyola College	237	(Regina and Saskatoon	
Manitoba, The University of	1,034	Campuses)	1,156
Marianopolis College	..	Sherbrooke, Université de	449
McGill University	1,178	Simon Fraser University	329
McMaster University	477	Sir George Williams University	351
		Toronto, University of	2,087
Memorial University of			
Newfoundland	500	Trent University	120
Moncton, Université de	160	Trinity College, University of	43
Montréal, Université de	964	Victoria, University of (B.C.)	417
Mount Allison University	109	Victoria University (Toronto)	104
Mount Saint Vincent University	52	Waterloo, University of	649
New Brunswick, University of	387	Waterloo Lutheran University	141
Notre Dame University of		Western Ontario,	
Nelson	40	The University of	867
Nova Scotia Agricultural College	..	Windsor, University of	477
Nova Scotia College of Art		Winnipeg, The University of	186
and Design	70	York University	636
Ontario Institute for Studies in			
Education	144		

.. Figures not available.   .. Chiffres non disponibles.

AUCC associate members   Membres associés, AUCC

Association of Canadian Faculties of Dentistry

Association des facultés dentaires du Canada

President
Dr. W.S. Leung
Dean, faculty of dentistry, The University of British Columbia, Vancouver 8, B.C.

Secretary-treasurer
Dr. D.V. Chaytor
Faculty of dentistry, Dalhousie University, 5981 University Ave., Halifax, N.S.

Président
Dr. S. W. Leung
Dean, faculty of dentistry, The University of British Columbia, Vancouver 8, B.C.

Secrétaire-trésorier
Dr. D.V. Chaytor
Faculty of dentistry, Dalhousie University, 5981 University Ave., Halifax, N.S.

The Association of Canadian Faculties of Dentistry was formed in 1967. Formerly, the Canadian schools were active members of the American Association of Dental Schools. ACFD now provides the official representative to the AADS in the person of its president. ACFD became an associate member of the AUCC in November 1969.

The membership consists of the 10 faculties of dentistry in Canada. Each is represented in the house of delegates by its dean and a delegate elected by faculty. From these, an executive council is elected, which meets twice annually. The house of delegates meets annually. Every two years a general session is held, during which time scientific papers are presented.

The association in the past has been supported by membership dues from its member faculties and by grants from the Canadian Fund for Dental Education.

Activities include the publication of a register of faculty staff members in Canada, a register of Canadian graduate students studying in Canada and abroad, a register of graduate and postgraduate programs available in Canada and a newsletter.

The association has conducted studies of staff demands in Canada, of the dental library services in Canada, and of student participation in university government. A major project at the present time is a study being conducted in co-operation with The University of Manitoba entitled "Delivery of dental health care on a national basis: its implications on the training of personnel".

L'Association des facultés dentaires du Canada a été formée en 1967. Auparavant, les facultés d'art dentaire du Canada étaient membres actifs de l'American Association of Dental Schools. Le président de l'AFDC représente maintenant cette association au sein de l'AADS. L'AFDC est devenue membre associé de l'AUCC, au mois de novembre 1969.

Cette association se compose des dix facultés d'art dentaire du Canada. Chacune d'elles est représentée par son doyen et un délégué élu par les professeurs. Les membres du conseil administratif sont élus parmi les doyens et les délégués; ce conseil se réunit deux fois par année. Les délégués se réunissent chaque année et tous les deux ans, une assemblée générale a lieu, au cours de laquelle des travaux scientifiques sont présentés.

Dans le passé, cette association a été financée par les cotisations de ses facultés membres et par des subventions du Fonds canadien pour l'enseignement de l'art dentaire.

Elle publie le répertoire des membres du personnel enseignant au Canada, le répertoire des étudiants gradués canadiens étudiant au Canada et à l'étranger, le répertoire des programmes d'études du niveau pré-grade et post-grade offerts au Canada et le bulletin de nouvelles.

Cette association a entrepris des études, sur les demandes de personnel au Canada, sur les services des bibliothèques d'art dentaire au Canada, et sur la participation des étudiants à l'administration des universités.

Elle a actuellement en chantier une importante étude, menée en collaboration

avec l'Université du Manitoba, et intitulée:
"Un régime de soins dentaires à l'échelle
nationale: ses conséquences pour la
formation du personnel".

Association of Canadian Medical Colleges

Association des facultés de médecine du Canada

151 Slater Street Ottawa, Ont., K1P 5H3

151, rue Slater, Ottawa (Ont.) K1P 5H3

President
Dr. J.R. Evans
Dean of medicine McMaster University,
Hamilton, Ont.

Président
Dr. J.R. Evans
Dean of medicine, McMaster University,
Hamilton, Ont.

Executive director
Dr. J.B. Firstbrook

Directeur administratif
Dr. J.B. Firstbrook

Research director
Dr. R.M. Grainger

Directeur des recherches
Dr. R.M. Grainger

In April 1943, the deans of the 10 then existing Canadian medical schools met in Ottawa at the request of the minister of health, to consider the accelerated training of physicians to meet war-time needs. On this occasion, the deans discovered many other areas of common concern, and decided to meet again in August 1943, for the inaugural meeting of the Association of Canadian Medical Colleges. All 10 schools became members at that time.

In July 1962 a secretariat was established in Ottawa. Dr. J. Wendell Macleod served as executive director, until his retirement in 1970.

ACMC provides information to prospective students and teachers of medicine. It provides for the accreditation of Canadian medical schools, and maintains close liaison with national and international bodies concerned in medical education.

The research division engages in studies of medical applicants, students, graduates and faculty, costs of medical education, and curriculum change.

There are now 16 medical schools in Canada. All belong to the association. ACMC is an associate member of the Association of Universities and Colleges of Canada and a member of the Pan American Federation of Associations of Medical Schools.

Au mois d'avril 1943, les doyens des dix facultés de médecine alors existantes se sont réunis à Ottawa, à la demande du ministre de la Santé, pour étudier la question de la formation accélérée des médecins en vue de répondre aux besoins engendrés par la guerre. A cette occasion, les doyens ont constaté qu'ils partageaient de nombreux autres domaines d'intérêt et ont décidé de se rencontrer de nouveau au mois d'août 1943, à la réunion inaugurale de l'Association des facultés de médecine du Canada. Les dix facultés de médecine en devinrent membres à cette occasion.

Au mois de juillet 1962, un secrétariat a été établi à Ottawa et le Dr Wendell Macleod a été directeur administratif jusqu'à sa retraite, en 1970.

Le secrétariat fournit des renseignements aux éventuels étudiants et professeurs de médecine. L'AFMC établit les formalités à suivre pour que les facultés de médecine soient reconnues officiellement et maintient d'étroites relations avec les organismes nationaux et internationaux qui s'intéressent à l'enseignement de la médecine.

La division des recherches poursuit des études sur les candidats en médecine, les étudiants, les diplômés et les professeurs, le coût des études de médecine et les changements dans les programmes.

Il y a maintenant seize facultés de médecine au Canada; elles sont toutes

membres de l'association. L'AFMC est
membre associé de l'Association des
Universités et Collèges du Canada et
membre de la Pan American Federation of
Associations of Medical Schools.

Association of Canadian University Information Bureaus

Association des bureaux de l'information des universités du Canada

President
Mr. Bruce Woodland
Director, information and alumni affairs,
Memorial University of Newfoundland, St. John's, Nfld.

Secretary-treasurer
Mrs. Rosemary Cavan
Information officer, Association of Universities and Colleges of Canada, 151 Slater St., Ottawa, Ont., K1P 5N1

Président
Mr. Bruce Woodland
Director, information and alumni affairs,
Memorial University of Newfoundland, St. John's, Nfld.

Secrétaire-trésorière
Mme Rosemary Cavan
Adjointe à l'information, Association des universités et collèges du Canada, 151, rue Slater, Ottawa (Ont.) K1P 5N1

The Association of Canadian University Information Bureaus was founded in July 1968 to further the interests of the universities of Canada. In November 1969, the association became affiliated with the AUCC.

ACUIB is the formalization of ad hoc meetings of university information and PR personnel held annually since 1965. These meetings began at McMaster University with a gathering of Ontario staff only; continued at Carleton University in 1966, with information people from other provinces invited to attend as observers; at Laval University in 1967, with almost full national representation; and in 1968 at The University of Calgary, when those present decided to form an association. All of these meetings were timed to coincide with the annual meeting of the Canadian Public Relations Society. Henceforth, they will be held at the time of the AUCC annual meeting.

Institutional membership is open to any member of the AUCC, with one person from that institution designated as its voting member in ACUIB. Associate membership is open to any person engaged in information or public relations work in a non-degree granting post-secondary educational institution, AUCC, Canada Council, National Research Council, provincial departments of education and university affairs, etc. Although ACUIB is for those engaged chiefly in information and PR work, some of its members have other responsibilities as well, usually alumni affairs or development or both.

L'Association des bureaux de l'information des universités du Canada a été fondée au mois de juillet 1968 afin de promouvoir les intérêts des universités du Canada. Au mois de novembre 1969, elle s'est affiliée à l'AUCC.

L'ABIUC a été établie à la suite de réunions spéciales que les membres du personnel de l'information et des relations extérieures des universités ont tenues chaque année depuis 1965. Ces réunions ont commencé à l'Université McMaster où s'était réuni un groupe de l'Ontario seulement; elles se sont continuées à l'Université Carleton en 1966 et des membres du personnel de l'information des autres provinces ont été invités à y assister à titre d'observateurs; puis, à l'Université Laval, en 1967, on comptait de représentants de presque tous les pays et en 1968, à l'Université de Calgary, tous ceux qui étaient présents ont décidé de former une association. Toutes ces réunions ont été prévues pour coïncider avec l'assemblée annuelle de la Société canadienne des relations publiques. Elles se tiennent maintenant en même temps que le Congrès annuel de l'AUCC.

Toute institution membre de l'AUCC peut devenir membre institutionnel et une personne de cet établissement est désignée comme ayant droit de voter aux réunions de l'ABIUC. Toute personne s'occupant d'information ou de relations extérieures au sein d'établissements d'enseignement post-secondaire ne conférant pas de grade, ainsi que de l'AUCC, du Conseil des arts

du Canada, du Conseil national de recherches, des ministères provinciaux de l'éducation et des affaires universitaires, etc. peut devenir membre associé. Bien que l'ABIUC soit composée de membres qui s'occupent principalement d'information et de relations extérieures, certains de ses membres ont aussi d'autres responsabilités qui se rapportent habituellement aux affaires relatives aux anciens étudiants ou au développement ou à ces deux domaines.

Association of Deans of Pharmacy of Canada

Association canadienne des doyens de pharmacie

175 College St., Toronto 130, Ont.

175 College St., Toronto 130, Ont.

President
Dr. J. R. Murray
Dean, faculty of pharmacy, The University of Manitoba, Winnipeg, Man.

Secretary-treasurer
Dr. A.W. Matthews

Président
Dr J. R. Murray
Doyen, faculté de pharmacie, Université de Manitoba, Winnipeg, Man.

Secrétaire-trésorier
Dr. A.W. Matthews

The association, formed in 1965, has as its members the administrative heads of the eight schools, colleges and faculties of pharmacy in Canada located in the following universities: Alberta, British Columbia, Dalhousie, Laval, Manitoba, Montréal, Saskatchewan and Toronto.

The initial impetus for the formation of the association stemmed from the growing need for a forum for a discussion of the increasingly complex administrative problems facing the deans within their respective universities. Matters pertaining to curriculum and teaching, on the other hand, fall within the jurisdiction of the Association of Faculties of Pharmacy of Canada. Nevertheless, the experience is that there are occasions when a joint statement of policy and of the viewpoint of pharmaceutical education has been put forward by the association representing the administrative heads. Recent examples of such activity are the briefs presented to the Medical Research Council and to the special Senate committee on science policy.

The association collects enrolment statistics and comparative data related thereto from its members. It currently has plans to update an earlier study of the employment opportunities in Canada for pharmacy graduates who subsequently proceed to advanced degrees in the faculties of pharmacy.

L'Association, formée en 1965, est composée des dirigeants des huit écoles, collèges et facultés de pharmacie des universités canadiennes suivantes: Alberta, Colombie-Britannique, Dalhousie, Laval, Manitoba, Montréal, Saskatchewan et Toronto.

Cette association est née du besoin croissant d'un forum pour la discussion des problèmes administratifs complexes et croissants que rencontraient les doyens dans leurs universités respectives. Les questions relatives aux programmes d'études et à l'enseignement relèvent par ailleurs de l'Association des facultés de pharmacie du Canada. L'association représentant les dirigeants a toutefois en certaines occasions fait un exposé de ses principes et de ses opinions sur les études en pharmacie comme dans les mémoires présentés récemment au Conseil des recherches médicales et au comité spécial du Sénat sur la politique scientifique.

L'association recueille de ses membres des statistiques et des données comparées sur les inscriptions. Elle prévoit présentement mettre à jour l'étude sur les débouchés professionnels au Canada pour les diplômés en pharmacie qui ont par la suite obtenu des grades supérieurs dans les facultés de pharmacie.

The Association of Faculties of Veterinary Medicine in Canada

L'Association des facultés de médecine vétérinaire du Canada

President
Dr Ephrem Jacques
Doyen, faculté de médecine vétérinaire,
Université de Montréal, C.P. 5000, St-Hyacinthe (Que.)

Secretary-treasurer
Dr Patrick Guay
Faculté de médecine vétérinaire, Université
de Montréal, C.P. 5000, St-Hyacinthe
(Que.)

Président
Dr Ephrem Jacques
Doyen, faculté de médecine vétérinaire,
Université de Montréal, C.P. 5000, St-Hyacinthe (Qué.)

Secrétaire-trésorier
Dr Patrick Guay
Faculté de médecine vétérinaire, Université
de Montréal, C.P. 5000, St-Hyacinthe
(Qué.)

The Association of Faculties of Veterinary Medicine in Canada was founded in 1969 when three faculties of veterinary medicine in Canada met to discuss common problems such as sources of funds, curriculum, graduate studies, research, etc.

The faculties of veterinary medicine in Canada intend to standardize teaching, and encourage exchange and research.

The teachers of each faculty of veterinary medicine were invited to attend a general meeting held in Windsor, Ontario, July 19, 1971. Some of the matters discussed included university policy concerning clinical clerkship curricula, reports, and discussions of various committees.

L'Association des facultés de médecine vétérinaire du Canada fut fondée en 1969 à la suite du désir des trois facultés de médecine vétérinaire de dialoguer sur des problèmes communs; par exemple, les sources de financement, le curriculum, les études supérieures, la recherche, etc.

Les facultés de médecine vétérinaire du Canada veulent uniformiser le plus possible l'enseignement, favoriser les échanges et stimuler la recherche.

Tous les professeurs de chacune des facultés de médecine vétérinaire ont tenu une assemblée générale à Windsor, Ontario, le 19 juillet 1971. Ils ont discuté de la politique universitaire en regard des programmes d'internat, de rapports et discussions de divers comités.

Association of Registrars of the Universities of Canada

L'Association des registraires d'université du Canada

President
Mr. D.J. Green
Registrar, Acadia University, Wolfville, N.S.

Secretary
Mrs. Jean Hadley
Assistant registrar, University of New Brunswick, Fredericton, N.B.

Président
Mr D.J. Green
Registrar, Acadia University, Wolfville, N.S.

Secrétaire
Mrs. Jean Hadley
Assistant registrar, University of New Brunswick, Fredericton, N.B.

The purpose of the association is to promote communication and exchange of information on the functions normally associated with the office of the registrar including changes in provincial secondary and post-secondary school systems and admission to Canadian universities.

Membership is institutional and any institution of high learning having membership in the Association of Universities and Colleges of Canada, or associated with an institution, is eligible for membership. Each institutional membership entitles the institution to one vote. Personnel representing eligible institutions shall be designated as regular members of the association.

Cette association a pour but de favoriser la communication et l'échange de renseignements sur les fonctions normalement en rapport avec la charge de registraire, y compris les changements dans les systèmes scolaires secondaires et postsecondaires des provinces et l'admission aux universités canadiennes.

Seule une institution peut devenir membre; toute institution d'études supérieures, membre de l'Association des Universités et Collèges du Canada, ou associée à une institution, est admissible à être membre. Chaque institution membre a droit à un seul vote. Les membres du personnel représentant des institutions admissibles seront désignés comme membres réguliers de cette association.

Canadian Association for Education in the Social Services

Association canadienne d'éducation pour les services sociaux

151 Slater St., Ottawa, Ont., K1P 5N1

151, rue Slater, Ottawa (Ont.) K1P 5N1

President
Dr. G.M. Hougham
Director, school of social work, The University of British Columbia, Vancouver 8, B.C.

Président
Dr. G.M. Hougham
Director, school of social work, The University of British Columbia, Vancouver 8, B.C.

Executive director
Prof. Marguerite Mathieu

Directrice administrative
Prof. Marguerite Mathieu

Prior to the 1940's, links between Canadian schools and departments of social work were maintained through participation in the American Association of Schools of Social Work. However, in the late 1940's the schools founded the National Committee of Canadian Schools of Social Work (NCCSSW) to provide for particular Canadian needs. Accreditation continued through the American Council on Social Work Education. In 1965, NCCSSW became an associate member of the Association of Universities and Colleges of Canada.

In 1968, the committee changed its name to the Canadian Association for Education in the Social Services (CAESS) and altered its constitution to include undergraduate as well as graduate programs and to include faculty as well as administrative representation in its governing body. With the assistance of the Laidlaw Foundation, CAESS was able to establish a secretariat.

At the unanimous request of its members, CAESS is now in the process of developing an accrediting authority for social work education in Canada replacing the Council on Social Work Education in this role. CAESS is being assisted by a grant from the Department of National Health and Welfare. Accreditation reviews are expected to commence in the fall of 1972.

The association has recently completed an extensive study of undergraduate education for social work in Canada that provides guidelines for new university programs and describes current changes. The study,

Avant les années 40, les liens entre les écoles canadiennes et les départements de service social étaient maintenus grâce à la participation à l'American Association of Schools of Social Work. Toutefois, vers la fin des années 40, les écoles ont fondé le Comité national des écoles canadiennes de service social (CNECSS) afin de répondre aux besoins particuliers des Canadiens, mais l'accréditation a continué à se faire par l'entremise de l'American Association on Social Work Education. En 1965, le CNECSS devint membre associé de l'Association de Universités et Collèges du Canada.

En 1968, le comité a changé son nom en celui de l'Association canadienne d'éducation pour les services sociaux (ACESS) et a modifié sa constitution afin d'y inclure les programmes d'études aussi bien de niveau pré-grade que post-grade et la représentation des professeurs ainsi que des administrateurs au sein de son organe administratif. Grâce à l'aide que lui a accordée la Fondation Laidlaw, l'ACESS a été capable d'établir son secrétariat.

A la demande unanime de ses membres et grâce à une subvention du ministère de la Santé nationale et du Bien-être social, l'ACESS est en train de devenir l'organisme d'accréditation des programmes d'études en service social du Canada, remplaçant ainsi le Council on Social Work Education qui jouait ce rôle auparavant. Les examens d'accréditation doivent commencer à l'automne de 1972.

L'association a terminé récemment une

published by CAESS, is entitled "The first university degree in social work". A similar study of graduate programs is now underway.

A major study of the employment of social service graduates from graduate, undergraduate, and community college programs has recently been initiated.

CAESS serves to represent the interests of Canadian social service education in a number of relationships. Of particular importance are international relationships through the International Association of Schools of Social Work and bilaterally with other countries as well as relationships with such Canadian organizations and institutions as AUCC, the Canada Welfare Council, the Canadian Association of Social Workers and the various departments and agencies of the government of Canada.

Finally, CAESS is studying its relationship to, and responsibility towards, the extensive growth of social service education that is occurring in Canada at the community college.

étude de l'ensemble des programmes d'études de niveau pré-grade en service social offerts au Canada, qui fournit des directives sur les nouveaux programmes universitaires et décrit les changements en cours. Cette étude, publiée par l'ACESS, s'intitule "Le premier grade universitaire en service social". Une étude semblable des programmes d'études supérieures est en cours.

Une étude importante sur l'emploi des diplômés en service social des programmes d'études post-grade, pré-grade et postsecondaires a été entreprise récemment.

L'ACESS entretient de nombreuses relations avec d'autres pays par l'entremise de l'Association internationale des écoles de service social ainsi qu'avec des organismes et institutions du Canada comme l'AUCC, le Conseil canadien du bien-être, l'Association canadienne des travailleurs sociaux et divers ministères et agences du gouvernement du Canada. Enfin, l'ACESS étudie le rôle et la responsabilité qu'elle a envers le progrès des études de service social qui se produit au Canada, au niveau du collège communautaire.

Canadian Association of College and University Libraries

Association canadienne des bibliothèques de collège et d'université

President
Rév. Daniel Croteau
Conservateur de la bibliothèque, Université de Sherbrooke, Sherbrooke (Qué.)

Secretary
Miss Rosemary Lyons
Head, acquisitions library, The University of Calgary, Calgary, Alta.

Président
Rév. Daniel Croteau
Conservateur de la bibliothèque, Université de Sherbrooke, Sherbrooke (Qué.)

Secrétaire
Miss Rosemary Lyons
Head, acquisitions library, The University of Calgary, Calgary, Alta.

CACUL was founded in 1963 as a section of the Canadian Library Association, with the object of furthering the interests of libraries of those institutions which offer formal education beyond the secondary level, and to support the highest aims of education and librarianship.

The same year CACUL became an associate member of the AUCC. Over the years, it has undertaken several worthwhile projects.

It co-operated with the AUCC on the Downs study of the *Resources of Canadian academic and research libraries.* CACUL has representations on AUCC library committees.

Apart from working with the AUCC, CACUL has initiated many projects on its own for the advancement of librarianship in Canada.

Three workshops on library automation have been held, and the proceedings published under the title: *Automation in libraries 1967, 1968 and 1970.* Included among its other publications are *Forecast of the cost of academic library services in Canada, 1965-1975; Guide to Canadian university library standards; Position classification and principles of academic status in Canadian university libraries;* and *Purchasing and copyright practices in Canadian libraries.* Salary and budget surveys and forecasts have been published for university libraries, and libraries of community colleges and technical institutes. In addition, reports are available on academic status; additions to academic library space in Canada 1965-1970; and position classification for supporting staff.

L'ACBCU a été fondée en 1963, comme division de la Canadian Library Association, dans le but de servir les intérêts des bibliothèques des établissements qui offrent des cours au-delà du niveau secondaire et d'appuyer les objectifs les plus élevés de l'enseignement de la bibliothéconomie et de la profession de bibliothécaire.

La même année, l'ACBCU devint membre associé de l'AUCC. Au cours des années, elle a entrepris plusieurs projets dignes d'être poursuivis.

Elle a collaboré avec l'AUCC à l'étude qu'a effectuée M. Downs sur *Les ressources des bibliothèques d'université et de recherche au Canada.* L'ACBCU compte des représentants au sein des comités de l'AUCC pour les bibliothèques.

En plus de travailler avec l'AUCC, l'ACBCU a elle-même entrepris de nombreux projets pour l'avancement de la profession de bibliothécaire au Canada.

On a tenu trois séances d'étude sur l'automatisation des bibliothèques et publié leurs délibérations sous le titre: *Automation in libraries 1967, 1968 and 1970.* Parmi ses autres publications on compte *Prévision du coût des services des bibliothèques académiques au Canada, 1965-1975; Guide to Canadian university library standards; Position classification and principles of academic status in Canadian university libraries (Plans de classification des fonctions professionnelles)* et *Purchasing and copyright practices in Canadian libraries.* On a publié des études et des prévisions sur les traitements et le budget pour les bibliothèques d'université, des

CACUL is involved in participatory programs with the CLA and the AUCC aimed at the development of professional librarianship in the field of higher education.

collèges communautaires et des instituts de technologie. En outre, on dispose de rapports sur la classification des fonctions professionnelles, les annexes aux bibliothèques universitaires du Canada de 1965 à 1970 et la classification des fonctions du personnel auxiliaire.

Conjointement avec la CLA et l'AUCC, l'ACBCU a participé à des programmes visant à développer la profession de bibliothécaire dans le domaine des études supérieures.

Canadian Association of Deans and Directors of University Faculties of Education

Association canadienne des doyens et directeurs de faculté de pédagogie

Chairman
Dean W.R. MacDonald
School of education, Acadia University,
Wolfville, N.S.

Secretary
Mr. Roger Black
University of Prince Edward Island,
Charlottetown, P.E.I.

Président
Dean W.R. MacDonald
School of education, Acadia University,
Wolfville, N.S.

Secrétaire-trésorier
Mr. Roger Black
University of Prince Edward Island,
Charlottetown, P.E.I.

The history of the Canadian Association of Deans and Directors of University Faculties of Education is a very brief one. It was the outcome of an informal meeting which was held by the deans on the occasion of the Canadian Association of Professors of Education meetings in Calgary in 1968. It was felt that it was very desirable that there should be an opportunity for the deans to meet once or twice a year to discuss problems that related specifically to the administration of faculties of education and the problems faced by deans of education rather than the more general educational problems discussed in the CAPE session. It was to meet these needs that the association was formed.

The association has held, since that time, two meetings in Ottawa, one in Winnipeg in 1970, and the 1971 meeting was held at Memorial University of Newfoundland.

L'Association canadienne des doyens et directeurs de faculté de pédagogie n'a pas une longue histoire. Elle a été formée à l'occasion d'une réunion sans formalité tenue par les doyens dans le cadre des réunions de l'Association canadienne des professeurs de pédagogie, à Calgary, en 1968. Les participants ont alors estimé qu'il était très souhaitable de permettre aux doyens de se réunir une ou deux fois par année afin de discuter des problèmes qui se rapportent particulièrement à l'administration des facultés de pédagogie et à ceux auxquels font face les doyens de ces facultés plutôt que des problèmes pédagogiques généraux discutés aux séances d'études de l'ACPP. L'association a été formée pour répondre à ces besoins.

L'association s'est réunie deux fois à Ottawa depuis ce temps; la réunion de 1970 s'est tenue à Winnipeg, et celle de 1971 à l'Université Memorial de Terre-Neuve.

Canadian Association of Departments of Extension and Summer Schools

Associations des services d'éducation des adultes et écoles d'été des universités du Canada

President
Mr. Donald Snowden
Director, extension service, Memorial University of Newfoundland, St. John's, Nfld.

Président
Mr. Donald Snowden
Director, extension service, Memorial University of Newfoundland, St. John's, Nfld.

Secretary-treasurer
Mr. R.S. Chapman
Associate director, division of continuing education, The University of Calgary, Calgary, Alta.

Secrétaire-trésorier
Mr. R. S. Chapman
Associate director, division of continuing education, The University of Calgary, Calgary, Alta.

CADESS began in 1950 as an association of directors of summer schools who gathered to discuss matters of common interest during the meetings of the learned societies. At the meeting held in 1954, the association was reorganized as a more inclusive organization, titled Canadian Association of Directors of Extension and Summer Schools.

For some time CADESS held its annual meetings with the learned societies, but more recently it has been in closer affiliation with the Association of Universities and Colleges of Canada, of which CADESS is an associate member.

In 1967, in recognition of the part that other staff, chiefly in extension, were playing in the association, the title was altered to Canadian Association of Departments of Extension and Summer Schools.

CADESS is concerned with the university's responsibility in credit and non-credit extension programs. It provides a national and regional forum for the discussion of matters relating to university extension and represents university extension in Canada and internationally.

It strives to encourage the maintenance and development of diploma and degree programs in extension and adult education in Canadian universities and colleges and promotes in-service and graduate training in existing and potential university extension staff. It desires to encourage and

En 1950, l'ASEAEEUC était une association des directeurs des écoles d'été, qui discutaient des questions d'intérêt commun durant les réunions des sociétés savantes. A sa réunion de 1954, cette association devint plus autonome et se nomma l'Association canadienne des directeurs des cours postscolaires et écoles d'été.

Durant quelques années, l'ASEAEEUC a tenu ses assemblées annuelles en même temps que celles des sociétés savantes, mais dernièrement elle les a tenues à l'occasion de l'assemblée annuelle de l'Association des Universités et Collèges du Canada, dont elle est membre associé.

En 1967, étant donné le rôle que jouait dans l'association le personnel des services d'éducation des adultes, le nom a été changé en celui de l'Association des services d'éducation des adultes et écoles d'été des universités du Canada.

L'ASEAEEUC s'occupe des programmes de cours postscolaires, de niveau universitaire, qui conduisent ou non à un grade. Elle joue le rôle d'un forum national et régional pour les discussions de questions relatives aux cours postscolaires, de niveau universitaire, et représente les services d'éducation des adultes, aux niveaux national et international.

Elle s'efforce d'encourager les universités et collèges du Canada à continuer à offrir et à mettre sur pied des programmes de cours postscolaires et pour adultes

conduct studies related to university extension activities and endeavours to maintain active liaison with other groups and associations which are concerned with adult education in Canada and elsewhere.

The membership of CADESS is made up of those member institutions of the AUCC which are interested in extension and summer school activities and which choose to join.

conduisant à l'obtention d'un diplôme et encourage la formation supérieure et les services offerts au personnel actuel et éventuel des cours postscolaires, au niveau universitaire. Elle désire encourager et effectuer des études sur les activités des services d'éducation des adultes, dans les universités, et s'efforce de maintenir les relations avec d'autres groupes et associations qui s'intéressent à l'éducation des adultes, au Canada et ailleurs.

L'ASEAEEUC se compose des institutions membres de l'AUCC qui sont intéressées aux cours postscolaires et aux écoles d'été et qui désirent se joindre à cette association.

Canadian Association of Graduate Schools

President
Dean M.A. Preston
Faculty of graduate studies, McMaster
University, Hamilton, Ont.

Secretary-treasurer
Dr. B.G. Hogg
Associate dean, Faculty of graduate
studies, The University of Manitoba,
Winnipeg, Man.

The Canadian Association of Deans and Directors of Graduate Schools was established in 1962. The aims and objectives of the association were: to exchange information, experience and views regarding a) the initiation, organization and administration of graduate students; b) the admission, support and supervision of students; c) the structure of degree programs; d) the promotion of research; e) other matters of concern to directors of graduate studies; and generally to promote the improvement of graduate education in Canadian universities.

The second meeting of the association was held in the fall of 1963, at which time it was agreed to change the name to the Canadian Association of Graduate Schools (CAGS). Since then the association has met annually in early November with the AUCC.

The topics discussed by the graduate deans have been: funds available for graduate studies; level of graduate support; NRC awards; other awards for graduate students; new graduate programs; requirements for the PhD; admission requirements and graduate status; and problems of foreign graduate students.

The association has prepared a number of briefs for other organizations including the Bladen Commission, the Rowat-Hurtubise Commission on the relationship between universities and governments, and the Senate committee on science policy.

The association prepares an annual statistical summary of numbers of graduate students, numbers of graduate

Association canadienne des écoles d'études supérieures

Président
Dean M.A. Preston
Faculty of graduate studies, McMaster
University, Hamilton, Ont.

Secrétaire-trésorier
Dr. B.G. Hogg
Associate dean, Faculty of graduate
studies, The University of Manitoba,
Winnipeg, Man.

L'Association canadienne des doyens et directeurs des écoles de gradués a été établie en 1962. Elle visait à échanger des renseignements, des expériences et des opinions sur a) la mise sur pied, l'organisation et l'administration des écoles de gradués, b) l'admission, l'appui et la surveillance des étudiants, c) la structure des programmes conduisant à un grade, d) la promotion de la recherche, e) d'autres questions qui préoccupent les directeurs des écoles de gradués, et d'une façon générale à favoriser l'amélioration de l'enseignement supérieur dans les universités du Canada.

L'association a tenu sa deuxiéme réunion à l'automne de 1963 et a décidé, à ce moment, de changer son nom en celui de l'Association canadienne des écoles de gradués (ACEG). Depuis, l'association s'est réunie chaque année, au début du mois de novembre, à l'occasion de la réunion annuelle de l'AUCC.

Les doyens des études supérieures ont discuté des sujets suivants: fonds accordés aux études supérieures, niveau d'aide aux études supérieures, bourses du CNR, autres bourses offertes aux étudiants gradués, nouveaux programmes d'études supérieures, conditions d'obtention du doctorat, conditions d'admission et situations de l'étudiant gradué, et problèmes des étudiants gradués étrangers.

L'association a préparé certains mémoires pour d'autres organisations dont la commission Bladen, la commission Rowat-Hurtubise sur les relations entre les universités et les gouvernements, et le comité du Sénat sur la politique scientifique.

degrees awarded, and financial support for graduate students in Canadian universities.

In 1971 the membership of CAGS included 32 universities.

Cette association prépare le relevé statistique annuel des étudiants gradués, des grades supérieurs conférés et l'aide financière accordée aux étudiants gradués dans les universités du Canada.

En 1971, l'ACES comptait 32 universités membres.

Canadian Association of Library Schools

Association canadienne des écoles de bibliothécaires

President
Miss Janette White
School of library and information science,
The University of Western Ontario,
London, Ont.

Secretary-treasurer
Miss Carmen Sprovieri
School of library and information science,
The University of Western Ontario,
London, Ont.

Président
Miss Janette White
School of library and information science,
The University of Western Ontario,
London, Ont.

Secrétaire-trésorière
Miss Carmen Sprovieri
School of library and information science,
The University of Western Ontario,
London, Ont.

The Canadian Association of Library Schools was founded in 1965 to promote the development and to foster the improvement of graduate library education in Canada, and to compile and exchange information on library education.

Personal membership in the association is open to any member of the instructional or administrative staff of a graduate library school in a Canadian university, including summer school faculty members. Institutional membership is open to the schools themselves.

The chief activity of the association at present is the compilation of statistics on enrolment, graduates, placement and employment opportunities

L'Association canadienne des écoles de bibliothécaires a été fondée en 1965 afin de promouvoir le développement et favoriser l'amélioration des études supérieures de bibliothéconomie au Canada ainsi que compiler et échanger des renseignements sur les études de bibliothéconomie.

Tous les membres du personnel enseignant ou administratif d'une école supérieure de bibliothéconomie, dans une université canadienne, y compris les professeurs d'une école d'été, sont admissibles à être membres institutionnels.

L'activité principlae de cette association à l'heure actuelle consiste à compiler des statistiques sur les inscriptions, les étudiants gradués, le placement de ces étudiants et les débouchés.

Canadian Association of University Development Officers

Association des dirigeants du service de développement des universités canadiennes

President
Mr. J. K. Babcock
Director, Alumni affairs and development,
University of Guelph, Guelph, Ont.

Secretary-treasurer
Mr. R.L. Jones
Director of development, University of
Toronto, Toronto 5, Ont.

Président
Mr. J. K. Babcock
Director, Alumni affairs and development,
University of Guelph, Guelph, Ont.

Secrétaire-trésorier
Mr. R. L. Jones
Director of development, University of
Toronto, Toronto 5, Ont.

CAUDO had its beginnings back in 1966 in Toronto when an informal group of university fund-raising administrators in Ontario began meeting to exchange information and ideas and to discuss mutual problems. At a meeting convened at Ottawa in 1968, a resolution establishing the association and appointing a provisional board of directors was signed by 24 representatives from 17 universities across Canada. A formal constitution was adopted by the provisional board and ratified by a general meeting of members held at Guelph on May 7, 1969. By 1971 membership had risen to over 70 members from 40 universities. CAUDO was elected an associate member of the AUCC in November 1968.

To accomplish its objects, CAUDO holds such functions as conferences with corporate donations administrators, development workshops, bequest seminars, general and regional meetings of members and directors. It also conducts studies and surveys on various aspects of fund-raising and organizes an annual development literature exchange program among its members. CAUDO publishes a bi-monthly newsletter, conference proceedings, selected survey results, and an annual membership directory.

Membership is open to the professional staff responsible for the development (fund-raising) functions at institutions which are members of the AUCC. Associate membership is available to part-time development staff members of the above institutions, to development staff at non-AUCC institutions, and to university personnel working in allied fields to

C'est en 1966 qu'a été formée à Toronto l'ADSDUC par un groupe d'administrateurs ontariens des campagnes de souscription des universités, réunis sans formalité pour échanger des renseignements et des idées ainsi que discuter de problèmes communs. A la réunion tenue à Ottawa en 1968, 24 représentants de 17 universités du Canada ont signé la résolution établissant l'assocation et nommant le conseil d'administration provisoire. Les statuts officiels ont été adoptés par le conseil provisoire et approuvés par l'assemblée générale des membres réunis à Guelph, le 7 mai 1969. En 1971, cette association se composait de plus de 70 membres provenant de 40 universités. L'ADSDUC est devenue membre associé de l'AUCC au mois de novembre 1968.

Afin de réaliser ses objectifs, l'ADSDUC tient des réunions avec les administrateurs des dons des sociétés, des séances d'études sur le développement, des colloques sur les biens mobiliers légués, des assemblées générales et régionales de ses membres et directeurs. Elle dirige aussi des études et des enquêtes sur divers aspects des campagnes de souscription et organise chaque année parmi ses membres un programme d'échanges littéraires sur le développement. L'ADSDUC publie un bulletin de nouvelles tous les deux mois, les délibérations de ses réunions, certains résultats de ses enquêtes et annuellement, le répertoire de ses membres.

Les cadres responsables du service de développement (campagnes de souscription) des établissements qui sont membres de l'AUCC, sont admissibles à être membres.

development work. Outside fund-raising consultants are not eligible for membership.

Les membres à temps partiel du personnel du service de développement des établissements sus-mentionnés, le personnel du service de développement des institutions qui ne sont pas membres de l'AUCC et le personnel universitaire travaillant dans des domaines connexes au développement sont admissibles à être membres associés. Les experts-conseils en campagnes de souscription non universitaires ne sont pas admissibles à être membres.

Canadian Association of University Schools of nursing

Association canadienne des écoles universitaires de nursing

President
Miss Elizabeth McCann
Acting Director, school of nursing, The University of British Columbia, Vancouver 8, B.C.

Secretary
Mrs. Helen Elfert
School of nursing, The University of British Columbia, Vancouver 8, B.C.

Présidente
Miss Elizabeth McCann
Acting Director, school of nursing, The University of British Columbia, Vancouver 8, B.C.

Secrétaire
Mrs. Helen Elfert
School of nursing, The University of British Columbia, Vancouver 8, B.C.

The CAUSN was established in 1967 to provide an organized body to promote the advancement of nursing education in universities.

The objectives of the association are to: a) develop criteria for university education in nursing; b) promote research in nursing; c) promote the interchange of nursing knowledge among members; d) represent views of the association to educational, professional, and other appropriate bodies; e) promote understanding by the public that university education in nursing can contribute to the development of health services in Canada.

The institutional members are faculties and schools of nursing of Canadian universities which are from time to time recommended for membership by the council and are approved by the affirmative votes of three-fourths of the institutional members present.

The association is an independent body which is an associate member of the AUCC.

L'ACEUN a été établie en 1967 afin de promouvoir l'avancement de l'enseignement des sciences infirmières dans les universités.

Les objectifs de cette association sont de: 1) élaborer les critères de l'enseignement universitaire des sciences infirmières; 2) promouvoir les recherches en sciences infirmières; 3) promouvoir les échanges de connaissances en sciences infirmières parmi les membres; 4) représenter les vues de l'association au sein d'organismes éducatifs, professionnels et d'autres organismes appropriés; 5) faire en sorte que le public comprenne que l'enseignement universitaire des sciences infirmières peut contribuer au développement des services de santé au Canada.

Les membres institutionnels sont les facultés et écoles de nursing des universités du Canada, qui sont, à l'occasion, recommandées par le conseil et approuvées par les trois quarts des voix des membres institutionnels présents.

Cette association est un organisme indépendant, membre associé de l'AUCC.

Canadian Intercollegiate Athletic Union

Union sportive interuniversitaire canadienne

President
Mr. Carl Totzke
Director of athletics, University of
Waterloo, Waterloo, Ont.

Executive director
Mr. R.W. Pugh
333 River Rd., Vanier City, Ont.

Président
M. Carl Totzke
Directeur des sports, Université de
Waterloo, Waterloo (Ont.)

Directeur administratif
M. R.W. Pugh
333 River Road, Vanier (Ont.)

The Canadian Intercollegiate Athletic Union was formed in 1961 as a co-ordinating body for the various intercollegiate athletic associations in Canada: Atlantic Intercollegiate Athletic Association; Ottawa-St. Lawrence Athletic Association; Ontario-Quebec Athletic Association; Western Canadian Intercollegiate Athletic Association; Ontario Intercollegiate Athletic Association.

In 1962, CIAU was recognized as a sports governing body by the Fitness and Amateur Sport Directorate; in 1966, CIAU was recognized as the sports governing body for intercollegiate sports by the AUCC and in addition the CIAU was approved as an associate member of the AUCC.

The CIAU appointed a special sub-committee to consider the best way in which to raise the standard of Canadian amateur athletics in colleges, secondary schools, and amateur athletic associations. This committee was instructed to look at athletics in general, with a view to formulating a plan to improve the conditions of athletics in Canadian educational institutions and, where possible, to compliment the amateur associations of Canada.

To this end, the CIAU is presently embarked on several important projects: a) AUCC/CIAU joint study on the "place of atiletics" in the university and educational environments; b) establishment of a CIAU national office; c) taking responsibility for Canadian membership in the Fédération internationale sportive universitaire and organizing Canadian representation for the world student summer games being held at

L'Union sportive interuniversitaire canadienne a été formée en 1961 comme organisme coordonnateur pour les diverses associations sportives interuniversitaires du Canada: Atlantic Intercollegiate Athletic Association; Ottawa-St. Lawrence Athletic Association; Ontario-Quebec Athletic Association; Western Canadian Intercollegiate Athletic Association; Ontario Intercollegiate Athletic Association.

En 1962, l'USIC a été reconnue comme l'organisme directeur des sports par la Direction de la santé et du sport amateur; en 1966, l'USIC a été reconnue comme l'organisme directeur des sports pour les sports interuniversitaires par l'AUCC et en outre l'USIC a été approuvée comme membre associé de l'AUCC.

L'USIC a nommé un sous-comité spécial chargé d'examiner le meilleur moyen d'élever le niveau des sports amateurs canadiens dans les collèges, les écoles secondaires et les associations des sports amateurs. Ce comité a été chargé d'examiner les sports en général dans le but de dresser un plan pour améliorer les conditions des sports dans les établissements d'enseignement du Canada et où cela serait possible, de récompenser les associations de sport amateur du Canada.

A cette fin, l'USIC est présentement engagée dans plusieurs projets importants: a) l'étude conjointe de l'AUCC et de l'USIC sur la "place des sports" dans l'université et les milieux scolaires; b) l'établissement du bureau national de l'USIC; c) responsabilité de la participation du Canada à la Fédération internationale sportive universitaire et de l'organisation

Lake Placid, U.S.A., February 25 - March 7, 1972; d) CIAU position regarding athletic scholarships currently under careful study; e) CIAU position in relation to the task force report on sport in Canada.

de la représentation canadienne aux jeux d'été mondiaux pour les étudiants qui seront tenus au Lac Placid, Etats-Unis, du 25 février au 7 mars 1972; d) position de l'USIC au sujet des bourses d'études sportives faisant présentement l'objet d'une étude attentive; e) position de l'USIC au sujet du rapport du groupe de travail sur le sport au Canada.

Canadian University Service Overseas

Service universitaire canadien outre-mer

151 Slater St., Ottawa, Ont., K1P 5N1

151, rue Slater, Ottawa (Ont.) K1P 5N1

President
Prof. Gérard Aubry
Institut de coopération internationale, 190 est, avenue Laurier, Ottawa (Ont.)

Président
Prof. Gérard Aubry
Institut de coopération internationale, 190 est, avenue Laurier, Ottawa (Ont.)

Executive directors
Mr. Charles Morin
Mr. David Catmur (acting)

Directeurs administratifs
M. Charles Morin
M. David Catmur (suppléant)

CUSO began in 1961 with the start of the first United Nations development decade, sending 17 people to work in four developing countries. Since then more than 2,500 Canadians have used the organization as a means of practical involvement in international development. Today, at the start of its second decade, the program has some 1,200 people working for more than 40 nations in Africa, Asia, the Caribbean and Latin America.

CUSO, an independent, non-profit organization, provides professionally and technically qualified Canadians in response to specific requests from overseas governments and agencies. CUSO personnel range in age from 18 to 80, and in occupation from town planners to motor mechanics. Currently in greatest demand are teachers (especially maths and science), nurses, doctors, medical technicians, engineers and agriculturalists.

CUSO workers are usually paid at approximately counterpart, not Canadian, salaries by their overseas employer, to whom they are directly responsible. This policy, which enables overseas governments to devote their all-too-scarce capital to other development tasks, is one of the features that distinguishes CUSO from many other manpower resource agencies.

A major priority in the past two years has been decentralization, recognizing that both initial planning and actual administration are most effectively conducted in the field. CUSO now has 25 full-time and eight part-time field staff officers, a total which

Fondé en 1961, au début de la première décennie du développement des Nations-Unies, le SUCO a alors recruté 17 volontaires pour travailler dans quatre pays en voie de développement. Depuis ce temps, plus de 2,500 Canadiens ont eu recours à cet organisme comme moyen de participer au développement international. Actuellement, au début de sa seconde décennie, le SUCO compte environ 1,200 personnes qui travaillent dans plus de 40 pays en Afrique, en Asie, dans les Antilles et en Amérique latine.

Le SUCO, organisme indépendant et sans but lucratif, envoie des Canadiens qualifiés au point de vue technique et professionnel pour répondre aux demandes précises des gouvernements et organismes d'outre-mer. Les volontaires du SUCO sont âgés de 18 à 80 ans et ont des professions aussi variées qu'urbanistes et mécaniciens d'automobiles. Présentement, les professeurs (spécialement de mathématiques et de sciences), les infirmières, les médecins, les techniciens en médecine, les ingénieurs et les agronomes sont très demandés.

En général, les coopérants reçoivent à peu près le même salaire que leurs homologues du pays dans lequel ils sont envoyés et sont directement responsables devant leur employeur d'outre-mer. Cette ligne de conduite qui permet aux gouvernements d'outre-mer de consacrer leurs modestes capitaux à d'autres travaux de développement, est l'une des caractéristiques qui distingue le SUCO d'un grand nombre d'autres organismes de ressources en personnel.

compares favourably with other similar organizations.

CUSO draws on four major sources for direct and indirect financial support: the Canadian International Development Agency (CIDA), overseas governments and agencies, Canadian educational institutions, and the private sector. In 1968-69 the CIDA grant totalled over $2 1/4 million, while the overseas government contributed over $2 1/2 million in salaries and housing supplements. Indirect support, estimated at $500,000, comes from such sources as universities and colleges providing office space, equipment and staff for local recruitment and selection committees; the advertising industry; the mass media, which carry recruitment advertising free of charge; and pharmaceutical and other companies donating medical kits packaged by the Department of National Health and Welfare. Finally, an estimated $400,000 comes from the private sector, including donations from individuals, corporations, foundations, community and service groups, and the thousands of Canadians who participate through the "Miles for Millions" marches.

Reconnaissant que la planification initiale et l'administration proprement dite sont très efficaces sur place, on a accordé la priorité principale, au cours des deux dernières années, à la décentralisation. Le SUCO compte maintenant 25 directeurs du personnel sur place, qui travaillent à plein temps et huit, à temps partiel. Ce nombre se compare avantageusement à celui d'autres organismes semblables.

L'aide financière directe et indirecte au SUCO provient de quatre sources principales: l'Agence canadienne de développement international (ACDI), les gouvernements et organismes d'outre-mer, les établissements d'enseignement du Canada et le secteur privé. En 1968-1969, les subventions de l'ACDI se sont élevées à plus de $2-1/4 millions, tandis que les gouvernements d'outre-mer ont versé plus de $2-1/2 millions en salaires et en suppléments au logement. L'aide indirecte, estimée à $500,000, provient des universités et collèges qui fournissent les locaux pour les bureaux, l'équipement et le personnel pour le recrutement local et les comités de sélection, des agences publicitaires, des organes d'information qui font gratuitement de la publicité au SUCO ainsi que des compagnies pharmaceutiques et autres qui donnent des médicaments empaquetés par le ministère de la Santé nationale et du Bien-être social. Enfin, environ $400,000, proviennent du secteur privé y compris les dons des individus, sociétés, fondations, groupes communautaires et des millions de Canadiens qui participent aux marches organisées par "Rallye Tiers-Monde".

Committee of Canadian Law Deans

Comité des doyens de droit du Canada

President
Prof. J.W. Durnford
Dean of law, McGill University, Montreal, Que.

Secretary
Prof. R.S. Mackay
Dean of law, The University of Western Ontario, London, Ont.

Président
Prof. J.W. Durnford
Dean of law, McGill University, Montreal, Que.

Secrétaire
Prof. R.S. Mackay
Dean of law, The University of Western Ontario, London, Ont.

The committee was formed in 1965 and was admitted to associate membership in the AUCC in 1966. It meets at least once yearly in connection with the AUCC annual meeting and sometimes as well in conjunction with the Association of Canadian Law Teachers.

The purpose of the organization is to share data and to discuss, and take steps to solve, mutual problems. This may involve, among other things, representations by the committee to various national associations or agreements to take parallel action within the university, the bar associations or with the outside community.

Among the matters which the committee has focussed on are: the financing of legal education in Canada; a survey of holdings of law libraries in Canada; admissions policies; graduate programs; curriculum changes and relations with the governing bodies of the legal profession.

Ce comité a été formé en 1965 et a été admis comme membre associé de l'AUCC, en 1966. Il se rencontre au moins une fois par année à l'occasion de l'assemblée annuelle de l'AUCC et tient parfois des réunions conjointes avec l'Association canadienne des professeurs de droit.

Cet organisme a pour but de partager des renseignements, discuter et prendre des mesures afin de résoudre les problèmes communs. Cela peut comprendre, entre autres, que ce comité fait des représentations à diverses associations nationales ou conclut, à l'intérieur de l'université, des associations du barreau ou avec la collectivité en général, des ententes visant à prendre des mesures semblables.

Ce comité s'est surtout occupé des questions suivantes: financement de l'enseignement du droit au Canada, relevé des collections des bibliothèques de droit au Canada, lignes de conduite en matière d'admission, programmes d'études supérieures, changements dans les programmes et relations avec les organes administratifs des professions juridiques.

Council of Associations of University Student Personnel Services

Conseil des associations des services universitaires aux étudiants

President
Dr. G.E. Wodehouse
Director, university health services,
University of Toronto, 256 Huron St.,
Toronto 181, Ont.

Secretary-treasurer
Miss Esther Brandon
Associate dean of students, Waterloo
Lutheran University, Waterloo, Ont.

Président
Dr. G.E. Wodehouse
Director, university health services,
University of Toronto, 256 Huron St.,
Toronto 181, Ont.

Secrétaire-trésorière
Miss Esther Brandon
Associate dean of students, Waterloo
Lutheran University, Waterloo, Ont.

The Council of Associations of University Student Personnel Services is a co-ordinating body for the following autonomous associations: Canadian College Health Services Association, Canadian Student Affairs Association, Canadian University Counselling Association, and University and College Placement Association.

The present organization has evolved from a concern in the immediate post-war years regarding counselling for veterans coming to the campus. As the years passed, many non-veterans availed themselves of the counselling services and the organization's name was changed from the University Advisory Service to the University Counselling and Placement Association.

In 1961 student affairs officers from universities and colleges in Ontario and Quebec met to share common concerns and possible solutions to such areas as student housing, discipline, government, etc. Initially it was proposed to have an organization separate from UCPA, but after discussion the two groups decided to meet as one body in 1963. In 1965, 20 years after the initial meeting of what became UCPA, the name of the association was changed to the Canadian Association of University Student Personnel Services and the "umbrella" concept was adopted. On January 1, 1968 the name was officially changed to the present "Council of Associations of University Student Personnel Services" and the divisions of counselling, student affairs, and placement, which in the interim had evolved into associations, became much more autonomous.

Le Conseil des associations des services universitaires aux étudiants est un organisme de coordination pour les associations autonomes suivantes: Canadian College Health Services Association, Canadian Student Affairs Association, Canadian University Counselling Association, and University and College Placement Association.

Cet organisme s'est développé à la suite de l'intérêt qu'on portait durant les années d'après guerre à l'orientation des anciens combattants qui entraient à l'université. Au cours des années qui ont suivi, plusieurs étudiants, qui n'étaient pas des anciens combattants, se sont prévalus des services d'orientation et le nom de l'organisme, qui était alors le University Advisory Service, est devenu la University Counselling and Placement Association.

En 1961, les directeurs des affaires étudiantes dans les universités et les collèges de l'Ontario et du Québec se sont rencontrés pour discuter de leurs intérêts communs et des solutions possibles qu'on pourrait apporter à des domaines tels que le logement, la discipline, la direction des étudiants, etc.

Tout d'abord, on a proposé de fonder un organisme distinct de l'UCPA. Mais après discussion les deux groupes ont décidé de se rencontrer en 1963, après fusion des deux organismes en un seul. En 1965, soit vingt ans après la première réunion qui a donné naissance à l'UCPA, le nom de l'association a été changé en celui de l'Association des services universitaires aux étudiants du Canada et est devenue l'organisation-mère. Le 1er janvier 1968,

Throughout this organizational evolution, the aim of the members of the associations was "the total and maximum development of college and university students". The council is the vehicle through which information from the component associations is shared and co-ordinated regarding research and other activities aimed at implementing this common concern.

In 1965 the Canadian College Health Services Association was founded and three years later became the fourth association under the council umbrella.

Some of the concerns of each of the associations are reflected in their programs over the years. The Canadian Student Affairs Association (CSAA) has addressed itself to questions of student unrest, housing, student government, drugs (including sponsorship of a national conference at Loyola College and the publication of papers delivered there), and the specialized interests of component groups such as deans of women, financial aid officers, and foreign student advisors.

The Canadian University Counselling Association (CUCA), as its name implies, brings together those people involved in providing professional counselling in Canadian universities. It is concerned with the effectiveness of various models of counselling programs and the training of counsellors as well as specific techniques and services designed to help students.

The University and College Placement Association (UCPA), with its own secretariat established in 1969, has an active program of publication, research, seminars for recruiters and university placement officers to help maintain a high ethical standard in student recruiting, co-ordination of recruiting schedules, production of video-tapes for career counselling, and so on.

The members of the Canadian College Health Services Association (CCHSA) are interested in the pursuit of all measures which may preserve or improve the health of university and college students and communities and to provide a means of exchange and sharing to this end.

cet organisme a officiellement modifié son nom et est devenu le "Conseil des associations des services universitaires aux étudiants", tandis que les départements de l'orientation, des affaires étudiantes et du placement, qui entre-temps étaient devenus des associations, ont acquis une plus grande autonomie.

Durant toute cette transformation, les membres des associations ont toujours visé au "développement complet et maximum des étudiants universitaires". Le conseil est un centre qui distribue aux associations constituantes les renseignements provenant de chacune d'elles et qui coordonne la recherche et les autres activités propres à la réalisation du but commun.

En 1965, la Canadian College Health Services Association a été fondée et, trois ans plus tard, est devenue la quatrième association relevant du conseil.

Les programmes mis sur pied dans le passé reflètent certaines des questions qui préoccupent chacune des associations. La Canadian Student Affairs Association (CSAA) s'est penchée sur l'agitation des étudiants, leurs logements, la direction des étudiants, les stupéfiants (y compris le parrainage d'une conférence nationale au Collège Loyola et la publication des thèses qui ont été exposées), ainsi que sur les intérêts spéciaux de groupes constituants tels que les directrices des étudiantes, les préposés à l'appui financier et les directeurs des étudiants étrangers.

La Canadian University Counselling Association (CUCA), groupe ensemble, comme l'indique son nom, les préposés à l'orientation professionnelle dans les universités canadiennes. Cette association s'intéresse à l'efficacité des diverses formes de programmes d'orientation, ainsi qu'à la formation des orienteurs de même qu'aux méthodes et services particuliers qui ont pour but d'aider les étudiants.

La University and College Placement Association (UCPA), qui a son propre secrétariat depuis 1969, met sur pied un programme actif de publication, de recherche, de colloques destinés aux recruteurs, ainsi qu'aux préposés au placement dans les universités, programme qui a pour but, entre autres, de maintenir une norme élevée dans le recrutement des étudiants, la coordination des programmes de recrutement, et la production de rubans magnétoscopiques sur l'orientation.

Les membres de la Canadian College Health Services Association (CCHSA) s'intéressent à toutes les mesures propres à conserver ou à améliorer la santé chez les étudiants universitaires et dans les collectivités, ainsi qu'à en faire un centre d'information à cette fin.

National Committee of Deans of Engineering and Applied Science

Comité national des doyens de génie et sciences appliquées

Chairman
Dean J. Hoogstraten
Faculty of engineering, The University of Manitoba, Winnipeg 19, Man.

Secretary
Dean G.W. Joly
Faculty of engineering, Loyola College, Montreal, Que.

Président
Dean J. Hoogstraten
Faculty of engineering, The University of Manitoba, Winnipeg 19, Man.

Secrétaire
Dean G.W. Joly
Faculty of engineering, Loyola College, Montreal, Que.

The National Committee of Deans of Engineering and Applied Science had its origin some years ago when the Engineering Institute of Canada invited deans to come together once a year at the time of the Institute's annual meeting in May or June. When the committee became associated with the AUCC, meetings were also frequently held at the time the AUCC met, so that lately two meetings per year have been held.

In 1969 the Engineering Institute of Canada changed its annual meeting date to September. It is likely in the future that one meeting will be held in the fall at the time of either the AUCC or EIC meetings with a second one being held in the spring, as required.

There are no specific terms of reference for the committee but in general it considers items of concern to the deans. These have included: engineering education and curricula; employment of engineers; co-operation with industry; accreditation; information retrieval; engineering research and engineering policy of government agencies.

The term of office for both the chairman and the secretary expires in May of each year.

Le Comité national des doyens de génie et sciences appliquées a été formé il y a quelques années lorsque l'Institut de génie du Canada a invité les doyens à se réunir une fois par année à l'occasion de l'assemblée annuelle de l'Institut, au mois de mai ou juin. Devenu associé à l'AUCC, le comité s'est souvent réuni à l'occasion de l'assemblée annuelle de l'AUCC de sorte que par la suite il a tenu deux réunions par année.

En 1969, l'Institut de génie du Canada a tenu son congrès au mois de septembre. Il y a des chances qu'à l'avenir une réunion se tienne à l'automne, à l'occasion de l'assemblée annuelle de l'AUCC ou de l'IGC et qu'une autre ait lieu au printemps, comme on l'a demandé.

Le comité n'a pas d'attributions précises, mais en général il étudie des questions qui préoccupent les doyens, comme les études de génie et les programmes d'études, les débouchés, la collaboration avec les industries, l'accréditation, la récupération de l'information, les recherches en génie et la ligne de conduite des organismes gouvernementaux à l'égard du génie.

Le mandat du président et du secrétaire expire au mois de mai, chaque année.

Service for Admission to College and University

Service d'admission au collège et à l'université

151 Slater St., Ottawa, Ont., K1P 5N2

151, rue Slater, Ottawa (Ont.) K1P 5N2

President
Mr. G.M. Davies
Associate deputy minister, Department of Youth and Education, 311 – 1181 Portage Ave., Winnipeg 10, Man.

Président
M. G.M. Davies
Sous-ministre associé, Ministère de la jeunesse et de l'éducation, 311 – 1181, avenue Portage, Winnipeg 10 (Man.)

Executive director
Mr. Léopold Lamontagne

Directeur général
M. Léopold Lamontagne

SACU, and interprovincial and interuniversity organization, was founded in 1966 to assist both French- and English-language educational institutions in connection with the transition of students from secondary schools to institutions of post-secondary education; to assist generally both secondary schools and post-secondary institutions in the identification and evaluation of student capacities, and in the admission of students to post-secondary studies; and to co-operate with organizations with similar objectives in other countries; and, without limiting the generality of the foregoing:

a) to arrange for the development and administration of suitable aptitude and achievement tests through not less than two test service centres: at least one located in the province of Quebec for French-speaking candidates and at least one located in a province or in provinces other than Quebec for English-speaking candidates;

b) to assist in the further development and improvement of selection and admission procedures and to aid, on request, in the awarding of scholarships and bursaries;

c) to assist member institutions of the association in the interpretation of the academic record of applicants for admission from other provinces in Canada or from other countries;

d) to conduct and support research on problems related to the admission of students to institutions of post-secondary education;

Le SACU est un organisme interprovincial et interuniversitaire, fondé en 1966 pour aider les établissements d'enseignement, tant de langue française que de langue anglaise, en ce qui a trait au passage des élèves des écoles secondaires aux établissements d'enseignement postsecondaire, aider de façon générale les écoles secondaires et les établissements postsecondaires en ce qui regarde la découverte et l'évaluation des aptitudes des élèves et l'admission de ces élèves aux études postsecondaires, collaborer avec les organismes qui poursuivent des buts semblables dans d'autres pays, et, sans restreindre la portée générale de ce qui précède:

a) faire établir des tests d'aptitudes et de connaissances pour aider à la sélection et au placement des élèves par au moins deux centres dont au moins un serait situé dans la province de Québec pour les étudiants francophones et au moins un autre dans une ou des provinces autres que le Québec pour les étudiants anglophones;

b) aider à mettre au point et perfectionner les méthodes de sélection et d'admission et aider, sur demande, à attribuer des bourses d'études et des bourses de soutien;

c) aider les établissements membres de l'association à interpréter le dossier scolaire des élèves venant d'autres provinces du Canada ou d'autres pays et qui sollicitent leur admission;

d) faire et favoriser des recherches sur les problèmes touchant l'admission des élèves

e) to gather and distribute information about entrance requirements, selection of students, admission procedures, scholarships and bursaries;

f) to provide a medium for the co-operation of secondary schools, universities, other institutions of post-secondary education, provincial departments of education, and other groups and organizations concerned with the transition of students from secondary to post-secondary institutions, and for the discussion of their common problems and other related matters.

A student directory entitled *Requirements for admission to Canadian colleges and universities* was published in September, 1971.

aux établissements d'enseignement postsecondaire;

e) recueillir et diffuser des renseignements sur les conditions d'admission, la sélection des élèves, les méthodes d'admission, les bourses d'études et les bourses de soutien;

f) constituer un organe de coopération entre les écoles secondaires, les universités, les autres établissements d'enseignement postsecondaire, les ministères provinciaux de l'éducation et les autres groupes et organisations qui s'occupent du passage des élèves du niveau secondaire aux établissements postsecondaires et leur permettre de discuter de leurs problèmes communs et d'autres questions connexes.

Un guide pour les étudiants, intitulé *Conditions d'admission dans les collèges et universités du Canada* a été publié au mois de septembre 1971.

AUCC honorary associates   Associés honoraires, AUCC

The Canada Council

Ottawa, Ont. (613-237-3400)

Principal officers

Chairman
John Prentice, LLD

Vice-chairman
Guy Rocher, PhD

Director
Peter Dwyer, BA

Associate director
Robert Elie, BA

Associate director for university affairs
F.A. Milligan, MA

Assistant director and treasurer
Paul Boisclair, BA, BCom

Assistant director and secretary
Claude Gauthier, BTh

Assistant director and chief, awards service
Jules Pelletier, BL, LLL, LScSoc, MCom

Secretary general, Canadian Commission for Unesco
David Bartlett, MSc

The Canada Council is an independent agency created by the government of Canada in 1957, to "foster and promote the study and enjoyment of, and the production of works in the arts, humanities and social sciences". It carries out its task mainly through a broad program of fellowships and grants. It also shares the responsibility for Canada's cultural relations with other countries, and administers, as a separate agency, the Canadian Commission for Unesco.

The council sets its own policies and makes its own decisions within the terms of The Canada Council act. It reports to Parliament through the Secretary of State and also appears before such parliamentary committees as the Public Accounts Committee and the Standing Committee on

Le Conseil des arts du Canada

Ottawa, Ont. (613-237-3400)

Direction

Président
John Prentice, LLD

Vice-président
Guy Rocher, PhD

Directeur
Peter Dwyer, BA

Directeur associé
Robert Elie, BA

Directeur adjoint pour les affaires universitaires
F.A. Milligan, MA

Directeur adjoint et trésorier
Paul Boisclair, BA, BCom

Directeur adjoint et secrétaire
Claude Gauthier, BTh

Directeur adjoint et chef du service des bourses
Jules Pelletier, BL, LLL, LScSoc, MCom

Secrétaire général de la commission canadienne pour l'Unesco
David Bartlett, MSc

Le Conseil des arts du Canada est un organisme indépendant, créé en 1957 par le gouvernement fédéral afin de "développer et favoriser l'étude et la jouissance des arts, des humanités et des sciences sociales, de même que la production d'oeuvres s'y rattachant". Son principal moyen d'action consiste à octroyer des bourses et des subventions de divers genres. En outre, il assure pour une part les relations culturelles du Canada avec l'étranger, et il administre la Commission canadienne pour l'Unesco, qui constitue un organisme distinct.

Dans les limites déterminées par la loi sur le Conseil des arts du Canada, le conseil jouit d'une entière liberté d'action et détermine ses

Broadcasting, Film and Assistance to the Arts.

The council is made up of 21 members appointed by the governor-in-council. The chairman and the vice-chairman serve for terms not exceeding five years, and other members for terms of three years. The day-to-day administrative work is carried out by a permanent staff in Ottawa, headed by a director and an associate director who are appointed by the governor-in-council.

In matters of policy and in the implementation of its programs, the council is assisted by two bodies of specialists, the advisory academic panel and the advisory arts panel.

The council's income is derived from three sources: an annual grant of the Canadian government which amounted to $26,310,000 for the 1971-72 fiscal year; the endowment fund established by parliament when it created the council, and which currently yields some $4.9 million per annum; and private funds willed or donated to the council. In addition, the council receives funds from the Department of External Affairs to administer some of Canada's cultural exchanges with foreign countries.

Assistance to the humanities and social sciences takes up the larger part of the council's budget. In 1970-71, this program accounted for $18,238,000. In support of research training the council awarded 2,456 doctoral fellowships worth $11,316,000; for research work, 164 leave fellowships totalling $1,269,000 and $4,345,000 in research grants; for research communication, a total of $893,000 in assistance to scholarly meetings and exchanges, and publication of learned journals and scholarly manuscripts. Beginning in 1972-73, the council will offer research fellowships for scholars who wish to do post-doctoral research at an early stage of their academic career.

In the arts, the council spent $10,269,000 of which $1,668,000 was used to finance some 750 bursaries, awards, and grants to individuals in the various art forms, and $8,601,000 was applied to grants to organizations, including $2,113,000 for music, $2,883,000 for the theatre, $1,612,000 for dance and opera, $1,208,000 for the visual arts and cinema and $279,000 for writing.

On behalf of the Canadian government, the council also administers several programs of cultural exchanges with foreign countries.

propres orientations. Il rend compte de son activité au parlement par l'intermédiaire du Secrétaire d'Etat, et aussi des comités parlementaires devant lesquels il est appelé à témoigner, notamment le Comité des comptes publics et le Comité permanent de la radiodiffusion, du film et de l'assistance aux arts.

Le Conseil des arts se compose de 21 membres nommés par le gouverneur en conseil. Le mandat du président est de cinq ans au maximum, et celui des autres membres, de trois ans. Le conseil se réunit au moins cinq fois l'an. Il a son siège à Ottawa, où un personnel permanent voit à la mise en oeuvre de ses programmes, sous la direction d'un directeur et d'un directeur associé nommés par le gouverneur en conseil.

Dans l'élaboration et la mise en oeuvre de ses programmes, le conseil bénéficie du concours de deux groupes de spécialistes, la Commission consultative des affaires universitaires et la Commission consultative des arts.

Les revenus du Conseil des arts du Canada proviennent de trois sources: une subvention annuelle du gouvernement fédéral, qui est de $26,310,000 pour l'exercice 1971-72; la caisse de dotation constituée lors de la création du conseil, et dont le rendement est d'environ $4.9 millions par année; et des dons et legs de sources privées.

L'aide aux humanités et aux sciences sociales absorbe la plus large part du budget du conseil. Cette aide a été en 1970-71 de l'ordre de $18,238,000. Au titre de la formation des chercheurs, le conseil a octroyé 2,456 bourses de doctorat d'une valeur totale de $11,316,000; au titre des travaux de recherche, 164 bourses de travail libre d'une valeur de $1,269,000 et des subventions de recherche d'une valeur de $4,345,000. Il a consacré $893,000 aux communications entre chercheurs (rencontres, échanges et publication de revues savantes et d'études manuscrites). A compter de l'année 1972-73, le conseil offrira des bourses d'un type nouveau, désignées "bourses de recherche". Elles s'adresseront en général aux titulaires d'un doctorat qui ont fait un peu d'enseignement postsecondaire et qui désirent faire de la recherche.

Dans le domaine des arts, les dépenses se sont élevées à $10,269,000, dont $1,668,000 ont servi à financer environ 750 bourses, et $8,601,000 ont servi à subventionner les institutions; sur cette dernière somme, les subventions se sont élevées à $2,113,000 pour

Under one of these, an amount of $746,000 in scholarships and fellowships for study in Canada was awarded in 1970-71 to nationals of France, Belgium, Switzerland, the Federal Republic of Germany, Italy, and the Netherlands. Under another program, Canadian universities and cultural institutions received grants totalling $115,000 to bring to Canada distinguished university professors, scholars, and artists; this program, which applied only to the above-mentioned countries, is being extended to continental Latin America. Under a special Canada-France program, travel grants worth a total of $9,000 were made to Canadian scholars in the humanities and social sciences wishing to conduct research in France; the recipients were paid a living allowance by the French authorities. The council also administers the funds of the Canadian Cultural Institute in Rome; the institute's annual income of some $25,000 is used to provide fellowships to one or two Canadian artists or scholars wishing to work or study in Italy.

The council, in co-operation with the Foreign Area Fellowship Program (U.S.), has initiated a program of training fellowships of $250 per month for graduate students proceeding to a master's degree in the social sciences, with provision for research in Latin America. Four such fellowships were granted for the year 1971-72.

Through the Izaak Walton Killman memorial awards of The Canada Council, $604,000 was awarded in 1970-71 to scholars of exceptional ability engaged in research projects of far-reaching significance. Young scholars who have recently completed their PhD studies and who wish to engage in cross-disciplinary research will be eligible for Killam awards in 1972-73 under a new category of special post-doctoral research scholarships. The senior research scholarships will be maintained, as in previous years.

Under its power to "make awards to persons in Canada for outstanding accomplishments in the arts, humanities and social sciences", the council annually awards the Molson prizes and finances the Governor General's Literary Awards.

As an agent of the council, the Canadian Commission for Unesco co-ordinates Unesco program activities abroad and administers a modest program in furtherance of Unesco objectives. In the year ending March 31, 1971, the council spent approximately $218,000 through the Canadian Commission for these purposes.

la musique, à $2,883,000 pour le théâtre, à $1,612,000 pour la danse et l'opéra, à $1,208,000 pour les arts plastiques et le cinéma, et à $279,000 pour les lettres.

D'autre part le conseil assure, pour le compte du gouvernement fédéral, l'exécution de plusieurs programmes d'échanges culturels avec l'étranger. Au titre d'un de ces programmes, il a octroyé en 1970-71 des bourses et subventions d'une valeur de $746,000 à des ressortissants de France, de Belgique, de Suisse, d'Italie, des Pays-Bas et de la République fédérale d'Allemange. Dans le cadre d'un autre programme, les universités et institutions culturelles canadiennes se sont partagé $115,000 pour faire venir de ces mêmes pays des professeurs, intellectuels et artistes éminents; ce programme sera étendu, à compter du prochain exercice, aux pays de l'Amérique latine continentale. En vertu d'un programme spécial d'échanges avec la France, des bourses de voyage d'une valeur globale de $9,000 ont été mises à la disposition des universitaires canadiens désireux de faire un stage de recherche en France; les frais de séjour des boursiers étaient assumés par les autorités françaises. Le conseil administre aussi les fonds de l'Institut culturel canadien à Rome. L'institut, dont les revenus sont de l'ordre de $25,000 par année, met une ou deux bourses par année à la disposition des artistes et des intellectuels canadiens désireux de faire un stage d'études ou de travail en Italie.

Avec le concours du Foreign Area Fellowship Program (E.-U.), le Conseil des arts du Canada a institué des bourses d'études comportant un stage de recherche en Amérique latine pour les étudiants de maîtrise en sciences sociales. Quatre de ces bourses on été accordées pour l'année 1972-73.

Dans le cadre du programme Killam, financé par la succession Izaak Walton Killam, le conseil a octroyé $604,000 en 1970-71 pour permettre à quelques universitaires canadiens de premier plan de se livrer à des travaux de recherche de grande portée. Des bourses postdoctorales spéciales, instituées récemment dans le cadre de ce programme, permettront aux jeunes titulaires d'un doctorat, à compter de l'année 1972-73, d'entreprendre des recherches interdisciplinaires. Les anciennes subventions Killam, désormais désignées "bourses de recherche Killam", demeureront accessibles à leurs aînés.

En vertu du pouvoir qui lui est dévolu de "décerner des récompenses à des personnes au Canada qui ont acquis un mérite exceptionnel dans les arts, les humanités ou

les sciences sociales", le conseil attribue
chaque année les prix Molson et finance les
prix littéraires du gouverneur général.

A titre d'agent du conseil, la Commission
canadienne pour l'Unesco assure la
coordination des activités du Canada à
l'étranger dans le cadre du programme de
l'Unesco et la mise en oeuvre d'un modeste
programme visant à promouvoir les objectifs
de l'Unesco. Au cours de l'année qui s'est
terminée le 21 mars 1971, le conseil a
consacré environ $218,000 à ces activités par
l'entremise de la Commission canadienne
pour l'Unesco.

Defence Research Board

Conseil de recherche pour la défense

Ottawa (Ont.) (613-992-0932)

Ottawa, Ont. (613-992-0932)

Principal officers

Direction

Chairman
L.J. L'Heureux, BA, BSc, ME, DEng

Président
L.J. L'Heureux, BA, BSc, ME, DEng

Vice-chairman
H. Sheffer, BA, MA, PhD, FCIC

Vice-président
H. Sheffer, BA, MA, PhD, FCIC

Deputy chairman (operations)
A.M. Pennie, BSc

Adjoint au président (administratif)
A.M. Pennie, BSc

Deputy chairman (scientific)
N.J.B. Wiggin, BSc, MSc, MDCM, PhD

Adjoint au président (scientifique)
N.J.B. Wiggin, BSc, MSc, MDCM, PhD

Secretary of the board
A.E. Léger, BA, BSc, DSc

Secrétaire du conseil
A.E. Léger, BA, BSc, DSc

Executive secretary, university grants program
R.H. Lowe, BA, MA

Secrétaire administratif du programme d'aide financière aux universités
R.H. Lowe, BA, MA

Defence research in Canada is the responsibility of the Defence Research Board which forms an integral part of the Department of National Defence and is staffed and directed by civilian scientists and administrators.

During the second world war, Canada developed a strong defence research capability. It was clear that a scientific organization was required to carry on research for the benefit of the armed forces and to maintain a close connection between the defence scientist and the serving officer. Thus the concept of a civilian service within the Department of National Defence, concentrating on research for the Canadian armed services, was finally decided upon, and the Defence Research Board came into being on April 1, 1947.

The Defence Research Board consists of two elements. The first of these is the board itself, composed of a chairman, a vice-chairman and a secretary, five ex-officio members comprising the chief of the defence staff, the vice-chief of the defence staff, the chief of technical services, the deputy minister of national defence and the president of the National Research Council, and other

La recherche pour la défense au Canada relève du Conseil de recherches pour la défense qui fait partie intégrale du ministère de la Défense nationale et dont le personnel et la direction se composent de savants et d'administrateurs civils.

La deuxième guerre mondiale a vu se développer au Canada un fort mouvement de recherche pour la défense. Il était clair qu'il fallait un organisme scientifique pour mener à bien la recherche au profit des forces armées et pour maintenir des relations étroites entre le chercheur pour la défense et l'officier militaire. Cette constatation a mené à la décision de créer un service civil au sein du ministère de la Défense nationale, qui se concentrerait sur la recherche pour les forces armées canadiennes. Le Conseil de recherches pour la défense a été établi le 1er avril 1947.

Ce conseil se compose de deux éléments. Le premier comprend le conseil lui-même, composé d'un président, d'un vice-président et d'un secrétaire, de cinq membres d'office: le chef de l'état-major de la défense, le sous-chef de l'état-major de la défense, le chef des services techniques, le sous-ministre de la défense nationale et le président du Conseil national de recherches, ainsi que d'autres

appointed members drawn from industry and universities.

The chairman and the vice-chairman are appointed by the governor-in-council and hold office during pleasure. In his capacity as scientific adviser to the minister, the chairman is a member of the defence council.

The members by appointment are appointed by the governor-in-council for a term of three years and are eligible for reappointment.

The board meets three times a year, or more frequently if the situation warrants. Through the chairman, it advises the minister of national defence on all matters affecting defence research and development.

Under the direction of the chairman as the chief executive officer, the board carries out a research program composed of projects and studies designed primarily to investigate military problems of both an immediate and long-range type. In many instances work on these problems must be considered classified, and as requiring not only the co-operation of the Canadian forces, but also specialized facilities not available elsewhere. In the intramural program are included joint or co-operative projects with Britain, the United States, and other western powers.

The second element of the board consists of the scientific and support staff necessary to carry out the duties inherent in the foregoing schedule of general responsibilities. In addition to a relatively small headquarters component, seven laboratories at various points in Canada conduct research in different aspects of defence science. The research establishments at Dartmouth, Nova Scotia, and Esquimalt, British Columbia, are engaged in maritime research. The research establishment at Valcartier near Quebec city has a diversified program in the fields of armament, explosives and propellants.

The laboratories at Shirley Bay and the Defence Research Establishment Suffield at Ralston, Alberta, are concerned with defence against biological and chemical agents that may be used as weapons, and with studies and experiments relative to the effects of nuclear weapons.

The research program of the Defence and Civil Institute of Environmental Medicine at Downsview, Ontario, studies the factors contributing to efficient performance of the human element in the Canadian forces.

membres choisis dans l'industrie et les universités.

Le président et le vice-président sont désignés par le gouverneur en conseil à titre amovible. A titre de conseiller scientifique auprès du ministre, le président est membre du conseil de la défense.

Les membres nommés sont désignés par le gouverneur en conseil pour un terme de trois années et leur mandat est renouvelable.

Le conseil se réunit trois fois par année ou davantage au besoin. Par l'intermédiaire du président, il conseille le ministre de la Défense nationale sur toute question se rapportant à la recherche pour la défense.

Sous la direction du président, qui en est le directeur administratif, le conseil poursuit un programme de recherche dont les projets et études visent à la solution de problèmes militaires à portée immédiate et à long terme. Souvent ces projets doivent être traités comme secrets et ils exigent non seulement la collaboration des forces armées mais également celle d'installations spécialisées qu'on ne trouve pas ailleurs. Le programme intra-muros comprend également les projets conjoints ou coopératifs avec la Grande-Bretagne, les Etats-Unis et les autres puissances du monde occidental.

Le second élément du conseil comprend le personnel scientifique et auxiliaire nécessaire pour remplir les fonctions d'ordre général qui entrent dans le programme précité. En plus d'un personnel relativement peu nombreux au siège même du conseil, ce dernier opère sept laboratoires situés à divers endroits au Canada qui poursuivent des recherches couvrant divers aspects de la science militaire de la défense. Les noms des laboratoires ont été changés cette année et la nouvelle désignation est utilisée ci-après. Le Centre de recherches pour la défense-Atlantique, à Dartmouth (Nouvelle-Ecosse) et le Centre de recherches pour la défense-Pacifique, à Esquimalt (Colombie-Britannique) s'occupent principalement de recherches maritimes. Le Centre de recherches à Valcartier, près de Québec, poursuit un programme diversifié dans le domaine des armements, des explosifs et des propulseurs.

Le Centre de recherches pour la défense à Shirley Bay et le Centre de recherches Suffield pour la défense à Ralston (Alberta) s'occupent non seulement de défense contre les agents biologiques et chimiques qui peuvent être utilisés comme armes mais ils poursuivent aussi des études et des

The Defence Research Analysis at Ottawa studies strategic problems, investigations of maritime, land, and tactical air operations and equipments, North American defence questions and problems relating to personnel, programming and logistics.

Through a system of extramural grants, the Defence Research Board supports a program of unclassified basic research in the universities and their affiliated institutes across Canada. In making this support available, the board has a threefold objective: to acquire new scientific knowledge of interest to defence science, to maintain a link with the academic community of the universities, and to assist in securing the services of competent younger scientists for its own laboratory operations. Although this program in the universities is broadly based in both the physical and the biosciences, emphasis is of necessity placed upon supporting work which bears a relationship to the problems of defence science.

Participation in the industrial aspects of defence science, although a relatively recent undertaking by the board, now forms an important part of the extramural program. The objective is to stimulate the research capability of the defence sector of Canadian industry and thus enhance Canada's position in competing for United States' and NATO military equipment orders. The method used is a cost-sharing arrangement whereby the board, through a research grant, pays one-half the cost of selected development projects which appear to have defence potential.

In addition to the responsibilities summarized above, the Defence Research Board maintains a close contact with the defence scientific community of other NATO and Commonwealth countries. Liaison offices, staffed by Defence Research Board personnel, operate in London, Washington, and Paris; the board's scientific staff contributes to international meetings and conferences for discussion of common problems in the technological development of defence systems. Through its scientific information service, the board ensures that the results of its research, both intramural and extramural, are made available to other western nations, and similarly that the information derived from research elsewhere is communicated to its own scientific staff.

expériences relatives aux effets des armes nucléaires. Le programme de recherches de la Defence et Civil Institute of Environmental Medicine à Downsview (Ontario), étudie une gamme étendue de facteurs contribuant à l'efficacité de l'élément humain dans les forces canadiennes.

Le travail du Centre analysé pour la défense, à Ottawa, comprend des études sur certains problèmes de stratégie, sur les opérations tactiques sur terre, sur mer et dans les airs et sur l'équipement alors utilisé, sur des questions concernant la défense du continent nord-américain et enfin sur tout problème qui touche le personnel, la programmation et la logistique.

Au moyen d'un régime d'aide financière à l'extérieur, le Conseil de recherches pour la défense appuie un programme de recherches fondamentales non secrètes qui se poursuit dans les universités et les instituts qui leur sont affiliés au Canada. Un tel appui financier sert un triple objectif: acquérir de nouvelles connaissances scientifiques intéressant la science militaire de la défense, maintenir un lien avec le monde universitaire et aider à obtenir les services de jeunes savants compétents pour ses propres laboratoires de recherches. Quoique ce programme concerne en général les recherches en physique et sur les sciences de la vie, l'appui financier est nécessairement accordé aux projets concernant les problèmes scientifiques de la défense.

Le programme de recherches industrielles pour la défense initié par le conseil, quoique de création récente, ne constitue pas moins une part importante du programme total d'aide extérieure. Il a pour but d'encourager la recherche dans le secteur de l'industrie canadienne produisant pour la défense afin de rendre les compagnies concernées compétitives sur le marché de l'équipement militaire nécessaire aux Etats-Unis et à l'OTAN. Pour y arriver, le conseil utilise la méthode du partage des frais. Dans le cadre de ce programme, le conseil paie la moitié du coût des projets choisis de développement qui présentent un intérêt défini pour la défense.

En plus des responsabilités déjà énumérées, le Conseil de recherches pour la défense maintient des relations étroites avec les organismes scientifiques de la défense des autres pays de l'OTAN et du Commonwealth. Des bureaux de liaison maintenus par un personnel du conseil existent à Londres, à Washington et à Paris; de plus, le personnel scientifique du conseil participe activement aux réunions et

conférences internationales où l'on discute de problèmes communs concernant le développement technologique des systèmes de défense. Enfin, au moyen de son Service d'information scientifique, le conseil s'assure que les résultats des recherches qu'il supporte, tant internes qu'externes, sont mis à la disposition des autres pays occidentaux et que par ailleurs, les résultats des recherches faites en dehors de ses cadres ou à l'étranger parviennent à son personnel scientifique.

Medical Research Council

Conseil des recherches médicales

Ottawa, Ontario
Telephone: 613-993-2358

Ottawa, Ontario
Téléphone: 613-993-2358

Principal officers

Direction

President
G. Malcolm Brown, MD, CM, DPhil, LLD, DSc, MD, FRSC, FRCP, FRCP(C), FACP

Président
G. Malcolm Brown, MD, CM, DPhil, LLD, DSc, MD, FRSC, FRCP, FRCP(C), FACP

Secretary
J.M. Roxburgh, PhD

Secrétaire
J.M. Roxburgh, PhD

The Medical Research Council was established in 1960 as a result of recommendations to the Privy council committee on scientific and industrial research by a special committee appointed to review extra-mural support of medical research by the government of Canada. For nine years it operated within the administrative framework of the National Research Council. In 1969 it became a separate crown corporation of the federal government, reporting to parliament through the minister of national health and welfare. The Medical Research Council has a membership of 21, selected on the basis of their competence and interest in health science research. It is served by a small secretariat, and has the invaluable advice of over 100 university-based scientists who serve on its 20 grants and selection committees.

It is the primary responsibility of the council to assist and promote the development of health science research in the university centres of Canada. Research in the faculties of medicine and their affiliated hospitals and institutes, in dentistry and in pharmacy, and research in other faculties, and in colleges of veterinary medicine, which is of high relevance to health, is supported chiefly through an extensive program of grants-in-aid. Personnel support is provided by means of studentships, fellowships, scholarships and associateships.

Operating grants, which may be awarded on an annual or a term basis, are designed to assist in defraying the normal operating costs of research — basic, applied or developmental, undertaken in clinical as well

Le Conseil des recherches médicales a été établi en 1960 par suite de recommandations au comité du conseil privé pour les recherches scientifiques et industrielles par un comité spécial chargé de passer en revue l'aide extra-murale apportée par le gouvernement du Canada à la recherche médicale au Canada. Pendant neuf ans il a fonctionné dans le cadre administratif du Conseil national de recherches du Canada. En 1969, il devint une société de la Couronne complètement autonome du gouvernement fédéral répondant au parlement par l'intermédiaire du ministre de la Santé nationale et du Bien-être social. Le Conseil des recherches médicales compte actuellement vingt et un membres, choisis d'après leur compétence et leur intérêt en recherche dans le domaine des sciences de la santé. Il est desservi par un secrétariat restreint, et jouit des services inestimables de plus de 100 chercheurs scientifiques universitaires membres de ses vingt comités de subventions et de sélection.

La responsabilité première du Conseil des recherches médicales est de stimuler et de promouvoir le développement de la recherche en sciences de la santé dans les centres universitaires canadiens. La recherche dans les facultés de médecine et leurs hôpitaux et instituts affiliés, les facultés de chirurgie dentaire et de pharmacie, et celle entreprise dans les autres facultés et dans les collèges de médecine vétérinaire et qui a un lien particulier au domaine de la santé, est encouragée principalement par un grand éventail de subventions. L'aide financière au personnel de recherche est accordée sous forme de "studentships", "fellowships", "scholarships", et "associateships".

as preclinical departments. Major equipment grants provide for the purchase of units of special research equipment costing $5,000 or more. The council also provides a general research grant to the dean of each Canadian school of medicine, pharmacy and dentistry to be used at his discretion for the development of research in his university.

The senior category of personnel support, and one which is now used particularly to strengthen the research effort in geographic or disciplinary areas in need of development in Canada, is the medical research associateship; under this phase of its program the council provides long-term salary support for a limited number of highly qualified independent investigators working in Canadian universities. Medical research scholarships provide for the salaries of a number of young investigators who have completed their formal training and have shown promise of becoming independent scientists; support under this program is limited to a five-year period in any one case. The council also provides medical research fellowships to enable qualified candidates at the postdoctoral level to take advanced training in research in the health sciences, and studentships to those at the predoctoral level who are working towards a higher degree in departments of medical, pharmacy or dental schools. To stimulate the interest of honor students and to afford them an opportunity to obtain early training in research, the council also provides each Canadian school of medicine, dentistry, and pharmacy with funds for a limited number of summer undergraduate awards valued at $1,200 each and tenable for a period of three months between the normal academic sessions.

In addition to these two main programs, the Medical Research Council sponsors several other programs to facilitate or promote health science research in Canada.

Development grants are made available to encourage local initiative and assist the health science centres in building up new research programs in areas which require stimulus. Council is also prepared to consider applications for the establishment of MRC groups within Canadian universities, a program designed to provide optimal conditions for collaborative research by groups of two or more highly qualified senior investigators who wish to devote the major portion of their time to an area of research which seems likely to be highly productive. Scientific collaboration and exchange of information is encouraged through council's sponsorship of visiting scientists and visiting

Les subventions destinées à la conduite d'une recherche, accordées pour une ou plusieurs années, ont pour but de défrayer une partie des dépenses de fonctionnement de la recherche fondamentale, appliquée et de développement, entreprise dans les départements cliniques et pré-cliniques.

La catégorie supérieure d'aide financière accordée au personnel de recherche, et qui maintenant est utilisée particulièrement afin de promouvoir la recherche dans des disciplines et régions géographiques peu développées, est celle de l' "associateship". Elle permet au conseil de rémunérer sur une base de long terme un nombre restreint de chercheurs de carrière de haute compétence, qui travaillent dans des universités canadiennes. Le poste de "scholar" permet de rémunérer un certain nombre de chercheurs qui ont complété leur formation et qui ont montré des aptitudes à effectuer des recherches individuelles; ce genre d'aide ne dépasse en aucun cas une période de cinq ans. Le conseil accorde en plus des "fellowships" qui permettent à des candidats qualifiés du niveau post-doctoral de recevoir une formation avancée en recherche dans les sciences de la santé, et des "studentships" à ceux du niveau pré-doctoral qui sont inscrits à un grade supérieur dans un département d'une école de médecine, de chirurgie dentaire ou de pharmacie. Pour stimuler l'intérêt à la recherche des étudiants brillants et pour faciliter leur formation, le conseil fournit des fonds à toutes les écoles de médecine, de chirurgie dentaire et de pharmacie du Canada, afin qu'elles puissent octroyer à un certain nombre d'étudiants non encore gradués des bourses d'une valeur de $1,200 chacune pour les trois mois de la saison estivale.

Outre ces deux programmes principaux, le conseil a institué plusieurs autres programmes visant à encourager la recherche dans le domaine des sciences de la santé au Canada. Parmi ceux-ci on compte les groupes de recherches créés dans le but d'établir les meilleures conditions possibles pour la recherche en groupe par des chercheurs de haute compétence qui désirent vouer la partie majeure de leur temps à un domaine de recherche qui semble promettre beaucoup de rendement; les subventions à caractère limité pour encourager l'initiative locale et aider aux écoles de médecine, de chirurgie dentaire et de pharmacie à créer de nouveaux programmes de recherche dans les domaines qui demandent à être stimulés; l'accommodation matérielle de scientifiques invités pour l'encouragement et l'avancement de la collaboration et l'échange de

professors, and support for research symposia and workshops.

As the occasion presents itself, the council also carries out or sponsors studies of specific problems of national interest.

A report on the support provided by the Medical Research Council to universities and their affiliated institutions is published annually.

connaissances scientifiques; l'aide accordée pour des symposia de recherche et un programme restreint d'indemnités de voyage pour permettre à des délégués d'assister à des congrès internationaux.

Lorsque l'occasion se présente, le conseil effectue ou appuie des études spéciales des problèmes particuliers d'intérêt national.

Un compte rendu de l'aide apportée par le Conseil des recherches médicales aux universités et aux hôpitaux et instituts affiliés est publié à chaque année.

National Research Council of Canada

Le Conseil national de recherches du Canada

Ottawa, Ont. (613-993-9114)

Ottawa (Ont.) (613-993-9114)

Principal officers

Direction

President
W.G. Schneider BSc, MSc, PhD, DSc, LLD, FRSC, FRS

Vice-president (scientific-industry)
R.D. Hiscocks, BASc, MBE

Vice-president (scientific-university)
D.J. LeRoy, BA, MA, PhD, FRSC

Délégué général (program planning and analysis)
W.H. Gauvin, BEng, MEng, PhD, DEng, FCIC, PEng

Vice-president (laboratories)
D.W.R. McKinley, OBE, BA, MS, PhD, FIEEE, FRSC

Executive director (external relations)
R.S. Rettie, BSc, DPhil

Assistant vice-presidents (laboratories)
W.A. Cumming, BSc
J.D. Keys, BSc, MSc, PhD

Secretary (acting)
A.W. Tickner, BE, MSc, PhD

Secretary for international relations
J.R.F. Martineau, DSc

Président
W.G. Schneider, BSc, MSc, PhD, DSc, LLD, FRSC, FRS

Vice-président (questions scientifiques-industrie)
R.D. Hiscocks, BASc, MBE

Vice-président (questions scientifiques-universités)
D.J. LeRoy, BA, MA, PhD, FRSC

Délégué général (groupe de planification et d'analyse de programme)
W.H. Gauvin, BEng, MEng, PhD, DEng, FCIC, PEng

Vice-président (laboratoires)
D.W.R. McKinley, OBE, BA, MS, PhD, FIEEE, FRSC

Directeur administratif (relations avec l'extérieur)
R.S. Rettie, BSc, DPhil

Vice-présidents adjoints (laboratoires)
W.A. Cumming, BSc
J.D. Keys, BSc, MSc, PhD

Secrétaire (par interim)
A.W. Tickner, BE, MSc, PhD

Secrétaire des relations internationales
J.R.F. Martineau, DSc

The National Research Council of Canada has the broad mandate of fostering and supporting scientific and industrial research in Canada. The NRC act assigns but does not limit NRC to the following functions: utilization of Canada's natural resources; improvement of technical methods and processes used in Canadian industry; maintain and improve the primary physical standards of measurement for Canada; set standards of the quality of material used in public works; standardization of scientific and technical apparatus used in Canadian industry and government; foster the carrying out of scientific and industrial research.

Le Conseil national de recherches du Canada a la charge globale de promouvoir et de soutenir la recherche scientifique et industrielle au Canada. La loi du Conseil national de recherches du Canada charge ce dernier des fonctions suivantes, sans le limiter à celles-ci: utilisation des richesses naturelles du Canada; perfectionnement des méthodes techniques et des procédés utilisés par l'industrie canadienne; maintenir et améliorer les étalons de premier ordre pour les mesures physiques au Canada; établir des normes pour la qualité des matériaux utilisés au cours des travaux publics; normaliser les appareils

The mandate of NRC is implemented mainly through: operation of research laboratories; financial assistance for research activities in Canadian universities; financial assistance and promotion of research in industry; operation of the National science library and the Technical information services.

The federal government designated the National Research Council of Canada as the co-ordinating body for the further development of a national scientific and technical information system (STI), under the general direction of the national librarian. The integrated national system, encompassing the natural sciences and engineering, will be decentralized and based on the existing resources and systems in industry, the universities, and government, all linked together.

On April 1, 1970, the government announced that federal research in astronomy would be consolidated under NRC. The council will be responsible for the operation of the Dominion Astrophysical Observatory, Victoria, B.C., and the Dominion Radio Astrophysical Observatory, Penticton, B.C. Also involved in the transfer are the Time Service of Canada, the solar and meteor programs of the Dominion Observatory in Ottawa, and the Meteorite Observation and Recovery Project which is a network of photographic stations with headquarters in Saskatoon.

The national research laboratories are organized into 10 divisions: the biochemistry laboratory; the biology laboratory; building research; chemistry; physics; mechanical engineering; radio and electrical engineering; the national aeronautical establishment; the Atlantic regional laboratory in Halifax and the Prairie regional laboratory in Saskatoon.

These laboratories carry out long-term applied and specific project research work, in areas for which commercial companies have neither sufficient money nor the required facilities. Results of research are disseminated through NRC publications which provide an international distribution for scientific information coming out of Canadian laboratories and institutes. Laboratory inventions are patented and made available to Canadian manufacturers.

From its inception the council has encouraged and supported research in Canadian universities. A system of postgraduate scholarships and postdoctorate fellowships is provided for the assistance of students, Canadians and landed immigrants, who have

scientifiques et techniques utilisés par l'industrie canadienne et les services du gouvernement canadien; promouvoir l'exécution de la recherche scientifique et industrielle.

Le conseil exécute son mandat par les principaux moyens suivants: l'exploitation de laboratoires de recherches; le soutien financier des travaux de recherches dans les universités canadiennes; le soutien financier et l'encouragement de la recherche dans l'industrie; l'exploitation de la Bibliothèque scientifique nationale et du Service de renseignements techniques.

Le Conseil national de recherches du Canada a été chargé par le gouvernement fédéral de continuer le développement d'un système national d'information technique et scientifique (SNITS ou STI) placé sous la direction générale du bibliothécaire national. Ce système national intégré couvrant les domaines techniques et scientifiques sera décentralisé et basé sur les ressources et les systèmes de l'industrie, des universités et du gouvernement travaillant ensemble.

Le 1er avril 1970, le gouvernement a annoncé la centralisation de tous les observatoires fédéraux et leur transfert administratif au CNRC. Le conseil administrera l'Observatoire fédéral d'astrophysique, situé à Victoria, C.-B., et l'Observatoire fédéral de radioastrophysique de Penticton, C.-B. Le Service de l'heure du Canada, les programmes d'observation du soleil et des météores de l'Observatoire fédéral, à Ottawa, ainsi que le programme d'observation et de récupération des météorites faisant appel à un réseau de stations photographiques dont le siège est à Saskatoon, sont inclus dans ce transfert.

Les laboratoires du Conseil national de recherches du Canada comptent dix divisions: le laboratoire de biochimie, le laboratoire de biologie, recherches en bâtiment, chimie, génie mécanique, radiotechnique et électrotechnique, l'établissement aéronautique national, physique, le laboratoire régional de l'Atlantique à Halifax et le laboratoire régional des Prairies à Saskatoon.

Ces laboratoires mènent à bien des programmes de recherches appliquées et spécifiques dans des domaines où les entreprises commerciales n'ont ni l'argent ni les installations nécessaires. Les inventions découlant de l'activité de ces laboratoires sont brevetées et rendues accessibles aux fabricants canadiens. Les résultats de la

shown promise of research ability. The awards are: postdoctorate fellowships; postgraduate scholarships; bursaries; 1967 science scholarships; post-industrial experience research (PIER) fellowships; and postgraduate scholarships in science librarianship and documentation. Awards are for advanced studies and/or research in science and engineering and are competitive, with academic excellence being the main criterion in the selection of successful candidates.

In addition to the support provided for research in Canadian universities, council now has a postdoctorate program for the support of research in Canadian industry which was introduced in 1970. These industrial postdoctorate fellowships are intended to encourage highly qualified science and engineering students to seek careers in industry.

Postdoctorate fellowships and industrial postdoctorate fellowships are awarded to candidates who have recently completed or who are about to complete their requirements for a doctorate degree. The purpose of the two programs is to enable those who have received a doctorate degree to undertake, prior to becoming permanently employed, postdoctoral research for up to two years after receiving their degree. Postdoctorate fellowships are tenable in Canadian universities and in universities and other institutions abroad. Industrial postdoctorate fellowships are tenable in industrial organizations in Canada.

Postgraduate scholarships are awarded for tenure in Canada and successful candidates may elect to carry out their program at the Canadian university of their choice. Although awards are intended for tenure in Canada only, successful candidates, for whom facilities for a PhD program are limited or lacking in Canada, may receive special permission of council to hold their scholarships at a university abroad.

Council modified the program in 1970 and winners of an award for a first year of graduate study now have the option of deferring tenure of their scholarship for up to two years to encourage them to investigate career opportunities in industry.

Bursaries are awarded to students nominated by universities. Canadian universities receive an annual quota of bursaries from the National Research Council of Canada and are responsible for the selection of students for these awards. Unlike postgraduate

recherche sont diffusés grâce aux publications du conseil, qui constituent un véhicule de portée internationale pour les données scientifiques provenant des laboratoires et des instituts canadiens.

Depuis sa création, le conseil encourage et aide la recherche dans les universités canadiennes. Cette aide consiste en un système de bourses d'études de deuxième et de troisième cycles et de bourses de recherche post-doctorale dont bénéficient les étudiants canadiens et les immigrants ayant fait preuve d'aptitudes pour la recherche. Ces différents types de bourses sont: les bourses de recherche post-doctorale; les bourses d'études de deuxième et de troisième cycles; les bourses d'entretien; les bourses d'études scientifiques 1967; les bourses de recherche après stage dans l'industrie (PIER) et les bourses d'études supérieures en bibliothéconomie et documentation scientifique. Elles sont destinées aux études supérieures et/ou aux recherches dans les sciences et les techniques (génie) et sont distribuées après un concours dont le critère principal est l'excellence scolaire des postulants.

Pour compléter son programme d'aide à la recherche universitaire canadienne, le conseil a mis en oeuvre en 1970 un programme de bourses de recherche industrielle post-doctorale. L'objet de ces bourses est d'encourager les étudiants hautement qualifiés dans les domaines scientifiques et techniques à faire carrière dans l'industrie.

Ces bourses post-doctorales de recherche universitaire et de recherche industrielle sont attribuées aux candidats ayant récemment satisfait, ou étant sur le point de satisfaire, aux conditions exigées pour le doctorat. Le but de ces deux programmes est de permettre à ceux qui ont obtenu un doctorat d'entreprendre une à deux années de recherche post-doctorale avant de trouver un emploi permanent. Ces bourses de recherche post-doctorale sont utilisables dans les universités canadiennes ainsi que dans les universités et autres institutions étrangères.

Les bourses de recherche industrielle post-doctorale sont utilisables dans des organismes industriels au Canada.

Les bourses d'études de deuxième et de troisième cycles ne sont valides qu'au Canada et leurs bénéficiaires ont la faculté d'exécuter leur programme dans l'université canadienne de leur choix. Bien que ces subventions ne soient utilisables qu'au Canada, les bénéficiaires pour lesquels les conditions

scholarships, bursaries are not transferable; tenure must be at the university that nominated the student for the award.

The 1967 science scholarship program was introduced to celebrate the Centennial of Canadian confederation and the 50th anniversary of the National Research Council of Canada. These awards are intended to encourage young men and women of outstanding intellectual promise to pursue postgraduate studies and research leading to doctorate degrees. It is intended that these awards should stimulate exchanges of students between different cultural and geographical regions in Canada. Scholars must select for graduate studies a university other than the one from which their first degree was obtained.

Post-industrial experience research (PIER) fellowships were introduced in 1966, with the object of providing an opportunity for persons with industrial experience to gain additional research experience and training. A limited number of these awards are made available each year to candidates who have had a minimum of five years' industrial experience.

Postgraduate scholarships in science librarianship and documentation were introduced in 1967 with the object of encouraging graduates with a degree in science or engineering to become science librarians, documentalists or science information specialists in an effort to meet the demand by universities, research laboratories, industrial firms and related organizations for properly qualified persons in this field.

NRC publishes annually a report on support of university research in science and engineering, and the report of the president to parliament which describes the scope and functions of NRC and the way in which the council serves the nation. *Science Dimension* (formerly *NRC Research News*), published every two months, in English and in French, enables the council to keep readers informed of its activities, comprising laboratory research and research support of universities and industries. In addition, the National Research Council of Canada *Newsletter* is published quarterly by the information services office, for industry, universities, government, economists, and the public.

The council also publishes nine primary research journals in the fields of biochemistry, botany, chemistry, earth sciences, geotechnology, microbiology, physics, physiology and pharmacology, and zoology.

d'études pour le PhD au Canada seraient insuffisantes ou inexistantes, pourraient obtenir du conseil une autorisation spéciale pour poursuivre leurs études dans une université étrangère.

Le conseil a modifié le programme en 1970 et les bénéficiaires de bourses pour une première année d'étude de deuxième cycle ont maintenant la possibilité d'en différer l'utilisation pour une période de deux ans au maximum afin de les encourager à rechercher un poste dans l'industrie.

Les universités reçoivent leur quota annuel de bourses d'entretien du conseil qu'elles attribuent aux étudiants de leur choix. Contrairement aux bourses d'étude de deuxième et de troisième cycles, ces bourses d'entretien ne sont pas transférables et ne sont donc utilisables qu'à l'université qui les a accordées.

Le Programme de bourses d'études scientifiques 1967 a été institué pour marquer le centenaire de la Confédération canadienne et le 50e anniversaire du Conseil national de recherches du Canada. Ces bourses ont pour objet d'encourager les étudiants ayant d'exceptionnelles aptitudes intellectuelles à poursuivre leurs études et des recherches jusqu'au doctorat. Elles visent à promouvoir les échanges d'étudiants canadiens provenant de différentes régions culturelles et géographiques. Les candidats doivent poursuivre leurs études de deuxième cycle dans une université autre que celle leur ayant décerné leur premier diplôme.

Les bourses de recherche après stage dans l'industrie (PIER) ont été créées en 1966 pour donner l'occasion aux personnes nanties d'une expérience industrielle d'acquérir une expérience et une formation supplémentaire dans la recherche. Un nombre limité de ces bourses est mis chaque année à la disposition des candidats possédant au moins cinq ans d'expérience industrielle.

Créées en 1967, les bourses d'études supérieures en bibliothéconomie et documentation scientifiques ont pour objet d'inciter les étudiants titulaires d'un diplôme scientifique ou technique à devenir des bibliothéconomes en sciences, des documentalistes ou des spécialistes en informatique. On pourrait ainsi pourvoir aux besoins en personnel spécialisé des universités, des laboratoires de recherche, des sociétés industrielles et d'autres organismes similaires.

Le conseil publie un rapport annuel sur l'aide qu'il apporte aux recherches universitaires en science et génie et un rapport du président adressé directement au Parlement, où l'on montre la portée et les fonctions du conseil ainsi que les services que le conseil rend à la nation. La revue bimestrielle *Science Dimension* (anciennement *NRC Research News*) publiée en anglais et en français, informe le public de ses recherches en laboratoire et de l'aide apportée aux universités et aux industries. De plus, le *Bulletin* du Conseil national de recherches du Canada est publié trimestriellement par l'Office des services d'information pour l'industrie, les universités, le gouvernement, les économistes, et le public en général.

Le conseil publie neuf revues de recherches en biochimie, botanique, chimie, sciences de la terre, géotechnique, microbiologie, physique, physiologie et pharmacologie, et zoologie.

General information

Renseignements généraux

Research institutes

Instituts de recherche

Note: A detailed description of how to use this section will be found in the guide on "How to use the handbook" located at the beginning of this book.

A noter: Les renseignements donnés au début sous le titre "Façon de se servir du répertoire" expliquent en détail comment se servir de la présente section.

Institut de recherche et de perfectionnement en **administration**
(Université de Sherbrooke)

Institute for **Aerospace** Studies
(University of Toronto)

Institute of **Air and Space Law**
(McGill University)

Centre de recherches en **aménagement régional**
(Université de Sherbrooke)

Wellcome **Anaesthesis** Research Department
(McGill University)

Institute of **Animal Resource Ecology**
(The University of British Columbia)

Centre canadien de recherches en **anthropologie**
(Université Saint-Paul)

Canadian Research Centre for **Anthropology**
(Saint Paul University)

Anthropology of Development Program
(McGill University)

Institute of **Applied Mathematics** and Statistics
(The University of British Columbia)

Institute of **Applied Statistics**
(University of Toronto)

Aquatic Biology Research Unit
(The University of Manitoba)

Morgan **Arboretum**
(McGill University)

Arctic Institute of North America
(McGill University)

Arctic and Alpine Research
(The University of British Columbia)

Institute of **Asian and Slavonic** Research
(The University of British Columbia)

Institut d'**astronomie**
(Université Laurentienne de Sudbury)

Institute of **Astronomy and Space Science**
(The University of British Columbia)

Centre de recherches sur les **atomes et les molécules**
(Université Laval)

Aviation Medical Research Unit
(McGill University)

Institute for **Behavioural** Research
(York University)

Bellairs Research Institute
(McGill University)

Centre international de recherches sur le **bilinguisme**
(Université Laval)

Research Unit in **Biochemistry, Biophysics and Molecular Biology**
(McMaster University)

Bio-Engineering Institute
(University of New Brunswick)

Matador Project, International **Biological** Program
(University of Saskatchewan, Saskatoon Campus)

Centre de recherche en productivité **biologique**
(Université du Québec à Chicoutimi)

Institute of **Biomedical Electronics**
(University of Toronto)

Biomedical Engineering Unit
(McGill University)

Centre de **biomédecine**
(Université Laval)

Centre de recherches en **bionique**
(Université Laval)

Brace Research Institute
(McGill University)

Canadian Plains Area Centre
(University of Saskatchewan, Regina Campus)

Cancer Research Institute
(The University of Alberta)

Cancer Research Laboratory
(The University of Western Ontario)

McGill **Cancer** Research Unit
(McGill University)

Centre de recherches **caraibes**
(Université de Montréal)

Cardio-Thoracic Research Institute
(Laurentian University of Sudbury)

Institut de recherche **cardio-thoracique**
(Université Laurentienne de Sudbury)

Manitoba Institute of **Cell Biology**
(The University of Manitoba)

Institute for **Child Guidance**
(The University of Saskatchewan, Saskatoon
Campus)

Clinical Research Centre
(Dalhousie University)

Coady International Institute
(St. Francis Xavier University)

Institute of **Commonwealth and Comparative**
Studies
(Queen's University at Kingston)

Centre de recherche en **communication
humaine**
(Université du Québec à Trois-Rivières)

Institute of **Comparative and Foreign Law**
(McGill University)

Computer Centre
(University of Toronto)

Institute of **Computing Science**
(University of Guelph)

Centre international de **criminologie
comparée**
(Université de Montréal)

Centre of **Criminology**
(University of Toronto)

Centre de recherches sur la **croissance
humaine**
(Université de Montréal)

Centre for **Culture and Technology**
(University of Toronto)

Dairy Herd Analysis Service
(McGill University).

McGill University Project for **Deaf Children**
(McGill University)

Centre for **Developing Area** Studies
(McGill University)

Centre de recherches en **développement
économique**
(Université de Montréal)

Centre de recherche en **didactique**
(Université du Québec à Montréal)

Centre for the Study of the **Drama**
(University of Toronto)

East-Asian Studies Program
(McGill University)

Centre de recherches sur l'**eau**
(Université Laval)

Centre de recherche en **écologie**
(Université du Québec à Montréal)

Institute for **Economic** Research
(Queen's University at Kingston)

Canadian International Centre of Research
and Information on Public and Cooperative
Economy
(Sir George Williams University)

Centre de recherche prospective en **éducation**
(Université du Québec à Trois-Rivières)

Ontario Institute for Studies in **Education**
(Ontario Institute for Studies in Education)

Centre for **Educational Disabilities**
(University of Guelph)

Centre de recherche en **énergie**
(Institut national de recherche scientifique de
l'Université du Québec)

Centre for Applied Research and **Engineering
Design**
(McMaster University)

Lyman **Entomological** Museum
(McGill University)

Environmental Sciences Centre (Kananaskis)
(The University of Calgary)

Institute of **Environmental Sciences**
(University of Toronto)

Centre de recherches de l'**état solide**
(Université Laval)

Centre d'**étude** du Québec
(Sir George Williams University)

University **Field** Station (Delta Marsh)
(The University of Manitoba)

University **Field** Station (Star Lake)
(The University of Manitoba)

Financial Research Institute
(McGill University)

Institute for **Fine Particle** Research
(Laurentian University of Sudbury)

Fire Science Centre
(The University of New Brunswick)

Centre for **French Area** Studies
(Queen's University at Kingston)

French Canada Studies Program
(McGill University)

Gastrointestinal Research Laboratory
(McGill University)

Gault Estate
(McGill University)

L'**Herbier** Louis-Marie
(Université Laval)

Centre de recherche en **histoire des religions**
et de la pensée
(Université du Québec à Trois-Rivières)

Centre de recherches en **histoire économique**
du Canada français
(Sir George Williams University)

Centre de recherche en **histoire religieuse** du
Canada
(Université Saint-Paul)

Institute for Research in **Human Abilities**
(Memorial University of Newfoundland)

Centre of **Human Relations** and Community
Studies
(Sir George Williams University)

Office of **Human Research**
(University of Waterloo)

Institute of **Immunology**
(University of Toronto)

Industrial Research Institute
(University of Windsor)

Industrial Relations Centre
(McGill University)

Industrial Relations Centre
(Queen's University at Kingston)

Centre for **Industrial Relations**
(University of Toronto)

Institute of **Industrial Relations**
(The University of British Columbia)

Atlantic **Industrial Research** Institute
(Nova Scotia Technical College)

Centre de traitement de l'**information**
(Université Laval)

Centre de recherche en **ingénierie des
télécommunications**
(Institut national de la recherche scientifique
de l'Université du Québec)

Institute of **Intergovernmental Relations**
(Queen's University at Kingston)

Centre for **International Programs**
(University of Guelph)

Institute of **International Relations**
(The University of British Columbia)

Institute of **Islamic** Studies
(McGill University)

Jewish Studies Program
(McGill University)

Institute of **Law** Research and Reform
(The University of Alberta)

Centre for **Learning and Development**
(McGill University)

Legal Research Institute
(The University of Manitoba)

Centre for **Linguistic** Studies
(University of Toronto)

Centre d'études des **littératures d'expression
françaises**
(Université de Sherbrooke)

Centre d'études en **liturgie**
(Université Saint-Paul)

Research Centre in **Liturgy**
(Saint Paul University)

Institute of **Local Government**
(Queen's University at Kingston)

Centre de recherche en **loisirs**
(Université du Québec à Trois-Rivières)

Management Development Institute
(McGill University)

Marine Sciences Centre
(McGill University)

Institute for **Materials** Research
(McMaster University)

Centre de recherches **mathématiques**
(Université de Montréal)

Pontifical Institute of **Mediaeval** Studies
(University of Toronto)

Banting and Best Department of **Medical**
Research
(University of Toronto)

Connaught **Medical** Research Laboratories
(University of Toronto)

Institute of **Medical Science**
(University of Toronto)

Centre for **Medieval** Studies
(University of Toronto)

Medieval and Renaissance Guild
(The University of Manitoba)

Atlantic Research Centre for **Mental
Retardation**
(Dalhousie University)

Centre for the Study of **Mental Retardation**
(The University of Alberta)

Centre for **Metal and Mineral** Technology
(Queen's University at Kingston)

Institut de recherche sur les **micro-particules**
(Université Laurentienne de Sudbury)

Institute for **Mineral Industry** Research
(McGill University)

Centre de recherche du **moyen-nord**
(Université du Québec à Chicoutimi)

Muskeg Research Institute
(The University of New Brunswick)

Natural Resource Institute
(The University of Manitoba)

Montreal **Neurological** Institute
(McGill University)

Centre d'études **nordiques**
(Université Laval)

Boreal Institute for **Northern** Studies
(The University of Alberta)

Northern Studies Committee
(The University of Manitoba)

Institute for **Northern** Studies
(University of Saskatchewan, Saskatoon
Campus)

Nuclear Research Centre
(The University of Alberta)

Centre de recherches en **nutrition**
(Université Laval)

David Dunlap **Observatory**
(University of Toronto)

Institute of **Oceanography**
(The University of British Columbia)

Institute of **Oceanography**
(Dalhousie University)

Institute of **Parasitology**
(McGill University)

Centre of **Pastoral Psychiatry**
(Saint Paul University)

Institute of **Pastoral Training**
(University of King's College, Halifax)

Institute of **Pathology**
(McGill University)

Centre d'étude et de recherches en
pédagogie du language oral et écrit
(Université Laval)

Institute of **Pedology**
(University of Saskatchewan, Saskatoon
Campus)

Pestology Centre
(Simon Fraser University)

Petroleum Recovery Research Institute
(The University of Calgary)

Phonetics Research Laboratory
(McGill University)

Planning and Resources Institute
(University of Waterloo)

Centre de **psychiatrie pastorale**
(Université Saint-Paul)

Allan Memorial Institute of **Psychiatry**
(McGill University)

Centre de recherche en **psychomathématique**
(Université de Sherbrooke)

Pulp and Paper Research Institute of Canada
(McGill University)

International Institute of **Quantitative Ecomonics**
(Sir George Williams University)

Foster **Radiation** Laboratory
(McGill University)

Research Centre in **Religious History** of Canada
(Saint Paul University)

Centre d'études de la **Renaissance**
(Université de Sherbrooke)

Centre for **Renaissance** Studies
(University of Toronto)

Waterloo **Research** Institute
(University of Waterloo)

Glenlea **Research** Station
(The University of Manitoba)

Centre for **Resources Development**
(University of Guelph)

Centre for **Russian and East European** Studies
(University of Toronto)

Institute for the History and Philosophy of **Science and Technology**
(University of Toronto)

Centre de recherche des **sciences de la santé**
(Institut national de la recherche scientifique de l'Université du Québec)

Centre de recherche des **sciences de la santé,** efficience physique et psycho-sociologique
(Université du Québec à Trois-Rivières)

Centre québécois des **sciences de l'eau**
(Institut national de la recherche scientifique de l'Université du Québec)

Institut supérieur des **sciences humaines**
(Université Laval)

Centre de recherche en **sciences neurologiques**
(Université de Montréal)

Centre for **Settlement** Studies
(The University of Manitoba)

Shastri Indo-Canadian Institute
(McGill University)

Institute for the Quantitative Analysis of **Social and Economic Policy**
(University of Toronto)

Institute of **Social and Economic Research**
(Memorial University of Newfoundland)

Social Sciences Statistics Laboratory
(McGill University)

Centre de recherches en **sociologie religieuse**
(Université Laval)

Soil Mechanics Laboratory
(McGill University)

Centre de **sondage**
(Université de Montréal)

Institute of **Space and Atmospheric** Studies
(University of Saskatchewan, Saskatoon Campus)

Centre for Research in Experimental **Space Science**
(York University)

McGill **Sub-Arctic** Research Laboratories
(McGill University)

Surgical-Medical Research Institute
(The University of Alberta)

Banque de **terminologie**
(Université de Montréal)

Institute of **Theoretical Physics**
(The University of Alberta)

Institute of **Theoretical Physics**
(McGill University)

Centre for Advanced Study in **Theoretical Psychology**
(The University of Alberta)

Transport Centre
(York University)

Canadian Institute of Guided Ground **Transportation**
(Queen's University at Kingston)

Centre for **Transportation** Studies
(The University of Manitoba)

Institute of **Transportation** Studies
(The University of Calgary)

Centre de recherches **urbaines et régionales**
(Institut national de la recherche scientifique de l'Université du Québec)

Institute of **Urban** Studies
(The University of Winnipeg)

Centre for **Urban and Community** Studies
(University of Toronto)

Agassiz Centre for **Water** Studies
(The University of Manitoba)

Water Resources Development Centre
(University of New Brunswick)

Associations and agencies related to higher education

Associations et organismes intéressés à l'enseignement supérieur

Note: A detailed description of how to use this section will be found in the guide on "How to use the handbook" located at the beginning of this book.

A noter: Les renseignements donnés au debut sous le titre "Façon de se servir du répertoire" expliquent en détail comment se servir de la présente section.

Index of acronyms and initialisms

Index des sigles

AAU
Association of Atlantic Universities

ACCC
Association of Canadian Community Colleges

ACEC
Association of Consulting Engineers of Canada, The

ACFD
Association of Canadian Faculties of Dentistry, The

ACLT
Association of Canadian Law Teachers

ACMC
Association of Canadian Medical Colleges

ACSB
Association of Canadian Schools of Business

ACU
Association of Commonwealth Universities

ACUIB
Association of Canadian University Information Bureaus

ACUTE
Association of Canadian University Teachers of English

AERCC
Agricultural Economics Research Council of Canada

AFPC
Association of Faculties of Pharmacy of Canada

AIC
Agricultural Institute of Canada

ARUC
Association of Registrars of the Universities of Canada

AUC
Alberta Universities Commission, The

AAMC
Association des archivistes médicales du Canada

AAPC
Association des architectes paysagistes du Canada, L'

ABC
Association bontanique de Canada, L'

ABIUC
Association des bureaux de l'information des universités du Canada

ACA
Association canadienne des anatomistes

ACAEN
Association canadienne pour l'avancement des études néerlandaises

ACBCU
Association canadienne des bibliothèques de collège et d'université

ACBLF
Association canadienne des bibliothécaires de langue française

ACCC
Association des collèges communautaires du Canada

ACD
Association canadienne des diététistes, L'

ACDAU
Association canadienne des directeurs athlétiques universitaires

ACDFP
Association canadienne des doyens et directeurs de faculté de pédagogie

ACDI
Agence canadienne de développement international, L'

ACE
Association canadienne d'économique, L'
Association canadienne d'éducation, L'
Association canadienne des ergothérapeutes

AUPELF
Association des universités partiellement ou
entierèment de langue française

BCC
Biological Council of Canada

CAA
Canadian Association of Anatomists

CAAE
Canadian Association for Adult Education

CAANS
Canadian Association for the Advancement
of Netherlandic Studies

CAAS
Canadian Association of African Studies

CAC
Classical Association of Canada, The

CACUL
Canadian Association of College and
University Libraries

CADESS
Canadian Association of Departments of
Extension and Summer Schools

CADUFE
Canadian Association of Deans and
Directors of University Faculties of
Education

CAESS
Canadian Association for Education in the
Social Services

CAG
Canadian Association of Geographers, The

CAGS
Canadian Association of Graduate Schools

CAH
Canadian Association of Hispanists

CAHPER
Canadian Association for Health, Physical
Education and Recreation

CALAS
Canadian Association of Latin American
Studies

CALS
Canadian Association of Library Schools

CAMRL
Canadian Association of Medical Record
Librarians

ACEA
Association canadienne des études
africaines, L'
Association canadienne des études
asiatiques

ACEB
Association canadienne des écoles de
bibliothécaires

ACEC
Association canadienne des écoles de
commerce

ACEES
Association canadienne des écoles des
études supérieures

ACELA
Association canadienne des études latino-
américaines

ACELF
Association canadienne d'éducation de
langue française

ACESS
Association canadienne d'éducation pour
les services sociaux

ACEUM
Association canadienne des écoles
universitaires de musique

ACEUN
Association canadienne des écoles
universitaires de nursing, L'

ACFAS
Association canadienne-française pour
l'avancement des sciences

ACG
Association canadienne des géographes, L'

ACH
Association canadienne des humanités

ACHP
Association canadienne d'hygiène publique,
L'

ACL
Association canadienne de linguistique

ACO
Association canadienne des optométristes,
L'

ACP
Association canadienne de physiothérapie,
L'
Association canadienne des pathologistes

CAO
Canadian Association of Optometrists

CAOT
Canadian Association of Occupational Therapists

CAP
Canadian Association of Pathologists
Canadian Association of Physicists

CAPE
Canadian Association of Professors of Education

CAS
Canadian Association of Slavists

CASI
Canadian Aeronautics and Space Institute

CASW
Canadian Association of Social Workers

CATSPM
Canadian Association of Teachers of Social and Preventive Medicine

CAUAD
Canadian Association of University Athletic Directors

CAUBO
Canadian Association of University Business Officers

CAUDO
Canadian Association of University Development Officers, The

CAUSM
Canadian Association of University Schools of Music

CAUSN
Canadian Association of University Schools of Nursing

CAUSPS
Council of Associations of University Student Personnel Services

CAUT
Canadian Association of University Teachers

CAUTF
Canadian Association of University Teachers of French

CAUTG
Canadian Association of University Teachers of German

Association canadienne des physiciens

ACPD
Association canadienne des professeurs de droit

ACPE
Association canadienne des professeurs d'éducation, L'

ACPMPS
Association canadienne des professeurs de médecine préventive et sociale

ACPU
Association canadienne des professeurs d'université

ACQ
Association des collèges du Québec

ACSP
Association canadienne de science politique, L'

ACTS
Association canadienne des travailleurs sociaux

ACTU
Association canadienne du théâtre universitaire

ACU
Association of Commonwealth Universities

ADC
Association dentaire canadienne, L'

ADSDUC
Association des dirigeants du service de développement des universités canadiennes

AFC
Association forestière canadienne

AFDC
Association des facultés dentaires du Canada, L'

AFMC
Association des facultés de médecine du Canada, L'

AFPC
Association des facultés de pharmacie du Canada

AHC
Association des hispanistes du Canada

AIC
Association des infirmières canadiennes

CBA
Canadian Botanical Association, The

CBS
Canadian Biochemical Society

CCIC
Canadian Council for International Co-operation

CCLD
Committee of Canadian Law Deans

CCPE
Canadian Council of Professional Engineers

CCRE
Canadian Council for Research in Education

CCURR
Canadian Council on Urban and Regional Research

CDA
Canadian Dental Association
Canadian Dietetic Association, The

CEA
Canadian Economics Association, The
Canadian Education Association, The

CFA
Canadian Forestry Association

CFBS
Canadian Federation of Biological Societies

CFI
Canadian Film Institute

CFUW
Canadian Federation of University Women

CGCA
Canadian Guidance and Counselling Association

CHA
Canadian Historical Association, The

CHEA
Canadian Home Economics Association

CIAE
Canadian Institute of Adult Education

CIAU
Canadian Intercollegiate Athletic Union

CIC
Chemical Institute of Canada, The

AICC
Association des ingénieurs-conseils du Canada

AIG
Association des industries graphiques

AIU
Association internationale des universités

AMC
Association des musées canadiens
Association médicale canadienne, L'
Association minière du Canada, L'

AMLFC
Association des médecins de langue française du Canada

APAUC
Association des professeurs d'allemand des universités canadiennes, L'

APC
Association de pétrole canadien, L'
Association des psychiatres du Canada
Association pharmaceutique canadienne, L'

APFUC
Association des professeurs de français des universités canadiennes

APUC
Association de placement universitaire et collégial

ARUC
Association des registraires d'université du Canada

AUA
Association des universités de l'Atlantique, L'

AUPELF
Association des universités partiellement ou entièrement de langue française

BNED
Bureau national d'examen dentaire du Canada

CADESS
Association des services d'éducation des adultes et écoles d'été des universités du Canada

CASUE
Conseil des associations des services universitaires aux étudiants

CICA
Canadian Institute of Chartered
Accountants, The

CIDA
Canadian International Development
Agency

CIESC
Comparative and International Education
Society of Canada

CIIA
Canadian Institute of International Affairs

CIM
Canadian Institute of Mining and
Metallurgy, The

CIPA
Canadian Institute of Public Affairs

CLA
Canadian Library Association
Canadian Linguistic Association

CMA
Canadian Medical Association, The
Canadian Museums Association, The

CMC
Canadian Mathematical Congress

CMEC
Council of Ministers of Education, Canada

CNA
Canadian Nuclear Association
Canadian Nurses' Association

COPSE
Commission on Post-Secondary Education
in Ontario

COU
Council of Ontario Universities

CPA
Canadian Petroleum Association
Canadian Physiotherapy Association
Canadian Psychiatric Association
Canadian Psychological Association

CPhA
Canadian Pharmaceutical Association

CPHA
Canadian Public Health Association

CPS
Canadian Paediatric Society
Canadian Physiological Society

CAUBO
Association canadienne du personnel
administratif universitaire

CCB
Conseil canadien de biologie

CCCI
Conseil canadien pour la coopération
internationale

CCI
Conseil canadien des ingénieurs

CCRE
Conseil canadien pour la recherche en
éducation

CCRH
Conseil canadien de recherches sur les
humanités, Le

CCRSS
Conseil canadien de recherche en sciences
sociales, Le

CCRUR
Conseil canadien de recherches urbaines et
régionales

CCT
Centre canadien du théâtre

CDDC
Comité des doyens de droit du Canada

CIM
Institut canadien des mines et de la
métallurgie, L'

CMEC
Conseil des ministres de l'éducation,
Canada

CNA
Association nucléaire canadienne

CNRC
Conseil national de recherches du Canada

CRCD(C)
Collège royal des chirurgiens dentistes du
Canada, Le

CRD
Conseil de recherches pour la défense

CRM
Conseil de recherches médicales

CRPUQ
Conférence des recteurs et des principaux
des universités du Québec

CPSA
Canadian Political Science Association

CPSE
Prince Edward Island Commission on Post-Secondary Education

CSAA
Canadian Sociology and Anthropology Association

CSAS
Canadian Society for Asian Studies

CSBS
Canadian Society of Biblical Studies

CSChE
Canadian Society for Chemical Engineering, The

CSEA
Canadian Society for Education Through Art

CSF
Canada Studies Foundation, The

CSI
Canadian Society for Immunology, The

CSLA
Canadian Society of Landscape Architects, The

CSM
Canadian Society of Microbiologists

CSPP
Canadian Society of Plant Physiologists

CSSHE
Canadian Society for the Study of Higher Education

CSWFB
Canadian Society of Wildlife and Fishery Biologists

CTC
Canadian Theatre Centre

CTF
Canadian Teachers' Federation

CUA
Committee on University Affairs of Ontario, The

CUSO
Canadian University Service Overseas

CSE
Conseil supérieur de l'éducation

CSWFB
Société canadienne des biologistes de la faune

CUA
Commission des universités de l'Alberta, La

CUO
Conseil des universités de l'Ontario

DGES
Direction générale de l'enseignement supérieur, Ministère de l'Education

ETRAC
Association canadienne de radio et de télévision éducatives, L'

EUMC
Entr'aide universitaire mondiale du Canada

FCE
Fédération canadienne des enseignants

FCFD
Fédération canadienne des femmes diplômées des universités

FCSB
Fédération canadienne des sociétés de biologie

FEC
Fondation d'études du Canada, La

FIUC
Fédération international des universités catholiques

FSJ
Fondation sciences jeunesse

IAC
Institut agricole du Canada, L'

IAPC
Institut d'administration publique du Canada, L'

IASC
Institut aéronautique et spatial du Canada, L'

ICAI
Institut canadien des affaires internationales

ICAP
Institut canadien des affaires publiques, L'

CUTA
Canadian University Theatre Association

DEC
Development Education Centre

DHEQ
Directorate of Higher Education, Quebec

DRB
Defence Research Board

EIC
Engineering Institute of Canada, The

ESC
Entomological Society of Canada

ETRAC
Educational Television and Radio
Association of Canada

GAIA
Graphic Arts Industries Association

HAC
Humanities Association of Canada

HEC
New Brunswick Higher Education
Commission

HRCC
Humanities Research Council of Canada

IAU
International Association of Universities

IFCU
International Federation of Catholic
Universities

IIQE
International Institute of Quantitative
Economics

IPAC
Institute of Public Administration of
Canada, The

IPCUR
Inter-Provincial Committee on University
Rationalization

MAC
Mining Association of Canada, The

MRC
Medical Research Council

NAVAC
National Audio-Visual Association of
Canada, The

ICC
Institut de chimie du Canada, L'

ICCA
Institut canadien des comptables agréés, L'

ICEA
Institut canadien d'éducation des adultes

ICF
Institut canadien du film

ICI
Institut canadien des ingénieurs, L'

IICS
Institut indo-canadien Shastri, L'

IIEQ
Institut international d'économie
quantitative

IRAC
Institut royal d'architecture du Canada, L'

NDC
Conseil national de l'esthétique

OCUFA
Union des associations des professeurs des
universités de l'Ontario

SACU
Service d'admission au collège et à
l'université

SCB
Société canadienne de biochimie, La

SCEA
Société canadienne d'éducation par l'art

SCEC
Société canadienne des études classiques,
La

SCECI
Société canadienne d'éducation comparée et
internationale, La

SCEES
Société canadienne pour l'étude de
l'enseignement supérieur, La

SCGC
Société canadienne du génie chimique, La

SCI
Société canadienne d'immunologie, La

SCITEC
Association des scientifiques, ingénieurs et
technologistes du Canada, L'

NDC
National Design Council

NDEB
National Dental Examining Board of
Canada

NRC
National Research Council of Canada

NSC
Nutrition Society of Canada

OCUFA
Ontario Confederation of University
Faculty Associations

OURA
Ontario University Registrars' Association

PSC
Pharmacological Society of Canada, The

RAIC
Royal Architectural Institute of Canada,
The

RASC
Royal Astronomical Society of Canada,
The

RCD(C)
Royal College of Dentists of Canada, The

RSC
Royal Society of Canada, The

SACU
Service for Admission to College and
University

SCE
Superior Council of Education

SCITEC
Association of the Scientific, Engineering
and Technological Community of Canada,
The

SICI
Shastri Indo-Canadian Institute, The

SINE
Society for Indian and Northern Education

SSRCC
Social Science Research Council of Canada

UAAC
Universities Art Association of Canada

SCM
Société canadienne des microbiologistes

SCN
Société canadienne de nutrition

SCOC
Société canadienne d'orientation et de
consultation

SCP
Société canadienne de pédiatrie
Société canadienne de physiologie
Société canadienne de psychologie

SCPV
Société canadienne de physiologie végétale

SCSA
Société canadienne de sociologie et
d'anthropologie

SCT
Société canadienne de théologie

SEC
Société entomologique du Canada, La

SHC
Société historique du Canada, La

SMC
Société mathématique de Canada

SPC
Société de pharmacologie du Canada, La

SRAC
Société royale d'astronomie du Canada, La

SRS
Société royale du Canada, La

SUCO
Service universitaire canadien outre-mer

Tourbec
Bureau de tourisme des étudiants du
Québec, Le

UAAC
Association universitaire des arts au
Canada

UNESCO
Commission canadienne pour l'UNESCO

USIC
Union sportive interuniversitaire canadienne

UCPA
University and College Placement
Association

UGCNS
University Grants Committee (Nova
Scotia)

UNESCO
Canadian Commission for UNESCO

WUSC
World University Service of Canada

YSF
Youth Science Foundation

Athletics
Canadian Association of University
Athletic Directors
Canadian Intercollegiate Athletic Union

Atlantic universities
Association of Atlantic Universities

Audio-visual
National Audio-Visual Association of
Canada, The

Awards
Canadian Association of Student Awards
Administrators

Biblical studies
Canadian Society of Biblical Studies

Biochemistry
Canadian Biochemical Society

Bio-engineering
Canadian Medical and Biological
Engineering Society

Biology
Biological Council of Canada
Canadian Federation of Biological Societies
Canadian Society of Wildlife and Fishery
Biologists

Botany
Canadian Botanical Association, The

Business
Association of Canadian Schools of
Business
Canadian Association of University
Business Officers

Canada studies
Canada Studies Foundation, The

Career planning
University and College Placement
Association

Chartered accountants
Canadian Institute of Chartered
Accountants, The

Chemical engineering
Canadian Society for Chemical
Engineering, The

Chemistry
Chemical Institute of Canada, The

Classics
Classical Association of Canada, The

Commonwealth
Association of Commonwealth Universities

Architectes paysagistes
Association des architectes paysagistes du
Canada, L'

Architecture
Institut royal d'architecture du Canada, L'

Archives médicales
Association des archivistes médicales du
Canada

Art dentaire
Association dentaire canadienne, L'
Association des facultés dentaires du
Canada, L'
Bureau national d'examen dentaire du
Canada

Arts
Conseil des arts du Canada, Le

Asiatiques, études
Association canadienne des études
asiatiques

**International associations of which
Canadian universities and colleges are
members**
Association des universités partiellement ou
entièrement de langue française
Association of Commonwealth Universities,
The
International Association of Universities
International Federation of Catholique
Universities

Astronomie
Société royale d'astronomie du Canada, La

Athlétisme
Association canadienne des directeurs
athlétiques universitaires

Atlantique, universités
Association des universités de l'Atlantique,
L'

Audio-visuel
Association canadienne de l'audio-visuel

Beaux-arts visuels
Association universitaire des arts au
Canada

Bibliothéconomie
Association canadienne des bibliothécaires
de langue française
Association canadienne des bibliothèques
de collège et d'université
Association canadienne des écoles de
bibliothécaires

Bibliques, études
Société canadienne des études bibliques

Community college
Association of Canadian Community
Colleges

Defence
Defence Research Board

Dentistry
Association of Canadian Faculties of
Dentistry, The
Canadian Dental Association
National Dental Examining Board of
Canada
Royal College of Dentists of Canada, The

Design
National Design Council

Development
Canadian Association of University
Development Officers, The

Development, International
Canadian International Development
Agency

Dietetics
Canadian Dietetic Association, The

Economics
Canadian Economics Association, The

Education
Canadian Association of Deans and
Directors of University Faculties of
Education
Canadian Association of Professors of
Education
Canadian College of Teachers, The
Canadian Council for Research in
Education
Canadian Education Association, The
Commission on Post-Secondary Education
in Ontario
Comparative and International Education
Society of Canada
Council of Ministers of Education, Canada
Development Education Centre
Division of Educational Services, Lutheran
Council in Canada
Education Division, Statistics Canada
Education Support Branch, Department of
the Secretary of State
Prince Edward Island Commission on
Post-Secondary Education
Superior Council of Education

Educational television
Educational Television and Radio
Association of Canada

Biochimie
Société canadienne de biochimie, La

Biologie
Conseil canadien de biologie
Fédération canadienne des sociétés de
biologie
Société canadienne des biologistes de la
faune, La

Botanique
Association botanique du Canada, L'

Bourses
Association canadienne des boursiers
Rhodes, L'
Institut indo-canadien Shastri, L'

Canada, études
Fondation d'études du Canada, La

CEGEP
Fédération des CEGEP

Chimie
Institut de chimie du Canada, L'

Chirurgiens dentistes
Collège royal des chirurgiens dentistes du
Canada, Le

Classiques, études
Société canadienne des études classiques,
La

Collèges
Association des collèges du Québec

Collèges communautaires
Association des collèges communautaires
du Canada

Commerce
Association canadienne des écoles de
commerce

Commonwealth
Association of Commonwealth Universities

Comptables agréés
Institut canadien des comptables agréés, L'

Coopération internationale
Service universitaire canadien outre-mer

Défense
Conseil de recherches pour la défense

Développement international
Agence canadienne de développement
international

Engineering
Association of Consulting Engineers of Canada, The
Association of the Scientific, Engineering and Technological Community of Canada, The
Canadian Council of Professional Engineers
Engineering Institute of Canada, The
National Committee of Deans of Engineering and Applied Science

English
Association of Canadian University Teachers of English
Canadian Council of Teachers of English

Entomology
Entomological Society of Canada

Examining board
National Dental Examining Board of Canada

Extension
Canadian Association of Departments of Extension and Summer Schools

Faculty
Ontario Confederation of University Faculty Associations

Family
Vanier Institute of the Family, The

Federal agencies
Canada Council, The
Canadian International Development Agency
Defence Research Board
Education Division, Statistics Canada
Education Support Branch, Department of the Secretary of State
Medical Research Council
National Research Council of Canada

Film
Canadian Film Institute

Forest conservation
Canadian Forestry Association

French
Canadian Association of University Teachers of French

Geographical
Royal Canadian Geographical Society, The

Geography
Canadian Association of Geographers, The

Diététique
Association canadienne des diététistes, L'

Droit
Association canadienne des professeurs de droit
Comité des doyens de droit du Canada

Economie
Association canadienne d'économique, L'

Economie agricole
Conseil de la recherche en économie agricole du Canada

Economie quantitative
Institut international d'économie quantitative

Education
Association canadienne d'éducation, L'
Association canadienne d'éducation de langue française
Association canadienne des professeurs d'éducation, L'
Collège canadien des enseignants, Le
Conseil canadien pour la recherche en éducation
Conseil supérieur de l'éducation
Direction de l'aide à l'éducation, Secrétariat d'Etat
Division de l'éducation, Statistique Canada
Services de l'éducation, Conseil luthérien au Canada
Société canadienne d'éducation comparée et internationale, La

Education des adultes
Institut canadien d'éducation des adultes

Education internationale
Bureau canadien de l'éducation internationale

Education par l'art
Société canadienne d'éducation par l'art

Education permanente
Association des services d'éducation des adultes et écoles d'été des universités du Canada

Education physique
Association canadienne pour la santé, l'éducation physique et la récréation, L'

Enseignants
Collège canadien des enseignants, Le
Fédération canadienne des enseignants

Enseignement supérieur
Commission de l'enseignement supérieur du Nouveau-Brunswick

German
Canadian Association of University
Teachers of German

Graduate studies
Canadian Association of Graduate Schools

Grants
Advisory Board for the Division of
University Grants in British Columbia
Universities Grants Commission (Manitoba)
University Grants Committee (Nova
Scotia)

Graphic arts
Graphic Arts Industries Association

Guidance
Canadian Guidance and Counselling
Association

Higher education
Canadian Society for the Study of Higher
Education
Directorate of Higher Education, Quebec
New Brunswick Higher Education
Commission

Hispanists
Canadian Association of Hispanists

History
Canadian Historical Association, The

Home economics
Canadian Home Economics Association

Humanities
Canada Council, The
Humanities Association of Canada
Humanities Research Council of Canada

Immunology
Canadian Society for Immunology, The

Indian education
Society for Indian and Northern Education

International affairs
Canadian Institute of International Affairs

**International associations of which
Canadian universities and colleges are
members**
Association des universités partiellement ou
entièrement de langue française
Association of Commonwealth Universities,
The
International Association of Universities
International Federation of Catholic
Universities

Direction générale de l'enseignement
supérieur, Québec
Société canadienne pour l'étude de
l'enseignement supérieur, La

Entomologie
Société entomologique du Canada, La

Ergothérapeutes
Association canadienne des ergothérapeutes

Esthétique
Conseil national de l'esthétique

Examen, Bureau d'
Bureau national d'examen dentaire du
Canada

Famille
Institut Vanier de la famille, L'

Faune
Fédération canadienne de la faune, La

Femmes diplômées
Fédération canadienne des femmes
diplômées des universités

Film
Institut canadien du film

Forêt
Association forestière canadienne

Français
Association des professeurs de français des
universités canadiennes

Génie
Association des scientifiques, ingénieurs et
technologistes du Canada, L'
Comité national des doyens de génie et
sciences appliquées
Institut canadien des ingénieurs, L'

Génie biologique
Société canadienne de génie médical et
biologique

Génie chimique
Société canadienne du génie chimique, La

Géographie
Association canadienne des géographes, L'

Géographique
Société géographique royale du Canada, La

Gestion
Institut canadien de gestion, L'

Hispanistes
Association des hispanistes du Canada

International co-operation
Canadian Council for International Co-operation

International education
Canadian Bureau for International Education

Landscape architects
Canadian Society of Landscape Architects, The

Latin American studies
Canadian Association of Latin American Studies

Law
Association of Canadian Law Teachers
Committee of Canadian Law Deans

Library
Canadian Association of College and University Libraries
Canadian Association of Library Schools
Canadian Library Association

Linguistics
Canadian Linguistic Association

Management
Canadian Institute of Management

Mathematics
Canadian Mathematical Congress

Medical records
Canadian Association of Medical Record Librarians

Medicine
Association of Canadian Medical Colleges
Canadian Medical Association, The
Medical Research Council

Meteorology
Canadian Meteorological Society

Microbiology
Canadian Society of Microbiologists

Mining
Canadian Institute of Mining and Metallurgy, The
Mining Association of Canada, The

Ministers of education
Council of Ministers of Education, Canada

Museums
Canadian Museums Association, The

Histoire
Société historique du Canada, La

Humanités
Association canadienne des humanités
Conseil canadien de recherches sur les humanités, Le
Conseil des arts du Canada, Le

Hygiène publique
Association canadienne d'hygiène publique, L'

Immunologie
Société canadienne d'immunologie, La

Industrie minière
Association minière du Canada, L'

Industries graphiques
Association des industries graphiques

Infirmières
Association des infirmières canadiennes

Information universitaire
Association des bureaux de l'information des universités du Canada

Ingénieurs
Association des ingénieurs-conseils du Canada
Conseil canadien des ingénieurs

Internationale
Association internationale des universités
Fédération internationale des universités catholiques

Internationale, coopération
Conseil canadien pour la coopération internationale

Internationales, affaires
Institut canadien des affaires internationales

Latino-américaines, études
Association canadienne des études latino-américaines

Linguistique
Association canadienne de linguistique

Mathématique
Société mathématique du Canada

Médecine
Association des facultés de médecine du Canada, L'
Association des médecins de langue française du Canada
Association médicale canadienne, L'
Conseil de recherches médicales

Music
Canadian Association of University Schools
of Music
Canadian Music Council

Netherlandic studies
Canadian Association for the Advancement
of Netherlandic Studies

News service
Canadian University Press

Nuclear
Canadian Nuclear Association

Nursing
Canadian Association of University Schools
of Nursing
Canadian Nurses' Association

Nutrition
Nutrition Society of Canada

Occupational therapy
Canadian Association of Occupational
Therapists

Ontario universities
Council of Ontario Universities

Optometrists
Canadian Association of Optometrists

Overseas development assistance
Canadian University Service Overseas

Paediatrics
Canadian Paediatric Society

Pathologists
Canadian Association of Pathologists

Petroleum
Canadian Petroleum Association

Pharmacology
Pharmacological Society of Canaaa, The

Pharmacy
Association of Deans of Pharmacy of
Canada, The
Association of Faculties of Pharmacy of
Canada
Canadian Pharmaceutical Association

Philosophy
Canadian Philosophical Association

Physical education
Canadian Association for Health, Physical
Education and Recreation

Médecine sociale
Association canadienne des professeurs de
médecine préventive et sociale

Medecine vétérinaire
Association des facultés de médecine
vétérinaire du Canada, L'

Médecins et chirurgiens
Collège royal des médecins et chirurgiens
du Canada, Le

Météorologie
Société météorologique du Canada, La

Microbiologie
Société canadienne des microbiologistes

Mines et métallurgie
Institut canadien des mines et de la
métallurgie, L'

Ministres de l'éducation
Conseil des ministres de l'éducation,
Canada

Musées
Association des musées canadiens

Musique
Association canadienne des écoles
universitaires de musique
Conseil canadien de la musique

Néerlandais
Association canadienne pour l'avancement
des études néerlandaises

Nucléaire
Association nucléaire canadienne

Nursing
Association canadienne des écoles
universitaires de nursing, L'

Nutrition
Société canadienne de nutrition

Octrois
Commission des octrois aux universités
(Manitoba), La

Ontario, universités
Conseil des universités de l'Ontario

Optométristes
Association canadienne des optométristes

Orientation
Société canadienne d'orientation et de
consultation

Physicians and surgeons
Royal College of Physicians and Surgeons of Canada, The

Physics
Canadian Association of Physicists

Physiology
Canadian Physiological Society

Physiotherapy
Canadian Physiotherapy Association

Plant physiology
Canadian Society of Plant Physiologists

Political science
Canadian Political Science Association

Post-secondary education
Commission on Post-Secondary Education in Ontario
Prince Edward Island Commission on Post-Secondary Education

Provincial associations
Academic Board for Higher Education in British Columbia
Advisory Board for the Division of University Grants in British Columbia
Alberta Universities Commission, The
Commission on Post-Secondary Education in Ontario
Committee on University Affairs of Ontario, The
Conference of Rectors and Principals of Quebec Universities
Council of Ontario Universities
Directorate of Higher Education, Quebec
New Brunswick Higher Education Commission
Ontario Confederation of University Faculty Associations
Ontario Universities' Council on Admissions
Ontario University Registrar's Association
Prince Edward Island Commission on Post-Secondary Education
Superior Council of Education, Quebec
Universities Grants Commission (Manitoba)
University Grants Committee (Nova Scotia)

Psychiatry
Canadian Psychiatric Association

Psychology
Canadian Psychological Association

Public administration
Institute of Public Administration of Canada, The

Orientation professionnelle
Association de placement universitaire et collégial

Pathologistes
Association canadienne des pathologistes

Pédagogie
Association canadienne des doyens et directeurs de faculté de pédagogie

Pédiatrie
Société canadienne de pédiatrie

Pétrole
Association de pétrole canadien, L'

Pharmacie
Association des doyens de pharmacie du Canada, L'
Association des facultés de pharmacie du Canada
Association pharmaceutique canadienne, L'

Pharmacologie
Société de pharmacologie du Canada, La

Philosophie
Association canadienne de philosophie

Physiologie
Société canadienne de physiologie

Physiologie végétale
Société canadienne de physiologie végétale

Physiothérapie
Association canadienne de physiothérapie, L'

Physique
Association canadienne des physiciens

Postsecondaire
Commission sur la formation postsecondaire en Ontario

Professeurs
Association canadienne des professeurs d'université
Union des associations des professeurs des universités de l'Ontario

Psychiatres
Association des psychiatres du Canada

Psychologie
Société canadienne de psychologie

Recherches
Conseil national de recherches du Canada

Public affairs
Canadian Institute of Public Affairs

Public health
Canadian Public Health Association

Quantitative economics
International Institute of Quantitative
Economics

Rationalization
Inter-Provincial Committee on University
Rationalization

Rectors
Conference of Rectors and Principals of
Quebec Universities

Regional associations
Association of Atlantic Universities
Inter-Provincial Committee on University
Rationalization

Registrars
Association of Registrars of the
Universities of Canada
Ontario University Registrars' Association

Research
National Research Council of Canada

Rhodes
Canadian Association of Rhodes Scholars,
The
Rhodes Scholarship Trust, The

Scholarships
Shastri Indo-Canadian Institute

Science
Youth Science Foundation

Shastri
Shastri Indo-Canadian Institute

Slavists
Canadian Association of Slavists

Social medicine
Canadian Association of Teachers of
Preventive and Social Medicine

Social sciences
Canada Council, The
Social Science Research Council of Canada

Social work
Canadian Association for Education in the
Social Services
Canadian Association of Social Workers

Recherches urbaines
Conseil canadien de recherches urbaines et
régionales

Recteurs
Conférence des recteurs et des principaux
des universités du Québec

Registraires
Association des registraires d'université du
Canada, L'

Rhodes
Association canadienne des boursiers
Rhodes, L'
Fondation des bourses Rhodes, La

Science politique
Association canadienne de science politique,
L'

Sciences
Association canadienne-française pour
l'avancement des sciences
Fondation sciences jeunesse

Sciences sociales
Conseil canadien de recherche en sciences
sociales, Le
Conseil des arts du Canada, Le

Services aux étudiants
Conseil des associations des services
universitaires aux étudiants

Service social
Association canadienne d'éducation pour
les services sociaux

Shastri
Institut indo-canadien Shastri, L'

Slavistes
Association canadienne des slavistes

Sociologie et anthropologie
Société canadienne de sociologie et
d'anthropologie

Spécialités dentaires
Collège royal des chirurgiens dentistes du
Canada, Le

Sport
Union sportive interuniversitaire canadienne

Supérieures, études
Association canadienne des écoles des
études supérieures

Télévision éducative
Association canadienne de radio et de
télévision éducatives, L'

Sociology and anthropology
Canadian Sociology and Anthropology
Association

Student personnel
Council of Associations of University
Student Personnel Services

Teachers
Canadian College of Teachers, The
Canadian Teachers' Federation

Theatre
Canadian Theatre Centre
Canadian University Theatre Association

UNESCO
Canadian Commission for UNESCO

Universities
Alberta Universities Commission, The
Committee on University Affairs of
Ontario, The
World University Service of Canada

University information
Association of Canadian University
Information Bureaus

University teachers
Canadian Association of University
Teachers

University women
Canadian Federation of University Women

Urban research
Canadian Council on Urban and Regional
Research

Veterinary medicine
Association of Faculties of Veterinary
Medicine in Canada

Visual arts
Universities Art Association of Canada

Wildlife
Canadian Wildlife Federation

Zoology
Canadian Society of Zoologists

Théâtre
Association canadienne du théâtre
universitaire
Centre canadien du théâtre

Théologie
Société canadienne de théologie

Tourbec
Bureau de tourisme des étudiants du
Québec, Le

Tourisme
Bureau de tourisme des étudiants du
Québec, Le

Travailleurs sociaux
Association canadienne des travailleurs
sociaux

UNESCO
Commission canadienne pour l'UNESCO

Universitaire
Comité sur les affaires universitaires de
l'Ontario, Le
Entr'aide universitaire mondiale du Canada

Universités
Association des universités partiellement ou
entièrement de langue française
Commission des universités de l'Alberta,
La

Zoologie
Société des zoologistes canadiens

Academic Board for Higher Education in British Columbia, The, 3611 W. Sixteenth Ave., Vancouver 8, B.C.
Chairman: Dean I. McTaggart-Cowan, faculty of graduate studies, The University of British Columbia, Vancouver 8, B.C.
Executive secretary: Mr. D. Franklin.

Advisory Board for the Division of University Grants in British Columbia, 1308 W. 48th Ave., Vancouver 13, B.C.
Chairman: Mr. W.G. Rathie.

Agricultural Economics Research Council of Canada (Conseil de la recherche en économie agricole du Canada), 55 Parkdale Ave., Ottawa 3, Ont.
President: Dr. Gordon MacEachern.

Agricultural Institute of Canada (Institut agricole du Canada, L'), suite 907, 151 Slater St., Ottawa, Ont., K1P 5H4.
President: Mr. R.E. Forbes, principal, Agricultural Extension Centre, Manitoba Department of Agriculture, Brandon, Man. General manager: Mr. W.E. Henderson.

Alberta Universities Commission, The (Commission des universités de l'Alberta, La), 202 The Sir John Franklin, 11111-87 Ave., Edmonton 61, Alta.
Chairman: Mr. D.L. Erickson. Secretary: Mr. H.W. Ford.

Association des universités partiellement ou entièrment de langue française, Université de Montréal, b.p. 6128, Montréal 101 (Qué.).
Président: M. Claude Renard, vice-président, Conseil d'administration, Université de Liège, Place du 20 Août, Liège, Belgique. Secrétairê général: M. Maurice Beutler.

Association of Atlantic Universities (Association des universités de l'Atlantique, L'), P.O. Box 24, Halifax, N.S.
Chairman: Dr. D.C. Duffie, president, St. Thomas University, Fredericton N.B.
Executive director: Mr. Jeffrey Holmes.

Association of Canadian Community Colleges (Association des collèges communautaires du Canada), 845 Ste-Croix Blvd., St-Laurent, Montreal 379, Que.
President: M. Normand Bumaylis, directeur général, CEGEP du Vieux-Montréal, 200 ouest, rue Sherbrooke, Montréal (Qué.).
Director: Mr. Jacques Fournier.

*Association of Canadian Faculties of Dentistry, The (Association des facultés

Agence canadienne de développement international, L' (Canadian International Development Agency), 122, rue Bank, Ottawa (Ont.), K1A 0G4.
Président: M. Paul Gérin-Lajoie.

Association botanique du Canada, L' (Canadian Botanical Association, The).
Président: Dr. H.N. Eydt, dept. of biology, University of Waterloo, Waterloo, Ont.
Secrétaire: Dr. J.E. Cruise, dept. of botany, University of Toronto, Toronto 181, Ont.

Association canadienne d'économique, L' (Canadian Economics Association, The).
Président: Prof. H.C. Eastman, dept. of political economy, University of Toronto, Toronto, Ont. Secrétaire: Prof. Gilles Paquet, Université Carleton, Ottawa (Ont.).

Association canadienne d'éducation de langue française, 3, place Jean-Talon, suite 338, Québec 2 (Qué.).
Président: Mgr Louis-Albert Vachon, recteur, Université Laval, Cité universitaire, Ste-Foy (Qué.). Secrétaire général: M. Jean-Jacques Bergeron.

Association canadienne d'éducation, L' (Canadian Education Association, The), 252 ouest, rue Bloor, Toronto 5 (Ont.).
Président: Dr. T.C. Byrne, president, Athabasca University, 406 IBM Bldg., 10808-99th Ave., Edmonton, Alta. Secrétaire administratif: M. F.K. Stewart.

*Association canadienne d'éducation pour les services sociaux (Canadian Association for Education in the Social Services), suite 209, 151, rue Slater, Ottawa (Ont.), K1P 5H3.
Président: Dr. George Hougham, director, school of social work, The University of British Columbia, Vancouver 8, B.C.
Directrice administrative: Mlle Marguerite Mathieu.

Association canadienne de l'audio-visuel (National Audio-Visual Association of Canada, The), 11e étage, 11 ouest, rue Adelaide, Toronto 1, (Ont.).
Président: Mr. D.G. McLeod, Ron Nelson Photography Ltd., 388 Horton St., London, Ont. Secrétaire administratif: M. Daniel Kay, Jr.

Association canadienne de linguistique (Canadian Linguistic Association).
Président: M. André Rigault, Université McGill, Montréal (Qué.). Secrétaire: M. Guy

---

dentaires du Canada, L'), 5981 University Ave., Halifax, N.S.
President: Dr. S.W. Leung, dean, faculty of dentistry, The University of British Columbia, Vancouver 8, B.C. Secretary: Dr. D.V. Chaytor.

Association of Canadian Law Teachers (Association canadienne des professeurs de droit).
President: Dean C.H.C. Edwards, faculty of law, The University of Manitoba, Robson Hall, Winnipeg 19, Man. Secretary-treasurer: Prof. D.W.M. Waters, faculty of law, McGill University, 3644 Peel St., P.O. Box 6070, Montreal 101, Que.

*Association of Canadian Medical Colleges (Association des facultés de médecine du Canada), 151 Slater St., Ottawa, Ont., K1P 5H3.
President: Dr. John Evans, dean of medicine, McMaster University, Hamilton, Ont.
Executive director: Dr. J.B. Firstbrook.

Association of Canadian Schools of Business (Association canadienne des écoles de commerce).
President: M. Roger Miller, Faculté d'administration, Université de Sherbrooke, Sherbrooke (Qué.). Secretary-treasurer: Dr. Herman Overgaard, school of business and economics, Waterloo Lutheran University, Waterloo, Ont.

*Association of Canadian University Information Bureaus (Association des bureaux de l'information des universités du Canada).
President: Mr. Bruce Woodland, director, information and alumni affairs, Memorial University of Newfoundland, St. John's, Nfld. Secretary: Mrs. Rosemary Cavan, information officer, Association of Universities and Colleges of Canada, 151 Slater St., Ottawa, Ont., K1P 5N1.

Association of Canadian University Teachers of English (Association des professeurs d'anglais des universités canadiennes).
President: Prof. Clara Thomas, 251 Winters College, York University, 4700 Keele St., Downsview, Ont. Secretary: Prof. Janet Lewis, dept. of English, York University, 4700 Keele St., Downsview, Ont.

Association of Commonwealth Universities, The, 36 Gordon Square, London, England. Chairman: Prof. A. Kwapong, vice-

Plastre, Université Laval, Pavillon de Koninck 0277, Québec 10e (Qué.).

Association canadienne de philosophie (Canadian Philosophical Association).
Président: Prof. David Braybrooke, dept. of philosophy, Dalhousie University, Halifax, N.S. Secrétaire: Prof. Robert Binkley, dept. of philosophy, The University of Western Ontario, London, Ont.

Association canadienne de physiothérapie, L' (Canadian Physiotherapy Association), 64 Avenue Rd., Toronto 5, Ont.
Présidente: Miss Margaret Finlayson, 107-4400 Ste-Catherine St. W., Westmount 215, Que. Directeur administratif: M. Peter Large.

Association canadienne de radio et de télévision éducatives, L' (Educational Television and Radio Association of Canada), a/s ACE, 252 ouest, rue Bloor, Toronto 5 (Ont.).
Président: Mr. H.H. Mamet, director, The University of Alberta Radio and Television CW 005, biological sciences bldg., Edmonton 7, Alta. Secrétaire: Mrs. Dorothy Patterson, director, public relations, The University of Calgary, Calgary, Alta.

Association canadienne des anatomistes (Canadian Association of Anatomists).
Président: Dr. David Dickson, head, division of morphological science, faculty of medicine, The University of Calgary, Calgary 44, Alta. Secrétaire: Dr Réal Gagnon, département d'anatomie, faculté de médecine, Université de Montréal, c.p. 6128, Montréal 101 (Qué.).

Association canadienne des bibliothécaires de langue française, 360, rue Le Moyne, Montréal 125 (Qué.).
Président: M. Réal Bosa, bibliothèque des sciences humaines et sociales, Université de Montréal, c.p. 6128, Montréal 101 (Qué.). Secrétaire général: M. Hubert Perron.

*Association canadienne des bibliothèques de collège et d'université (Canadian Association of College and University Libraries).
Président: Rév. Daniel Croteau, directeur des bibliothèques, Université de Sherbrooke, Cité universitaire, Sherbrooke (Qué.). Secrétaire: Miss Rosemary Lyons, acquisitions librarian, The University of Calgary, Calgary 44, Alta.

Association canadienne des boursiers Rhodes, L' (Canadian Association of Rhodes

---

chancellor, University of Ghana, P.O. Box 25, Legon, West Africa. Secretary-general: Sir Hugh Springer.

Association of Consulting Engineers of Canada, The (Association des ingénieurs-conseils du Canada), suite 616, 130 Albert St., Ottawa, Ont., K1P 5G4.
President: Mr. J.A. Merchant, Swan Wooster Engineering Co. Ltd., 1525 Robson St., Vancouver 5, B.C. General manager: Mr. H.R. Pinault.

*Association of Deans of Pharmacy of Canada, The (Association des doyens de pharmacie du Canada, L'), 175 College St., Toronto, Ont.
President: Dr. Randolph Murray, faculty of pharmacy, The University of Manitoba, Winnipeg, Man. Secretary-treasurer: Dr. A.W. Matthews.

Association of Faculties of Pharmacy of Canada (Association des facultés de pharmacie du Canada).
President: Dr. J.G. Nairn, faculty of pharmacy, University of Toronto, Toronto 181, Ont. Secretary: Dr. R.A. Locock, faculty of pharmacy, The University of Alberta, Edmonton, Alta.

*Association of Faculties of Veterinary Medicine in Canada (Association des facultés de médecine vétérinaire du Canada, L').
President: Dr Ephrem Jacques, doyen, faculté de médecine vétérinaire, Université de Montréal, c.p. 5000, St-Hyacinthe (Qué.).
Secretary-treasurer: Dr Patrick Guay, faculté de médecine vétérinaire, Université de Montréal, c.p. 5000, St-Hyacinthe (Qué.).

*Association of Registrars of the Universities of Canada (Association des registraires d'université du Canada, L').
President: Mr. David Green, registrar, Acadia University, Wolfville, N.S. Secretary: Mrs. Jean Hadley, admissions officer and assistant registrar, University of New Brunswick, Fredericton, N.B.

Association of the Scientific, Engineering and Technological Community of Canada, The (Association des scientifiques, ingénieurs et technologistes du Canada, L'), 151 Slater St., Ottawa, Ont., K1P 5H3.
President: M. L. Berlinguet, vice-président à la recherche, Université du Québec, 2525, boul. Laurier, Québec (Qué.). General manager: Mr. T.H.G. Michael.

Scholars, The), 7e étage, 100, avenue University, Toronto 116 (Ont.).
Président: Mr. Clarence Campbell, president, National Hockey League, 922 Sun Life Bldg., Montreal 110, Que. Secrétaire: M. Hugh Morrison.

Association canadienne de science politique, L' (Canadian Political Science Association).
Président: Prof. J.E. Hodgetts, Victoria University, Toronto 5, Ont. Secrétaire: Prof. J.E. Trent, département de science politique, Université d'Ottawa, Ottawa (Ont.).

Association canadienne des diététistes, L' (Canadian Dietetic Association, The), suite 215, 1393, rue Yonge, Toronto 290 (Ont.).
Présidente: Mrs. Phyllis McFeat, director of food service, The Montreal Children's Hospital, Montreal 108, Que. Secrétaire générale: Mlle Joan Brown.

Association canadienne des directeurs athlétiques universitaires (Canadian Association of University Athletic Directors).
Président: Mr. John Kennedy, athletic director, McMaster University, Hamilton, Ont. Secretary: Mr. William Mitchell, athletic director, University of Guelph, Guelph, Ont.

*Association canadienne des doyens de pharmacie, L' (Association of Deans of Pharmacy of Canada), 175, rue College, Toronto (Ont.).
Président: Dr. Randolph Murray, faculty of pharmacy, The University of Manitoba, Winnipeg, Man. Secrétaire-trésorier: Dr. A.W. Matthews.

*Association canadienne des doyens et directeurs de faculté de pédagogie (Canadian Association of Deans and Directors of University Faculties of Education).
Président: Dean W.R. MacDonald, school of education, Acadia University, Wolfville, N.S. Secrétaire: Mr. Roger Black, University of Prince Edward Island, Charlottetown, P.E.I.

*Association canadienne des écoles de bibliothécaires (Canadian Association of Library Schools).
Présidente: Miss Janette White, school of library and information science, The University of Western Ontario, London, Ont. Secrétaire: Miss Carmen Sprovieri, school of library and information science, The University of Western Ontario, London, Ont.

Biological Council of Canada (Conseil canadien de biologie), suite 907, 151 Slater St., Ottawa, Ont., K1P 5H4.
President: Dr. J.B. Armstrong, executive director (médical), Canadian Heart Foundation, 270 Laurier Ave. W., Ottawa, Ont., K1P 5K1. Secretary: Dr. R.L. Taylor, office of the botanical, The University of British Columbia, Vancouver 8, B.C.

†Canada Council, The (Conseil des arts du Canada, Le), P.O. Box 1047, Ottawa, Ont., K1P 5V8.
Chairman: Dr. John Prentice. Assistant director and secretary: Mr. Claude Gauthier.

Canada Studies Foundation, The (Fondation d'études du Canada, La), suite 716, 252 Bloor St. W., Toronto 5, Ont.
Director: Mr. A.B. Hodgetts. Secretary: Miss Gillian Hawes.

Canadian Aeronautics and Space Institute (Institut aéronautique et spatial du Canada, L'), suite 406, 77 Metcalfe St., Ottawa, Ont., K1P 5L6.
President: Brig. Gen. E.P. Bridgland, chief aeronautical engineer, Ministry of Transport, Ottawa, Ont. Secretary-treasurer: Mr. H.C. Luttman.

Canadian Association for Adult Education, 238 St. George St., Toronto 5, Ont.
President: Dr. D.H. Brundage, office of graduate studies, Ontario Institute for Studies in Education, 252 Bloor St. W., Toronto, Ont. Executive director: Mr. G.A. Hodge.

Canadian Association for American Studies (Association canadienne d'études américaines).
President: Dr. Virginia Rock, master, 314 Stong College, York University, Downsview, Ont. Secretary: Prof. Ernest Redekop, dept. of English, The University of Western Ontario, London, Ont.

*Canadian Association for Education in the Social Services (Association canadienne d'éducation pour les services sociaux), room 209, 151 Slater St., Ottawa, Ont., K1P 5H3.
President: Dr. George Hougham, director, school of social work, The University of British Columbia, Vancouver 8, B.C. Executive director: Miss Marguerite Mathieu.

Association canadienne des écoles de commerce (Association of Canadian Schools of Business).
Président: M. Roger Miller, Faculté d'administration, Université de Sherbrooke, Sherbrooke (Qué.). Secrétaire-trésorier: Dr. Herman Overgaard, school of business and economics, Waterloo Lutheran University, Waterloo, Ont.

*Association canadienne des écoles d'études supérieures (Canadian Association of Graduate Schools).
Président: Dr. M.A. Preston, faculty of graduate studies, McMaster University, Hamilton, Ont. Secrétaire-trésorier: Dr. B.G. Hogg, faculty of graduate studies, The University of Manitoba, Winnipeg 19, Man.

*Association canadienne des écoles universitaires de nursing, L' (Canadian Association of University Schools of Nursing).
Présidente: Miss Elizabeth McCann, school of nursing, The University of British Columbia, Vancouver 8, B.C. Secrétaire: Miss H. Elfert, school of nursing, The University of British Columbia, Vancouver 8, B.C.

Association canadienne des ergothérapeutes (Canadian Association of Occupational Therapists), suite 412, 57 ouest, rue Bloor, Toronto (Ont.).
Présidente: Mme Sheila Irvine.

Association canadienne des études africaines, L' (Canadian Association of African Studies).
Président: Prof. André Lux, département de sociologie et d'anthropologie, Université Laval, Québec (Qué.). Secrétaire: Dr. D.R.F. Taylor, dept. of geography, Carleton University, Ottawa, Ont., K1S 5B6.

Association canadienne des études asiatiques (Canadian Society for Asian Studies).
Président: Dr. E. Pulleyblank, head, dept. of Asian studies, The University of British Columbia, Vancouver 8, B.C. Secrétaire: Dr. George Kurian, dept. of sociology and anthropology, The University of Calgary, Calgary 44, Alta.

Association canadienne des études latino-américaines (Canadian Association of Latin American Studies).
Président: Prof. Hugues-G. Hambleton, département d'économie, Université Laval, Québec 10e (Qué.). Secrétaire-trésorier: Prof. Myron Frankman, department of economics, McGill University, Montreal, Que.

---

*Associate member, AUCC.

†Honorary associate, AUCC.

*Membre associé de l'AUCC.

Canadian Association for Health, Physical Education and Recreation (Association canadienne pour la santé, l'éducation physique et la récréation, L'), 333 River Road, Vanier City, Ont., K1L 8B9. President: Dr. William Orban, director, school of physical education and recreation, University of Ottawa, Ottawa, Ont., K1N 6N5. Executive director: Mr. C.R. Blackstock.

Canadian Association for the Advancement of Netherlandic Studies (Association canadienne pour l'avancement des études néerlandaises). President: Mr. Jack Riedé, vice-president and director, Longmans Canada Ltd., 55 Barber Greene Rd., Don Mills, Ont. Secretary: Prof. Christopher Levenson, English dept., Carleton University, Ottawa, Ont., K1S 5B6.

Canadian Association of African Studies (Association canadienne des études africaines, L'). President: Prof. André Lux, département de sociologie et d'anthropologie, Université Laval, Québec (Qué.). Secretary: Dr. D.R.F. Taylor, dept. of geography, Carleton University, Ottawa, Ont., K1S 5B6.

Canadian Association of Anatomists (Association canadienne des anatomistes). President: Dr. David Dickson, head, division of morphological science, faculty of medicine, The University of Calgary, Calgary 44, Alta. Secretary: Dr Réal Gagnon, département d'anatomie, faculté de médecine, Université de Montréal, c.p. 6128, Montréal 101 (Qué.).

*Canadian Association of College and University Libraries (Association canadienne des bibliothèques de collège et d'université). President: Rév. Daniel Croteau, directeur des bibliothèques, Université de Sherbrooke, Cité universitaire, Sherbrooke (Qué.). Secretary: Miss Rosemary Lyons, acquisitions librarian, The University of Calgary, Calgary 44, Alta.

*Canadian Association of Deans and Directors of University Faculties of Education (Association canadienne des doyens et directeurs de faculté de pédagogie). Chairman: Dean W.R. MacDonald, school of education, Acadia University, Wolfville, N.S. Secretary: Mr. Roger Black, University of Prince Edward Island, Charlottetown, P.E.I.

Association canadienne des géographes, L' (Canadian Association of Geographers, The). Président: Prof. L.-E. Hamelin, centre d'études nordiques, Université Laval, Québec 10e (Qué.). Secrétaire: Dr. J.T. Parry, Burnside Hall, McGill University, P.O. Box 6070, Montreal 101, Que.

Association canadienne des humanités (Humanities Association of Canada). Président: Dr. John Matthews, dept. of Commonwealth studies, Queen's University at Kingston, Kingston, Ont. Secrétaire: Prof. M.G. Wiebe, dept. of English, Queen's University at Kingston, Kingston, Ont.

Association canadienne des optométristes, L' (Canadian Association of Optometrists), suite 807, 88, rue Metcalfe, Ottawa (Ont.), K1P 5L7. Président: Dr. R.W. Macpherson, Napanee, Ont. Secrétaire administratif: M. G.J. Walsh.

Association canadienne des pathologistes (Canadian Association of Pathologists). Président: Dr. D.E.O. Magner, University of Ottawa, Ottawa, Ont. Secrétaire: Dr. D.W. Penner, dept. of pathology, Winnipeg General Hospital, Winnipeg 3, Man.

Association canadienne des physiciens (Canadian Association of Physicists), suite 903, 151, rue Slater, Ottawa (Ont.), K1P 5H3. Président: M. Gilles-G. Cloutier, directeur des recherches, Institut de recherches de l'Hydro-Québec, c.p. 1000, Varennes (Qué.). Secrétaire: Dr C.C. Costain.

Association canadienne des professeurs de droit (Association of Canadian Law Teachers). Président: Dean C.H.C. Edwards, faculty of law, The University of Manitoba, Robson Hall, Winnipeg 19, Man. Secrétaire-trésorier: Prof. D.W.M. Waters, faculty of law, McGill University, 3644 Peel St., P.O. Box 6070, Montreal 101, Que.

Association canadienne des professeurs d'éducation, L' (Canadian Association of Professors of Education). Président: Dr. Eigil Pedersen, faculty of education, McGill University, Montreal 110, Que. Secrétaire-trésorier: Dr. Norman Henchey, faculty of education, McGill University, Montreal 110, Que.

Association canadienne des professeurs de médecine préventive et sociale (Canadian Association of Teachers of Preventive and Social Medicine). Président: Dr. D.J. Hosking, faculty of

---

*Canadian Association of Departments of Extension and Summer Schools (Association des services d'éducation des adultes et écoles d'été des universités du Canada).
President: Mr. Donald Snowden, director, extension service, Memorial University of Newfoundland, St. John's, Nfld. Secretary: Mr. R.S. Chapman, associate director, division of continuing education, The University of Calgary, Calgary, Alta.

Canadian Association of Geographers, The (Association canadienne des géographes, L'). President: Prof. L.-E. Hamelin, centre d'études nordiques, Université Laval, Québec 10e (Qué.). Secretary: Dr. J.T. Parry, Burnside Hall, McGill University, P.O. Box 6070, Montreal 101, Que.

*Canadian Association of Graduate Schools (Association canadienne des écoles d'études supérieures).
President: Dr. M.A. Preston, faculty of graduate studies, McMaster University, Hamilton, Ont. Secretary-treasurer: Dr. B.G. Hogg, faculty of graduate studies, The University of Manitoba, Winnipeg 19, Man.

Canadian Association of Hispanists (Association des hispanistes du Canada). President: Prof. H.W. Hilborn, dept. of Spanish and Italian, Queen's University at Kingston, Kingston, Ont. Secretary: Prof. J.A. Valverde, head, dept. of Spanish, Acadia University, Wolfville, N.S.

Canadian Association of Latin American Studies (Association canadienne des études latino-américaines).
President: Prof. Hugues-G. Hambleton, département d'économie, Université Laval, Québec 10e (Qué.). Secretary-treasurer: Prof. Myron Frankman, department of economics, McGill University, Montreal, Que.

*Canadian Association of Library Schools (Association canadienne des écoles de bibliothécaires).
President: Miss Janette White, school of library and information science, The University of Western Ontario, London, Ont. Secretary: Miss Carmen Sprovieri, school of library and information science, The University of Western Ontario, London, Ont.

Canadian Association of Medical Records Librarians (Association des archivistes médicales du Canada), 770 Glenforest St., Oshawa, Ont.

medicine, University of Saskatchewan, Saskatoon, Sask. Secrétaire: Dr. J. Owen, faculty of medicine, University of Saskatchewan, Saskatoon, Sask.

Association canadienne des professeurs d'université (Canadian Association of University Teachers), 66, rue Lisgar, Ottawa (Ont.), K2P 0C1.
Président: M. Robert Bertrand, faculté de droit, Université de Montréal, c.p. 6128, Montréal 101 (Qué.). Secrétaire administratif: Prof. Alwyn Berland.

Association canadienne des slavistes (Canadian Association of Slavists).
Président: Prof. D. Dorotich, department of education foundations, University of Saskatchewan, Saskatoon, Sask. Secrétaire: Prof. R. Serbyn, département d'histoire, Université du Québec, Montréal 110 (Qué.).

Association canadienne des travailleurs sociaux (Canadian Association of Social Workers), suite 400, 55, ave Parkdale, Ottawa (Ont.), K1Y 1E5.
Président: Dr. Albert Rose, director, school of social work, University of Toronto, 246 Bloor St., Toronto 5, Ont. Directrice administrative: Mlle Florence Philpott.

Association canadienne d'études américaines (Canadian Association for American Studies).
Présidente: Dr. Virginia Rock, master, 314 Stong College, York University, Downsview, Ont. Secrétaire: Prof. Ernest Redekop, dept. of English, The University of Western Ontario, London, Ont.

Association canadienne d'hygiène publique, L' (Canadian Public Health Association), 1255, rue Yonge, Toronto 7 (Ont.).
Président: Dr. V. L. Matthews, head, dept. of social and preventive medicine, University of Saskatchewan, Saskatoon, Sask. Directeur administratif: M. C.D. Noble.

Association canadienne du personnel administratif universitaire (Canadian Association of University Business Officers).
Président: Mr. B.R. James, controller, McMaster University, Hamilton, Ont. Secrétaire-trésorier: Mr. D.S. Claringbold, Simcoe Hall, University of Toronto, Toronto 181, Ont.

Association canadienne du théâtre universitaire (Canadian University Theatre Association).
Président: Prof. R. Skene, dept. of English, theatre division, The University of Winnipeg, Winnipeg, Man. Secrétaire intérimaire: Mr.

President: Sister Pauline Leblanc, St. Joseph's Hospital, Chatham, Ont. Executive director: Mrs. Janet Milner.

Canadian Association of Occupational Therapists (Association canadienne des ergothérapeutes), suite 412, 57 Bloor St. W., Toronto, Ont.
President: Mrs. Sheila Irvine.

Canadian Association of Optometrists (Association canadienne des optométristes, L'), suite 807, 88 Metcalfe St., Ottawa, Ont., K1P 5L7.
President: Dr. R.W. Macpherson, Napanee, Ont. Executive secretary: Mr. G.J. Walsh.

Canadian Association of Pathologists (Association canadienne des pathologistes).
President: Dr. D.E.O. Magner, University of Ottawa, Ottawa, Ont. Secretary: Dr. D.W. Penner, dept. of pathology, Winnipeg General Hospital, Winnipeg 3, Man.

Canadian Association of Physicists (Association canadienne des physiciens), suite 903, 151 Slater St., Ottawa, Ont., K1P 5H3.
President: M. Gilles-G. Cloutier, directeur des recherches, Institut de recherches de l'Hydro-Québec, c.p. 1000, Varennes (Qué.).
Secretary: Dr. C.C. Costain.

Canadian Association of Professors of Education (Association canadienne des professeurs d'éducation, L').
President: Dr. Eigil Pedersen, faculty of education, McGill University, Montreal 110, Que. Secretary-treasurer: Dr. Norman Henchey, faculty of education, McGill University, Montreal 110, Que.

Canadian Association of Rhodes Scholars, The (Association canadienne des boursiers Rhodes, L'), 7th floor, 100 University Ave., Toronto 116, Ont.
President: Mr. Clarence Campbell, president, National Hockey League, 922 Sun Life Bldg., Montreal 110, Que. Secretary: Mr. Hugh Morrison.

Canadian Association of Slavists (Association canadienne des slavistes).
President: Prof. D. Dorotich, department of educational foundations, University of Saskatchewan, Saskatoon, Sask. Secretary: Prof. R. Serbyn, département d'histoire, Université du Québec, Montréal 110 (Qué.).

Canadian Association of Social Workers (Association canadienne des travailleurs sociaux), suite 400, 55 Parkdale Ave., Ottawa, Ont., K1Y 1E5.

David Hewlett, theatre division, The University of Winnipeg, Winnipeg, Man.

Association canadienne-française pour l'avancement des sciences, 2730, chemin de la Côte Ste-Catherine, Montréal 250 (Qué.).
Président: M. Jean-Marc Lalancette, doyen, Faculté des sciences, Université de Sherbrooke, Sherbrooke (Qué.). Directeur général: M. Serge Hamel.

Association canadienne pour la santé, l'éducation physique et la récréation, L' (Canadian Association for Health, Physical Education and Recreation), 333 River Road, Vanier (Ont.), K1L 8B9.
Président: M. William Orban, directeur, Ecole d'éducation physique et récréation, Université d'Ottawa, Ottawa (Ont.), K1N 6N5. Directeur administratif: M. C.R. Blackstock.

Association canadienne pour l'avancement des études néerlandaises (Canadian Association for the Advancement of Netherlandic Studies).
Président: Mr. Jack Riedé, vice-president and director, Longmans Canada Ltd., 55 Barber Greene Rd., Don Mills, Ont. Secrétaire: Prof. Christopher Levenson, English dept., Carleton University, Ottawa (Ont.), K1S 5B6.

Association dentaire canadienne, L' (Canadian Dental Association), 234, rue St. George, Toronto 180 (Ont.).
Directeur administratif: Dr W.G. McIntosh.

Association de pétrole canadien, L' (Canadian Petroleum Association), 625-404 6th Ave. S.W., Calgary 1, Alta.
Directeur: Mr. D.B. Furlong, 400-130 Albert St., Varette Bldg., Ottawa, Ont., K1P 5C4. Gérant et secrétaire-trésorier: M. R.J. Frocklage.

Association de placement universitaire et collégial (University and College Placement Association), 254A nord, rue Main, Markham (Ont.).
Président: Mr. W.G. Donnelly, vice-president, Alcan Canada Products, Box 269, Toronto-Dominion Centre, Toronto 111, Ont. Secrétaire: M. S. Musgrave.

Association des architectes paysagistes du Canada, L' (Canadian Society of Landscape Architects, The), c.p. 3304, succursale postale C, Ottawa (Ont.), K1Y 4J5.
Président: Mr. Edwin Skapsts, suite 290, 755 Berri St., Montreal 127, Que. Secrétaire: Mrs. J.V. Stensson, 1300 Winston Churchill Blvd., Oakville, Ont.

President: Dr. Albert Rose, director, school of social work, University of Toronto, 246 Bloor St., Toronto 5, Ont. Executive director: Miss Florence Philpott.

Canadian Association of Student Awards Administrators.
President: Mr. A.R. Dejeet, student awards officer, University of Waterloo, Waterloo, Ont. Secretary: Mrs. A.T. Loates, awards officer, Carleton University, 1231 Colonel By Drive, Ottawa, Ont., K1S 5B6.

Canadian Association of Teachers of Preventive and Social Medicine (Association canadienne des professeurs de médecine préventive et sociale).
President: Dr. D.J. Hosking, faculty of medicine, University of Saskatchewan, Saskatoon, Sask. Secretary: Dr. J. Owen, faculty of medicine, University of Saskatchewan, Saskatoon, Sask.

Canadian Association of University Athletic Directors (Association canadienne des directeurs athlétiques universitaires).
President: Mr. John Kennedy, athletic director, McMaster University, Hamilton, Ont. Secretary: Mr. William Mitchell, athletic director, University of Guelph, Guelph, Ont.

Canadian Association of University Business Officers (Association canadienne du personnel administratif universitaire).
President: Mr. B.R. James, controller, McMaster University, Hamilton, Ont. Secretary-treasurer: Mr. D.S. Claringbold, Simcoe Hall, University of Toronto, Toronto 181, Ont.

*Canadian Association of University Development Officers, The (Association des dirigeants du service de développement des universités canadiennes).
President: Mr. John Babcock, director, alumni affairs and development, University of Guelph, Guelph, Ont. Secretary: Mr. R.L. Jones, director of development, University of Toronto, Toronto 181, Ont..

Canadian Association of University Schools of Music (Association canadienne des écoles universitaires de musique).
President: M. Lucien Brochu, directeur, école de musique, Université Laval, Québec 10e (Qué.). Secretary: M. Armand Ferland, école de musique, Université Laval, Québec 10e (Qué.).

Association des archivistes médicales du Canada (Canadian Association of Medical Records Librarians), 770, rue Glenforest, Oshawa (Ont.).
Présidente: Rév. Soeur Pauline Leblanc, Hôpital St. Joseph's, Chatham (Ont.). Directrice administrative: Mme Janet Milner.

*Association des bureaux de l'information des universités du Canada (Association of Canadian University Information Bureaus).
Président: Mr. Bruce Woodland, director, information and alumni affairs, Memorial University of Newfoundland, St. John's, Nfld. Secrétaire: Mme Rosemary Cavan, adjointe à l'information, Association des Universités et Collèges du Canada, 151, rue Slater, Ottawa (Ont.), K1P 5N1.

Association des collèges communautaires du Canada (Association of Canadian Community Colleges), 845, boul. Ste-Croix, St-Laurent, Montréal 379 (Qué.).
Président: M. Normand Bumaylis, directeur général, CEGEP du Vieux-Montréal, 200 ouest, rue Sherbrooke, Montréal (Qué.). Directeur: M. Jacques Fournier.

Association des collèges du Québec, 1940 est, boulevard Henri-Bourassa, Montréal 360 (Qué.).
Vice-président: Père Georges Legault. Secrétaire général: M. Jean-Marie Saint-Germain.

*Association des dirigeants du service de développement des universités canadiennes (Canadian Association of University Development Officers).
Président: Mr. John Babcock, director, alumni affairs and development, University of Guelph, Guelph, Ont. Secrétaire: Mr. R.L. Jones, director of development, University of Toronto, Toronto 181, Ont.

*Association des facultés de médecine du Canada, L' (Association of Canadian Medical Colleges), 151, rue Slater, Ottawa (Ont.), K1P 5H3.
Président: Dr. John Evans, dean of medicine, McMaster University, Hamilton, Ont. Directeur administratif: Dr. J.B. Firstbrook.

*Association des facultés de médecine vétérinaire du Canada, L' (Association of Faculties of Veterinary Medicine in Canada).
Président: Dr Ephrem Jacques, doyen, faculté de médecine vétérinaire, Université de Montréal, 5000, St-Hyacinthe (Qué.).

---

*Associate member, AUCC.

*Membre associé de l'AUCC.

*Canadian Association of University Schools of Nursing (Association canadienne des écoles universitaires de nursing, L').
President: Miss Elizabeth McCann, school of nursing, The University of British Columbia, Vancouver 8, B.C. Secretary: Miss. H. Elfert, school of nursing, The University of British Columbia, Vancouver 8, B.C.

Canadian Association of University Teachers (Association canadienne des professeurs d'université), 66 Lisgar, Ottawa, Ont., K2P OC1.
President: M. Robert Bertrand, faculté de droit, Université de Montréal, c.p. 6128, Montréal 101 (Qué.). Executive secretary: Prof. Alwyn Berland.

Canadian Association of University Teachers of French (Association des professeurs de français des universités canadiennes).
President: Dr. R. Bismuth, dept. of French, Brock University, St. Catharines, Ont. Secretary: Dr. M.J. Cardy, dept of French, Brock University, St. Catharines, Ont.

Canadian Association of University Teachers of German (Association des professeurs d'allemand des universités canadiennes, L').
President: Dr. J.B. MacLean, dept. of Germanic languages and literature, University of Victoria, Victoria, B.C. Secretary-treasurer: Dr. R.T.K. Symington, dept. of Germanic languages and literature, University of Victoria, Victoria, B.C.

Canadian Biochemical Society (Société canadienne de biochimie, La).
President: Dr. G.R. Williams, dept. of biochemistry, University of Toronto, Toronto, Ont. Secretary: Dr Bégin Heick, département de biochimie, faculté de médecine, Université Laval, Québec 10 (Qué.).

Canadian Botanical Association, The (Association botanique du Canada, L').
President: Dr. H.N. Eydt, dept. of biology, University of Waterloo, Waterloo, Ont. Secretary: Dr. J.E. Cruise, dept. of botany, University of Toronto, Toronto 181, Ont.

Canadian Bureau for International Education (Bureau canadien de l'éducation internationale), suite 408, 151 Slater St., Ottawa, Ont., K1P 5H3.
President: Dr. W.C. Winegard, president, University of Guelph, Guelph, Ont. Executive director: Mr. Allan Rix.

Secrétaire-trésorier: Dr Patrick Guay, faculté de médecine vétérinaire, Université de Montréal, 5000, St-Hyacinthe (Qué.).

*Association des facultés dentaires du Canada, L' (Association of Canadian Faculties of Dentistry, The), 5981, avenue de l'Université, Halifax (N.-E.).
Président: Dr. S.W. Leung, dean, faculty of dentistry, The University of British Columbia, Vancouver 8, B.C. Secrétaire: M. D.V. Chaytor.

Association des facultés de pharmacie du Canada (Association of Faculties of Pharmacy of Canada).
Président: M. J.G. Nairn, faculty of pharmacy, University of Toronto, Toronto 181, Ont. Secrétaire: Mr. R.A. Locock, faculty of pharmacy, The University of Alberta, Edmonton, Alta.

Association des hispanistes du Canada (Canadian Association of Hispanists).
Président: Prof. H.W. Hilborn, dept. of Spanish and Italian, Queen's University at Kingston, Kingston, Ont. Secrétaire: Prof. J.A. Valverde, head, dept. of Spanish, Acadia University, Wolfville, N.S.

Association des industries graphiques (Graphic Arts Industries Association), #906, 75, rue Albert, Ottawa (Ont.), K1P 5E7.
Président: Mr. D.M. Alloway, president, Consolidated Graphics Ltd., 24 Ferrand Dr., Don Mills, Ont. Gérant général: M. D. Maclellan.

Association des infirmières canadiennes (Canadian Nurses' Association), 50, Le Driveway, Ottawa (Ont.), K2P 1E2.
Présidente: Mlle Louise Miner. Directrice administrative: Dr Helen Mussallem.

Association des ingénieurs-conseils du Canada (Association of Counsulting Engineers of Canada, The), pièce 616, 130, rue Albert, Ottawa (Ont.), K1P 5G4.
Président: Mr. J.A. Merchant, Swan Wooster Engineering Co. Ltd., 1525 Robson St., Vancouver 5, B.C. Gérant général: M. H.R. Pinault.

Association des médecins de langue française du Canada, 5064, avenue du Parc, Montréal 152 (Qué.).
Président: Dr Jacques Léger. Secrétaire: Dr Georges Desrosiers. Association des musées canadiens (Canadian Museums Association,

---

Canadian College of Teachers, The (Collège canadien des enseignants, Le), box 760, 39 Leacock Way, Kanata, Ont. President: Mr. R.J. Carter, 2049 W. 61st St., Vancouver 14, B.C. Secretary-treasurer: Mr. S.R. Berry.

Canadian Commission for UNESCO (Commission canadienne pour l'UNESCO), 5th floor, 151 The Mall, Ottawa, Ont., K1P 5E3. President: M. Napoléon LeBlanc, vicerecteur, Université Laval, Québec (Qué.). Secretary general: Mr. David Bartlett.

Canadian Conference of University Schools of Architecture. Chairman: Mr. Douglas Shadbolt, head of schools committee, c/o Carleton University, Ottawa 1, Ont, K1S 5B6.

Canadian Council for International Cooperation (Conseil canadien pour la coopération internationale), 75 Sparks St., Ottawa, Ont., K1P 5A5. President: Hon. Maurice Sauvé, vicepresident administration, Consolidated Bathurst Ltd., 800 Dorchester Blvd., Montreal 101, Que. Executive director: Mr. Angus Archer.

Canadian Council for Research in Education (Conseil canadien pour la recherche en éducation), 265 Elgin St., Ottawa, Ont., K2P 1L8. President: Dr. W.C. Lorimer, deputy minister of education, Department of Education, room 162, Legislative Bldg., Winnipeg 1, Man. Interim director: Mr. Léo Desmarteau.

Canadian Council of Professional Engineers (Conseil canadien des ingénieurs), suite 401, 116 Albert St., Ottawa, Ont., K1P 5G3. President: Mr. H.L. Morrison, 14004-88th Ave., Edmonton 51, Alta. General manager: Mr. L.M. Nadeau.

Canadian Council of Teachers of English. President: Mrs. Evelyn Pearce, 906-1106 St. Mary's Rd., Winnipeg 8, Man. Secretary: Dr. Emma Plattor, faculty of education, The University of Calgary, Calgary, Alta.

Canadian Council on Urban and Regional Research (Conseil canadien de recherches urbaines et régionales), suite 511, 151 Slater St., Ottawa, Ont., K1P 5H3. President: Mr. Allan O'Brien. Secretarytreasurer: Mr. Alan Armstrong.

Canadian Dental Association (Association dentaire canadienne, L'), 234 St. George St., Toronto 180, Ont. Executive director: Dr. W.G. McIntosh.

The), suite 505-6, 56, rue Sparks, Ottawa 4 (Ont.). Président: M. Louis Lemieux, Musée national des sciences naturelles, Ottawa (Ont.). Directeur administratif: M. W.S. Bragg.

Association des professeurs d'allemand des universités canadiennes, L'(Canadian Association of University Teachers of German). Président: Dr. J.B. MacLean, dept. of Germanic languages and literature, University of Victoria, Victoria, B.C. Secrétaire-trésorier: Dr. R.T.K. Symington, dept. of Germanic languages and literature, University of Victoria, Victoria, B.C.

Association des professeurs d'anglais des universités canadiennes (Association of Canadian University Teachers of English). Présidente: Prof. Clara Thomas, 251 Winters College, York University, 4700 Keele St., Downsview, Ont. Secrétaire: Prof. Janet Lewis, dept. of English, York University, 4700 Keele St., Downsview, Ont.

Association des professeurs de français des universités canadiennes (Canadian Association of University Teachers of French). Président: M. R. Bismuth, département de français, Université Brock, St. Catharines (Ont.) Secrétaire: M. M.J. Cardy, département de français, Université Brock, St. Catharines (Ont.)

Association des psychiatres du Canada (Canadian Psychiatric Association), suite 103, 225, rue Lisgar, Ottawa (Ont.), K2P 0C6. Président: Dr Gérard Beaudoin, directeur, département de psychiatrie, Université de Montréal, c.p. 6128, Montréal 26³ (Qué.). Secrétaire: Dr André Côté.

*Association des registraires d'université du Canada, L' (Association of Registrars of the Universities of Canada). Président: Mr. David Green, registrar, Acadia University, Wolfville, N.S. Secrétaire: Mrs. Jean Hadley, admissions officer and assistant registrar, University of New Brunswick, Fredericton, N.B.

Association des scientifiques, ingénieurs et technologistes du Canada, L' (Association of the Scientific, Engineering and Technological Community of Canada), 151, rue Slater, Ottawa (Ont.), K1P 5H3. Président: M. L. Berlinguet, vice-président à

_____

*Membre associé de l'AUCC.

Canadian Dietetic Association, The (Association canadienne des diététistes, L'), suite 215, 1393 Yonge St., Toronto 290, Ont. President: Mrs. Phyllis McFeat, director of food service, The Montreal Children's Hospital, Montreal 108, Que. General secretary: Miss Joan Brown.

Canadian Economics Association, The (Association canadienne d'économique, L'). President: Prof. H.C. Eastman, dept. of political economy, University of Toronto, Toronto, Ont. Secretary: Prof. Gilles Paquet, Carleton University, Ottawa, Ont., K1S 5B6.

Canadian Education Association, The (Association canadienne d'éducation, L'), 252 Bloor St. W., Toronto 5, Ont. President: Dr. T.C. Byrne, president, Athabasca University, 406 IBM Bldg., 10808-99th Ave., Edmonton, Alta. Executive secretary: Dr. F.K. Stewart.

Canadian Federation of Biological Societies (Fédération canadienne des sociétés de biologie). Chairman: Dr. Mark Nickerson, dept. of pharmacology, McGill University, Montreal 110, Que. Honorary secretary: Dr. D.T. Armstrong, dept. of physiology, The University of Western Ontario, London 72, Ont.

Canadian Federation of University Women (Fédération canadienne des femmes diplômées des universités), c/o Mount Allison University, P.O. Box 69, Sackville, N.B. President: Mrs. J.L. Black. Executive secretary: Mrs. Laing Fergusson.

Canadian Film Institute (Institut canadien du film), 1762 Carling Ave., Ottawa, Ont., K2A 2H7. President: Mr. Jean Clavel, Public and Industrial Relations, 1808 Sherbrooke St. W., Montreal, Que. Executive director: Mr. Gordon Noble.

Canadian Forestry Association (Association forestière canadienne), 185 Somerset St. W., Ottawa, Ont., K2P 0J2. President: Mr. E.G. Shorter, MacMillan Bloedel Limited, 1075 W. Georgia St., Vancouver 5, B.C. Executive director: Mr. A.D. Hall.

Canadian Guidance and Counselling Association (Société canadienne d'orientation et de consultation), suite 302, 1000 Yonge St., Toronto 289, Ont. President: Dr. J.G. Paterson, dept. of educational psychology, faculty of education, The University of Alberta, Edmonton, Alta. Treasurer: Mr. Rolland Fobert.

la recherche, Université du Québec, 2525, boul. Laurier, Québec (Qué.). Gérant général: M. T.H.G. Michael.

*Association des services d'éducation des adultes et écoles d'été des universités du Canada (Canadian Association of Departments of Extension and Summer Schools). Président: Mr. Donald Snowden, director, extension service, Memorial University of Newfoundland, St. John's, Nfld. Secrétaire: Mr. R.S. Chapman, associate director, division of continuing education, The University of Calgary, Calgary, Alta.

Association des universités de l'Atlantique, L' (Association of Atlantic Universities), b.p. 24, Halifax (N.-E.). Président: Dr. D.C. Duffie, president, St. Thomas University, Fredericton, N.B. Directeur administratif: M. Jeffrey Holmes.

Association des universités partiellement ou entièrement de langue française, Université de Montréal, b.p. 6128, Montréal 101 (Qué.). Président: M. Claude Renard, vice-président, Conseil d'administration, Université de Liège, Place du 20 Août, Liège, Belgique. Secrétaire général: M. Maurice Beutler.

Association forestière canadienne (Canadian Forestry Association), 185 ouest, rue Somerset, Ottawa (Ont.), K2P 0J2. Président: Mr. E.G. Shorter, MacMillan Bloedel Limited, 1075 W. Georgia St., Vancouver 5, B.C. Directeur administratif: M. A.D. Hall.

Association internationale des universités (International Association of Universities), 1, rue Miollis, 75-Paris 15e, France. Président: Prof. V. Merikowski, University of Helsinki, Fabianinkatu 33, Helsinki 17, Finland. Secrétaire général: M. H.M. Keyes.

Association médicale canadienne, L' (Canadian Medical Association, The), c.p. 8650, 1867, Alta Vista Dr., Ottawa (Ont.), K1G 0G8. Président: Dr. Harry Roberts, 95 Le Marchant Rd., St. John's, Nfld. Secrétaire général: Dr J.D. Wallace.

Association minière du Canada, L' (Mining Association of Canada, The), suite 2100, tour A, Place de Ville, Ottawa (Ont.) Président: Mr. F.F. Todd, 9th floor, 20 Toronto St., Toronto 210, Ont. Directeur général: M. J.L. Bonus.

*Membre associé de l'AUCC.

Canadian Historical Association, The (Société historique du Canada, La), Public Archives of Canada, Ottawa, Ont., K1A 0N3.
President: Prof. Ivo Lambi, dept. of history, University of Saskatchewan, Saskatoon, Sask. Secretary: Father Jacques Monet, s.j., dept. of history, University of Ottawa, Ottawa, Ont.

Canadian Home Economics Association, room 901, 151 Slater St., Ottawa, Ont., K1P 5H3.
President: Mrs. Maxine Cochran, 1004-5885 Spring Garden Rd., Halifax, N.S. Secretary: Mrs. Dalia Jocys.

Canadian Institute of Adult Education (Institut canadien d'éducation des adultes), suite 800, 506 Ste-Catherine St. E., Montreal 132, Que.
President: M. Maurice Chartrand, directeur général, Le Petit Journal, 5460 Royalmount, Montreal (Qué.). Executive director: Miss Madeleine Joubert.

Canadian Institute of Chartered Accountants, The (Institut canadien des comptables agréés, L'), 250 Bloor St. E., Toronto 285, Ont.
President: Mr. F.S. Capon, c/o Riddell Stead & Co., suite 2500, 630 Dorchester Blvd. W., Montreal 101, Que. Executive director: Mr. R.D. Thomas.

Canadian Institute of International Affairs (Institut canadien des affaires internationales), 31 Wellesley St. E., Toronto 284, Ont.
President: Mr. David Golden, president, Telesat Canada, 333 River Rd., Vanier, Ottawa 7, Ont. National secretary: Miss Edna Neale.

Canadian Institute of Management (Institut canadien de gestion, L'), 51 Eglinton Ave. E., Toronto 315, Ont.
President: M. Jacques Viau, Radio Canada, Montréal (Qué.). Secretary: Mr. E.C. Luke.

Canadian Institute of Mining and Metallurgy, The (Institut canadien des mines et de la métallurgie, L'), 906-1117 Ste-Catherine St. W., Montreal 110, Que.
President: Mr. T.H. Patching, dept. of mining and metallurgy, The University of Alberta, Edmonton 7, Alta. Secretary: Mr. G.F. Skilling.

Canadian Institute of Public Affairs (Institut canadien des affaires publiques, L'), Box 952, Postal station Q, Toronto 7, Ont.
President: Mr. Harry Wolfson, 318 Vesta Dr., Toronto, Ont. Secretary-treasurer: Mr. Mel James.

Association nucléaire canadienne (Canadian Nuclear Association), suite 1002, 11 ouest, rue Adelaide, Toronto 105 (Ont.).
Président: Mr. W.M. Gilchrist, president, Eldorado Nuclear, Port Hope, Ont. General manager: Mr. R.F. Gross.

Association of Commonwealth Universities, The, 36 Gordon Square, London, England.
Chairman: Prof. A. Kwapong, vice-chancellor, University of Ghana, P.O. Box 25, Legon, West Africa. Secretary general: Sir Hugh Springer. Association pharmaceutique canadienne, L' (Canadian Pharmaceutical Association), 175, rue College, Toronto 2B (Ont.).
Président: Mr. R.J. Edgar, Edgar Drugs, Westlock, Alberta. Directeur administratif: M. J.C. Turnbull.

Association universitaire des arts du Canada (Universities Art Association of Canada).
Président: Prof. R.E. Williams, school of art, The University of Manitoba, Winnipeg, Man. Secrétaire-trésorier: Prof. Virgil Hammock, school of art, The University of Manitoba, Winnipeg, Man.

Bureau canadien de l'éducation internationale (Canadian Bureau of International Education), suite 408, 151, rue Slater, Ottawa (Ont.), K1P 5H3.
Président: Dr. W.C. Winegard, president, University of Guelph, Guelph, Ont. Directeur administratif: M. Allan Rix.

Bureau de tourisme des étudiants du Québec, Le, bureau 200, 112 ouest, rue St-Paul, Montréal 125 (Qué.).
Président: M. Robert Panet-Raymond, Ducharme Déom et Associés, Cité du Havre, Aile #3, Montréal 101 (Qué.). Secrétaire: M. Jean Pelletier.

Bureau national d'examen dentaire du Canada (National Dental Examining Board of Canada), suite 600, 287, rue MacLaren, Ottawa (Ont.).
Président: Dr. J.D. Purves, 170 St. George St., Toronto 180, Ont. Secrétaire: Mme Juliette Matte.

Centre canadien du théâtre (Canadian Theatre Centre), 49 est, rue Wellington, Toronto 181 (Ont.).
Présidente: Mme Mercedes Palomino. Secrétaire général (intérimaire): M. Jack Gray.

Collège canadien des enseignants, Le (Canadian College of Teachers, The), c.p. 760, 39, Leacock Way, Kanata (Ont.).
Président: Mr. R.J. Carter, 2049 W. 61st St.,

*Canadian Intercollegiate Athletic Union (Union sportive interuniversitaire canadienne), 333 River Rd., Vanier City, Ont., K1L 8B9.
President: Mr. Carl Totzke, director of athletics, University of Waterloo, Waterloo, Ont. Executive director: Mr. Robert Pugh.

Canadian International Development Agency (Agence canadienne de développement international, L'), 122 Bank St., Ottawa, Ont., K1A 0G4.
President: Mr. Paul Gérin-Lajoie.

Canadian Library Association, 9th floor, 151 Sparks St., Ottawa, Ont., K1P 5E3.
President: Mr. Dean Halliwell, University of Victoria Library, Victoria, B.C. Executive director: to be appointed.

Canadian Linguistic Association (Association canadienne de linguistique).
President: Mr. André Rigault, McGill University, Montreal, Que. Secretary: M. Guy Plastre, Université Laval, Pavillon de Koninck 0277, Québec 10ᵉ (Qué.).

Canadian Mathematical Congress (Société mathématique du Canada).
President: Prof. N.S. Mendelsohn, dept. of mathematics, The University of Manitoba, Winnipeg, Man. English-language secretary: Rev. R.E. O'Connor, Thomas More Institute, 3421 Drummond St., Montreal 109, Que. French-language secretary: Prof. J.L. Lavoie, département de mathématiques, Université Laval, Québec (Qué.).

Canadian Medical and Biological Engineering Society (Société canadienne de génie médical et biologique).
President: Dr. David Winter, associate director, prosthetics/orthotics program, Shriners Hospital, 633 Wellington Cres., Winnipeg, Man. Secretary: Mr. Harry Callan, Department of National Health and Welfare, health facilities design division, Brooke Claxton Bldg., Ottawa, Ont.

Canadian Medical Association, The (Association médicale canadienne, L'), Box 8650, 1867 Alta Vista Dr., Ottawa, Ont., K1G 0G8.
President: Dr. Harry Roberts, 95 Le Marchant Rd., St. John's, Nfld. General secretary: Dr. J.D. Wallace.

Canadian Meteorological Society (Société météorologique du Canada, La), P.O. Box

Vancouver 14, B.C. Secrétaire-trésorier: M. S.R. Berry.

Collège royal des chirurgiens dentistes du Canada, Le (Royal College of Dentists of Canada, The), suite 164, 170, rue St. George, Toronto 180 (Ont.).
Président: Dr. A.M. Hayes, 1004-750 West Broadway, Vancouver 9, B.C. Secrétaire-registraire-trésorier: M. J.E. Speck.

Collège royal des médecins et chirurgiens du Canada, Le (Royal College of Physicians and Surgeons of Canada, The), 74, ave Stanley, Ottawa (Ont.), K1M 1P4.
Président: Dr. Robert Dickson, Sir Charles Tupper Medical Bldg., Halifax, N.S. Secrétaire: Dr James Graham.

*Comité des doyens de droit du Canada (Committee of Canadian Law Deans).
Président: Dean John Durnford, faculty of law, McGill University, 3644 Peel St., Montreal 112, Que. Secrétaire: Dean R.S. Mackay, faculty of law, The University of Western Ontario, London, Ont.

*Comité national des doyens de génie et sciences appliquées (National Comittee of Deans of Engineering and Applied Science).
Président: Dr. J. Hoogstraten, dean of engineering, The University of Manitoba, Winnipeg 19, Man. Secrétaire: Dr. George Joly, dean of engineering, Loyola College, Montreal, Que.

Comité sur les affaires universitaires, Le (Comittee on University Affairs of Ontario, The), 5ᵉ étage, édifice Mowat, edifices du Parlement, Toronto 5 (Ont.).
Président: M. D.T. Wright. Secrétaire: M. H.H. Walker.

Commission canadienne pour l'UNESCO (Canadian Commission for UNESCO), 5ᵉ étage, Le Mall, Ottawa (Ont), K1P 5E3.
Président: M. Napoléon LeBlanc, vice-recteur, Université Laval, Québec (Qué.). Secrétaire général: M. David Bartlett.

Commission de l'enseignement supérieur du Nouveau-Brunswick (New Brunswick Higher Education Commission), 766, rue King, Fredericton (N.-B.).
Vice-président: M. W.B. Thompson.

Commission des octrois aux universités (Manitoba), La [University Grants Commission (Manitoba)], 11-395, rue Berry, Winnipeg 12 (Man.).

---

*Associate member, AUCC.

*Membre associé de l'AUCC.

851, Adelaide St. Post Office, Toronto 210, Ont.
President: Mr. Donald McMullen. Corresponding secretary: Mr. G.A. McPherson.

Canadian Museums Association, The (Association des musées canadiens), suite 505-6, 56 Sparks St., Ottawa 4, Ont.
President: Dr. Louis Lemieux, National Museum of Natural Sciences, Ottawa, Ont. Executive director: Mr. W.S. Bragg.

Canadian Music Council (Conseil canadien de la musique).
President: Mr. Françoys Bernier, director, music dept., University of Ottawa, 180 Waller St., Ottawa, Ont. Secretary: Mr. John Cozens, 188 Elmwood Ave., Willowdale, Ont.

Canadian Nuclear Association (Association nucléaire canadienne), suite 1002, 11 Adelaide St. W., Toronto 105, Ont.
President: Mr. W.M. Gilchrist, president, Eldorado Nuclear, Port Hope, Ont. General manager: Mr. R.F. Gross.

Canadian Nurses' Association (Association des infirmières canadiennes), 50 The Driveway, Ottawa, Ont., K2P 1E2.
President: Miss Louise Miner. Executive director: Dr. Helen Mussallem.

Canadian Paediatric Society (Société canadienne de pédiatrie).
President: Dr. Michael Rigg, 3195 Granville St., Vancouver, B.C. Secretary: Dr Victor Marchessault, division des sciences cliniques, centre hospitalier universitaire, Université de Sherbrooke, Sherbrooke (Qué.).

Canadian Petroleum Association (Association de pétrole canadien, L'), 625-404 6th Ave. S.W., Calgary 1, Alta.
Managing director: Mr. D.B. Furlong, 400-130 Albert St., Varette Bldg., Ottawa, Ont., K1P 5C4. Assistant manager and secretary-treasurer: Mr. R.J. Frocklage.

Canadian Pharmaceutical Association (Association pharmaceutique canadienne, L'), 175 College St., Toronto 2B, Ont.
President: Mr. R.J. Edgar, Edgar Drugs, Westlock, Alberta. Executive director: Mr. J.C. Turnbull.

Canadian Philosophical Association (Association canadienne de philosophie).
President: Prof. David Braybrooke, dept. of philosophy, Dalhousie University, Halifax, N.S. Secretary: Prof. Robert Binkley, dept. of philosophy, The University of Western Ontario, London, Ont.

Président: M. Scott Bateman. Directeur administratif: M. Douglas Chevrier.

Commission des universités de l'Alberta, La (Alberta Universities Commission, The), 202 The Sir John Franklin, 11111-87e avenue, Edmonton 61 (Alta.).
Président: M. D.L. Erickson, Secrétaire: M. H.W. Ford.

Commission sur la formation postsecondaire en Ontario (Commission on Post-Secondary Education in Ontario), suite 203, 505, ave de l'Université, Toronto 101 (Ont.).
Président: M. D.T. Wright. Secrétaire: M. B.B. Kymlicka.

Conférence des recteurs et des principaux des universités du Québec (Conference of Rectors and Principals of Quebec Universities, The), suite 300, 6,600, chemin de la Côte des Neiges, Montréal 249 (Qué.).
Directeur administratif: M. Pierre-Paul Proulx. Directrice du secrétariat: Mme Fernande Gervais.

Conseil canadien de biologie (Biological Council of Canada), suite 907, 151, rue Slater, Ottawa (Ont.), K1P 5H4.
Président: Dr. J.B. Armstrong, executive director (medical), Canadian Heart Foundation, 270 Laurier Ave. W., Ottawa, Ont., K1P 5K1.
Secrétaire: Dr. R.L. Taylor, office of the botanical, The University of British Columbia, Vancouver 8, B.C.

Conseil canadien de la musique (Canadian Music Council).
Président: M. Françoys Bernier, directeur, département de musique, Université d'Ottawa, 180, rue Waller, Ottawa (Ont.). Secrétaire: M. John Cozens, 188, avenue Elmwood, Willowdale (Ont.).

Conseil canadien de recherche en sciences sociales, Le (Social Science Research Council of Canada), suite 415, 151, rue Slater, Ottawa (Ont.), KIP 5H3.
Président: Dean Daniel Soberman, faculty of law, Queen's University at Kingston, Kingston, Ont. Secrétaire administratif: M. John Banks.

Conseil canadien de recherches sur les humanités, Le (Humanities Research Council of Canada), suite 415, 151, rue Slater, Ottawa (Ont.), K1P 5H3.
Présidente: Mme Eva Kushner, département de littérature comparée, Université Carleton, Ottawa (Ont.). Secrétaire administratif: M. John Banks.

Canadian Physiological Society (Société canadienne de physiologie).
President: Dr. A. Naimark, dept. of physiology, The University of Manitoba, Emily and Bannatyne, Winnipeg 3, Man. Secretary: Dr. C. Heath, dept. of pharmacology, The University of Alberta, Edmonton 7, Alta.

Canadian Physiotherapy Association (Association canadienne de physiothérapie, L'), 64 Avenue Rd., Toronto 5, Ont. President: Miss Margaret Finlayson, 107-4400 Ste-Catherine St. W., Westmount 215, Que. Executive director: Mr. Peter Large.

Canadian Political Science Association (Association canadienne de science politique, L').
President: Prof. J.E. Hodgetts, Victoria University, Toronto 5, Ont. Secretary: Prof. J.E. Trent, dept. of political science, University of Ottawa, Ottawa, Ont.

Canadian Psychiatric Association (Association des psychiatres du Canada), suite 103, 225 Lisgar St., Ottawa, Ont., K2P 0C6.
President: Dr Gérard Beaudoin, directeur, département de psychiatrie, Université de Montréal, c.p. 6128, Montréal 26e (Qué.). Secretary: Dr André Côté.

Canadian Psychological Association (Société canadienne de psychologie), 1390 Sherbrooke St. W., Montreal 109, Que.
President: Dr. D.E. Berlyne, dept. of psychology, University of Toronto, Toronto 181, Ont. Secretary-treasurer: Miss Suzanne Edwards.

Canadian Public Health Association (Association canadienne d'hygiène publique, L'), 1255 Yonge St., Toronto 7, Ont. President: Dr. V.L. Matthews, head, dept. of social and preventive medicine, University of Saskatchewan, Saskatoon, Sask. Executive director: Mr. C.D. Noble.

Canadian Society for Asian Studies (Association canadienne des études asiatiques).
President: Dr. E. Pulleyblank, head, dept. of Asian studies, The University of British Columbia, Vancouver 8, B.C. Secretary: Dr. George Kurian, dept. of sociology and anthropology, The University of Calgary, Calgary 44, Alta.

Canadian Society for Chemical Engineering (Société canadienne du génie chimique, La), 151 Slater St., Ottawa, Ont., K1P 5H3. President: Dr. W.M. Campbell, manager,

Conseil canadien de recherches urbaines et régionales (Canadian Council on Urban and Regional Research), suite 511, 151, rue Slater, Ottawa (Ont.), K1P 5H3. Président: M. Allan O'Brien. Secrétaire-trésorier: M. Alan Armstrong.

Conseil canadien des ingénieurs (Canadian Council of Professional Engineers), suite 401, 116, rue Albert, Ottawa (Ont.), K1P 5G3. Président: Mr. H.L. Morrison, 14004-88th Ave., Edmonton 51, Alta. Gérant général: M. L.M. Nadeau.

Conseil canadien pour la coopération internationale (Canadian Council for International Co-operation), 75, rue Sparks, Ottawa (Ont.), K1P 5A5.
Président: Hon. Maurice Sauvé, vice-président (administration), Consolidated Bathurst Ltd., 800, boul. Dorchester, Montréal 101 (Qué.). Directeur administratif: M. Angus Archer.

Conseil canadien pour la recherche en éducation (Canadian Council for Research in Education), 265, rue Elgin, Ottawa (Ont.), K2P 1L8.
Président: Dr. W.C. Lorimer, deputy minister of education, Department of Education, room 162, Legislative Bldg., Winnipeg 1, Man. Directeur intérimaire: M. Léo Desmarteau.

Conseil d'admissions des universités de l'Ontario (Ontario Universities' Council on Admissions).
Président: Dean A.D. Allen, faculty of arts and science, University of Toronto, Toronto, Ont. Secrétaire-trésorier: M. M.A. Bider, registrar, York University, 4700 Keele St., Downsview 463, Ont.

Conseil de la recherche en économie agricole du Canada (Agricultural Economics Research Council of Canada), 55, avenue Parkdale, Ottawa (Ont.).
Président: M. Gordon MacEachern.

†Conseil de recherches médicales (Medical Research Council), édifice des recherches nationales, M-58, chemin de Montréal, Ottawa (Ont.), K1A 0R6.
Président: Dr Malcolm Brown. Secrétaire: Dr J.M. Roxburgh.

†Conseil de recherches pour la défense (Defence Research Board), 125, rue Elgin, Ottawa (Ont.), K1A 0Z3. Président: M. L.J. L'Heureux. Secrétaire: M. A. Léger.

---

†Associé honoraire de l'AUCC.

Industrial Applications Power Projects, Atomic Energy of Canada Ltd., Sheridan Park, Ont. General manager: Mr. T.H.G. Michael.

Canadian Society for Education Through Art (Société canadienne d'éducation par l'art), 451 Park St. W., Windsor, Ont. President: Prof. Sam Black, The University of British Columbia, Vancouver 8, B.C. Secretary general: Mr. Garnet Humphrey.

Canadian Society for Immunology, The (Société canadienne d'immunologie, La). President: Dr. Bram Rose, division of immunochemistry and allergy, Royal Victoria Hospital, Montreal, Que. Secretary: Dr. Phil Gold, division of clinical immunology and allergy, room 7135, The Montreal General Hospital, Montreal, Que.

Canadian Society for the Study of Higher Education (Société canadienne pour l'étude de l'enseignement supérieur, La). President: M. Pierre-Paul Proulx, directeur administratif, Conférence des recteurs et principaux des universités du Québec, suite 300, 6600, chemin de la Côte des Neiges, Montréal 249 (Qué.). Secretary: Mr. Jeffrey Holmes, executive director, Association of Atlantic Universities, P.O. Box 24, Halifax, N.S.

Canadian Society of Biblical Studies (Société canadienne des études bibliques). President: Prof. R.B.Y. Scott, 215 Varsity Ave., Princeton, N.J., U.S.A. Secretary-treasurer: Prof. R.C. Culley, faculty of religious studies, McGill University, Montreal 110, Que.

Canadian Society of Landscape Architects, The (Association des architectes paysagistes du Canada, L'), Box 3304, Postal station C, Ottawa, Ont., K1Y 4J5. President: Mr. Edwin Skapsts, suite 290, 755 Berri St., Montreal 127, Que. Secretary: Mrs. J.V. Stensson, 1300 Winston Churchill Blvd., Oakville, Ont.

Canadian Society of Microbiologists (Société canadienne des microbiologistes). President: Dr J. deRepentigny, département de microbiologie et d'immunologie, faculté de médecine, Université de Montréal, c.p. 6128, Montréal 101 (Qué.). Secretary: Dr. G.A. Jones, dept. of dairy and food science, University of Saskatchewan, Saskatoon, Sask.

Canadian Society of Plant Physiologists, C.D.A. (Société canadienne de physiologie végétale), Research station, 2560 chemin Gomin, Ste-Foy, Que.

†Conseil des arts du Canada, Le (Canada Council, The), b.p. 1047, Ottawa (Ont.), K1P 5V8. Président: M. John Prentice. Directeur adjoint et secrétaire: M. Claude Gauthier.

*Conseil des associations des services universitaires aux étudiants (Council of Associations of University Student Personnel Services). Président: Dr. G.E. Wodehouse, director, university health services, University of Toronto, 256 Huron St., Toronto 181, Ont. Secrétaire-trésorière: Miss Esther Brandon, associate dean of students, Waterloo Lutheran University, Waterloo, Ont.

Conseil des ministres de l'éducation, Canada (Council of Ministers of Education, Canada), suite N1201, 252 ouest, rue Bloor, Toronto 181 (Ont.). Secrétaire général: M. Maurice Richer.

Conseil des universités de l'Ontario (Council of Ontario Universities), 102 ouest, rue Bloor, Toronto 181 (Ont.). Directeur administratif: M. J.B. Macdonald. Secrétaire: M. G.G. Clark .

Conseil national de l'esthétique, 112, rue Kent, Ottawa (Ont.), K1A 0H5. Président: M. I.C. Pollack, Letourneau et Associés, 65, rue Ste-Anne, Québec 4 (Qué.). Secrétaire général: M. E.P. Weiss.

†Conseil national de recherches du Canada (National Research Council of Canada), Ottawa (Ont.), K1A 0R6. Président: M. W.G. Schneider. Secrétaire: M. B.D. Leddy.

Conseil supérieur de l'éducation (Superior Council of Education), Hôtel du Gouvernement, Québec (Qué.). Président: M. Léopold Garant. Secrétaire général: M. Gilbert Desrosiers.

Direction de l'aide à l'éducation, Secrétariat d'Etat (Education Support Branch, Department of the Secretary of State), 130, rue Slater, Ottawa 4 (Ont.). Président: M. D.C. Munroe.

Direction générale de l'enseignement supérieur, Québec (Directorate of Higher Education, Quebec), ministère de l'Education, 917, Mgr Gradin, Ste-Foy, Québec 10 (Qué.).

---

*Membre associé de l'AUCC.

†Associé honoraire de l'AUCC.

President: Dr. Mary Spencer, dept. of plant biochemistry, south laboratory, The University of Alberta, Edmonton, Alta. Secretary: Dr. C. Willemot.

Canadian Society of Wildlife and Fishery Biologists (Société canadienne des biologistes de la faune, La), P.O. Box 2292, Station D, Ottawa, Ont., K1P 5K0. President: Mr. R.C. Passmore. Secretary-treasurer: Mr. Wm. J. Thurlow, Environmental Control Consultants, Ltd., P.O. Box 2728, Station D, Ottawa, Ont., K1P 5K0.

Canadian Society of Zoologists (Société des zoologistes canadiens). President: Dr. H.H. Harvey, dept. of zoology, University of Toronto, Toronto 5, Ont.

Canadian Sociology and Anthropology Association (Société canadienne de sociologie et d'anthropologie). President: Prof. Hubert Guindon, dept. of sociology, Sir George Williams University, Montreal, Que. Secretary-treasurer: Prof. Kurt Jonassohn, dept. of sociology, Sir George Williams University, Montreal, Que.

Canadian Teachers' Federation (Fédération canadienne des enseignants), 320 Queen St., Ottawa, Ont., K1R 5A3. President: Mr. R.G. Fredericks. Secretary general: Mr. Norman Goble.

Canadian Theatre Centre (Centre canadien du théâtre), 49 Wellington St. E., Toronto 181, Ont. President: Mrs. Mercedes Palomino. Acting secretary general: Mr. Jack Gray.

Canadian University Press, suite 205, 160 Chapel St., Ottawa 2, Ont. President: Mr. Larry Calvert.

*Canadian University Service Overseas (Service universitaire canadien outre-mer), 151 Slater St., Ottawa, Ont., K1P 5H5. President: M. Gérard Aubry, Institut de coopération internationale, 190 est, rue Laurier, Ottawa (Ont.). Executive director: Mr. Charles Morin.

Canadian University Theatre Association (Association canadienne du théâtre universitaire). President: Prof. R. Skene, dept. of English, theatre division, The University of Winnipeg, Winnipeg, Man. Acting secretary: Mr. David

Directeur général: M. Louis Rousseau. Secrétaire administratif: M. Réginald Lapointe.

Division de l'éducation, Statistique Canada (Education Division, Statistics Canada), Ottawa (Ont.). Directeur: M. M. Wisenthal.

Entr'aide universitaire mondiale du Canada (World University Service of Canada), 328 ouest, rue Adelaide, Toronto 133 (Ont.). Président: Dr. James Brasch, dept. of English, McMaster University, Hamilton, Ont. Secrétaire général: M. Roger Roy.

Fédération canadienne de la faune, La (Canadian Wildlife Federation), 1419, avenue Carling, Ottawa (Ont.), K1Z 7L7. Président: Mr. Jack O'Dette, Canadian Wildlife Federation, 377 Bath Rd., Kingston, Ont. Directeur administratif: M. R.C. Passmore.

Fédération canadienne des enseignants (Canadian Teachers' Federation), 320, rue Queen, Ottawa (Ont.), K1R 5A3. Président: M. R.G. Fredericks. Secrétaire général: M. Norman Goble.

Fédération canadienne des femmes diplômées des universités (Canadian Federation of University Women), a/s Université Mount Allison, c.p. 69, Sackville N.-B. Président: Mme J.L. Black. Secrétaire administrative: Mme Laing Fergusson.

Fédération canadienne des sociétés de biologie (Canadian Federation of biological Societies). Président: Dr. Mark Nickerson, dept. of pharmacology, McGill University, Montreal 110, Que. Secrétaire honoraire: Dr. D.T. Armstrong, dept. of physiology, The University of Western Ontario, London 72, Ont.

Fédération des CEGEP, 1940 est, boul. Henri-Bourassa, Montréal 360 (Qué.). Président: M. Jacques Laberge, directeur des services pédagogiques, Collège St-Jean-sur-Richelieu, 30, boul. du Séminaire, c.p. 310, St-Jean (Qué.). Secrétaire: M. Jean-Jacques Deguire.

Fédération international des universités catholiques (International Federation of Catholic Universities), 77 bis, rue de Grenelle, Paris 7eme, France. President: R.P. Hervé Carrier, recteur, Université Gregoriana, Roma, Italy, Secretary: Msgr. Georges Leclercq.

Hewlett, theatre division, The University of Winnipeg, Winnipeg, Man.

Canadian Wildlife Federation (Fédération canadienne de la faune, La), 1419 Carling Ave., Ottawa, Ont., K1Z 7L7.
President: Mr. Jack O'Dette, Canadian Wildlife Federation, 377 Bath Rd., Kingston, Ont. Executive director: Mr. R.C. Passmore.

Chemical Institute of Canada, The (Institut de chimie du Canada, L'), 151 Slater St., Ottawa, Ont., K1P 5H3.
President: Dr. H.R.L. Streight, principal research engineer, DuPont of Canada Ltd., P.O. Box 660, Montreal 101, Que. General manager: Mr. T.H.G. Michael.

Classical Association of Canada, The (Société canadienne des études classiques, La).
President: Prof. E.G. Berry, dept. of classics, The University of Manitoba, Winnipeg, Man. Secretary: Prof. A.A. Barrett, dept. of classics, The University of British Columbia, Vancouver 8, B.C.

Commission on Post-Secondary Education in Ontario (Commission sur la formation postsecondaire en Ontario), suite 203, 505 University Ave., Toronto 101, Ont.
Chairman: Dr. D.T. Wright. Secretary: Dr. B.B. Kymlicka.

*Committee of Canadian Law Deans (Comité des doyens de droit du Canada).
President: Dean John Durnford, faculty of law, McGill University, 3644 Peel St., Montreal 112, Que. Secretary: Dean R.S. Mackay, faculty of law, The University of Western Ontario, London, Ont.

Committee on University Affairs of Ontario, The (Comité sur les affaires universitaires de l'Ontario, Le), 5th floor, Mowat Block, Parliament Buildings, Toronto 5, Ont.
Chairman: Dr. D.T. Wright. Deputy minister: Mr. H.H. Walker.

Comparative and International Education Society of Canada (Société canadienne d'éducation comparée et internationale, La).
President: Dr. Roger Magnuson, faculty of education, McGill University, 3700 McTavish St., Montreal 112, Que. Secretary: Dr. Douglas Ray, Althouse College of Education, The University of Western Ontario, London, Ont.

Conference of Rectors and Principals of Quebec Universities, The (Conférence des recteurs et des principaux des universités du Québec), suite 300, 6,600, chemin de la Côte des Neiges, Montréal 249 (Qué.).

Fondation des bourses Rhodes, La (Rhodes Scholarship Trust, The), 14GHième étage, 320, rue Bay, Toronto 105 (Ont.).
Secrétaire général (Canada): M. J.L. Stewart.

Fondation d'études du Canada, La (Canada Studies Foundation, The), suite 716, 252 ouest, rue Bloor, Toronto 5, (Ont.).
Directeur: M. A.B. Hodgetts. Secrétaire: Mlle Gillian Hawes.

Fondation sciences jeunesse (Youth Science Foundation), suite 302, 151, rue Slater, Ottawa (Ont.), K1P 5H3.
Président: Prof. D.G. Andrews, dept. of chemical engineering, University of Toronto, Toronto, Ont. Secrétaire: M. N.S. Helm.

Institut aéronautique et spatial du Canada, L' (Canadian Aeronautics and Space Institute), suite 406, 77, rue Metcalfe, Ottawa (Ont.), K1P 5L6.
Président: Brig. Gen. E.P. Bridgland, chief aeronautical engineer, Ministry of Transport, Ottawa, Ont. Secrétaire-trésorier: M. H.C. Luttman.

Institut agricole du Canada, L' (Agricultural Institute of Canada), suite 907, 151, rue Slater, Ottawa (Ont.), K1P 5H4.
Président: Mr. R.E. Forbes, principal, Agricultural Extension Centre, Manitoba Department of Agriculture, Brandon, Man. Gérant général: M. W.E. Henderson.

Institut canadien d'éducation des adultes (Canadian Institute of Adult Education), suite 800, 506 est, Ste-Catherine, Montréal 132 (Qué.).
Président: M. Maurice Chartrand, directeur général, Le Petit Journal, 5460 Royalmount, Montréal (Qué.). Directrice générale: Mlle Madeleine Joubert.

Institut canadien de gestion, L' (Canadian Institute of Management), 51 est, avenue Eglinton, Toronto 315 (Ont.).
Président: M. Jacques Viau, Radio Canada, Montréal (Qué.). Secrétaire: M. E.C. Luke.

Institut canadien des affaires internationales (Canadian Institute of International Affairs), 31 est, rue Wellesley, Toronto 284 (Ont.).
Président: Mr. David Golden, president, Telesat Canada, 333 River Rd., Vanier, Ottawa 7, Ont. Secrétaire: Mlle Edna Neale.

Institut canadien des affaires publiques, L' (Canadian Institute of Public Affairs), c.p. 952, succursale postale Q, Toronto 7 (Ont.).
Président: Mr. Harry Wolfson, 318 Vesta Dr., Toronto, Ont. Secrétaire-trésorier: M. Mel James.

Executive director: Mr. Pierre-Paul Proulx.
Secretariat director: Mrs. Fernande Gervais.

*Council of Associations of University
Student Personnel Services (Conseil des
associations des services universitaires aux
étudiants).
President: Dr. G.E. Wodehouse, director,
university health services, University of
Toronto, 256 Huron St., Toronto 181, Ont.
Secretary-treasurer: Miss Esther Brandon,
associate dean of students, Waterloo
Lutheran University, Waterloo, Ont.

Council of Ministers of Education, Canada
(Conseil des ministres de l'education,
Canada), suite N1201, 252 Bloor St. W.,
Toronto 181, Ont.
Secretary general: Dr. Maurice Richer.

Council of Ontario Universities (Conseil des
universités de l'Ontario), 102 Bloor St. W.,
Toronto 181, Ont.
Executive director: Dr. J.B. Macdonald.
Secretary: Mr. G.G. Clarke.

†Defence Research Board (Conseil de
recherches pour la défense), 125 Elgin St.,
Ottawa, Ont., K1A 0Z3.
Chairman: Dr. L.J. L'Heureux. Secretary: Dr.
A. Léger.

Development Education Centre, 25 Prince
Arthur St., Toronto 181, Ont.
Chairman: Mr. J.A. O'Grady. Secretary-
treasurer: Mr. Derek Wynne.

Directorate of Higher Education, Quebec
(Direction générale de l'enseignement
superieur, Québec), Department of
Education, 917, Mgr Grandin, Ste-Foy,
Quebec 10 (Que.).
Executive director: Mr. Louis Rousseau.
Executive secretary: Mr. Réginald Lapointe.

Division of Educational Services, Lutheran
Council in Canada (Services de l'éducation,
Conseil luthérien au Canada), 500-365
Hargrave St., Winnipeg 2, Man.
Executive secretary: Rev. D.H. Voigts.

Educational Television and Radio
Association of Canada (Association
canadienne de radio et de télévision
éducatives, L'), c/o CEA, 252 Bloor St. W.,
Toronto 5, Ont.
President: Mr. H.H. Mamet, director, The
University of Alberta Radio and Television

Institut canadien des comptables agréés, L'
(Canadian Institute of Chartered
Accountants, The), 250 est, rue Bloor,
Toronto 285 (Ont.).
Président: Mr. F.S. Capon, c/o Riddell Stead
& Co., suite 2500, 630 Dorchester Blvd. W.,
Montreal 101, Que. Directeur administratif:
M. R.D. Thomas.

Institut canadien des ingénieurs, L'
(Engineering Institute of Canada, The), suite
700, édifice E.I.C., 2050, rue Mansfield,
Montréal 110 (Qué.).
Président: Mr. W.L. Hutchison, president,
Fluid Power Ltd., 282 Belfield Rd., Rexdale,
Ont. Gérant général: M. Pierre Bournival.

Institut canadien des mines et de la
métallurgie, L' (Canadian Institute of Mining
and Metallurgy, The), 906-1117, Ste-
Catherine, Montréal 110 (Qué.).
Président: Mr. T.H. Patching, dept. of
mining and metallurgy, The University of
Alberta, Edmonton 7, Alta. Secrétaire: M.
G.F. Skilling.

Institut canadien du film (Canadian Film
Institute), 1762 ave Carling, Ottawa (Ont.),
K2A 2H7.
Président: M. Jean Clavel, Relations
publiques et industrielles, 1808 ouest, rue
Sherbrooke, Montréal (Que.). Directeur
administratif: M. Gordon Noble.

Institut d'administration publique du
Canada, L' (Institute of Public
Administration of Canada, The), 897, rue
Bay, Toronto 5 (Ont.).
Président: Mr. Edgar Gallant, deputy
secretary to the Cabinet (federal-provincial
relations), Privy Council Office, East Block,
Ottawa 4, Ont. Secrétaire: Mme Jean
Stewart.

Institut de chimie du Canada, L' (Chemical
Institute of Canada, The), 151, rue Slater,
Ottawa (Ont.), K1P 5H3.
Président: Dr. H.R.L. Streight, principal
research engineer, DuPont of Canada Ltd.,
P.O. Box 660, Montreal 101, Que. Gérant
général: M. T.H.G. Michael.

Institut indo-canadien Shastri, L' (Shastri
Indo-Canadian Institue, The), 3511, rue Peel,
Montreal 112 (Qué.).
Président: Prof. E.C. Moulton, dept. of
history, The University of Manitoba,
Winnipeg, Man. Directrice administrative:
Mme Kathleen de la Ronde.

Institut international d'économie quantitative
(International Institute of Quantitative
Economics), suite 225, 1550 ouest, boul. de

CW 005, biological sciences bldg., Edmonton 7, Alta. Secretary: Mrs. Dorothy Patterson, director, public relations, The University of Calgary, Calgary, Alta.

Education Division, Statistics Canada (Division de l'éducation, Statistique Canada), Ottawa, Ont.
Director: Dr. M. Wisenthal.

Education Support Branch, Department of the Secretary of State (Direction de l'aide à l'éducation, Secrétariat d'Etat), 130 Slater St., Ottawa 4, Ont.
Director: Dr. D.C. Munroe.

Engineering Institute of Canada, The (Institut canadien des ingénieurs, L'), 700 E.I.C. Bldg., 2050 Mansfield St., Montreal 110, Que.
President: Mr. W.L. Hutchison, president, Fluid Power Ltd., 282 Belfield Rd., Rexdale, Ont. General manager: Mr. Pierre Bournival.

Entomological Society of Canada (Société entomologique du Canada, La), K.W. Neatby Bldg., C.E.F., Ottawa, Ont., K1A 0C6.
President: Dr. W.F. Baldwin, biology and health physics division, Atomic Energy of Canada Ltd., Chalk River, Ont. Secretary: Mr. D.G. Peterson.

Graphic Arts Industries Association (Association des industries graphiques), #906, 75 Albert St., Ottawa, Ont., K1P 5E7.
President: Mr. D.M. Alloway, president, Consolidated Graphics Ltd., 24 Ferrand Dr., Don Mills, Ont. General manager: Mr. D. Maclellan.

Humanities Association of Canada (Association canadienne des humanités).
President: Dr. John Matthews, dept. of Commonwealth studies, Queen's University at Kingston, Kingston, Ont. Secretary: Prof. M.G. Wiebe, dept. of English, Queen's University at Kingston, Kingston, Ont.

Humanities Research Council of Canada (Conseil canadien de recherches sur les humanités, Le), suite 415, 151 Slater St., Ottawa, Ont., K1P 5H3.
Chairman: Mrs. Eva Kushner, dept. of comparative literature, Carleton University, Ottawa, Ont. Executive secretary: Mr. John Banks.

Institute of Public Administration of Canada, The (Institut d'administration publique du Canada, L'), 897 Bay St., Toronto 5, Ont.
President: Mr. Edgar Gallant, deputy secretary to the Cabinet (federal-provincial

Maisonneuve, Montréal 107 (Qué.).
Directeur: M. M. Inagaki.

Institut royal d'architecture du Canada, L' (Royal Architectural Institute of Canada, The), suite 1104, 151, rue Slater, Ottawa (Ont.), K1P 5H3.
Président: M. Jean-Louis Lalonde, FRAIC, 430, rue Bonsecours, Montréal (Qué.). Secrétaire administratif: M. Maurice Holdham.

Institut Vanier de la famille, L' (Vanier Institute of the Family, The), 151, rue Slater, Ottawa (Ont.), K1P 5H3.
Présidente: Mme A.F.W. Plumptre. Secrétaire général: M. Stewart Sutton.

*Service d'admission au collège et à l'université (Service for Admission to College and University), 151, rue Slater, Ottawa (Ont.) K1P 5N1.
Président: Mr. G.M. Davies, associate deputy minister, Department of Youth and Education, 311-1181 Portage Ave., Winnipeg 10, Man. Directeur général: M. Léopold Lamontagne.

Services de l'éducation, Conseil luthérien au Canada (Division of Educational Services, Lutheran Council in Canada), 500-365, rue Hargrave, Winnipeg 2 (Man.).
Secrétaire administratif: Rev. D.H. Voigts.

*Service universitaire canadien outre-mer (Canadian University Service Overseas), 151, rue Slater, Ottawa (Ont.), K1P 5H5.
Président: M. Gérard Aubry, Institut de coopération internationale, 190 est, rue Laurier, Ottawa (Ont.). Directeur exécutif: M. Charles Morin.

Société canadienne de biochimie, La (Canadian Biochemical Society).
Président: Dr. G.R. Williams, dept. of biochemistry, University of Toronto, Toronto, Ont. Secrétaire: Dr Bégin Heick, département de biochimie, faculté de médecine, Université Laval, Québec 10 (Qué.).

Société canadienne d'éducation comparée et internationale, La (Comparative and International Education Society of Canada).
Président: Dr. Roger Magnuson, faculty of education, McGill University, 3700 McTavish St., Montreal 112, Que. Secrétaire: Dr. Douglas Ray, Althouse College of Education, The University of Western Ontario, London, Ont.

_____

*Membre associé de l'AUCC.

relations), Privy Council Office, East Block, Ottawa 4, Ont. Secretary: Mrs. Jean Stewart.

International Association of Universities (Association internationale des universités), 1, rue Miollis, 75 — Paris 15e, France. Président: Prof. V. Merikowski, University of Helsinki, Fabianinkatu 33, Helsinki 17, Finland. Secretary-general: Mr. H.M. Keyes.

International Federation of Catholic Universities (Fédération international des universités catholiques), 77 bis, rue de Grenelle, Paris 7ème, France.
W President: R.P. Hervé Carrier, recteur, Universite Gregoriana, Rome, Italy. Secretary: Msgr. Georges Leclercq.

International Institute of Quantitative Economics (Institut international d'économie quantitative), suite 225, 1550 de Maisonneuve Blvd. W., Montreal 107, Que. Director: Mr. M. Inagaki.

Inter-Provincial Committee on University Rationalization.
Chairman: Mr. L.H. Bergstrom, Department of Education, 2002 Victoria Ave., Regina, Sask. Secretary: Dr. W.A. Riddell, College Bldg., University of Saskatchewan, Regina Campus, Regina, Sask.

†Medical Research Council (Conseil de recherches médicales), National Research Bldg., M-58, Montreal Rd., Ottawa, Ont., K1A 0R6.
President: Dr. Malcolm Brown. Secretary: Dr. J.M. Roxburgh.

Mining Association of Canada, The (Association minière du Canada, L'), suite 2100, Tower A, Place de Ville, Ottawa, Ont. President: Mr. F.F. Todd, 9th floor, 20 Toronto St., Toronto 210, Ont. Managing director: Mr. J.L. Bonus.

National Audio-Visual Association of Canada, The (Association canadienne de l'audio-visuel), 11th floor, 11 Adelaide St. W., Toronto 1, Ont.
President: Mr. D.G. McLeod, Ron Nelson Photography Ltd., 388 Horton St., London, Ont. Executive secretary: Mr. Daniel Kay, Jr.

*National Committee of Deans of Engineering and Applied Science (Comité

Société canadienne d'éducation par l'art (Canadian Society for Education Through Art), 451 ouest, rue Park, Windsor (Ont.). Président: Prof. Sam Black, The University of British Columbia, Vancouver 8, B.C. Secrétaire général: M. Garnet Humphrey.

Society canadienne de génie médical et biologique (Canadian Medical and Biological Engineering Society).
Président: Dr. David Winter, associate director, prosthetics/orthotics program, Shriners Hospital, 633 Wellington Cres., Winnipeg, Man. Secrétaire: Mr. Harry Callan, Department of National Health and Welfare, health facilities design division, Brooke Claxton Bldg., Ottawa, Ont.

Société canadienne de nutrition (Nutrition Society of Canada).
Président: Dr. A.B. Morrison, director-general, research and operations, Food and Drug Directorate, Tunney's Pasture, Ottawa, Ont., K1A 0L2. Secrétaire: M. René Belzile, département de zootechnie, faculté d'agriculture, Université Laval, Québec 10GHe (Qué.).

Société canadienne de pédiatrie (Canadian Paediatric Society).
Président: Dr. Michael Rigg, 3195 Granville St., Vancouver, B.C. Secrétaire: Dr Victor Marchessault, division des sciences cliniques, centre hospitalier universitaire, Université de Sherbrooke, Sherbrooke (Qué.).

Société canadienne de physiologie (Canadian Physiological Society).
Président: Dr. A. Naimark, dept. of physiology, The University of Manitoba, Emily and Bannatyne, Winnipeg 3, Man. Secrétaire: Dr. C. Heath, dept. of pharmacology, The University of Alberta, Edmonton 7, Alta.

Société canadienne de physiologie végétale (Canadian Society of Plant Physiologists), C.D.A., Research Station, 2560, chemin Gomin, Ste-Foy (Qué.). Présidente: Dr. Mary Spencer, dept. of plant biochemistry, south laboratory, The University of Alberta, Edmonton, Alta. Secrétaire: M. C. Willemot.

Société canadienne de psychologie (Canadian Psychological Association), 1390 ouest, rue Sherbrooke, Montréal 109 (Qué.). Président: Dr. D.E. Berlyne, dept. of psychology, University of Toronto, Toronto 181, Ont. Secrétaire-trésorière: Mlle Suzanne Edwards.

---

*Associate member, AUCC.

†Honorary associate, AUCC.

national des doyens de génie et sciences appliquées).
President: Dr. J. Hoogstraten, dean of engineering, The University of Manitoba, Winnipeg 19, Man. Secretary: Prof. George Joly, dean of engineering, Loyola College, Montreal, Que.

National Dental Examining Board of Canada (Bureau national d'examen dentaire du Canada), suite 600, 287 MacLaren St., Ottawa, Ont.
President: Dr. J.D. Purves, 170 St. George St., Toronto 180, Ont. Secretary: Mrs. Juliette Matte.

National Design Council (Conseil national de l'esthétique), 112 Kent St., Ottawa, Ont., K1A 0H5.
Chairman: Mr. I.C. Pollack, Letourneau and Associates, 65 Ste-Anne St., Quebec 4, Que. Secretary general: Mr. E.P. Weiss.

†National Research Council of Canada (Conseil national de recherches du Canada, Le), Ottawa, Ont., K1A 0R6.
President: Dr. W.G. Schneider. Secretary: Mr. B.D. Leddy.

New Brunswick Higher Education Commission (Commission de l'enseignement supérieur du Nouveau-Brunswick), 766 King St., Fredericton, N.B.
Vice-chairman: Mr. W.B. Thompson.

Nutrition Society of Canada (Société canadienne de nutrition).
President: Dr. A.B. Morrison, director-general, research and operations, Food and Drug Directorate, Tunney's Pasture, Ottawa, Ont., K1A 0L2. Secretary: Dr René Belzile, département de zootechnie, faculté d'agriculture, Université Laval, Québec 10ᵉ (Qué.).

Ontario Confederation of University Faculty Associations (Union des associations des professeurs des universités de l'Ontario), 40 Sussex Ave., Toronto 181, Ont.
President: Prof. G.I. Clarke, dept. of classics, Laurentian University of Sudbury, Sudbury, Ont. Secretary: Prof. C.M.T. Hanly.

Ontario Universities' Council on Admissions (Conseil d'admissions des universités de l'Ontario).
Chairman: Dean A.D. Allen, faculty of arts and science, University of Toronto, Toronto, Ont. Secretary-treasurer: Mr. M.A. Bider,

Société canadienne des biologistes de la faune, La (Canadian Society of Wildlife and Fishery Biologists), c.p. 2292, succursale postale D, Ottawa (Ont.), K1P 5K0.
Président: M. R.C. Passmore. Secrétaire-trésorier: Mr. Wm. J. Thurlow, Environmental Control Consultants, Ltd., P.O. Box 2728, Station D, Ottawa, Ont., K1P 5K0.

Société canadienne des études bibliques (Canadian Society of Biblical Studies).
Président: Prof. R.B.Y. Scott, 215 Varsity Ave., Princeton, N.J., U.S.A. Secrétaire-trésorier: Prof. R.C. Culley, faculty of religious studies, McGill University, Montreal 110, Que.

Société canadienne des études classiques, La (Classical Association of Canada, The).
Président: Prof. E.G. Berry, dept. of classics, The University of Manitoba, Winnipeg, Man. Secrétaire: Prof. A.A. Barrett, dept. of classics, The University of British Columbia, Vancouver 8, B.C.

Société canadienne des microbiologistes (Canadian Society of Microbiologists).
Président: Dr J. deRepentigny, département de microbiologie et d'immunologie, Faculté de médecine, Université de Montréal, c.p. 6128, Montréal 101 (Qué.). Secrétaire: Dr. G.A. Jones, dept. of dairy and food science, University of Saskatchewan, Saskatoon, Sask.

Société canadienne de sociologie et d'anthropologie (Canadian Sociology and Anthropology Association).
Président: Prof. Hubert Guindon, département de sociologie, Université Sir George Williams, Montréal (Qué.). Secrétaire-trésorier: Prof. Kurt Jonassohn, dept. of sociology, Sir George Williams University, Montreal, Que.

Société canadienne de théologie.
Président: M. André Naud, Faculté de théologie, Université de Montréal, c.p. 6128, Montréal 101 (Qué.). Secrétaire: M. Jean-Louis d'Aragon, Faculté de théologie, Université de Montréal, c.p. 6128, Montréal 101 (Qué.).

Société canadienne d'immunologie, La (Canadian Society for Immunology, The).
Président: Dr. Bram Rose, division of immunochemistry and allergy, Royal Victoria Hospital, Montreal, Que. Secrétaire: Dr. Phil Gold, division of clinical immunology and allergy, room 7135, The Montreal General Hospital, Montreal, Que.

---

†Honorary associate, AUCC.

registrar, York University, 4700 Keele St., Downsview 463, Ont.

Ontario University Registrars' Association. President: Mr. H.W. Sterne, assistant registrar (admissions), Queen's University at Kingston, Kingston, Ont. Secretary-treasurer: Mr. J.L. Sevigny, assistant registrar (admissions), Carleton University, Ottawa, Ont., K1S 5B6.

Pharmacological Society of Canada, The (Société de pharmacologie du Canada, La). President: Dr. J.G. Aldous, head, dept. of pharmacology, Dalhousie University, Halifax, N.S. Secretary: Dr. P.E. Dresel, dept. of pharmacology and therapeutics, faculty of medicine, The University of Manitoba, 770 Bannatyne Ave., Winnipeg 3, Man.

Prince Edward Island Commission on Post-Secondary Education, P.O. Box 335, Charlottetown, P.E.I. President: Mr. R.D. Manning, Currie Bldg., Charlottetown, P.E.I. Secretary: Mrs. Grace Nicholson.

Rhodes Scholarship Trust, The (Fondation des bourses Rhodes, La), 14th floor, 320 Bay St., Toronto 105, Ont. General secretary for the Rhodes scholarships in Canada: Mr. J.L. Stewart.

Royal Architectural Institute of Canada, The (Institut royal d'architecture du Canada, L'), suite 1104, 151 Slater St., Ottawa, Ont., K1P 5H3. President: M. Jean-Louis Lalonde, FRAIC, 430, rue Bonsecours, Montréal (Que.). Executive secretary: Mr. Maurice Holdham.

Royal Astronomical Society of Canada, The (Société royale d'astronomie du Canada, La), 252 College St., Toronto 130, Ont. President: M. Henri Simard, 5340, rue Radisson, Montréal 410 (Qué.). Secretary: Mr. C.E. Hodgson.

Royal Canadian Geographical Society, The (Société géographique royale du Canada, La), 488 Wilbrod St., Ottawa, Ont., K1N 6M8. President: Dr. Pierre Camu, president, St. Lawrence Seaway Authority, 473 Albert St., Ottawa, Ont., K1R 5B4. Executive secretary: Major-General W.J. Megill.

Royal College of Dentists of Canada, The (Collège royal des chirurgiens dentistes du Canada, Le), suite 164, 170 St. George St., Toronto 180, Ont.

Société canadienne d'orientation et de consultation (Canadian Guidance and Counselling Association), suite 302, 1000, rue Yonge, Toronto 289 (Ont.). Président: Dr. J.G. Paterson, dept. of educational psychology, faculty of education, The University of Alberta, Edmonton, Alta. Trésorier: M. Rolland Fobert.

Société canadienne du génie chimique, La (Canadian Society for Chemical Engineering, The), 151, rue Slater, Ottawa (Ont.), K1P 5H3. Président: Dr. W.M. Campbell, manager, Industrial Applications Power Projects, Atomic Energy of Canada Ltd., Sheridan Park, Ont. Gérant général: M. T.H.G. Michael.

Société canadienne pour l'étude de l'enseignement supérieur, La (Canadian Society for the Study of Higher Education). Président: M. Pierre-Paul Proulx, directeur administratif, Conférence des recteurs et principaux des universités du Québec, suite 300, 6600, chemin de la Côte des Neiges, Montréal 249 (Qué.). Secrétaire: M. Jeffrey Holmes, directeur administratif, Association des universités de l'Atlantique, c.p. 24, Halifax (N.-E.).

Société de pharmacologie du Canada, La (Pharmacological Society of Canada, The). Président: Dr. J.G. Aldous, head, dept. of pharmacology, Dalhousie University, Halifax, N.S. Secrétaire: Dr. P.E. Dresel, dept. of pharmacology and therapeutics, faculty of medicine, The University of Manitoba, 770 Bannatyne Ave., Winnipeg 3, Man.

Société des zoologistes canadiens (Canadian Society of Zoologists). Président: Dr. H.H. Harvey, dept. of zoology, University of Toronto, Toronto 5, Ont.

Société entomologique du Canada, La (Entomological Society of Canada), édifice K.W. Neatby, C.E.F., Ottawa (Ont.), K1A 0C6. Président: Dr. W.F. Baldwin, biology and health physics division, Atomic Energy of Canada Ltd., Chalk River, Ont. Secrétaire: M. D.G. Peterson.

Société géographique royale du Canada, La (Royal Canadian Geographical Society), 488, rue Wilbrod, Ottawa (Ont.), K1N 6M8. Président: M. Pierre Camu, président, Administration de la voie maritime, 473, rue Albert, Ottawa (Ont.), K1R 5B4. Secrétaire administratif: Maj.-Gén. W.J. Megill.

President: Dr. A.M. Hayes, 1004-750 West Broadway, Vancouver 9, B.C. Secretary-registrar-treasurer: Dr. J.E. Speck.

Royal College of Physicians and Surgeons of Canada, The (Collège royal des médecins et chirurgiens du Canada, Le), 74 Stanley Ave., Ottawa, Ont., K1M 1P4. President: Dr. Robert Dickson, Sir Charles Tupper Medical Bldg., Halifax, N.S. Secretary: Dr. James Graham.

Royal Society of Canada, The (Société royale du Canada, La), 395 Wellington St., Ottawa, Ont., K1A 0N4. President: Dr. H.E. Duckworth, president, The University of Winnipeg, 515 Portage Ave., Winnipeg 2, Man. Executive secretary: Mr. E.H.P. Garneau.

*Service for Admission to College and University (Service d'admission au collège et à l'université), 15i Slater St., Ottawa, Ont., K1P 5N1. President: Mr. G.M. Davies, associate deputy minister, Department of Youth and Education, 311-1181 Portage Ave., Winnipeg 10, Man. Executive director: Dr. Léopold Lamontagne.

Shastri Indo-Canadian Institute, The (Institut indo-canadien Shastri,L'), 3511 Peel St., Montreal 112, Que. President: Prof. E.C. Moulton, dept. of history, The University of Manitoba, Winnipeg, Man. Executive officer: Mrs. Kathleen de la Ronde.

Social Science Research Council of Canada (Conseil canadien de recherche en sciences sociales, Le), suite 415, 151 Slater St., Ottawa, Ont., K1P 5H3. President: Dean Daniel Soberman, faculty of law, Queen's University at Kingston, Kingston, Ont. Executive secretary: Mr. John Banks.

Society for Indian and Northern Education. Secretary: Miss Joan Drummond, Indian and Northern education program, College of education, University of Saskatchewan, Saskatoon, Sask.

Superior Council of Education (Conseil supérieur de l'éducation), Hôtel du Gouvernement, Québec (Qué.). President: Mr. Léopold Garant. Secretary: Mr. Gilbert Desrosiers.

Société historique du Canada, La (Canadian Historical Association, The), Les archives publiques du Canada, Ottawa (Ont.), K1A 0N3. Président: Prof. Ivo Lambi, dept. of history, University of Saskatchewan, Saskatoon, Sask. Secrétaire: R.P. Jacques Monet, s.j., département d'histoire, Université d'Ottawa, Ottawa (Ont.).

Société mathématique du Canada (Canadian Mathematical Congress). Président: Prof. N.S. Mendelsohn, dept. of mathematics, The University of Manitoba, Winnipeg, Man. Secrétaire de langue anglaise: Rev. R.E. O'Connor, Thomas More Institute, 3421 Drummond St., Montreal 109, Que. Secrétaire de langue française: Prof. J.L. Lavoie, département de mathématiques, Université Laval, Québec (Qué.).

Société météorologique du Canada, La (Canadian Meteorological Society), P.O. Box 851, Adelaide St. Post Office, Toronto 210, Ont. Président: M. Donald McMullen. Secrétaire: M. G.A. McPherson.

Société royale d'astronomie du Canada, La (Royal Astronomical Society of Canada, The), 252, rue College, Toronto 130 (Ont.). Président: M. Henri Simard, 5340, rue Radisson, Montréal 410 (Qué.). Secrétaire: M. C.E. Hodgson.

Société royale du Canada, La (Royal Society of Canada, The), 395, rue Wellington, Ottawa (Ont.), K1A 0N4. Président: Dr. H.E. Duckworth, president, The University of Winnipeg, 515 Portage Ave., Winnipeg 2, Man. Secrétaire administratif: M. E.H.P. Garneau.

Union des associations des professeurs des universités de l'Ontario (Ontario Confederation of University Faculty Associations), 40, ave Sussex, Toronto 181 (Ont.). Président: Prof. G.I. Clarke, dept. of classics, Laurentian University of Sudbury, Sudbury, Ont. Secrétaire: Prof. C.M.T. Hanly.

*Union sportive interuniversitaire canadienne (Canadian Intercollegiate Athletic Union), 333, River Rd., Vanier (Ont.), K1L 8B9. Président: Mr. Carl Totzke, director of athletics, University of Waterloo, Waterloo, Ont. Directeur administratif: M. Robert Pugh.

---

*Associate member, AUCC.

*Membre associé de l'AUCC.

Universities Art Association of Canada
(Association universitaire des arts du
Canada).
President: Prof. R.E. Williams, school of art,
The University of Manitoba, Winnipeg, Man.
Secretary-treasurer: Prof. Virgil Hammock,
school of art, The University of Manitoba,
Winnipeg, Man.

Universities Grants Commission (Manitoba)
[Commission des octrois aux universités
(Manitoba), La], 11-395 Berry St.,
Winnipeg 12, Man.
Chairman: Mr. Scott Bateman. Executive
director: Mr. Douglas Chevrier.

University and College Placement
Association (Association de placement
universaire et collégial), 254a Main St. N.,
Markham, Ont.
President: Mr. W.G. Donnelly, vice-
president, Alcan Canada Products, Box 269,
Toronto-Dominion Centre, Toronto 111, Ont.
Secretary: Mr. S. Musgrave.

University Grants Committee (Nova Scotia),
5413 Spring Garden Rd., Halifax, N.S.
Chairman: Dr. A.L. Murphy. Executive
secretary: Mr. B.E. Robinson.

Vanier Institute of the Family, The (Institut
Vanier de la famille, L'), 151 Slater St.,
Ottawa, Ont., K1P 5H3.
President: Mrs. A.F.W. Plumptre. Secretary
general: Mr. Stewart Sutton.

World University Service of Canada
(Entr'aide universitaire mondiale du
Canada), 328 Adelaide St. W., Toronto 133,
Ont.
President: Dr. James Brasch, dept. of English,
McMaster University, Hamilton, Ont.
General secretary: Mr. Roger Roy.

Youth Science Foundation (Fondation
sciences jeunesse), suite 302, 151 Slater St.,
Ottawa, Ont., K1P 5H3.
President: Prof. D.G. Andrews, dept. of
chemical engineering, University of Toronto,
Toronto, Ont. Secretary: Mr. N.S. Helm.

Abbreviations of degrees, diplomas and certificates awarded by Canadian universities

Abréviations des grades, diplômes et certificats offerts par les universités canadiennes

Note: A detailed description of how to use this section will be found in the guide on "How to use the handbook" located at the beginning of this book.

A noter: Les renseignements donnés au début sous le titre "Façon de se servir du répertoire" expliquent en détail comment se servir de la présente section.

AA
Associate in arts
Saskatchewan — Saskatoon

AdvDipSW
Diploma in advanced social work
Toronto

AKC(NS)
Associate of King's College (Nova Scotia)
King's — Halifax

AMus
Associate in music
Saskatchewan — Regina

AMusWesternBoard
Associate in music
Manitoba

ANSCAD
Associate of the Nova Scotia College of Art and Design
N.S. College of Art and Design

ArtDipMus
Artist diploma in music
Toronto

ATh
Associate in theology
King's — Halifax

BA
Baccalauréat ès arts
Jean-de-Brébeuf (Montréal), Laurentienne, Moncton, Montréal, Ottawa, Québec à Montréal, Québec à Trois-Rivières

BA
Baccalauréat ès arts appliquées en études françaises (littérature canadienne)
Laval

BA
Baccalauréat ès arts spécialisé en études allemandes
Laval

BA
Baccalauréat ès arts spécialisé en études anciennes (archéologie)
Laval

BA
Baccalauréat ès arts spécialisé en études anciennes (études grecques)
Laval

BA
Baccalauréat ès arts spécialisé en études anciennes (études latines)
Laval

BA
Baccalauréat ès arts spécialisé en études anglaises (linguistique)
Laval

BA
Baccalauréat ès arts spécialisé en études anglaises (littérature)
Laval

BA
Baccalauréat ès arts spécialisé en études françaises (linguistique)
Laval

BA
Baccalauréat ès arts spécialisé en études françaises (littérature françaises)
Laval

BA
Baccalauréat ès arts spécialisé en études hispaniques
Laval

BA
Baccalauréat ès arts spécialisé en français (pour non francophones)
Laval

BA
Baccalauréat ès arts spécialisé en géographie
Laval

BA
Baccalauréat ès arts spécialisé en histoire
Laval

BA
Baccalauréat ès arts spécialisé en histoire de l'art
Laval

BA
Baccalauréat ès arts spécialisé en traduction
Laval

BA
Bachelor of arts
Acadia, Alberta, Bishop's, Brandon, Brescia (Western Ontario), British Columbia, Brock, Calgary, Carleton, Dalhousie, Guelph, Huron (Western Ontario), King's — Halifax (Dalhousie), King's — London (Western Ontario), Lakehead, Laurentian,

Loyola (Montréal), Manitoba, Marianopolis (Montréal), McGill, McMaster, Memorial, Mount Allison, Mount Saint Vincent, New Brunswick, Notre Dame, Ottawa, Prince Edward Island, Queen's, Royal Military, St. Francis Xavier, St. Jerome's (Waterloo), St. John's (Manitoba), Saint Mary's, St. Michael's (Toronto), St. Paul's — Winnipeg (Manitoba), St. Thomas More (Saskatchewan, Saskatoon), Saskatchewan — Regina, Saskatchewan — Saskatoon, Simon Fraser, Sir George Williams, Toronto, Trent, Trinity (Toronto), Victoria — Toronto (Toronto), Victoria — B.C., Waterloo, Waterloo Lutheran, Western Ontario, Windsor, Winnipeg, York

BA
Bachelor of arts and science
Lethbridge

BA
Bachelor of arts with honors in public administration
Carleton

BA
Bachelor of arts with major in music
Mount Allison

BAA
Baccalauréat en administration des affaires
Montréal

BA(BusinessAdministration)
Bachelor of arts in business administration
Bishop's

BAdm
Baccalauréat en administration
Sherbrooke

BAdmin
Bachelor of administration
Saskatchewan — Regina

BAdPub
Baccalauréat en administration publique avec spécialisation
Ottawa

BAE
Bachelor of art education
Queen's

BA(Ed)
Bachelor of arts (education)
Memorial

BA(général)
Baccalauréat ès arts général
Montréal

BA(lettres)
Baccalauréat ès arts général (lettres)
Montréal

BA(Mus)
Bachelor of arts (major in music)
Acadia

BAP
Baccalauréat en architecture paysagiste
Montréal

BA(PE)
Bachelor of arts in physical education
Saskatchewan — Saskatoon

BA(Ph)
Baccalauréat ès arts avec mention philosophie
Ottawa

BA(Ph)
Bachelor of arts with a major in philosophy
Ottawa

BArch
Baccalauréat en architecture
Laval, Montréal

BArch
Bachelor of architecture
British Columbia, Carleton, McGill, Nova Scotia Technical, Toronto, Waterloo

BA(Recreation)
Bachelor of arts in recreation
Waterloo

Bartsvis
Baccalauréat en arts visuels (arts plastiques)
Laval

Bartsvis
Baccalauréat en arts visuels (communication graphique)
Laval

BASc
Bachelor of applied science
British Columbia, Lakehead, Ottawa, Toronto, Waterloo, Windsor

BA(spPh)
Baccalauréat ès arts avec spécialisation en philosophie
Ottawa

BAwithsecretarialcertificate
Bachelor of arts with secretarial certificate
Mount Allison

BBA
Bachelor of business administration
Acadia, New Brunswick, Prince Edward Island, St. Francis Xavier

BCat
Baccalauréat en catéchèse
Laval

BCL
Bachelor of canon law
Ottawa

BCL
Bachelor of civil law
McGill

BCom
Baccalauréat en commerce
Laurentienne

BCom
Baccalauréat en sciences commerciales avec
spécialisation
Ottawa

BCom
Bachelor of commerce
Alberta, British Columbia, Carleton,
Dalhousie, Lakehead, Laurentian, Loyola
(Montréal), McGill, McMaster, Memorial,
Ottawa, Queen's, St. Michael's (Toronto),
Sir George Williams, Toronto, Trinity
(Toronto), Victoria — Toronto (Toronto)

BComm
Bachelor of commerce
Calgary, Guelph, Manitoba, Mount Allison,
Saint Mary's, Saskatchewan — Saskatoon,
Windsor

BCS
Bachelor of computer science
Windsor

BD
Bachelor of divinity
Acadia Divinity College, Bishop's, King's
— Halifax, Queen's Theological College

BDC
Baccalauréat en droit canonique
Ottawa, Saint-Paul — Ottawa (Ottawa)

BDes
Bachelor of design
N.S. College of Art and Design

BDI
Baccalauréat en design industriel
Montréal

BE
Bachelor of science in engineering
Saskatchewan — Regina, Saskatchewan —
Saskatoon

BEAD
Bachelor of education
Saskatchewan — Regina

BEd
Baccalauréat en éducation
Moncton, Ottawa

BEd
Baccalauréat en éducation (administration
scolaire)
Laval

BEd
Baccalauréat en éducation (enseignement
aux inadaptés)
Laval

BEd
Baccalauréat en éducation (enseignement
élémentaire)
Laval

BEd
Baccalauréat en éducation (enseignement
secondaire)
Laval

BEd
Baccalauréat en éducation (enseignement
technique et professionnel)
Laval

BEd
Baccalauréat en éducation (orientation
scolaire et professionnelle)
Laval

BEd
Baccalauréat en éducation (technologie de
l'enseignement)
Laval

BEd
Bachelor of education
Acadia, Alberta, Brandon, British
Columbia, Calgary, Dalhousie, Lethbridge,
Manitoba, McGill, Memorial, Mount
Allison, Mount Saint Vincent, New
Brunswick, Notre Dame, Ottawa, Prince
Edward Island, Queen's, St. Francis
Xavier, Saint Mary's, Saskatchewan —
Regina, Saskatchewan — Saskatoon, Simon
Fraser, Toronto, Victoria — B.C.

BEdPhy
Baccalauréat en éducation — physique
Moncton

BEdPhys
Baccalauréat en éducation physique
Ottawa

BEdPhys
Bachelor of physical education
Ottawa

BEE
Baccalauréat d'enseignement à l'élémentaire
Moncton

BEng
Bachelor of engineering
Carleton, McGill, McMaster, Memorial,
Nova Scotia Technical, Royal Military, Sir
George Williams

BEngM
Bachelor of engineering and management
McMaster

BES
Bachelor of environmental studies
Manitoba, St. Jerome's (Waterloo),
Waterloo

BESc
Bachelor of engineering science
Western Ontario

BFA
Bachelor of fine arts
Alberta, Calgary, Manitoba, Mount Allison,
Notre Dame, N.S. College of Art and
Design, Saskatchewan — Regina,
Saskatchewan — Saskatoon, Sir George
Williams, Victoria — B.C., Windsor

BGS
Bachelor of general studies
Simon Fraser

BHD
Baccalauréat en hygiène dentaire
Montréal

BHE
Bachelor of home economics
British Columbia

BHEc
Bachelor of home economics
Manitoba

BHSc
Bachelor of household science
Guelph

BID
Bachelor of interior design
Manitoba

BIS
Bachelor of independent studies
Waterloo

BJ
Bachelor of journalism
Carleton

BL
Bachelor of laboratory technology
Saskatchewan — Regina

BLA
Bachelor of landscape architecture
Guelph, Manitoba

BLArch
Bachelor of landscape architecture
Toronto

BLS
Bachelor of library science
Alberta, Ottawa

BManSc
Bachelor of management sciences
Ottawa

BMath
Bachelor of mathematics
St. Jerome's (Waterloo), Waterloo

BMEd
Bachelor of music education
Mount Allison

BMin
Bachelor of Ministry
Huron

BMS
Bachelor of medical science
Memorial

BMus
Baccalauréat en musique
Montréal

BMus
Baccalauréat en musique avec spécialisation
Ottawa

BMus
Baccalauréat en musique (composition)
Laval

BMus
Baccalauréat en musique (éducation
musicale)
Laval

BMus
Baccalauréat en musique (historie et
littérature musicales)
Laval

BMus
Baccalauréat en musique (interprétation
—   )
Laval

BMus
Baccalauréat en musique (interprétation —
chant)
Laval

BMus
Baccalauréat en musique (interprétation —
flûte à bec)
Laval

BMus
Baccalauréat en musique (interprétation —
flûte traversière)
Laval

BMus
Baccalauréat en musique (interprétation —
guitare)
Laval

BMus
Baccalauréat en musique (interprétation —
orgue)
Laval

BMus
Baccalauréat en musique (interprétation —
piano)
Laval

BMus
Baccalauréat en musique (interprétation —
saxophone)
Laval

BMus
Baccalauréat en musique (interprétation —
violon)
Laval

BMus
Baccalauréat en musique (interprétation —
violoncelle)
Laval

BMus
Baccalauréat en musique (rythmique)
Laval

BMus
Baccalauréat en musique — sans mention
Laval

BMus
Bachelor of music
Acadia, Alberta, Brandon, British
Columbia, Calgary, Manitoba, McGill,
Mount Allison, Ottawa, Prince Edward
Island, Queen's, Saskatchewan — Regina,
Victoria — B.C., Waterloo Lutheran,
Windsor

BMusandBMusEd
Bachelor of music and bachelor of music
education
Saskatchewan — Saskatoon

BMusEd
Bachelor of music education
Acadia, Dalhousie, Saskatchewan — Regina

BMus(Perf)
Bachelor of music in performance
Manitoba

BN
Bachelor of nursing
Calgary, Dalhousie, Manitoba, McGill,
Memorial, New Brunswick

BN
Degree program for registered nurses
New Brunswick

BNurs
Baccalauréat en nursing
Montréal

BOT
Bachelor of occupational therapy
Alberta, Manitoba

BPaed
Bachelor of pedagogy
Manitoba

BPE
Bachelor of physical education
Alberta, British Columbia, Calgary,
Dalhousie, Manitoba, McMaster, Memorial,
New Brunswick

BPh
Baccalauréat en philosophie
Laval, Montréal, Saint-Paul — Ottawa,
Sherbrooke

BPh
Bachelor of philosophy
Saint Paul — Ottawa

BPharm
Baccalauréat en pharmacie
Laval

BPHE
Baccalauréat en éducation physique et
hygiène
Laurentienne

BPHE
Bachelor of physical and health education
Lakehead, Laurentian, Queen's, Toronto,
Windsor

BPs
Baccalauréat en psychologie
Sherbrooke

BPsy
Baccalauréat en psychologie
Laval

BPT
Bachelor of physical therapy
Alberta, Manitoba

BPubAd
Bachelor of public administration
Ottawa

BRE
Bachelor of recreation education
British Columbia

BSA
Bachelor of science in agriculture
Manitoba, Saskatchewan – Saskatoon

BSA
Bachelor of secretarial administration
Acadia

BSA
Bachelor of secretarial arts
Notre Dame

BSc
Baccalauréat ès sciences
Laurentienne, Moncton, Montréal,
Sherbrooke

BSc
Baccalauréat ès sciences (biochimie)
Laval

BSc
Baccalauréat ès sciences (biologie)
Laval

BSc
Baccalauréat ès sciences (chimie)
Laval

BSc
Baccalauréat ès sciences (géologie)
Laval

BSc
Baccalauréat ès sciences (informatique de
génie)
Laval

BSc
Baccalauréat ès sciences (informatique de
gestion)
Laval

BSc
Baccalauréat ès sciences (informatique
mathématique)
Laval

BSc
Baccalauréat ès sciences (mathématiques)
Laval

BSc
Baccalauréat ès sciences (microbiologie)
Laval

BSc
Baccalauréat ès sciences (physique)
Laval

BSc
Baccalauréat ès sciences (spécialisé)
Montréal

BSc
Bachelor of science
Acadia, Alberta, Bishop's, Brandon, British
Columbia, Brock, Calgary, Carleton,
Dalhousie, Guelph, King's – Halifax
(Dalhousie), Lakehead, Laurentian, Loyola
(Montréal), Manitoba, Marianopolis
(Montréal), McGill, McMaster, Memorial,
Mount Allison, Mount Saint Vincent, New
Brunswick, Notre Dame, Ottawa, Prince
Edward Island, Queen's, Royal Military,
St. Francis Xavier, St. John's (Manitoba),
Saint Mary's, St. Michael's (Toronto), St.
Paul's – Winnipeg (Manitoba), St.
Thomas More (Saskatchewan, Saskatoon),
Saskatchewan – Regina, Saskatchewan –
Saskatoon, Simon Fraser, Sir George
Williams, Toronto, Trent, Trinity
(Toronto), Victoria – Toronto (Toronto),
Victoria – B.C., Waterloo, Waterloo
Lutheran, Western Ontario, Windsor, York

BSc
Bachelor of science (applied)
Royal Military

BSc
Bachelor of science in agriculture
Alberta

BSc
Bachelor of science in engineering
Alberta, Calgary

BSc
Bachelor of science in medical laboratory
science
Alberta

BSc
Bachelor of science in medicine
Alberta

BSc
Bachelor of science in nursing
Alberta

BSc
Bachelor of science in nursing for
registered nurses
Alberta

BSc
Bachelor of science in pharmacy
Alberta

BSc
Bachelor of science in speech pathology
and audiology
Alberta

BScA
Baccalauréat ès sciences appliquées
Moncton, Sherbrooke

BScA
Baccalauréat ès sciences appliquées et
diplôme d'ingénieur
Montréal

BSc(AAMed)
Bachelor of science (art as applied to
medicine)
Toronto

BScact
Baccalauréat ès sciences de l'actuariat
(administration)
Laval

BScact
Baccalauréat ès sciences de l'actuariat
(économie)
Laval

BScact
Baccalauréat ès sciences de l'actuariat
(mathématiques)
Laval

BScadm
Baccalauréat en sciences de l'administration
Laval

BSc(AE)
Bachelor of science in agricultural
engineering
Manitoba

BSc(Agr)
Bachelor of science in agriculture
British Columbia, Guelph, McGill

BSc(AgrEng)
Bachelor of science in agricultural
engineering
McGill

BScapp
Baccalauréat ès sciences appliquées (agro-
économie)
Laval

BScapp
Baccalauréat ès sciences appliquées
(arpentage)
Laval

BScapp
Baccalauréat ès sciences appliquées (bio-
agronomie)
Laval

BScapp
Baccalauréat ès sciences appliquées
(consommation)
Laval

BScapp
Baccalauréat ès sciences appliquées (génie
chimique)
Laval

BScapp
Baccalauréat ès sciences appliquées (génie
civil)
Laval

BScapp
Baccalauréat ès sciences appliquées (génie
électrique)
Laval

BScapp
Baccalauréat ès sciences appliquées (génie
forestier)
Laval

BScapp
Baccalauréat ès sciences appliquées (génie
géologique)
Laval

BScapp
Baccalauréat ès sciences appliquées (génie
mécanique)
Laval

BScapp
Baccalauréat ès sciences appliquées (génie
métallurgique)
Laval

BScapp
Baccalauréat ès sciences appliquées (génie
minier)
Laval

BScapp
Baccalauréat ès sciences appliquées (génie physique)
Laval

BScapp
Baccalauréat ès sciences appliquées (génie rural)
Laval

BScapp
Baccalauréat ès sciences appliquées (vivres)
Laval

BSc(Arch)
Bachelor of science (architecture)
McGill

BSc(CE)
Bachelor of science in civil engineering
Manitoba

BScCom
Baccalauréat ès sciences commerciales
Moncton

BScD
Bachelor of science in dentistry
Toronto

BSc(Diét)
Baccalauréat ès sciences avec spécialisation en diététique
Ottawa

BSc(Diet)
Bachelor of science in dietetics
Ottawa

BScDom
Baccalauréat en sciences domestiques
Moncton

BSc(E)
Bachelor of science en engineering
New Brunswick

BScEd
Baccalauréat ès sciences de l'éducation
Sherbrooke

BSc(Ed)
Baccalauréat ès sciences (éducation)
Montréal

BScEd
Bachelor of science in education
St. Francis Xavier

BSc(Edphys)
Baccalauréat ès sciences (éducation physique)
Montréal

BSc(éducprésensélém)
Baccalauréat ès sciences (éducation préscolaire et enseignement élémentaire)
Montréal

BSc(EE)
Bachelor of science in electrical engineering
Manitoba

BSc(Eng)
Bachelor of science in engineering
Guelph

BSc(EnginPhys)
Bachelor of science in engineering physics
Dalhousie

BSc(erg)
Baccalauréat ès sciences (ergothérapie)
Montréal

BScF
Bachelor of science in forestry
Lakehead, New Brunwsick, Toronto

BSc(FdSc)
Bachelor of science in food science
Alberta

BScFE
Bachelor of science in forest engineering
New Brunswick

BSc(FoodSci)
Bachelor of science in food science
Toronto

BSc(FSc)
Bachelor of science in food science
McGill

BSc(GE)
Bachelor of science in geological engineering
Manitoba

BScGest
Baccalauréat en sciences de la gestion
Ottawa

BSc(HE)
Bachelor of science (home economics)
Acadia

BScHEc
Bachelor of science in home economics
Mount Saint Vincent, St. Francis Xavier

BSc(HEc)
Bachelor of science in household economics
Alberta

BSc(HEcon)
Bachelor of science in home economics
Ottawa

BSc(Inf)
Baccalauréat en sciences infirmières
Moncton

BSc(Kin)
Baccalauréat ès sciences kinanthropologie
Ottawa

BSc(Kin)
Bachelor of science in kinanthropology
Ottawa

BSc(Kinesiology)
Bachelor of science in kinesiology
Simon Fraser, Waterloo

BSc(ME)
Bachelor of science in mechanical
engineering
Manitoba

BSc(Med)
Bachelor of science in medicine
Manitoba, McMaster, Saskatchewan —
Saskatoon

BSc(MLT)
Degree in medical laboratory technology
Saskatchewan — Saskatoon

BScMR
Bachelor of science in medical
rehabilitation
Western Ontario

BSc(MR)
Bachelor of science (medical records)
Notre Dame

BScN
Baccalauréat en sciences infirmières
Laurentienne

BScN
Bachelor of science in nursing
Lakehead, Laurentian, McMaster, Mount
Saint Vincent, Ottawa, St. Francis Xavier,
Toronto, Western Ontario, Windsor

BSc(N)
Bachelor of science in nursing
McGill

BSc(NEd)
Bachelor of science in nursing education
Ottawa

BSc(nut)
Baccalaurat ès sciences (nutrition)
Montréal

BSc(OccTher)
Bachelor of science in occupational therapy
McGill

BSc(ortho)
Baccalauréat ès sciences (orthopédagogie)
Montréal

BSc(orthoetaudio)
Baccalauréat ès sciences (orthophonie et
audiologie)
Montréal

BSc(OT)
Bachelor of science in occupational therapy
Queen's, Toronto

BSc(PE)
Bachelor of science in physical education
Guelph

BSc(Pharm)
Bachelor of science in pharmacy
British Columbia, Dalhousie, Manitoba

BSc(phm)
Baccalauréat ès sciences (pharmacie)
Montréal

BScPhm
Bachelor of science in pharmacy
Toronto

BSc(PHN)
Bachelor of science in public health
nursing
Ottawa

BScPhysEd
Bachelor of science in physical education
St. Francis Xavier

BSc(physio)
Baccalauréat ès sciences (physiothérapie)
Montréal

BSc(PhysTher)
Bachelor of science in physical therapy
McGill

BSc(Ps)
Baccalauréat ès sciences (psychologie)
Montréal

BSc(psed)
Baccalauréat ès sciences (psychoéducation)
Montréal

BSc(PT)
Bachelor of science in physical therapy
Queen's, Toronto

BSc(Réc)
Baccalauréat ès sciences en récréologie
Ottawa

BSc(Rec)
Bachelor of science in recreology
Ottawa

BScsanté
Baccalauréat ès sciences de la santé
(diététique)
Laval

BScsanté
Baccalauréat ès sciences de la santé
(ergothérapie)
Laval

BScsanté
Baccalauréat ès sciences de la santé
(médecine)
Laval

BScsanté
Baccalauréat ès sciences de la santé
(médecine dentaire)
Laval

BScsanté
Baccalauréat ès sciences de la santé
(pharmacie)
Laval

BScsanté
Baccalauréat ès sciences de la santé
(physiothérapie)
Laval

BScsanté
Baccalauréat ès sciences de la santé
(sciences infirmières)
Laval

BSc(ScDom)
Baccalauréat ès sciences avec spécialisation
en sciences domestiques
Ottawa

BScsoc
Baccalauréat en sciences sociales
Ottawa

BScsoc
Baccalauréat ès sciences sociales
(anthropologie)
Laval

BScsoc
Baccalauréat ès sciences sociales (économie)
Laval

BScsoc
Baccalauréat ès sciences sociales (politique)
Laval

BScsoc
Baccalauréat ès sciences sociales (relations
industrielles)
Laval

BScsoc
Baccalauréat ès sciences sociales (sociologie)
Laval

BSectA
Bachelor of secretarial arts
St. Francis Xavier

BServsoc
Baccalauréat en service social
Laval

BServSoc
Baccalauréat en service social
Sherbrooke

BSF
Bachelor of science in forestry
British Columbia

BSHEc
Bachelor of science in home economics
Saskatchewan — Saskatoon

BSL
Baccalauréat en sciences du langage
Laurentienne

BSL
Bachelor of science in language
Laurentian

BSLitt
Bachelor of sacred letters
King's — Halifax

BSN
Bachelor of science in nursing
British Columbia, Saskatchewan —
Saskatoon

BSocSc
Bachelor of social sciences
Ottawa

BSP
Bachelor of science in pharmacy
Saskatchewan — Saskatoon

BSpAdm
Baccalauréat spécialisé en administration
Québec à Chicoutimi, Québec à Montréal,
Québec à Rimouski, Québec à Trois-
Rivières

BSpAdm(sciencescomptables)
Baccalauréat spécialisé en administration
(sciences comptables)

Québec à Chicoutimi, Québec à Trois-Rivières

BSpAnimCult
Baccalauréat spécialisé en animation
culturelle
Québec à Montréal

BSpAnimCult(esthétique)
Baccalauréat spécialisé en animation
culturelle (esthétique)
Québec à Montréal

BSpAnimCult(étudesétrangères)
Baccalauréat spécialisé en animation
culturelle (études étrangères)
Québec à Montréal

BSpAnimCult(étudeslittéraires)
Baccalauréat spécialisé en animation
culturelle (études littéraires)
Québec à Montréal

BSpAnimCult(étudesthéâtrales)
Baccalauréat spécialisé en animation
culturelle (études théâtrales)
Québec à Montréal

BSpAnimCult(linguistique)
Baccalauréat spécialisé en animation
culturelle (linguistique)
Québec à Montréal

BSpArtsPl
Baccalauréat spécialisé en arts plastiques
Québec à Chicoutimi, Québec à Montréal,
Québec à Trois-Rivières

BSpArtsPl(gravure)
Baccalauréat spécialisé en arts plastiques
(gravure)
Québec à Montréal

BSpArtsPl(peinture)
Baccalauréat spécialisé en arts plastiques
(peinture)
Québec à Montréal

BSpArtsPl(sculpture)
Baccalauréat spécialisé en arts plastiques
(sculpture)
Québec à Montréal

BSpDesign(2D)
Baccalauréat spécialisé en design (2D)
Québec à Montréal

BSpDesign(3D)
Baccalauréat spécialisé en design (3D)
Québec à Montréal

BSpEc
Baccalauréat spécialisé en économique

Québec à Montréal, Québec à Trois-Rivières

BSpEdCult
Baccalauréat spécialisé en éducation
culturelle
Québec à Montréal

BSpEdCult(esthétique)
Baccalauréat spécialisé en éducation
culturelle (esthétique)
Québec à Montréal

BSpEdCult(étudesétrangères)
Baccalauréat spécialisé en éducation
culturelle (études étrangères)
Québec à Montréal

BSpEdCult(étudeslittéraires)
Baccalauréat spécialisé en éducation
culturelle (études littéraires)
Québec à Montréal

BSpEdCult(étudesthéâtrales)
Baccalauréat spécialisé en éducation
culturelle (études théâtrales)
Québec à Montréal

BSpEdCult(linguistique)
Baccalauréat spécialisé en éducation
culturelle (linguistique)
Québec à Montréal

BSpEdPh
Baccalauréat spécialisé en éducation
physique
Québec à Chicoutimi, Québec à Trois-Rivières

BSpEnfInad
Baccalauréat spécialisé en enfance
inadaptée
Québec à Chicoutimi, Québec à Montréal,
Québec à Rimouski, Québec à Trois-Rivières

BSpEns(éducationphysique)
Baccalauréat spécialisé d'enseignement
(éducation physique)
Québec à Montréal, Québec à Trois-Rivières

BSpEnsEl
Baccalauréat spécialisé d'enseignement
élémentaire
Québec à Chicoutimi, Québec à Montréal,
Québec à Rimouski, Québec à Trois-Rivières

BSpEns(enfanceinadaptée)
Baccalauréat spécialisé d'enseignement
(enfance inadaptée)
Québec à Trois-Rivières

BSpEns(musique)
Baccalauréat spécialisé d'enseignement
(musique)
Québec à Trois-Rivières

BSpEnsPrésc
Baccalauréat spécialisé d'enseignement
préscolaire
Québec à Montréal, Québec à Rimouski,
Québec à Trois-Rivières

BSpEnsProf(électrotechnique)
Baccalauréat spécialisé d'enseignement
professionnel (électrotechnique)
Québec à Montréal

BSpEnsProf(techniquesdelamécanique)
Baccalauréat spécialisé d'enseignement
professionnel (techniques de la mécanique)
Québec à Montréal

BSpEnsSec(administration)
Baccalauréat spécialisé d'enseignement
secondaire (administration)
Québec à Chicoutimi, Québec à Montréal,
Québec à Rimouski, Québec à Trois-
Rivières

BSpEnsSec(anglais)
Baccalauréat spécialisé d'enseignement
secondaire (anglais)
Québec à Chicoutimi, Québec à Rimouski,
Québec à Trois-Rivières

BSpEnsSec(artsplastiques)
Baccalauréat spécialisé d'enseignement
secondaire (arts plastiques)
Québec à Trois-Rivières

BSpEnsSec(biologie)
Baccalauréat spécialisé d'enseignement
secondaire (biologie)
Québec à Chicoutimi, Québec à Montréal,
Québec à Rimouski, Québec à Trois-
Rivières

BSpEnsSec(chimie)
Baccalauréat spécialisé d'enseignement
secondaire (chimie)
Québec à Chicoutimi, Québec à Montréal,
Québec à Rimouski, Québec à Trois-
Rivières

BSpEnsSec(étudesfrançaises)
Baccalauréat spécialisé d'enseignement
secondaire (études françaises)
Québec à Rimouski

BSpEnsSec(géographie)
Baccalauréat spécialisé d'enseignement
secondaire (géographie)
Québec à Chicoutimi, Québec à Montréal,

Québec à Rimouski, Québec à Trois-
Rivières

BSpEnsSec(histoire)
Baccalauréat spécialisé d'enseignement
secondaire (histoire)
Québec à Chicoutimi, Québec à Montréal,
Québec à Rimouski, Québec à Trois-
Rivières

BSpEnsSec(latin)
Baccalauréat spécialisé d'enseignement
secondaire (latin)
Québec à Montréal

BSpEnsSec(latin-grec)
Baccalauréat spécialisé d'enseignement
secondaire (latin-grec)
Québec à Montréal

BSpEnsSec(lettresfrançaises)
Baccalauréat spécialisé d'enseignement
secondaire (lettres françaises)
Québec à Chicoutimi, Québec à Trois-
Rivières

BSpEnsSec(mathématiques)
Baccalauréat spécialisé d'enseignement
secondaire (mathématiques)
Québec à Chicoutimi, Québec à Montréal,
Québec à Rimouski, Québec à Trois-
Rivières

BSpEnsSec(physique)
Baccalauréat spécialisé d'enseignement
secondaire (physique)
Québec à Chicoutimi, Québec à Montréal,
Québec à Rimouski, Québec à Trois-
Rivières

BSpEnsSec(sciencesreligieuses)
Baccalauréat spécialisé d'enseignement
secondaire (sciences religieuses)
Québec à Montréal, Québec à Rimouski,
Québec à Trois-Rivières

BSpEns(sexologie)
Baccalauréat spécialisé d'enseignement
sexologie
Québec à Montréal

BSpGénagogie
Baccalauréat spécialisé en génagogie
Québec à Trois-Rivières

BSpGéogHum
Baccalauréat spécialisé en géographie
humaine
Québec à Montréal

BSpGéogr
Baccalauréat spécialisé en géographie

Québec à Chicoutimi, Québec à Trois-Rivières

BSpH
Baccalauréat spécialisé en histoire
Québec à Chicoutimi, Québec à Montréal,
Québec à Trois-Rivières

BSpHdel'art
Baccalauréat spécialisé en histoire de l'art
Québec à Montréal

BSpInformCult
Baccalauréat spécialisé en information
culturelle
Québec à Montréal

BSpInformCult(esthétique)
Baccalauréat spécialisé en information
culturelle (esthétique)
Québec à Montréal

BSpInformCult(étudesétrangères)
Baccalauréat spécialisé en information
culturelle (études étrangères)
Québec à Montréal

BSpInformCult(étudeslittéraires)
Baccalauréat spécialisé en information
culturelle (études littéraires)
Québec à Montréal

BSpInformCult(étudesthéâtrales)
Baccalauréat spécialisé en information
culturelle (études théâtrales)
Québec à Montréal

BSpInformCult(linguistique)
Baccalauréat spécialisé en information
culturelle (linguistique)
Québec à Montréal

BSpInformScoletProf
Baccalauréat spécialisé en enformation
scolaire et professionnelle
Québec à Montréal

BSpLangMod(étudesanglaises)
Baccalauréat spécialisé en langues modernes
(études anglaises)
Québec à Trois-Rivières

BSpLCl(étudesanciennes)
Baccalauréat spécialisé en lettres classiques
(études anciennes)
Québec à Montréal

BSpLCl(grec)
Baccalauréat spécialisé en lettres classiques
(grec)
Québec à Trois-Rivières

BSpLCl(latin)
Baccalauréat spécialisé en lettres classiques
(latin)
Québec à Montréal, Québec à Trois-Rivières

BSpLCl(latin-grec)
Baccalauréat spécialisé en lettres classiques
(latin-grec)
Québec à Montréal, Québec à Trois-Rivières

BSpL(étudesfrançaises)
Baccalauréat spécialisé en lettres (études
françaises)
Québec à Chicoutimi, Québec à Montréal,
Québec à Rimouski, Québec à Trois-Rivières

BSpL(étudesquébécoises)
Baccalauréat spécialisé en lettres (études
québécoises)
Québec à Trois-Rivières

BSpLing
Baccalauréat spécialisé en linguistique
Québec à Montréal, Québec à Trois-Rivières

BSpMus
Baccalauréat spécialisé en musique
Québec à Montréal, Québec à Trois-Rivières

BSpPh
Baccalauréat spécialisé en philosophie
Québec à Chicoutimi, Québec à Montréal,
Québec à Trois-Rivières

BSpPs
Baccalauréat spécialisé en psychologie
Québec à Chicoutimi, Québec à Montréal,
Québec à Trois-Rivières

BSpRechCult
Baccalauréat spécialisé en recherche
culturelle
Québec à Montréal

BSpRechCult(esthétique)
Baccalauréat spécialisé en recherche
culturelle (esthétique)
Québec à Montréal

BSpRechCult(étudesétrangères)
Baccalauréat spécialisé en recherche
culturelle (études étrangères)
Québec à Montréal

BSpRechCult(étudeslittéraires)
Baccalauréat spécialisé en recherche
culturelle (études littéraires)
Québec à Montréal

BSpRechCult(étudesthéâtrales)
Baccalauréat spécialisé en recherche
culturelle (études théâtrales)
Québec à Montréal

BSpRechCult(linguistique)
Baccalauréat spécialisé en recherche
culturelle (linguistique)
Québec à Montréal

BSpRécréol
Baccalauréat spécialisé en récréologie
Québec à Trois-Rivières

BSpRelHum
Baccalauréat spécialisé en relations
humaines
Québec à Montréal

BSpROp
Baccalauréat spécialisé en recherche
opérationnelle
Québec à Trois-Rivières

BSpScA(géniechimique)
Baccalauréat spécialisé en sciences
appliquées (génie chimique)
Québec à Chicoutimi, Québec à Trois-
Rivières

BSpScA(génieélectrique)
Baccalauréat spécialisé en sciences
appliquées (génie électrique)
Québec à Chicoutimi, Québec à Trois-
Rivières

BSpScA(géniemédical)
Baccalauréat spécialisé en sciences
appliquées (génie médical)
Québec à Chicoutimi, Québec à Trois-
Rivières

BSpScA(géniephysique)
Baccalauréat spécialisé en sciences
appliquées (génie physique)
Québec à Chicoutimi, Québec à Trois-
Rivières

BSpSc(biochimie)
Baccalauréat spécialisé en sciences
(biochimie)
Québec à Trois-Rivières

BSpSc(biologie)
Baccalauréat spécialisé en sciences
(biologie)
Québec à Chicoutimi, Québec à Montréal,
Québec à Rimouski, Québec à Trois-
Rivières

BSpSc(biologiehumaine)
Baccalauréat spécialisé en sciences (biologie
humaine)
Québec à Trois-Rivières

BSpSc(chimie)
Baccalauréat spécialisé en sciences (chimie)
Québec à Chicoutimi, Québec à Montréal,
Québec à Rimouski, Québec à Trois-
Rivières

BSpScdel'Ed
Baccalauréat spécialisé en sciences de
l'éducation
Québec à Chicoutimi, Québec à Trois-
Rivières

BSpSc(géographie-physique)
Baccalauréat spécialisé en sciences
(géographie-physique)
Québec à Montréal

BSpSc(géolgie)
Baccalauréat spécialisé en sciences
(géologie)
Québec à Montréal

BSpSc(mathématiques)
Baccalauréat spécialisé en sciences
(mathématiques)
Québec à Chicoutimi, Québec à Montréal,
Québec à Rimouski, Québec à Trois-
Rivières

BSpSc(physique)
Baccalauréat spécialisé en sciences
(physique)
Québec à Chicoutimi, Québec à Montréal,
Québec à Rimouski, Québec à Trois-
Rivières

BSpScPol
Baccalauréat spécialisé en science politique
Québec à Montréal

BSpScRel
Baccalauréat spécialisé en sciences
religieuses
Québec à Montréal

BSpScSanté(nursing)
Baccalauréat spécialisé en sciences de la
santé (nursing)
Québec à Trois-Rivières

BSpSoc
Baccalauréat spécialisé en sociologie
Québec à Montréal

BSpTh
Baccalauréat spécialisé en théologie
Québec à Rimouski, Québec à Trois-
Rivières

BSpTravSoc
Baccalauréat spécialisé en travail social
Québec à Montréal

BSR
Bachelor of science in rehabilitation
British Columbia

BSSoc
Baccalauréat en service social
Moncton

BST
Bachelor of sacred theology
King's — Halifax

BSW
Baccalauréat en service social
Laurentienne

BSW
Bachelor of social welfare
King's — London (Western Ontario),
Western Ontario

BSW
Bachelor of social work
Calgary, Laurentian, Manitoba, McGill,
McMaster, Memorial, Windsor

BT
Bachelor of teaching
New Brunswick

BTh
Baccalauréat en théologie
Laval, Montréal, Ottawa, Saint-Paul —
Ottawa (les grades civils sont conférés par
l'Université d'Ottawa et les grades
canoniques sont conférés par l'Université
Saint-Paul), Sherbrooke

BTh
Bachelor of theology
Acadia Divinity College, McGill, Ottawa,
Queen's Theological College, Saint Paul —
Ottawa (civil degree conferred by the
University of Ottawa, canonical degree
conferred by Saint Paul)

BThPast
Baccalauréat en théologie pastorale
Montréal

BTrad
Baccalauréat en traduction
Montréal

CAPES
Certificat d'aptitudes pédagogiques à
l'enseignement secondaire
Sherbrooke

CEAServSoc
Certificat d'études avancées en service
social
Sherbrooke

CEC
Certificat pour l'enseignement au cours
collégial
Laval

CEE
Certificat pour l'enseignement au cours
élémentaire
Laval

CertAppSci
Certificate of applied science
Acadia

CertPHN
Certificate in public health nursing, general
Toronto

CES
Certificat pour l'enseignement au cours
secondaire
Laval

CPA
Certificate in public administration
Dalhousie

CPH
Certificate in public health
Toronto

CPSS
Certificate in public service studies
Carleton

DCC
Diploma in clincial chemistry
Toronto

DCL
Doctor of civil law
McGill

DD
Doctor of divinity
Bishop's

DDPH
Diploma in dental public health
Toronto

DDS
Doctorat en chirurgie dentaire
Montréal

DDS
Doctor of dental surgery
Alberta, Dalhousie, McGill, Toronto,
Western Ontario

DEd
Doctor of education
McGill

DEng
Doctor of engineering
Sir George Williams

DENS
Diplôme de l'Ecole normale supérieure
Montréal

DèsL
Doctorat ès lettres
Sherbrooke

DHP
Diplôme en hygiène publique
Montréal

DIH
Diploma in industrial health
Toronto

DipAnaes
Diploma in anaesthesia
Toronto

DipBact
Diploma in bacteriology
Toronto

DipBusAdmin
Diploma in business administration
Lakehead, Toronto, Western Ontario

DipClinPsychol
Diploma in clinical psychology
Dalhousie

DipCS
Diploma in child study
Toronto

DipDentHyg
Diploma in dental hygiene
British Columbia, Toronto

DipEandCH
Diploma in epidemiology and community
health
Toronto

DipEdAdmin
Postgraduate diploma in education
administration
Saskatchewan – Regina

Dip(Eng)
Diploma in engineering
Saint Mary's

DipEngTechnol
Diploma in engineering technology
Lakehead

DipForTechnol
Diploma in forest technology
Lakehead

DipHA
Diploma in hospital administration
Toronto

Dipladm
Diplôme en administration
Laval

DipLibTechnol
Diploma in library technology
Lakehead

DiplPHN
Diploma in public health nursing
Winnipeg

DipNutrit
Diploma in nutrition
Toronto

DipOphthSc
Diploma in ophthalmic science
Toronto

DipOralSurg
Diploma in oral surgery and anaesthesia
Toronto

DipOrthodont
Diploma in orthodontics
Toronto

DipPaedodont
Diploma in paedodontics
Toronto

DipPandOT
Diploma in physical and occupational
therapy
Toronto

DipPeriodont
Diploma in periodontics
Toronto

DipSpeechPathandAud
Diploma in speech pathology and
audiology
Toronto

DipUandRP
Diploma in urban and regional planning
Toronto

DJur
Doctor juris
Toronto

DJur
Doctor of jurisprudence
York

DLitt
Doctor of letters
Saskatchewan — Saskatoon

DMD
Doctor of dental medicine
British Columbia, Manitoba

DMD
Doctor of dentistry
Saskatchewan — Saskatoon

DMR
Diploma in medical radiology
Toronto

DMR(D)
Diploma in radiology (diagnosis)
Queen's

DMus
Doctorat en musique
Montréal

DMV
Doctorat en médecine vétérinaire
Montréal

DPA
Graduate diploma in public administration
Carleton

DPH
Diploma in public health
Toronto

DPh
Docteur en philosophie
Ottawa, Saint-Paul — Ottawa

DPh
Doctor of philosophy
Ottawa

DPH
Doctor of philosophy
Saint Paul — Ottawa

DPs
Doctorat en psychologie
Montréal

DPsych
Diploma in psychiatry
Toronto

DSc
Doctor of science
Saskatchewan — Saskatoon

DScA
Doctorat ès sciences appliquées
Montréal

DScH
Doctorat ès sciences en hygiène
Montréal

DSW
Doctor of social work
Toronto

DTh
Doctorat en théologie
Montréal, Saint-Paul — Ottawa

DTh
Doctor of theology
St. Michael's, Saint Paul — Ottawa

DTh(Miss)
Doctorat en théologie en sciences
missionnaires
Saint-Paul — Ottawa

DTh(Miss)
Doctor in theology in mission studies
Saint Paul — Ottawa

DVM
Doctor of veterinary medicine
Guelph, Saskatchewan — Saskatoon

DVPH
Diploma in veterinary public health
Toronto

EdD
Doctor of education
Alberta, British Columbia

EngDip
Diploma in engineering
Dalhousie

HLT
Certificate in hospital laboratory technology
Saskatchewan — Regina

JCB
Baccalauréat en droit canonique
Saint-Paul — Ottawa

JCB
Bachelor of canon law
Saint Paul — Ottawa (civil degree
conferred by the University of Ottawa;
canonical degree conferred by Saint Paul)

JCD
Doctorat en droit canonique
Saint-Paul — Ottawa

JCD
Doctor in canon law
Saint Paul — Ottawa

JCL
Licence en droit canonique
Saint-Paul — Ottawa

JCL
Licentiate in canon law
Saint Paul — Ottawa

Ld'ensél
Licence d'enseignement élémentaire
Sherbrooke

Ld'enssec
Licence d'enseignement secondaire
Sherbrooke

LicDipMus
Licentiate diploma in music
Toronto

LLB
Baccalauréat en droit
Laval

LLB
Bachelor of laws
Alberta, British Columbia, Dalhousie,
Manitoba, McGill, New Brunswick,
Ottawa, Queen's, Saskatchewan —
Saskatoon, Toronto, Western Ontario,
Windsor, York

LLD
Doctorat en droit
Montréal, Ottawa

LLL
Licence en droit
Montréal, Ottawa, Sherbrooke

LLM
Maîtrise en droit
Montréal, Ottawa, Sherbrooke

LLM
Master of laws
Alberta, British Columbia, Dalhousie,
Manitoba, McGill, Queen's, Saskatchewan
— Saskatoon, Toronto, York

LMus
Licentiate in music
McGill, Saskatchewan — Regina

LMusWesternBoard
Licentiate in music
Manitoba

LPh
Licence en philosophie
Saint-Paul — Ottawa

LPh
Licentiate in philosophy
Saint Paul — Ottawa

LSccompt
Licence en sciences comptables
Laval

LScO
Licence en optométrie
Montréal

LST
Licentiate in sacred theology
Bishop's

LTh
Licence en théologie
Montréal, Saint-Paul — Ottawa

LTh
Licentiate in theology
King's — Halifax, Saint Paul — Ottawa,
Victoria — Toronto

MA
Maîtrise ès arts
Moncton, Montréal, Ottawa, Sherbrooke

MA
Master of arts
Acadia, Alberta, Bishop's, British
Columbia, Brock, Calgary, Carleton,
Dalhousie, Guelph, Lakehead, Manitoba,
McGill, McMaster, Memorial, Mount Saint
Vincent, New Brunswick, Ontario Institute
for Studies in Education (Toronto),
Ottawa, Queen's, Royal Military, St.
Francis Xavier, St. John's (Manitoba), St.
Paul's — Winnipeg (Manitoba),
Saskatchewan — Regina, Saskatchewan —
Saskatoon, Simon Fraser, Sir George.
Williams, Toronto, Trent, Victoria — B.C.,
Waterloo, Waterloo Lutheran, Western
Ontario, Windsor, York

MA
Master of arts in education
McGill, Saint Mary's

MA
Master of arts in history
Saint Mary's

MA
Master of arts in musicology
Western Ontario

MA
Master of arts in philosophy
Saint Mary's

MA
Master of arts in public administration
Carleton

MA
Master of arts in theology
St. Michael's

MAA
Maîtrise en administration des affaires
Montréal

MAC
Maîtrise en administration correctionnelle
Ottawa

MA(CL)
Master of arts in canon law
Ottawa, Saint Paul — Ottawa (Ottawa)

MA(Crim)
Maîtrise ès arts en criminologie
Ottawa

MA(Crim)
Master of arts in criminology
Ottawa

MA(DC)
Maîtrise ès arts en droit canonique
Ottawa, Saint-Paul — Ottawa (Ottawa)

MA(Ed)
Maîtrise ès arts en éducation
Moncton, Ottawa

MA(Ed)
Master of arts in education
Dalhousie, Ottawa

MA(Education)
Master of arts (education)
Simon Fraser

MA(ens)
Maîtrise ès arts (enseignement)
Montréal

MAGuid
Master of arts in guidance
St. Francis Xavier

MAineducation
Master of arts in education
British Columbia

MAinGuidance
Master of arts in guidance
St. Francis Xavier

MAinteaching
Master of arts in teaching
St. Francis Xavier

MAm(Arch)GB. Maîtrise en aménagement
Montréal

MA(Miss)
Maîtrise ès arts en sciences missionnaires
Saint-Paul — Ottawa (Ottawa)

MA(Miss)
Master of arts in mission studies
Saint Paul — Ottawa (Ottawa)

MA(MissStud)
Master of arts in mission studies
Ottawa

MA(Ph)
Maîtrise ès arts en philosophie
Montréal, Ottawa

MA(Ph)
Master of arts in philosophy
Ottawa

MA(Ps)
Maîtrise ès arts en psychologie
Moncton, Montréal, Ottawa

MA(Ps)
Master of arts in psychology
Ottawa

MArch
Master of architecture
British Columbia, Manitoba, McGill, Nova
Scotia Technical, Toronto

MAS
Maîtrise en administration de la santé
Montréal

MASc
Master of applied science
British Columbia, Ottawa, Toronto,
Waterloo, Windsor

MA(sciencesmédiévales)
Maîtrise ès arts en sciences médiévales
Montréal

MA(ScMiss)
Maîtrise ès arts en sciences missionnaires
Ottawa

MA(Th)
Master of arts in theology

MA(Th)
Maîtrise ès arts en théologie
Ottawa, Saint-Paul — Ottawa (Ottawa)

MBA
Maîtrise en administration des affaires
Sherbrooke

MBA
Maîtrise en gestion des affaires
Moncton

MBA
Master of business administration
Alberta, British Columbia, Dalhousie,
Manitoba, McGill, McMaster, Queen's,
Saskatchewan — Saskatoon, Simon Fraser,
Sir George Williams, Toronto, Western
Ontario, Windsor, York

MBibl
Maîtrise en bibliothéconomie
Montréal

MCA
Master of correctional administration
Ottawa

MCEd
Master of continuing education
Saskatchewan — Saskatoon

MCL
Master of canon law
Ottawa

MCL
Master of civil law
McGill

MCISc
Master of clinical science
Western Ontario

MCom
Master of commerce
McGill

MCP
Master of city planning
Manitoba

MD
Doctorat en médecine
Laval, Montréal, Sherbrooke

MD
Doctor of medicine
Alberta, British Columbia, Calgary,

Dalhousie, Manitoba, McMaster, Ottawa,
Queen's, Saskatchewan — Saskatoon,
Toronto, Western Ontario.

MDC
Maîtrise en droit canonique
Ottawa, Saint-Paul — Ottawa (Ottawa)

MDC
Master of canon law
Saint Paul — Ottawa (Ottawa)

MD,CM
Doctor of medicine and master of surgery
McGill

MDiv
Master of divinity
Huron, McMaster Divinity College
(McMaster), St. Michael's, Victoria —
Toronto, Waterloo Lutheran

MEd
Maîtrise en éducation
Moncton, Montréal, Ottawa

MEd
Master of education
Acadia, Alberta, Bishop's, British
Columbia, Calgary, Manitoba, McGill,
Memorial, New Brunswick, Ontario
Institute for Studies in Education
(Toronto), Ottawa, Queen's, St. Francis
Xavier, Saskatchewan — Saskatoon,
Toronto

MEdAdmin
Master of education administration
Saskatchewan — Regina

MEdAdmScol
Maîtrise en éducation option administration
scolaire
Sherbrooke

MEdPhys
Maîtrise en éducation physique
Ottawa

MEng
Master of engineering
Alberta, British Columbia, Calgary,
Carleton, McGill, McMaster, Memorial,
New Brunswick, Nova Scotia Technical,
Ottawa, Royal Military, Sir George
Williams, Toronto, Western Ontario

MEng(Mining)
Master of engineering (mining)
McGill

MESc
Master of engineering science
Western Ontario

MF
Master of forestry
British Columbia, New Brunswick

MFA
Master of fine arts
Alberta, Victoria — B.C.

MHA
Master of hospital administration
Ottawa

MHP
Master of hospital administration
Alberta

MHSA
Master of health services administration
Alberta

MIng
Maîtrise en ingénierie
Montréal

MLabSc
Master of laboratory science
Dalhousie

MLS
Master of library science
British Columbia, McGill, Ottawa, Toronto,
Western Ontario

MLS
Master of library service
Dalhousie

MMA
Master of musical arts
McGill

MManSc
Master of management science
Ottawa

MMath
Master of mathematics
Waterloo

MMus
Maîtrise en musique
Montréal

MMus
Master of music
Alberta, British Columbia, Victoria — B.C.

MMuseol
Master of museology
Toronto

MNRM
Master of natural resources management
Manitoba

MN(Teaching)
Master of nursing (teaching)
McGill

MNurs
Maîtrise en nursing
Montréal

MOA
Maîtrise en orthophonie et audiologie
Montréal

MOr
Maîtrise en orientation
Montréal

MPA
Master of public administration
Queen's, York

MPAandDPA
Master of public administration and
graduate diploma in public administration
Dalhousie

MPast
Maîtrise en pastorale
Ottawa

MPast
Master of pastoral studies
Ottawa

MPE
Master of physical education
British Columbia, Dalhousie, Windsor

MPhil
Master of philosophy
Memorial, Waterloo

MPhysEd
Master of physical education
Ottawa

MPs
Maîtrise en psychologie
Moncton, Montréal, Ottawa

MPs
Master of psychology
Ottawa

MPsed
Maîtrise en psychoéducation
Montréal

MRE
Master of religious education
McMaster Divinity College (McMaster), St.
Michael's, Victoria — Toronto

MSc
Maîtrise ès sciences
Laurentienne, Moncton, Montréal,
Sherbrooke

MSc
Master of science
Acadia, Alberta, Bishop's, British
Columbia, Brock, Calgary, Carleton,
Dalhousie, Guelph, Lakehead, Laurentian,
Manitoba, McGill, McMaster, Memorial,
Mount Allison, New Brunswick, Ottawa,
Queen's, Royal Military, St. Francis
Xavier, Saskatchewan — Regina,
Saskatchewan — Saskatoon, Simon Fraser,
Sir George Williams, Toronto, Trent,
Victoria — B.C., Waterloo, Western
Ontario, Windsor, York

MSc
Master of science in commerce
Saskatchewan — Saskatoon

MSc
Master of science in engineering
Saskatchewan — Regina

MSc
Master of science in medicine
Memorial

MSc
Master of science in pharmacy
British Columbia

MSc
Master of science (medical science)
McMaster

MScA
Maîtrise ès sciences appliquées
Montréal, Sherbrooke

MSc(Appl)
Master of science (applied)
McGill

MSc(biologiedentaire)
Maîtrise en biologie dentaire
Montréal

MSc(ComputerScience)
Master of science in computer science
Toronto

MScCS
Master of science in computer science
New Brunswick

MScD
Master of science in dentistry
Toronto

MScE
Master of science in engineering
New Brunswick

MScEd
Maîtrise ès sciences de l'éducation
Sherbrooke

MSc(Edphys)
Maîtrise ès sciences (éducation physique)
Montréal

MSc(Education)
Master of science (education)
Simon Fraser

MSc(Eng)
Master of science in engineering
Queen's

MScF
Master of science in forestry
New Brunswick, Toronto

MScGest
Maîtrise en sciences de la gestion
Ottawa

MScH
Maîtrise ès sciences en hygiène
Montréal

MSc(Kin)
Maîtrise ès sciences en kinanthropologie
Ottawa

MSc(Kin)
Master of science in kinanthropology
Ottawa

MSc(Kinesiology)
Master of science (kinesiology)
Simon Fraser

MScN
Master of science in nursing
Toronto, Western Ontario

MSc(nut)
Maîtrise ès sciences (nutrition)
Montréal

MSc(orthodontie)
Maîtrise ès sciences en orthodontie
Montréal

MScPhm
Master of science in pharmacy
Toronto

MSc(Pl)
Master of science in urban and regional planning
Toronto

MScV
Maîtrise en sciences vétérinaires
Montréal

MSD
Doctorate in mediaeval studies
St. Michael's (Pontifical Institute of Mediaeval Studies)

MServSoc
Maîtrise en service social
Sherbrooke

MSL
Licentiate in mediaeval studies
St. Michael's (Pontifical Institute of Mediaeval Studies)

MSN
Master of science in nursing
British Columbia

MST
Master of sacred theology
King's — Halifax

MSW
Master of social work
British Columbia, Calgary, Carleton, Dalhousie, Manitoba, McGill, Toronto, Waterloo Lutheran, Windsor

MTh
Maîtrise en théologie
Ottawa, Saint-Paul — Ottawa (Ottawa), Sherbrooke

MTh
Master of theology
Acadia Divinity College, Ottawa, St. Michael's, Saint Paul — Ottawa (Ottawa), Trinity

MTrad
Maîtrise en traduction
Montréal

MusB
Bachelor of music
Western Ontario

MusBac
Bachelor of music
McMaster, Toronto

MusBac
Bachelor of music in performance
Toronto

MusDoc
Doctor of music
Toronto

MusM
Master of music
Toronto, Western Ontario

OD
Doctor of optometry
Waterloo

PhD
Doctorat
Montréal, Sherbrooke

PhD
Doctorat en aménagement
Montréal

PhD
Doctorat en philosophie
Ottawa

PhD
Doctorat ès sciences appliquées
Sherbrooke

PhD
Doctor of philosophy
Alberta, British Columbia, Calgary, Carleton, Dalhousie, Guelph, Manitoba, McGill, McMaster, Memorial, New Brunswick, Nova Scotia Technical, Ontario Institute for Studies in Education (Toronto), Ottawa, Queen's, Saskatchewan — Regina, Saskatchewan — Saskatoon, Simon Fraser, Sir George Williams, Toronto, Victoria — B.C., Waterloo, Western Ontario, Windsor, York

PhD
Doctor of philosophy in engineering
Carleton

PhD
Doctor of philosophy in medicine
Memorial

PhD
Doctor of philosophy in theology
St. Michael's

PhD
Doctor of philosophy (medical science)
McMaster

PhD
Philosophiae doctor
Montréal

PhD(CL)
Doctor of philosophy in canon law
Ottawa, Saint Paul — Ottawa (Ottawa)

PhD(DC)
Doctorat en philosophie en droit canonique
Ottawa, Saint-Paul — Ottawa (Ottawa)

PhD(phil)
Philosophiae doctor (philosophie)
Montréal

PhD(psy)
Philosophiae doctor en psychologie
Montréal

PhD(sciencesmédiévales)
Philosophie doctor en sciences médiévales
Montréal

PhD(Th)
Doctorat en philosophie en théologie
Ottawa, Saint-Paul — Ottawa (Ottawa)

PhD(Th)
Doctor of philosophy in theology
Ottawa, Saint Paul — Ottawa (Ottawa)

PhilM
Master of philosophy
Ontario Institute for Studies in Education
(Toronto), Toronto

STB
Bachelor of sacred theology
Bishop's, Trinity

STM
Master of sacred theology
Winnipeg

TchrCertOccTher
Certificate as a teacher of occupational
therapy
Toronto

TchrCertPhysTher
Certificate as a teacher of physical therapy
Toronto

ThD
Doctor of theology
Trintiy, Victoria — Toronto

ThM
Master of theology
Victoria — Toronto

Glossary

Lexique

Explanations of terms are intended as an interpretation of common usage in Canada. Exceptional uses will be noted throughout the handbook, but usually in a context which makes the meaning clear.

Affiliated college. A college which is administratively independent but whose academic affairs are governed by the senate of the university to which it is affiliated. Instruction is given to the college but degrees are awarded by the university.

Approved teaching centre. The term used by The University of Manitoba to indicate an unaffiliated college whose students may prepare for and write the examinations set by the university, for credit toward the degree of the university in a limited number of courses.

Assistantship. An award, usually to a graduate student, in return for which part-time instructional service is to be given.

Associated institutions. A generic term including federated universities and colleges, and affiliated colleges.

Associated university. Rare. See federated university.

Bursary. A monetary award to assist a student in the pursuit of his studies, based on financial need and satisfactory academic achievement.

Campus. University buildings and the site on which they are located.

Co-educational. Refers to a university or college which admits both men and women.

College. An institution of post-secondary education which usually has only one faculty. If may award a first degree but is more likely to be affiliated to a university by which degrees are conferred on its students. This word is also used in the names of secondary schools, teacher training institutions, private and business training schools.

College of applied arts and technology. The term used in Ontario to designate a two- or three-year post-secondary institute of higher education offering courses which lead to non-university diplomas.

College of general and vocational education. A college in the province of Quebec offering the 13th and 14th years of schooling.

L'explication des termes se fonde sur l'usage commun au Canada. Les usages exceptionnels seront notés dans le manuel mais, généralement, le contexte en précise nettement les sens.

Aide aux étudiants. Aide financière accordée aux étudiants afin de leur permettre de poursuivre leurs études.

Bourse. Octroi monétaire destiné à aider l'étudiant à poursuivre ses études; l'octroi se fonde sur les succès scolaires ou le besoin financier, ou les deux à la fois.

Centre d'études universitaires. Institution prévue pour la province de Québec et destinée à assurer une partie de l'enseignement du premier grade universitaire (la première année ou les deux premières années) dans un nombre suffisant de disciplines de base et de spécialités.

Cité universitaire. Les pavillons d'une université et le site où ils se trouvent.

Coéducationnelle. A trait à une université qui admet les hommes et les femmes.

Collège affilié. Collège indépendant du point de vue administratif, mais dont les programmes scolaires sont régis par le sénat de l'université à laquelle il est affilié. Le collège donne l'enseignement, mais l'université confère les grades.

Collège constituant. Collège faisant partie intégrante d'une université, régi par l'administration de l'université et émargeant au budget de l'université.

Collège d'enseignement général et professionnel (CEGEP). Institution de la province de Québec, 13e et 14e années.

Collège universitaire. Un collège constituant. (Voir au-dessus.)

Cours avec mention. Cours collégial qui met l'accent sur une discipline, mais à un degré moindre que le "cours avec spécialisation".

Cours ordinaire. Parfois désigné: cours général. Cours collégial non spécialisé, qui donne droit généralement au baccalauréat ès arts en quatre ans après l'immatriculation. Cours simple — même que le cours ordinaire.

Community college. One of the terms current with reference to a two- or three-year post-secondary, non-university institution of higher education offering courses which may be credited toward a university degree and also courses which lead to non-university diplomas.

Constituent college. A college which is an integral part of a university, governed by the university administration and sharing the university's budget.

Credit. When a student is given credit for a university subject, he is exempted from it and the number of subjects required for the degree is thus reduced. This word is also used to indicate a unit of study which has been completed and may be counted toward a degree.

Department. A sub-division of a faculty or school, usually devoted to a single discipline, e.g. history.

Exhibition. Rare. Similar to a scholarship.

Extension department courses. Programs for those not enroled as full-time candidates for degrees. Sometimes conducted on campus, sometimes in centres away from the campus. Essentially adult education.

Faculty. Most university teaching is organized in a group of faculties, e.g. arts, law, medicine. Occasionally the word "college" is used in this way. The word "faculty" is used also to mean the teaching staff.

Federated college or university. An institution which holds its degree-granting powers (usually with the exception of those in theology) in abeyance during the term of federation with another university. The working relationship between the two institutions is much the same as between an affiliated college and its parent university.

Fellowship. Similar to a scholarship, but usually for graduate studies and research. Sometimes some teaching service is expected of the recipient.

First year, second year, etc., of course. Counting from junior or senior matriculation, depending on which is the minimum level of admission to the faculty concerned.

Foreign student, international student, student from abroad. One who is temporarily resident in Canada for the purpose of securing education.

Cours avec spécialisation. Cours collégial spécialisé, généralement d'une durée égale à celle du cours ordinaire, mais qui comporte parfois une année de plus.

Crédit. Lorsqu'un étudiant obtient crédit (équivalence) pour une matière universitaire, il en est exempté et le nombre de cours requis pour obtenir le grade est ainsi réduit. Ce mot sert également à indiquer une unité d'étude complétée qui entre en ligne de compte dans l'obtention d'un grade.

Culture populaire. Même sens que cours postscolaires (extension).

Département. Subdivision d'une faculté ou d'une école, qui se consacre généralement à une seule discipline, par exemple: l'histoire.

Ecole. Généralement une subdivision d'une faculté. S'emploie parfois dans la même acception que le mot "faculté".

Ecole affiliée ou annexée. Ecole alliée à la faculté d'une université à peu près de la même façon qu'un collège affilié est allié à une université.

Etudiant étranger. Etudiant qui habite temporairement au Canada afin de s'instruire.

Etudiant du niveau post-grade. Celui qui a obtenu un premier grade universitaire et prépare un grade ou diplôme supérieur.

Etudiant du niveau pré-grade. Celui qui cherche à obtenir son premier diplôme ou grade universitaire dans une discipline donnée.

Externat. Collège pour étudiants qui habitent à l'extérieur du collège.

Faculté. Dans la plupart des universités, l'enseignement est réparti entre un groupe de facultés, par exemple: les facultés des arts, de droit, de médecine.

Grand séminaire. Institution donnant la formation nécessaire aux hommes qui possèdent le baccalauréat ès arts et qui se destinent à la prêtrise.

Immatriculation junior. Fin du cycle de quatre ans d'études secondaires.

Immatriculation senior. Fin d'un cours préparatoire d'un an après le niveau de l'immatriculation junior.

Freshman, sophomore, junior, senior year of course. First, second, third, fourth year, usually counting from the junior matriculation level.

General course. Sometimes referred to as a general program. An unspecialized university course, commonly leading to a bachelor's degree in four years beyond junior matriculation, or three years beyond senior matriculation.

Graduate student. One working toward a higher degree or diploma in a given discipline.

Grant-in-aid. Ordinarily, of research.

Honors course. Sometimes referred to as an honors program. A specialized university course, sometimes of the same length as the pass or general course, more often one year longer.

Institute. Usually a sub-division of a faculty or school, or a grouping of disciplines in more than one faculty or school, e.g. northern studies. Sometimes the equivalent of a school or faculty.

Junior college. A college which ordinarily gives instruction to within two years of a first or baccalaureate degree.

Junior matriculation. Eligibility for admission to university at the lower of the two common levels of entry. A student holding a secondary school graduation certificate may or may not have "junior matriculation" standing, depending on the number and pattern of the subjects taken and his standing on the examinations.

Loan. Similar to a bursary except that it must be repaid, usually following termination of studies, and with interest.

Ordinary course. Same as "general course".

Pass course. Same as "general course".

Post-secondary. Describes a wide range of institutions open to high school matriculants and others who may qualify.

Preliminary year. When a university calls the course-year beyond senior matriculation "first year", but offers instruction in a course-year following junior matriculation, the latter is usually referred to as the "preliminary year".

Institut. Subdivision d'une faculté ou d'une école, ou groupement de disciplines dans plus d'une faculté ou d'une école, par exemple: l'institut de géographie.

Institutions associées. Terme générique qui comprend les collèges et les séminaires affiliés, ainsi que les écoles annexées.

Première année, deuxième année, etc., du cours. A compter de l'immatriculation junior, de l'immatriculation senior ou du baccalauréat ès arts, selon le niveau minimum d'admission à la faculté intéressée.

Prêt. Semblable à une bourse, sauf qu'il doit être remboursé, généralement après la fin des études et avec intérêt.

Secondaire V. Dernière année du cours secondaire (12e année) dans la province de Québec.

Semestre. Un des termes ou sessions de cours formant une année universitaire composée de deux termes, chacun étant environ de quinze semaines.

Trimestre. Un des termes ou sessions de cours formant une année universitaire composée de trois termes, chacun étant environ de quinze semaines.

Unité. Voir "crédit".

Université. Institution d'enseignement supérieur, en vue des carrières libérales et de recherches, qui confère les premiers grades ainsi que des grades supérieurs.

Qualifying year. Usually a course-year of further preparation, beyond the first degree, before entry as a candidate for a higher degree.

Regional college. The term used in British Columbia to designate a two- or three-year post-secondary institution of higher education administered by two or more neighboring school districts. Usually offers courses which may be credited toward a university degree and also courses which lead to non-university diplomas.

Scholarship. A monetary award to assist a student in the pursuit of his studies, based on outstanding academic achievement but usually not on financial need.

School. Usually a sub-division of a faculty. Sometimes used in the same way as the word "faculty".

School district college. The term used in British Columbia to designate a two- or three-year post-secondary institution of higher education administered by a single school district. Usually offers courses which may be credited toward a university degree and also courses which lead to non-university diplomas.

Semester. One of the terms or periods of instruction in a two-term academic year, usually of about fifteen weeks' duration.

Seminary. A theological training institution.

Senior matriculation. Eligibility for admission to university at the higher of the two common levels of entry. Involves one year of study beyond the junior matriculation level.

Student aid. Financial assistance to students to enable them to pursue their studies.

Terminal. Sometimes used to designate technical or occupational programs.

Transfer. Often used in reference to a program of studies designed to provide credits toward a baccalaureate degree.

Trimester. One of the terms or periods of instruction in a three-term academic year, usually of about fifteen weeks' duration.

Undergraduate student. One working toward a first certificate, diploma or degree in a given discipline.

University. An institution of post-secondary education, professional training, and research, which awards first and advanced degrees.

University college. A "constituent college". (See above.)

Unit. See "Credit".

Bibliography

Bibliographie

Academic Board for Higher Education. *A guide to post-secondary education in British Columbia.* Victoria, 1967. 26 p.

Association of Universities and Colleges of Canada/Association des Universités et Collèges du Canada. *Proceedings/ Délibérations.* Ottawa. (Annual/annuel).

Association of Universities and Colleges of Canada/Association des Universités et Collèges du Canada. *Select bibliography on higher education/ Une bibliographie sur l'enseignement supérieur.* Ottawa, 1961. (Quarterly/trimestriel).

Association of Universities and Colleges of Canada/Association des Universités et Collèges du Canada. *University Affairs/ Affaires universitaires.* Ottawa. (Ten times a year with supplements/dix fois par année avec suppléments).

Canada. Bureau of Statistics. Education Division. *Awards for graduate study and research.* Ottawa, Queen's Printer, 1969. 455 p. ($4.00).

Canada. Bureau of Statistics. Education Division/Bureau de la statistique. Division de l'éducation. *Survey of libraries*: Part II, academic libraries; Part III, library education/ *Relevé des bibliothèques*: Partie II, bibliothèques scolaires; Partie III, la formation professionnelle. Ottawa, Queen's Printer/Imprimeur de la Reine. (Annual/annuel).

Canada. Bureau of Statistics. Education Division. *University student expenditure and income in Canada*: Part I, non-Canadian students; Part II, Canadian undergraduate students; Part III, Canadian graduate students. Ottawa, Queen's Printer. (Occasional).

Canada. Bureau of Statistics. Higher Education Section/Bureau de la statistique. Section de l'enseignement supérieur. *Canadian universities, income and expenditures/ Universités canadiennes, recettes et dépenses.* Ottawa, Queen's Printer/ Imprimeur de la Reine. (Annual/annuel).

Canada. Bureau of Statistics. Higher Education Section/Bureau de la statistique. Section de l'enseignement supérieur. *Salaries and qualifications of teachers in universities and colleges/ Traitements et qualifications des professeurs des universités et collèges.* Ottawa, Queen's Printer/ Imprimeur de la Reine. (Annual/annuel).

Canada. Bureau of Statistics. Higher Education Section/Bureau de la statistique. Section de l'enseignement supérieur. *Survey of higher education*: Part I, Fall enrolment in universities and colleges; Part II, degrees, staff and summary/ *Relevé de l'enseignement supérieur*: Partie I, Inscriptions d'automne aux universités et collèges; Partie II, grades, personnel et résumé. Ottawa, Queen's Printer/Imprimeur de la Reine. (Annual/ annuel).

Canada. Department of External Affairs/ Ministère des Affaires extérieures. *Notes for the guidance of students considering university study in Canada/ Guide pour les étudiants étrangers qui désirent poursuivre des études universitaires au Canada.* Prepared by/ Préparé par: AUCC, Ottawa, 1967. 26 p. (Available outside Canada from Canadian missions abroad or the department; in Canada from AUCC/ Disponible à l'étranger des missions canadiennes et du ministère; au Canada de l'AUCC).

Canada. Department of Industry, Trade and Commerce. Industrial Research and Development Incentives Act. *Federal grants for industrial R & D how to apply.* Ottawa, 1970. 78 p.

Canada. Secretary of State. Education Support Branch. *Federal expenditures on research in the academic community. 1966-67, 1967-68.* Ottawa, Queen's Printer, 1969. 113 p. (Bilingual).

Canada Council/Conseil des arts du Canada. *Guide to applicants for research grants in the humanities and social sciences/ Guide des candidats aux subventions de recherches en humanités et en sciences sociales.* Ottawa, 1970. 32 p.

Canadian Association of Departments of Extension and Summer Schools. *Canadian university correspondence courses.* Saskatoon, University of Saskatchewan. (Annual).

Canadian Association of University Teachers/Association canadienne des professeurs d'université "C.A.U.T. Bulletin/ Bulletin de l'A.C.P.U." Ottawa. (Quarterly/ trimestriel).

Canadian Council for Research in Education/Conseil canadien pour la recherche en éducation. *Canadian education index/ Répertoire canadien sur l'éducation.* Ottawa, 1965. (Quarterly/trimestriel).

Canadian Scholarship Trust Foundation. *National student aid information service/ Service de renseignements, aide nationale aux étudiants.* Don Mills, Ontario, 300 North American Tower, 797 Don Mills Road.

Canadian Teachers' Federation. *Bibliographies in education series.* Ottawa, 1969–. (Occasional).

Centre d'animation et de recherche en éducation. *Prospectives.* Montréal. (Bimestriel).

Commission d'étude sur les relations entre les universités et les gouvernements. *L'Université, la société et le gouvernement*; rapport. Ottawa, Editions de l'Université d'Ottawa, 1970. 268 pp.

Commission of inquiry on forty Catholic church-related colleges and universities. *A commitment to higher education in Canada.* Ottawa, National Education office, 1970. 272 p.

Commission on the Financing of Higher Education/Commission sur le financement de l'enseignement supérieur. *Financing higher education in Canada*; being the report of a commission to the Association of Universities and Colleges of Canada/ *Le financement de l'enseignement supérieur au Canada*; rapport d'une commission d'enquête à l'Association des Universités et Collèges du Canada. Toronto/Québec, University of Toronto Press/ Presses de l'Université Laval, 1965. 98 p. ($2.00).

Commission on the relations between universities and governments. *Studies on the university, society and government prepared for the commission/ Etudes sur l'université, la société et le gouvernement préparées pour la commission.* Ottawa, University of Ottawa Press/Editions de l'Université d'Ottawa, 1970. 2 v.

Commission on the relations between universities and government. *The university, society and government*; report. Ottawa, University of Ottawa Press, 1970. 252 p.

Downs, R. B. *Resources of Canadian academic and research libraries.* Ottawa, AUCC, 1967. 301 p.

Downs, R. B. *Ressources des bibliothèques d'université et de recherche au Canada.* Ottawa, AUCC, 1967. 325 pp.

Duff, Sir James and/et Berdahl, R.O. *University government in Canada/ Structures administratives des universités au Canada.* Ottawa, Association of Universities and Colleges of Canada and Canadian Association of University Teachers/ Association des Universités et Collèges du Canada et l'Association canadienne des professeurs d'université. 1966. 97 p. ($2.00).

Economic Council of Canada/Conseil économique du Canada. *Enrolment in school and universities,* 1951-52 to 1975-76/ *Inscriptions aux écoles et aux universités,* 1951-52 à 1975-76. By/Par W. M. Illing and/et Z. E. Zsigmond. Ottawa, Queen's Printer/Imprimeur de la Reine, 1967. 166 p. ($1.25).

Finley, E. G. *Sources à consulter en vue d'une compilation bibliographique sur l'évolution de l'éducation au Canada-français.* Ottawa, Secrétariat d'Etat, 1969. 60 pp.

Harris, R. S. and/et Tremblay, A. *A bibliography of higher education in Canada/ Bibliographie de l'enseignement supérieur au Canada.* Toronto/Québec, University of Toronto Press/Presses de l'Université Laval, 1960. 158 p. (Studies in higher education in Canada/Etudes dans l'enseignement supérieur au Canada, no./n° 1. ($6.50).

Harris, R. S. ed. *Changing patterns of higher education in Canada.* Toronto, University of Toronto Press, 1966. 106 p.

Harris, R. S. *Supplement to A bibliography of higher education in Canada/ Supplément à la Bibliographie de l'enseignement supérieur au Canada.* Toronto/Québec, University of Toronto Press/ Presses de l'Université Laval, 1965. 107 p. (Studies in higher education in Canada/Etudes dans l'enseignement supérieur au Canada, no./n° 3. ($6.50).

LeBel, M. "Collèges classiques, classical colleges". In *Encyclopedia Canadiana.* Montreal, Grolier, 1966. p. 20-22, v. 3.

Masters, D. C. C. *Protestant church colleges in Canada.* Ottawa, University of Toronto Press, 1966. 225 p.

Mitchener, R. D. ed. *Canadian universities and colleges.* Ottawa, Department of External Affairs, Information Division, 1964. (Reference paper no. 106). (Available outside Canada only, from the department or from Canadian missions abroad/Pour usage à l'extérieur du Canada, disponible du ministère des Affaires extérieures ou des missions canadiennes à l'étranger).

National Research Council of Canada/
Conseil national de recherches du Canada.
*Annual report on support of university
research/Compte rendu annuel sur l'aide
apportée à la recherche dans les universités.*
Ottawa. (Annual/annuel).

National Research Council of Canada.
Scientific meetings and conferences. Ottawa.
(Quarterly).

New Brunswick. Committee on the Financing
of Higher Education. *Report,* 1967.
Fredericton, 1967. 74 p.

New Brunswick. Higher education
commission. *First annual report,* 1967-68.
Fredericton, 1968. 20 p.

New Brunswick. Royal Commission on
Higher Education in New Brunswick. *Report
of the Royal ...* Fredericton, Queen's Printer,
1962.

Newfoundland. Royal Commission on
Education and Youth, *Report.* St. John's
Queen's Printer, 1967-68. 2 v.

Nouveau-Brunswick. Commission de
l'enseignement supérieur. *Premier rapport
annuel,* 1967-68. Fredericton, 1968. 22 pp.
(Bilingue).

Nova Scotia. University Grants Committee.
Higher education in Nova Scotia; the annual
report of the University Grants Committee
for the year ending December 31, 1967.
Halifax, 1968. 53 p.

Ontario. Department of University Affairs.
Horizons; a guide to education opportunities
in Ontario beyond secondary schools.
Toronto. (Annual).

Ontario. Department of University Affairs.
Report. Toronto, 1968. 130 p.

Organization for Economic Co-operation and
Development. *Reviews of National Science
Policy in Canada.* Ottawa, Queen's Printer,
1969. 453 p. (Bilingual).

Prince Edward Island. *Policy statement on
post-secondary education.* Charlottetown,
1968. 39 p.

Prince Edward Island. Royal Commission on
Higher Education. *Report of the Royal
Commission ...* Charlottetown, Queen's
Printer, 1965.

Québec (Prov.). Commission royale d'enquête
sur l'enseignement dans la province de
Québec/ Royal commission of inquiry on
education in the province of Quebec. *Rapport
de la Commission .../ Report of the Royal
commission ...* Québec, Queen's Printer/
Imprimeur de la Reine, 1963-1966. 5 v.

Québec (Prov.). Ministère de l'Education.
Service d'information. *Annuaire de
l'enseignement supérieur et postsecondaire.*
Québec, Imprimeur de la Reine. (Annuel).

Qu'bec (Prov.). Ministère de l'Education.
Service d'information. *L'Enseignement
collégial et les collèges d'enseignement général
et professionnel.* Québec, Imprimeur de la
Reinc, 1967. 222 pp. (Documents
d'éducation, n° 3).

Science Council of Canada. *The role of the
federal government in support of research in
Canadian universities with a minority report.*
Ottawa, Queen's Printer, 1969. 361 p.
(Bilingual).

Service for Admission to College and
University/Service d'admission au collège et
à l'université. *Requirements for admission to
Canadian colleges and universities/Conditions
d'admission dans les collèges et universités du
Canada.* Ottawa, 1971. 150 p.

Service for Admission to College and
University/Service d'admission au collège et
à l'université. *Proceedings/Délibérations.*
Ottawa, 1969. (Annual/annuel).

Sheffield, E. F. "The universities of Canada".
In: Association of Commonwealth
Universities. *Commonwealth universities
yearbook.* London, 1969. pp. 1031-1047.

United Nations Educational, Scientific and
Cultural Organization. *Study abroad/Etudes
à l'étranger/Estudios en el extranjero.* Paris,
(Annual/annuel). ($4.00) (Available from
Queen's Printer/disponible chez l'Imprimeur
de la Reine).

Wilson, J.D. and others. *Canadian education;
a history.* Scarborough, Prentice-Hall, 1970.
528 p.

Zsigmend, Z.E. and Wenass, C. S. *Enrolment
in educational institutions by province 1951-52
to 1980-81.* Ottawa, Economic Council of
Canada 1970. 311 p.

Undergraduate and
graduate diploma and
degree courses at Canadian
universities and colleges,
1972

Cours préparatoires
à un premier diplôme et à
des diplôme supérieurs
dans les universités
et collèges du Canada, 1972

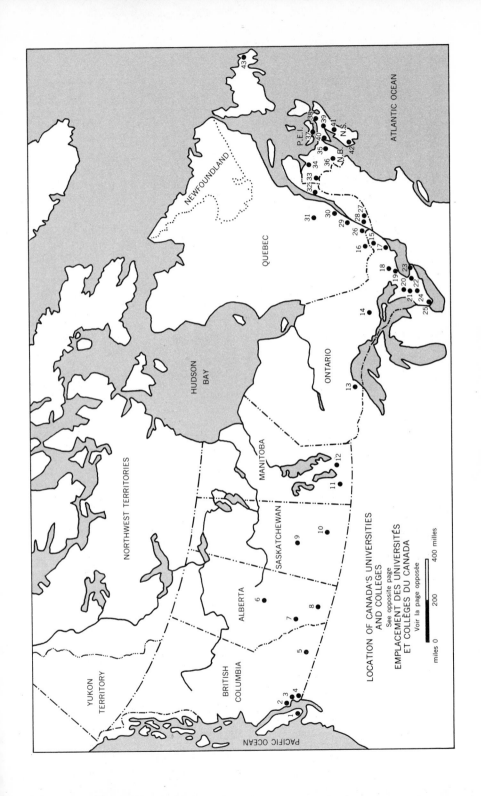

LOCATION OF CANADA'S UNIVERSITIES
AND COLLEGES
See opposite page
EMPLACEMENT DES UNIVERSITÉS
ET COLLÈGES DU CANADA
Voir la page opposée

miles 0   200   400 milles

General information

Renseignements généraux

On the following pages is a list of the degree programs offered by Canadian universities and colleges. The list is based upon information provided by the institutions for inclusion in the 1972 edition of the AUCC handbook *Universities and Colleges of Canada* and the 1971-72 calendars of the universities and colleges.

It is intended that the lists be used in the following manner. First, check the index of courses to know how the programs which interest you are listed. They may appear more than once according to the designation given by the university. For example: engineering, civil engineering, mechanical engineering. Check also the French equivalent.

Programs are arranged alphabetically and are listed in the language of instruction (French or English). If a course name is spelled the same in English and in French (e.g. commerce), the symbols (E) and (F) are used. At the end of the index is a key which explains the numbers used to indicate the level at which the program is offered.

There are footnotes following the list of programs. These refer to colleges which offer degree programs but which do not always confer their own degrees on their students. The notes are numbered to match the notations which appear in the list (e.g. Brescia[3]).

For general information concerning courses available within a program (for example: history — European, Commonwealth, Canadian, etc.), please contact AUCC information (151 Slater Street, Ottawa, Ont., K1P 5N1, Canada).

For details regarding a specific undergraduate program, contact the registrar of the university. For details regarding a graduate program, contact the dean of graduate studies of the university. All application forms must be obtained from the university.

For general information concerning a university or college, consult the AUCC handbook *Universities and Colleges of Canada*, the *Commonwealth Universities Yearbook*, or the universities' own calendars and brochures

Renseignements généraux

On trouvera dans les pages qui suivent la liste des programmes d'études conduisant à un grade, offerts par les universités et collèges du Canada. Cette liste se fonde sur les renseignements que ces établissements nous ont fournis afin de les inclure dans le répertoire de l'AUCC, pour 1972, intitulé *Universités et Collèges du Canada* et les annuaires (1971-72) des universités et collèges.

Voici comment utiliser cette liste. D'abord, consultez l'index des cours pour trouver les programmes qui vous intéressent. Ils peuvent figurer plus d'une fois selon l'appellation donnée par l'université. Par exemple, génie, génie civil, génie mécanique. Vérifier aussi l'équivalence en anglais.

Les programmes sont énumérés par ordre alphabétique d'après la langue d'enseignement (français ou anglais). Si un cours porte le même nom en anglais et en français (par exemple, commerce), il est suivi des lettres (E) et (F). A la fin de l'index des cours on trouvera les explications sur les numéros utilisés pour indiquer les niveaux auxquels le programme est offert.

A la suite de la liste des programmes vous trouverez les renvois concernant les collèges qui offrent des programmes d'études conduisant à un grade, mais qui ne confèrent pas toujours leur propre grade à leurs étudiants. Ces notes sont numérotées afin de se reporter aux renvois qui figurent dans les listes. (Par exemple, Brescia[3].)

Pour obtenir des renseignements généraux sur les cours offerts dans le cadre d'un programme d'études (par exemple: histoire européenne, du Commonwealth, canadienne, etc.), veuillez communiquer avec le service d'information de l'AUCC, 151, rue Slater, Ottawa (Ontario), K1P 5N1, Canada.

Pour obtenir des détails sur un programme d'études pré-grade particulier, communiquez avec le secrétaire général de l'université. Pour obtenir des détails sur un programme d'études post-grade, commmuniquez avec le directeur des études supérieures à l'université. Toutes les formules d'admission doivent être obtenues de l'université.

Pour obtenir des renseignements généraux
sur une université ou un collège
quelconque, consultez le répertoire de
l'AUCC, intitulé *Universités et Collèges du
Canada,* le *Commonwealth Universities
Yearbook* ou l'annuaire et les brochures de
l'université.

C

Canadian Northern studies
Canadian Plains Area studies
Canadian politics
Canadian studies
Cancer research
Canon law
Cartographie
Cell biology
Celtic studies
Ceramics
Chemical engineering
Chemical physics
Chemistry
Child clinical psychology
Child psychology (education)
Child study
Chimie
Chimie industrielle
Chimie médicinale
Chinese, Chinese studies
Chinois
Chirurgie
Chirurgie dentaire
Christian ethics
Church history
Cinéma
City planning
Civil engineering
Classics, classical studies
Clinical chemistry
Clinical psychology
Clinical psychology (education)
Clinical sciences (medicine)
Clinical sciences (veterinary medicine)
Clothing and textiles
Combinatorics, optimization (mathematics)
Commerce (E)
Commerce, sciences commerciales
Commercial education, teaching
Commonwealth studies
Communication arts, communications
Communication design (fine art)
Communication disorders (human)
Communications(F)
Communications graphiques
Communications sociales
Community and regional planning or
development
Community health
Community health nursing
Community resource development
Comparative and foreign law
Comparative education
Comparative linguistics
Comparative literature
Comparative political studies
Comparative religion
Composition (music)
Composition (musique)

Comptabilité, sciences comptables
Computer applications (education)
Computer science, computing science
Consommation
Consumer studies, consumer education
Continuing education
Control engineering
Coopération internationale
Coptic
Correctional administration
Counselling scolaire (éducation)
Creative writing
Cree language
Criminologie
Criminology
Crop ecology
Crop science
Crystallography
Cytology
Czech

D

Dairying, dairy science
Dance
Démographie
Dental hygiene
Dental public health
Dental science
Dentistry
Design (E)
Design (F)
Design industriel
Development studies
Didactique des langues secondes
Dietetics
Diététique
Divinity
Drama, dramatic art
Drawing
Droit
Droit canonique

E

Early childhood education
Earth sciences
East Asian studies
Ecologie
Ecology
Economics
Economie, économie appliquée, science
économique
Economie familiale
Economie rurale
Education (E)

Education culturelle
Education en nursing
Education musicale
Education, pédagogie, sciences de l'éducation
Education physique
Education psychology, school psychology
Educational administration
Educational foundations
Educational planning
Educational technology
Educational theory
Egyptian
Electrical communications
Electrical engineering
Electrothermique
Elementary education
Embryologie
Embryology
Engineering
Engineering and management
Engineering materials
Engineering physics
Engineering science
Engineering technology
English
Enseignement à l'enfance exceptionnelle
Enseignement à l'enfance inadaptée
Enseignement de l'éducation physique
Enseignement des métiers
Enseignement élémentaire
Enseignement en arts plastiques
Enseignement en musique
Enseignement préscolaire
Enseignement secondaire
Entomology (agriculture)
Environmental biology
Environmental design (fine art)
Environmental design control (engineering)
Environmental engineering
Environmental horticulture
Environmental studies, conservation planning
Epidemiology
Ergothérapie
Eskimo language
Espagnol
Etudes africaines
Etudes anciennes
Etudes canadiennes
Etudes classiques
Etudes dramatiques
Etudes étrangères
Etudes françaises
Etudes littéraires
Etudes médiévales
Etudes québécoises
Etudes slaves
Exceptional children (education)
Exécution (musique)
Experimental medicine
Experimental psychology
Experimental surgery
Exploitation forestière

F

Family studies, family science
Far Eastern studies
Farm management
Field crops and plant breeding
Film cinema
Finance (E)
Finance (F)
Fisheries
Folklore
Fondements théoriques de l'éducation
Food chemistry
Food management, administration
Food processing and food microbiology
Food science
Foods and nutrition
Forest engineering
Forest hydrology
Forest management
Forest technology
Forestry
Français
French
French studies
French-Canadian studies

G

Gaelic
Génagogie
Genetics
Génétique
Génie
Génie aérospatial
Génie chimique
Génie civil
Génie électrique
Génie forestier
Génie géologique
Génie industriel
Génie mécanique
Génie médical
Génie métallurgique
Génie minier
Génie physique
Génie rural
Geochemistry
Géodésie
Géographie
Geography
Geological engineering
Géologie
Geology, geological sciences
Geophysical engineering
Geophysics
German, German language and literature, studies

Gestion des affaires
Gestion du bureau
Glaciology
Graphics, graphic design, graphics
technology
Gravure
Grec, études grecques
Greek
Guidance, counselling

H

Health administration
Hébreu
Hebrew
Hellenistic Greek
Hindi, Urdu
Hispanic studies
Histoire
Histoire de l'art
Histologie
Histology (pure science)
Histology (veterinary medicine)
History
History and philosophy of religion
History and philosophy of science,
technology
History of canon law
History of Christian worship
History of education
Home economics, household science
Home economics management
Home economics teaching
Horticulture
Hospital administration
Hospital pharmacy
Hotel and food administration
Housing and design (home economics)
Housing and housing design (architecture)
Human development (home economics)
Human relations (psychology)
Human resources development
Humanités
Humanities and social sciences
Humanities of science
Hydrology
Hygiene
Hygiène
Hygiène mentale (nursing)

I

Icelandic
Illustration
Immunologie
Immunology (medicine)

Immunology (veterinary medicine)
India studies
Indian-Eskimo studies
Industrial administration (commerce)
Industrial engineering
Industrial health
Industrial relations
Information culturelle
Information scolaire et professionnelle
Informatique
Intercultural education
Interior design
International affairs, relations, studies
International co-operation
International programs
Islamic studies
Italian
Italien

J

Japanese, Japanese studies
Journalism
Journalisme et information
Judaic studies, Jewish studies

K

Kinanthropologie
Kinanthropology
Kinesiology

L

Laboratory science, technology
Labor relations
Landscape architecture
Langue crise
Langue esquimaude
Latin (E)
Latin (F)
Latin-American studies
Law
Lettres
Library science, library service
Life sciences
Linguistics
Linguistics — translation
Linguistique
Linguistique — traduction
Littérature canadienne
Littérature comparée
Logging

M

Machinery (engineering)
Management, management sciences
Man-environment studies
Marine biology, marine sciences
Marketing (E)
Marketing (F)
Materials engineering, materials handling
Materials science
Mathematical physics
Mathematics
Mathematics(teaching of)
Mathématiques
Mechanical engineering
Médecine
Médecine dentaire
Médecine et chirurgie expérimentales
Médecine vétérinaire
Mediaeval studies
Medical biophysics
Medical laboratory science and technology
Medical microbiology
Medical records science
Medical science
Medical secretarial science
Medical-surgical nursing
Medicine
Mesure et expérimentation (éducation)
Metallurgical engineering
Métallurgie
Metallurgy
Meteorology
Microbial genetics
Microbiologie et immunologie
Microbiology
Microbiology (veterinary medicine)
Minéralogie
Mineral and mining engineering
Missiologie (théologie)
Missiology (theology)
Mission studies
Molecular biology
Museology
Music
Music education
Music history and literature
Musicologie
Musicology
Musique

N

Natural resource management
Natural sciences
Near Eastern studies
Neurologie
Neurology

Neurosurgery
North American studies
Norwegian
Nursing
Nursing education
Nursing service administration
Nutrition(F)
Nutrition (agriculture)
Nutrition (applied human)
Nutritional biochemistry

O

Obstetrics and gynaecology
Obstetrique et gynécologie
Occupational therapy
Occupational therapy (teaching of)
Ocean engineering
Oceanography
Ophthalmic science, ophthalmology
Opthalmologie
Optométrie
Optometry
Oral biology
Oral surgery
Organizational behavior (commerce)
Orientation (F)
Orthodontics, paedodontics, periodontics
Orthodontie, pédodontie
Orthopédagogie
Orthophonie et audiologie
Otolaryngology
Oth-rhino-laryngologie
Outpost nursing

P

Pacific studies
Paediatrics
Painting
Palaeobiology
Pali
Parasitologie
Parasitology
Parasitology (veterinary medicine)
Pastoral counselling
Pastorale familiale
Pastorale scolaire
Pastoral studies
Pathological chemistry
Pathologie
Pathologie (médecine vétérinaire)
Pathology (human)
Pathology (veterinary medicine)
Pédologie (forestière)
Peinture

Performance (music)
Persian
Petroleum engineering
Pharmaceutical chemistry
Pharmaceutics, pharmaceutical science
Pharmacie
Pharmacognosie
Pharmacognosy
Pharmacologie
Pharmacology
Pharmacy
Philosophie
Philosophy
Philosophy of education
Phonétique
Photogrammétrie
Physiatrie
Physical education, physical and health
education
Physics
Physiological hygiene
Physiological optics
Physiologie
Physiologie animale
Physiology
Physiology (veterinary medicine)
Physiothérapie
Physiotherapy
Physiotherapy (teaching of)
Physique
Phytotéchnie
Planification régionale
Plant ecology
Plant physiology
Plant science
Polish
Political philosophy
Politics, political science, studies
Polonais
Portuguese
Poultry science
Power engineering
Preventive medicine
Print-making
Processing, process control (engineering)
Product manufacturing, development
(pharmacy)
Psychiatric nursing
Psychiatrie
Psychiatrie (nursing)
Psychiatry
Psychobiology
Psycho-éducation
Psychologie
Psychologie clinique, psychologie clinique de
l'enfant
Psychologie scolaire, psychologie
éducationnelle
Psychology
Psycho-mathématiques
Psycho-pédagogie
Psychopedagogy

Public administration
Public health
Public health nursing

Q

Quantitative analysis
Quantitative methods, operations research

R

Radioactive tracer work (pharmacy)
Radiologie, radiothérapie
Radiology
Réadaptation
Recherche culturelle
Recherche opérationnelle (administration)
Recreation
Recreation administration
Recreation education
Récréologie
Recreology
Regional planning
Rehabilitation medicine
Relations de travail
Relations humaines
Relations industrielles
Religion, religious studies, education
Resource management (forestry)
Resources, resources development
Restorative dentistry and prosthodontics
Retailing (business)
Roman studies
Rural sociology
Russe
Russian

S

Sanskrit
School music
Science (E) general program
Sciences (F) cours général
Science politique
Sciences agronomiques
Sciences cliniques
Sciences de la gestion
Sciences de la santé
Sciences de la terre
Sciences de l'eau
Sciences domestiques
Sciences du bois
Sciences forestières

Sciences humaines de la religion
Sciences infirmières, nursing
Sciences missionnaires
Sciences religieuses
Sciences secrétarielles
Scottish studies
Sculpture (E)
Sculpture (F)
Secondary school education
Secretarial administration
Secretarial science, secretarial arts
Serbo-Croatian
Service social, travail social
Silvics, silviculture
Slavonics, Slavic studies
Social action, development, theory
Social communications
Social leadership, development
Social, political and economic thought
Social work, social welfare
Sociologie
Sociology
Soil science
Sols
Soviet studies, Russian studies, East
European studies
Space science (experimental)
Spanish
Spanish-American studies
Special education
Speech pathology and audiology
Statistics
Structures (architecture, engineering)
Studio art
Surgery
Surgery (veterinary medicine)
Surveying engineering
Sylviculture (F)
Syriac, Aramaic
Systems design

T

Taiga studies
Teaching and supervision in nursing
Technologie de l'enseignement
Technologie médicale
Testing and measurement, experimentation
(education)
Textiles and design
Théâtre
Theatre, theatre arts
Théologie
Theology, theological studies
Theory and composition (music)
Therapeutics
Tibetan
Traduction
Translation and interpretation

Transportation and utilities, transportation
planning
Turkish

U

Ukrainian
Ukrainien
Urban and regional planning, studies
Urban forestry
Urbanisme
Urban planning
Urban studies
Urology

V

Vernacular literature
Veterinary medicine
Veterinary public health
Visual arts
Vivres

W

War studies
Water resources engineering
West Indian studies
Wildlife biology
Wildlife management
Wildlife resources

Y

Yiddish

Z

Zoologie
Zoology
Zootechnie

Key	Explication des numéros

1 Doctorate

1 Doctorat

2 Master of philosophy (University of Toronto, University of Waterloo, Memorial University of Newfoundland)

2 Maîtrise en philosophie (Université de Toronto, Université de Waterloo, Université Memorial de Terre-Neuve)

3 Master

3 Maîtrise

4 Licence

4 Licence

5 Graduate diploma

5 Diplôme d'études supérieures

6 Bachelor and first professional (e.g., BA, BSc, MD, DVM, DMD, LLB)

6 Baccalauréat et premier diplôme professionnel (p. ex. BA, BSc, MD, DMV, DCD, LLB)

7 Undergraduate diploma

7 Diplôme d'études pré-grade

8 Special certificate

8 Certificat spécial

9 Minor specialization only or courses offered

9 Spécialisation mineure seulement ou cours offerts

Accounting

		6	Alberta
1	4	6	British Columbia
		6	Calgary
		6	Carleton
		6	Loyola[9]
		6	Manitoba
		6	McGill
		6	Memorial
		6	Mount Allison
		6	Ottawa
		6	St. Francis Xavier
		6	Saint Mary's
	3	6	Saskatchewan (Sask.)
		6	Sir George Williams
		6	Windsor

Actuarial science

	3	6	Manitoba
		6	Toronto
		6	Waterloo
1	3	6	Western Ontario

Actuariat

		6	Laval

Administration (F)

1	3	6	Laval
	3		Moncton
		6	Québec (Chicoutimi)
		6	Québec (Montréal)
		6	Québec (Rimouski)
		6	Québec (Trois-Rivières)
		6	Sherbrooke

Administration, administrative studies

		6	Brock
		6	Calgary
		6	Saskatchewan (Regina)
		7	Windsor
		6	Winnipeg
1	3	6	York

Administration correctionnelle

	3		Ottawa

Administration des affaires

1	3	6	Montréal
		7	Ottawa
	3		Sherbrooke

Administration du nursing

	3		Montréal

Administration hospitalière

	3		Montréal
	3		Ottawa

Administration publique

	6	7	Ottawa
	3		Québec (l'Ecole nationale d'administration publique)

Administration scolaire

		6	Laval
	3		Moncton
	3		Ottawa
	3		Sherbrooke

Adult education

	3		Guelph
1	3		Ontario Institute for Studies in Education[11]
	3	6	St. Francis Xavier

Aeronautical engineering

1	3		Carleton

Aerospace studies

1	3	6	Toronto

African studies, Middle East studies

		6	McGill
		6	Simon Fraser

Agricultural biology

		6	Guelph
		6	Saskatchewan (Sask.)

Agricultural chemistry

1	3	6	McGill
		6	Saskatchewan (Sask.)

Agricultural commerce, business

		6	Manitoba
		6	McGill
		7	Nova Scotia Agricultural

Agricultural economics

1	3	6	Alberta
	3	6	British Columbia
	3	6	Guelph
	3	6	Manitoba
1	3	6	McGill
1	3	6	Saskatchewan (Sask.)

Agricultural engineering

	3	6	Alberta
	3	6	British Columbia
		6	Guelph
	3	6	Manitoba
1	3	6	McGill
		6	Nova Scotia Technical
1	3	6	Saskatchewan (Sask.)

Agricultural extension
3 British Columbia
3 Guelph

Agricultural land planning and development
6 McGill

Agricultural mechanics, mechanization
3 6 Alberta
3 British Columbia
6 Saskatchewan (Sask.)

Agricultural microbiology
6 Guelph
3 6 Saskatchewan (Sask.)

Agriculture (E)
1 3 6 Alberta
1 3 6 British Columbia
1 3 6 Guelph
1 3 6 7 Manitoba
1 3 6 7 McGill
7 Nova Scotia Agricultural
1 3 5 6 7 Saskatchewan (Sask.)

Agriculture (F)
1 3 6 Laval

Agrobiologie
1 3 6 Laval

Agro-économie
6 Laval

Agrometeorology
1 3 Guelph

Agronomy
1 3 6 McGill

Air and space law
3 5 McGill

Akkadian
9 Dalhousie
9 King's (Halifax)[7]
9 Toronto

Allemand, études allemandes
6 Laurentienne
1 3 6 Laval
9 Moncton
1 3 6 Montréal
3 6 Ottawa
6 Québec (Montréal)
6 Québec (Trois-Rivières)

Aménagement
1 3 6 Laval
1 3 Montréal

Aménagement du territoire et developpement régional
3 Laval

Aménagement forestier, écologie forestière
1 3 Laval

American studies
6 Mount Allison

Anaesthesia
5 McGill
5 Queen's
5 Toronto
5 Western Ontario

Anatomie
1 3 Laval
1 3 Montréal
1 3 Sherbrooke

Anatomie comparée (médecine vétérinaire)
3 Montréal

Anatomy (human)
1 3 Alberta
1 3 British Columbia
3 Dalhousie
1 3 Manitoba
1 3 6 McGill
1 3 Ottawa
1 3 Queen's
1 3 Saskatchewan (Sask.)
1 3 6 Toronto
1 3 6 Western Ontario

Anatomy (pure science)
3 Dalhousie
3 Manitoba
1 3 6 Saskatchewan (Sask.)
6 Western Ontario

Anatomy (veterinary medicine)
1 3 Guelph
3 6 Saskatchewan (Sask.)

Ancient history
1 3 6 Alberta
6 Brock
3 Dalhousie
3 Ottawa
1 2 3 6 Toronto

Anesthésie
5 Laval

Anglais, études anglaises
6 Laurentienne
1 3 6 Laval
1 3 6 Montréal
6 Ottawa
6 Québec (Montréal)
6 Québec (Trois-Rivières)
6 Sainte-Anne
6 Sherbrooke

Animal behavior
6 McGill

Animal genetics
1 3 6 British Columbia
1 3 6 McGill

Animal pathology
1 3 McGill

Animal physiology
6 British Columbia
1 3 McGill

Animal resource ecology
1 3 British Columbia

Animal science
1 3 6 Alberta
1 3 6 British Columbia
1 3 6 Guelph
1 3 6 Manitoba
1 3 6 McGill
7 Nova Scotia Agricultural
1 3 6 Saskatchewan (Sask.)

Animation culturelle
6 Québec (Montréal)

Anthropologie
1 3 6 Laval
1 3 6 Montréal

Anthropology
1 3 6 Alberta
1 3 6 British Columbia
3 6 Calgary
6 Carleton
3 6 Guelph
6 Lakehead
6 Lethbridge
3 6 Manitoba
1 3 6 McGill
3 6 McMaster
2 3 6 Memorial
6 New Brunswick
6 St. Jerome's[12]
6 St. John's[13]
6 Saint Mary's
6 Saskatchewan (Regina)
6 Saskatchewan (Sask.)
1 3 6 Simon Fraser
1 2 3 6 Toronto
6 Trent
3 6 Victoria (B.C.)
6 Waterloo
6 Waterloo Lutheran
6 Western Ontario
6 Windsor
6 Winnipeg
6 York

Apiculture
1 3 Guelph

Applied linguistics
6 Marianopolis[10]
3 Ottawa
1 3 Simon Fraser

Applied mathematics
6 Alberta
1 3 British Columbia
1 3 6 Calgary
1 3 Carleton
6 Lakehead
6 Laurentian
6 McMaster
1 3 6 Nova Scotia Technical
1 3 6 Toronto
1 2 3 6 Waterloo
1 3 6 Western Ontario

Applied psychology
3 McGill
3 Sir George Williams
3 Waterloo

Applied social science
6 Sir George Williams
6 Waterloo

Arabic
9 Dalhousie
9 Manitoba
9 McGill
9 Sir George Williams
9 Toronto

Archéologie classique
1 3 6 Laval

Archeology
3 6 Alberta
1 3 6 Calgary
1 3 6 Simon Fraser
1 2 3 6 Toronto

Architectural design

3			McGill

Architecture (E)

3	6		British Columbia
3			Calgary
	6		Carleton
3	6		Manitoba
3	6		McGill
3	6		Nova Scotia Technical
3	6		Toronto
	6		Waterloo

Architecture (F)

	3	6	Laval
1	3	6	Montréal

Architecture paysagiste

6	Montréal

Arid land development

5	McGill

Arpentage

1	3	6	Laval

Art as applied to medicine

6	Toronto

Art dramatique

6	Moncton
6	Québec (Montréal)

Art education

6		British Columbia
6		N.S. College of Art and Design
6		Queen's
6		Saskatchewan (Sask.)
3	5	Sir George Williams

Art, fine arts

3	6		Alberta
3	6		British Columbia
	6		Calgary
	6		Carleton
	6		Guelph
	6		Lethbridge
	6	7	Manitoba
1	3	6	McGill
	6		McMaster
	6		Mount Allison
	6	7	N.S. College of Art and Design
	6		Notre Dame
		7	Ottawa
	6		Saskatchewan (Regina)
3	6		Saskatchewan (Sask.)
	6		Sir George Williams
	6		Toronto
1	3	6	Victoria (B.C.)

6	Waterloo
6	Western Ontario
6	Windsor
6	York

Art history

		6	Alberta
		6	British Columbia
		6	Carleton
1	3	6	McGill
		6	McMaster
		6	Queen's
		6	Saskatchewan (Regina)
	3	6	Saskatchewan (Sask.)
		6	Sir George Williams
1 2	3		Toronto
	3	6	Victoria (B.C.)
		6	Windsor
		6	York

Arts (E) (general program)

6	Acadia
6	Alberta
6	Bishop's
6	Brandon
6	Brescia[3]
6	British Columbia
6	Brock
6	Calgary
6	Carleton
6	Christ the King
6	Dalhousie
6	Guelph
6	Huron[5]
6	King's (Halifax)[7]
6	King's (London)[8]
6	Lakehead
6	Laurentian
6	Lethbridge
6	Loyola[9]
6	Manitoba
6	Marianopolis[10]
6	McGill
6	McMaster
6	Memorial
6	Mount Allison
6	Mount Saint Vincent
6	New Brunswick
6	Notre Dame
6	Ottawa
6	Prince Edward Island
6	Queen's
6	Royal Military
6	St. Francis Xavier
6	St. Jerome's[12]
6	St. John's[13]
6	Saint Mary's
6	St. Michael's[14]
6	St. Paul's (Winnipeg)[14]
6	St. Thomas More[18]
6	Sainte-Anne
6	Saskatchewan (Regina)

(Arts (E)) general program cont'd)

		6	Saskatchewan (Sask.)
		6	Simon Fraser
		6	Sir George Williams
		6	Toronto
		6	Trent
		6	Trinity[19]
		6	Victoria (B.C.)
		6	Victoria (Toronto)[19]
		6	Waterloo
		6	Waterloo Lutheran
		6	Western Ontario
		6	Windsor
		6	Winnipeg
		6	York

Arts (F) (cours général)

		6	Jean-de-Brébeuf[6]
		6	Laurentienne
		6 7	Laval
		6	Manitoba
		6	Moncton
		6	Ottawa
		6	Québec (Montréal)
		6	Québec (Trois-Rivières)
		6	Sainte-Anne
		6	Sherbrooke

Arts management and administration

3		York

Arts plastiques

		6	Laval
		6 7	Ottawa
		6	Québec (Chicoutimi)
		6	Québec (Montréal)
		6	Québec (Trois-Rivières)

Arts visuels

		6	Laval
		6	Moncton

Asian studies

	3	6	British Columbia
		6	Brock
		6	Guelph
		9	Manitoba
		6	Saint Mary's
		6	Waterloo Lutheran
		6	Windsor

Astronomy

1	3		British Columbia
1	3	6	Toronto
1	3	6	Victoria (B.C.)
1	3	6	Western Ontario

Bactériologie vétérinaire

3		Montréal

Bacteriology

	3		Alberta
1	3	6	Dalhousie
1			Manitoba
1	3	6	Saskatchewan (Sask.)
	5		Toronto
		6	Victoria (B.C.)
1	3	6	Western Ontario

Beaux-arts

	6	Moncton
7		Ottawa

Bibliothéconomie

3	Montréal

Biochemical engineering

1	3	6	Western Ontario

Biochemistry

1	3	6	Alberta
		6	Bishop's
1	3	6	British Columbia
		6	Calgary
		6	Carleton
1	3	6	Dalhousie
1	3		Guelph
		6	Loyola[9]
1	3		Manitoba
1	3	6	McGill
1	3	6	McMaster
1	3	6	Memorial
	3		New Brunswick
1	3	6	Ottawa
1	3	6	Queen's
1	3	6	Saskatchewan (Regina)
1	3	6	Saskatchewan (Sask.)
1	3	6	Simon Fraser
		6	Sir George Williams
1	3	6	Toronto
1	3	6	Victoria (B.C.)
1	3	6	Western Ontario
1	3	6	Windsor

Biochimie

1	3	6	Laval
	3	6	Moncton
1	3	6	Montréal
		6	Québec (Trois-Rivières)
1	3		Sherbrooke

Biologie

	3	6	Laval
		6	Moncton
		6	Montréal
		6	Québec (Chicoutimi)
		6	Québec (Montréal)
		6	Québec (Rimouski)
		6	Québec (Trois-Rivières)
1	3	6	Sherbrooke

Biologie dentaire

	Institution
3	Montréal

Biologie pharmacodynamique et clinique

		Institution
1	3	Montréal

Biology, biological sciences

1	3	6	8	Institution
	3	6		Acadia
1	3	6		Alberta
	3	6		Bishop's
1	3	6		British Columbia
	3	6		Brock
1	3			Calgary
1	3	6		Carleton
1	3	6		Dalhousie
1	3	6		Guelph
	3	6		Lakehead
	3	6		Laurentian
		6		Lethbridge
		6		Loyola[9]
		6		Marianopolis[10]
1	3	6		McGill
1	3	6		McMaster
1	3	6	8	Memorial
	3	6		Mount Allison
		6		Mount Saint Vincent
1	3	6		New Brunswick
		6		Notre Dame
1	3	6		Ottawa
		6		Prince Edward Island
1	3	6		Queen's
	3	6		St. Francis Xavier
		6		Saint Mary's
1	3	6		Saskatchewan (Regina)
1	3	6		Saskatchewan (Sask.)
1	3	6		Simon Fraser
	3	6		Sir George Williams
		6		Toronto
		6		Trent
1	3	6		Victoria (B.C.)
1	3	6		Waterloo
		6		Waterloo Lutheran
1	3	6		Windsor
		6		Winnipeg
1	3	6		York

Biomedical engineering

1	3	Institution
1	3	McGill
1	3	Saskatchewan (Sask.)
1	3	Toronto

Biomedical sciences

1	3	Institution
1	3	McGill

Biomedical sciences (veterinary medicine)

1	3	Institution
1	3	Guelph

Biometrics

1	3	Institution
1	3	Toronto

Biophysics

1	3	6	Institution
1	3		Dalhousie
		6	McGill
	3		McMaster
		6	Saskatchewan (Sask.)
1	3	6	Western Ontario

Biophysique

1	3	Institution
1	3	Sherbrooke

Botanique

1	3	Institution
1	3	Montréal

Botany

1	3	6	Institution
1	3	6	Alberta
		6	Brandon
1	3	6	British Columbia
		6	Calgary
1	3	6	Guelph
1	3	6	Manitoba
1	3	6	McGill
		6	Notre Dame
1	3	6	Toronto

Business, business administration

1	3	5	6	7	8	Institution
			6			Acadia
	3					Alberta
			6			Bishop's
1	3					British Columbia
	3					Dalhousie
		5		7		Lakehead
		5				Laurentian
			6			Loyola[9]
			6			Manitoba
1	3					McGill
	3		6			McMaster
			6			Mount Saint Vincent
			6		8	New Brunswick
				7		Ottawa
			6			Prince Edward Island
	3	5				Queen's
			6			St. Francis Xavier
			6			Saint Mary's
	3					Saskatchewan (Sask.)
	3					Simon Fraser
	3		6			Sir George Williams
1	3	5				Toronto
			6			Waterloo Lutheran
1	3	5	6			Western Ontario
	3	5	6	7		Windsor
	3		6			York

Canadian Northern studies

	Institution
6	Alberta

Canadian Plains Area studies

	Institution
6	Saskatchewan (Regina)

Canadian politics

			Institution
		6	Sir George Williams

Canadian studies

			Institution
		6	Alberta
	3		Carleton
	3		Guelph
		6	Loyola[9]
		9	Manitoba
		6	McGill
		6	McMaster
		6	Lakehead
		6	Mount Allison
	3	6	Saskatchewan (Regina)
		6	Simon Fraser
		6	Sir George Williams
		6	Trent
		6	Waterloo
		6	Winnipeg
		6	York

Cancer research

		Institution
1	3	Saskatchewan (Sask.)

Canon law

				Institution
1	3		6	Ottawa
1	3	4	6	Saint Paul (Ottawa)[15]

Cartographie

		Institution
1	3	Laval

Cell biology

			Institution
		6	McGill
		6	Sir George Williams
1	3		Toronto

Celtic studies

		Institution
3	6	St. Francis Xavier

Ceramics

	Institution
6	Manitoba

Chemical engineering

					Institution
				7	Acadia
1	3		6		Alberta
1	3		6		British Columbia
1	3		6		Calgary
				7	Lakehead
				7	Laurentian
1	3	5	6		McGill
1	3		6		McMaster
	3		6		New Brunswick
1	3		6		Nova Scotia Technical
1	3		6		Ottawa
1	3		6		Queen's
	3		6		Royal Military
	3		6		Saskatchewan (Regina)
1	3		6		Saskatchewan (Sask.)
1	3		6		Toronto
1	3		6		Waterloo
1	3		6		Western Ontario
1	3		6		Windsor

Chemical physics

			Institution
1	3		McMaster
1	3	6	Queen's
1	3	6	Simon Fraser

Chemistry

			Institution
	3	6	Acadia
1	3	6	Alberta
	3	6	Bishop's
		6	Brandon
1	3	6	British Columbia
	3	6	Brock
1	3	6	Calgary
1	3	6	Carleton
1	3	6	Dalhousie
1	3	6	Guelph
	3	6	Lakehead
	3	6	Laurentian
		6	Lethbridge
		6	Loyola[9]
1	3	6	Manitoba
		6	Marianopolis[10]
1	3	6	McGill
1	3	6	McMaster
1	3	6	Memorial
	3	6	Mount Allison
		6	Mount Saint Vincent
1	3	6	New Brunswick
		6	Notre Dame
1	3	6	Ottawa
		6	Prince Edward Island
1	3	6	Queen's
	3		Royal Military
	3	6	St. Francis Xavier
	3	6	St. John's[13]
		6	Saint Mary's
1	3	6	Saskatchewan (Regina)
1	3	6	Saskatchewan (Sask.)
1	3	6	Simon Fraser
1	3	6	Sir George Williams
1	3	6	Toronto
	3	6	Trent
1	3	6	Victoria (B.C.)
1	3	6	Waterloo
		6	Waterloo Lutheran
1	3	6	Western Ontario
1	3	6	Windsor
		6	Winnipeg
1	3	6	York

Child clinical psychology

	Institution
1	Ottawa

Child psychology (education)

		Institution
1	3	Alberta

Child study

		Institution
3	6	Guelph
5		Toronto

Chimie

			Institution
1	3	6	Laval
	3	6	Moncton

(Chimie cont'd)

1	3 4	6	Montréal
		6	Québec (Chicoutimi)
		6	Québec (Montréal)
		6	Québec (Rimouski)
		6	Québec (Trois-Rivières)
1	3	6	Sherbrooke

Chimie industrielle

6	Québec (Montréal)

Chimie médicinale

1 3	Montréal

Chinese, Chinese studies

1	3	6	British Columbia
		9	Guelph
		6	McGill
		9	Ottawa
		9	Saskatchewan (Sask.)
1 2 3		6	Toronto
		9	Victoria (B.C.)
		9	Windsor
		9	York

Chinois

9	Ottawa

Chirurgie

1 3 5	Laval

Chirurgie dentaire

6	Laval
6	Montréal

Christian ethics

1 3	McGill

Church history

1 3	McGill

Cinéma

9	Montréal
9	Ottawa

City planning

3 5	Manitoba

Civil engineering

		7	Acadia
1	3	6	Alberta
1	3	6	British Columbia
1	3	6	Calgary
1	3	6	Carleton
	3		Guelph
		7	Lakehead
		7	Laurentian
		6	Loyola[9]
1	3	5 6	Manitoba
1	3	5 6	McGill
1	3	6	McMaster

	3	6	Memorial
	3	6	New Brunswick
1	3	6	Nova Scotia Technical
1	3	6	Ottawa
1	3	6	Queen's
	3	6	Royal Military
	3	6	Saskatchewan (Regina)
1	3	6	Saskatchewan (Sask.)
1	3	6	Sir George Williams
1	3	6	Toronto
1	3	6	Waterloo
1	3	6	Western Ontario
1	3	6	Windsor

Classics, classical studies

	3		Acadia
1	3	6	Alberta
		6	Bishop's
1	3	6	British Columbia
		6	Brock
		6	Calgary
	3	6	Carleton
	3	6	Dalhousie
		6	Guelph
		6	King's (London)[8]
		6	Loyola[9]
	3	6	Manitoba
		6	Marianopolis
	3	6	McGill
	3	6	McMaster
		6	Memorial
		6	Mount Allison
	3	6	New Brunswick
		6	Ottawa
		6	Prince Edward Island
	3	6	Queen's
		6	St. Francis Xavier
		6	St. John's[13]
		6	Saint Mary's
		6	Saskatchewan (Regina)
	3	6	Saskatchewan (Sask.)
1 2 3		6	Toronto
		6	Trent
		6	Victoria (B.C.)
		6	Waterloo
		6	Waterloo Lutheran
1	3	6	Western Ontario
		6	Windsor
		6	Winnipeg
		6	York

Clinical chemistry

5	Toronto

Clinical psychology

5	Dalhousie
3	Lakehead
1	Ottawa

Clinical psychology (education)

1 3	Alberta
5	Queen's

			Clinical sciences (medicine)
	5		Toronto
3			Western Ontario

			Clinical studies (veterinary medicine)
3	5		Guelph

			Clothing and textiles
		6	Alberta
1	3	6	Guelph
	3	6	Manitoba
		6	Marianopolis
		6	Saskatchewan (Sask.)
		6	Toronto

			Combinatorics, optimization (mathematics)
		6	Sir George Williams
1 2 3		6	Waterloo

			Commerce (E)
		6	Alberta
		6	British Columbia
		6	Calgary
		6	Carleton
		6	Dalhousie
		6	Guelph
		6	Lakehead
		6	Laurentian
		6	Loyola[9]
		6	Manitoba
		6	McGill
		6	McMaster
		6	Memorial
		6	Mount Allison
		6	Ottawa
		6	Queen's
		6	Royal Military
		6	Saint Mary's
		6	St. Michael's[14]
		6	Saskatchewan (Sask.)
3		6	Simon Fraser
		6	Sir George Williams
		6	Toronto
		6	Trinity[19]
		6	Victoria (Toronto)[19]
		6	Windsor

			Commerce, sciences commerciales
3		6	Moncton
		6	Ottawa

			Commercial education, teaching
		6	New Brunswick
		6	Saskatchewan (Regina)

			Commonwealth studies
		6	Queen's

				Communication arts, communications
3				Guelph
		6		Loyola[9]
3				Saskatchewan (Regina)
3				Simon Fraser
			9	Toronto
		6		Windsor

			Communication design (fine art)
		6	N.S. College of Art and Design

			Communication disorders (human)
1	3		McGill
		6	Western Ontario

			Communications (F)
3			Montréal

			Communications graphiques
		6	Laval

				Communications sociales
		6	7	Saint-Paul (Ottawa)[15]

			Community and regional planning or development
3			Alberta
3			British Columbia
3	5		Manitoba
3			McGill

		Community health
3		Queen's

			Community health nursing
	7		British Columbia
3			Toronto

			Community resource development
		6	McGill

		Comparative and foreign law
1	3	McGill

		Comparative education
3		McGill

		Comparative linguistics
1	3	Simon Fraser

			Comparative literature
1	3	6	Alberta
3			British Columbia
3			Carleton

(Comparative literature cont'd)

		6	King's (London)[8]
1	3		Toronto
		6	Windsor

Comparative political studies

	6	Sir George Williams

Comparative religion

1	3	McGill

Composition (music)

		6	Acadia
	3	6	British Columbia
3	4	6	McGill
		6	Ottawa
	3	6	Toronto
	3		Victoria (B.C.)

Composition (musique)

6	Laval
6	Montréal
6	Ottawa

Comptabilité, sciences comptables

4		Laval
	6	Moncton
	6	Ottawa
	6	Québec (Chicoutimi)
	6	Québec (Rimouski)
	6	Québec (Trois-Rivières)
3	6	Sherbrooke

Computer applications (education)

1	3	Ontario Institute for Studies in Education[11]

Computer science, computing science

		6	Acadia
1	3	6	Alberta
1	3	6	British Columbia
		6	Calgary
		6	Guelph
		6	Lakehead
		6	Loyola[9]
	3	6	Manitoba
	3	6	McGill
		6	McMaster
		6	New Brunswick
		6	Ottawa
	3	6	Queen's
		6	St. John's[13]
		6	Saskatchewan (Regina)
		6	Saskatchewan (Sask.)
		6	Simon Fraser
1	3	6	Toronto
	3	6	Victoria (B.C.)

1 2 3		6	Waterloo
3		6	Western Ontario
		6	Windsor
		6	York

Consommation

6	Laval

Consumer studies, consumer education

6	Guelph
6	McGill

Continuing education

3	5	Saskatchewan (Sask.)

Control engineering

1	3	Saskatchewan (Sask.)

Coopération internationale

5	Ottawa

Coptic

9	Dalhousie
9	King's (Halifax)[7]

Correctional administration

3	Ottawa

Counselling scolaire (éducation)

3	Ottawa

Creative writing

3	6	British Columbia
3	6	Victoria (B.C.)
3		Windsor

Cree language

9	Ottawa

Criminologie

1	3	6	Montréal
	3		Ottawa

Criminology

	8	British Columbia
3		Ottawa
3		Toronto

Crop ecology

1	3	6	Alberta

Crop science

1	3		Guelph
1	3	6	Saskatchewan (Sask.)

Crystallography

3	6	McGill

Cytology
5 McGill

Czech
9 Toronto

Dairying, dairy science
7 Manitoba
1 3 6 Saskatchewan (Sask.)

Dance
6 York

Démographie
1 3 6 Montréal

Dental hygiene
7 Acadia
7 Alberta
7 British Columbia
7 Dalhousie
7 Manitoba
7 Toronto

Dental public health
5 Toronto

Dental science
3 Manitoba

Dentistry
3 6 Alberta
6 British Columbia
6 Dalhousie
1 3 6 8 Manitoba
5 6 McGill
6 Saskatchewan (Sask.)
1 3 6 Toronto
6 Western Ontario

Design (E)
6 7 N.S. College of Art and Design

Design (F)
6 Québec (Montréal)

Design industriel
6 Montréal

Development studies
5 Toronto

Didactique des langues secondes
1 3 4 Laval

Dietetics
6 McGill
6 Mount Saint Vincent
6 Ottawa

Diététique
3 6 Laval
6 Moncton
6 Ottawa

Divinity
6 Acadia
6 Alberta
6 Bishop's
3 6 7 King's (Halifax)[7]
6 McGill
3 McMaster
6 Queen's
6 St. John's[13]
3 6 Saint Mary's
6 Victoria (Toronto)[19]
3 7 Waterloo Lutheran
3 Winnipeg

Drama, dramatic art
3 6 Alberta
6 Brock
6 Calgary
6 Guelph
6 Queen's
6 Saskatchewan (Regina)
3 6 Saskatchewan (Sask.)
1 2 3 Toronto
6 Waterloo
9 Western Ontario
6 Windsor
6 Winnipeg
6 York

Drawing
6 Manitoba

Droit
1 3 6 Laval
1 3 4 Montréal
1 3 6 Ottawa
4 6 Sherbrooke

Droit canonique
1 3 6 Ottawa
1 3 4 6 Saint-Paul (Ottawa)[15]

Early childhood education
6 Guelph
8 Manitoba
7 McGill
6 Sir George Williams

Earth sciences
3 6 Guelph
6 Lethbridge
1 3 6 Manitoba
3 6 Waterloo

East Asian studies
6 McGill

(East Asian studies cont'd)

1	2	3	5	6	Institution
1	2	3		6	Toronto
				6	York

Ecologie

1	3	6	Institution
1	3	6	Laval

Ecology

6	Institution
6	McGill
6	Sir George Williams

Economics

1	2	3	5	6	Institution
		3		6	Acadia
1		3		6	Alberta
				6	Bishop's
				6	Brandon
1		3		6	British Columbia
				6	Brock
1		3		6	Calgary
1		3		6	Carleton
1		3		6	Dalhousie
		3		6	Guelph
				6	King's (London)[8]
		3		6	Lakehead
				6	Laurentian
				6	Lethbridge
				6	Loyola[9]
1		3		6	Manitoba
1		3		6	McGill
1		3		6	McMaster
	2	3		6	Memorial
				6	Mount Allison
				6	Mount Saint Vincent
		3		6	New Brunswick
				6	Notre Dame
		3		6	Ottawa
				6	Prince Edward Island
1		3		6	Queen's
		3		6	Royal Military
				6	St. Francis Xavier
				6	St. Jerome's[12]
				6	St. John's[13]
				6	Saint Mary's
		3		6	Saskatchewan (Regina)
1		3		6	Saskatchewan (Sask.)
1		3		6	Simon Fraser
1		3		6	Sir George Williams
1	2	3	5	6	Toronto
				6	Trent
		3		6	Victoria (B.C.)
		3		6	Waterloo
				6	Waterloo Lutheran
1		3		6	Western Ontario
		3		6	Windsor
				6	Winnipeg
		3		6	York

Economie, économie appliquée, science économique

1	3	6	Institution
		6	Laurentienne
1	3	6	Laval

1	3	6	Institution
	3	6	Moncton
1	3	6	Montréal
1	3	6	Ottawa
		6	Québec (Montréal)
		6	Québec (Rimouski)
		6	Québec (Trois-Rivières)
	3	6	Sherbrooke

Economie familiale

6	Institution
6	Laval

Economie rurale

3	Institution
3	Laval

Education (E)

1	2	3	5	6	7	8	Institution
		3		6	7		Acadia
1		3	5	6			Alberta
		3	5	6			Bishop's
				6		8	Brandon
1		3		6			British Columbia
						8	Brock
		3	5	6			Calgary
		3	5	6			Dalhousie
				6		8	Lakehead
				6			Lethbridge
1		3		6	7	8	Manitoba
1		3	5	6	7		McGill
		3	5	6	7		Memorial
				6			Mount Allison
		3		6			Mount Saint Vincent
		3		6			New Brunswick
				6			Notre Dame
1	2	3					Ontario Institute for Studies in Education[11]
1		3		6			Ottawa
				6	7		Prince Edward Island
				6			Queen's
		3		6			St. Francis Xavier
		3		6			Saint Mary's
		3	5	6			Saskatchewan (Regina)
		3	5	6			Saskatchewan (Sask.)
		3		6			Simon Fraser
				6			Sir George Williams
1	2	3		6			Toronto
1		3		6			Victoria (B.C.)
			5	6			Western Ontario
						8	Windsor

Education culturelle

6	Institution
6	Québec (Montréal)

Education en nursing

3	Institution
3	Montréal

Education musicale

6	Institution
6	Laval
6	Moncton
6	Québec (Trois-Rivières)

Education, pédagogie, sciences de l'éducation

1	3	6	Institution
1	3	6	Laval

(Education, pédagogie,
sciences de l'éducation cont'd)

	3		6	Moncton
1	3 4		6	Montréal
1	3		6	Ottawa
			6	Québec (Chicoutimi)
			6	Québec (Rimouski)
			6	Québec (Trois-Rivières)
	3 4		6	Sherbrooke

Education physique

		6	Laval
		6	Moncton
3		6	Montréal
3		6	Ottawa
		6	Québec (Trois-Rivières)
		6	Sherbrooke

Educational administration

	3			Acadia
1	3			Alberta
			6	Brandon
	3	5		Calgary
1	3			Manitoba
	3			McGill
	3	5		Memorial
1	3			Ontario Institute for Studies in Education[11]
	3			Ottawa
			6	Queen's
	3	5		Saskatchewan (Regina)
	3	5		Saskatchewan (Sask.)
	3			Simon Fraser
	3			Victoria (B.C.)

Educational foundations

1	3			Alberta
			6	Brandon
	3	5		Calgary
	3			Manitoba
	3	5		Memorial
	3			Ottawa
	3	5		Saskatchewan (Sask.)

Educational planning

1	3	Ontario Institute for Studies in Education[11]

Educational psychology,
school psychology

1	3		Alberta
1	3	5	Calgary
	3		Manitoba
	3		McGill
	3	5	Memorial
	3		Mount Saint Vincent
1	3		Ontario Institute for Studies in Education[11]
1			Ottawa
	3	5	Saskatchewan (Sask.)
1	3		Victoria (B.C.)
	3		Waterloo

Educational technology

		6	Alberta
		9	British Columbia
3			Sir George Williams

Educational theory

1 2 3		Toronto

Egyptian

9	Toronto

Electrical
communications

1	3	McGill

Electrical engineering

			7	Acadia
1	3		6	Alberta
1	3		6	British Columbia
1	3		6	Calgary
1	3		6	Carleton
	3		6	Guelph
			7	Lakehead
			7	Laurentian
			6	Loyola[9]
1	3		6	Manitoba
1	3	5	6	McGill
1	3		6	McMaster
	3		6	Memorial
	3		6	New Brunswick
1	3		6	Nova Scotia Technical
1	3		6	Ottawa
1	3		6	Queen's
	3		6	Royal Military
	3		6	Saskatchewan (Regina)
1	3		6	Saskatchewan (Sask.)
1	3		6	Sir George Williams
1	3		6	Toronto
1	3		6	Waterloo
1	3		6	Western Ontario
1	3		6	Windsor

Electrothermique

3	Québec (Trois-Rivières)

Elementary education

1	3	6		Alberta
		6		Brandon
	3	6		British Columbia
			8	Brock
		6		Calgary
		6		Dalhousie
		6	8	Lakehead
		6		Lethbridge
			8	Manitoba
		7		McGill
		6 7		Memorial
		6 7		Mount Saint Vincent
		6		New Brunswick
		6		Notre Dame
		6		Queen's
		6		St. Francis Xavier
		6		Saskatchewan (Regina)

(Elementary education cont'd)

	6		Saskatchewan (Sask.)
	6		Simon Fraser
	6		Toronto
	5 6		Victoria (B.C.)
	6		Western Ontario
		8	Windsor

Embryologie

1	3	Laval

Embryology

1	3	Ottawa

Engineering

		7	Acadia
1	3	6	Alberta
1	3	6	British Columbia
1	3	6	Calgary
1	3	6	Carleton
		5 6	Dalhousie
1	3	6	Guelph
		6 7	Lakehead
		7	Laurentian
		6	Loyola[9]
1	3	5 6	Manitoba
1	3	5 6	McGill
1	3	6	McMaster
1	3	6	Memorial
		8	Mount Allison
	3	6 7	New Brunswick
1	3	6	Nova Scotia Technical
1	3	6	Ottawa
		7	Prince Edward Island
1	3	5 6	Queen's
	3	6	Royal Military
		7 8	St. Francis Xavier
		7	Saint Mary's
	3	6	Saskatchewan (Regina)
1	3	5 6	Saskatchewan (Sask.)
1	3	6	Sir George Williams
1	3	6	Toronto
1	3	6	Waterloo
1	3	6	Western Ontario
1	3	6	Windsor

Engineering and management

6	McMaster
6	Royal Military

Engineering materials

	3 6	Memorial
1	3 6	Windsor

Engineering physics

1	3	6	British Columbia
		6	Dalhousie
	3	6	McMaster
		6	Queen's
	3	6	Royal Military
1	3	6	Saskatchewan (Sask.)

Engineering science

		6	Toronto
1	3	6	Western Ontario

Engineering technology

7	Lakehead

English

	3	6	Acadia
1	3	6	Alberta
	3	6	Bishop's
		6	Brandon
		6	Brescia[3]
1	3	6	British Columbia
		6	Brock
	3	6	Calgary
	3	6	Carleton
1	3	6	Dalhousie
	3	6	Guelph
		6	Huron[5]
		6	King's (London)[8]
	3	6	Lakehead
		6	Laurentian
		6	Lethbridge
		6	Loyola[9]
1	3	6	Manitoba
		6	Marianopolis[10]
1	3	6	McGill
1	3	6	McMaster
1	3	6	Memorial
		6	Mount Allison
	3	6	Mount Saint Vincent
1	3	6	New Brunswick
		6	Notre Dame
1	3	6	Ottawa
		6	Prince Edward Island
1	3	6	Queen's
		6	Royal Military
		6	St. Francis Xavier
		6	St. Jerome's[12]
		6	St. John's[13]
		6	Saint Mary's
		6	Sainte-Anne
	3	6	Saskatchewan (Regina)
1	3	6	Saskatchewan (Sask.)
1	3	6	Simon Fraser
	3	6	Sir George Williams
1 2	3	6	Toronto
		6	Trent
1	3	6	Victoria (B.C.)
1 2	3	6	Waterloo
		6	Waterloo Lutheran
1	3	6	Western Ontario
	3	6	Windsor
		6	Winnipeg
1	3	6	York

Enseignement à l'enfance exceptionnelle

8	Québec (Chicoutimi)
8	Québec (Montréal)
8	Québec (Rimouski)
8	Québec (Trois-Rivières)

			Enseignement à l'enfance inadaptée				**Entomology (agriculture)**
1	3	6	Laval	1	3	6	Alberta
		6	Québec (Chicoutimi)	1	3	6	Guelph
		6	Québec (Montréal)	1	3	6	Manitoba
		8	Québec (Rimouski)	1	3	6	McGill
		8	Québec (Trois-Rivières)				
							Environmental biology
			Enseignement de l'éducation physique			8	Memorial
	4		Laval				**Environmental design (fine art)**
		6	Québec (Chicoutimi)			6	N. S. College of Art and
		6	Québec (Montréal)				Design
		6	Québec (Trois-Rivières)				
							Environmental design control (engineering)
			Enseignement des métiers				
		6	Moncton		3	6	Guelph
			Enseignement élémentaire				**Environmental engineering**
1	3 4		Laval		3		Western Ontario
		6	Moncton				
	5 6		Montréal				**Environmental horticulture**
		6	Québec (Chicoutimi)			6	Guelph
		6	Québec (Montréal)				
		6	Québec (Rimouski)				**Environmental studies, planning, conservation**
		6	Québec (Trois-Rivières)		3		Calgary
	4	6	Sherbrooke			6	Carleton
						6 8	Lakehead
			Enseignement en arts plastiques			6	Manitoba
		6	Québec (Montréal)			6	McGill
		6	Québec (Trois-Rivières)			8	Memorial
						6	St. Jerome's[12]
			Enseignement en musique			6	Saskatchewan (Sask.)
		6	Ottawa			6	Waterloo
		6	Québec (Montréal)			6	Winnipeg
		6	Québec (Trois-Rivières)		3		York
			Enseignement préscolaire				**Epidemiology**
		6	Montréal				
		6	Quebec (Chicoutimi)	1	3	5	McGill
		6	Québec (Montréal)		3		Queen's
		6	Québec (Rimouski)	1	3	5	Toronto
		6	Québec (Trois-Rivières)	1	3		Western Ontario
			Enseignement secondaire				**Ergothérapie**
1	3 4		Laval			6	Laval
	3		Moncton			6	Montréal
	4		Montréal				
		6	Québec (Chicoutimi)				**Eskimo language**
		6	Québec (Montréal)			9	Ottawa
		6	Québec (Rimouski)				
		6	Québec (Trois-Rivières)				**Espagnol, études hispaniques**
	4	6	Sherbrooke			6	Laurentienne
				1	3	6	Laval
			Enseignement secondaire – administration			9	Moncton
		6	Laval		3	6	Montreal
		6	Québec (Chicoutimi)			6	Ottawa
		6	Québec (Montréal)			6	Québec (Montréal)
		6	Québec (Rimouski)				
		6	Québec (Trois-Rivières)				

Etudes africaines

5 Montréal

Etudes anciennes

6 Laval
6 Québec (Montréal)
6 Québec (Trois-Rivières)

Etudes canadiennes

1 3 6 Laval

Etudes dramatiques

6 Québec (Montréal)

Etudes étrangères

6 Québec (Montréal)

Etudes françaises

1 3 6 Laval
1 3 6 Montréal
6 Québec (Chicoutimi)
6 Québec (Montréal)
6 Québec (Rimouski)
6 Québec (Trois-Rivières)
3 Sherbrooke

Etudes littéraires

3 6 Québec (Montréal)

Etudes médiévales

1 3 Montréal

Etudes québécoises

3 6 Québec (Trois-Rivières)

Etudes slaves

1 3 6 Montréal
1 3 6 Ottawa

Exceptional children (education)

1 3 Alberta

Exécution (musique)

6 Laval
6 Montréal
6 Ottawa

Experimental medicine

1 3 Alberta
1 McGill

Experimental psychology

1 3 6 Calgary
3 Lakehead
3 Memorial
1 Ottawa
3 Sir George Williams

Experimental surgery

1 3 Alberta
1 McGill

Exploitation forestière

1 3 Laval

Family studies, family science

6 Alberta
6 British Columbia
3 6 Guelph
6 Manitoba

Far Eastern studies

3 6 Saskatchewan (Sask.)

Farm management

3 6 Manitoba

Field crops and plant breeding

6 Alberta

Film, cinema

9 British Columbia
9 McGill
9 McMaster
9 Ottawa
6 Queen's
6 Sir George Williams
6 Toronto
6 York

Finance (E)

6 Alberta
1 6 British Columbia
6 Calgary
6 Carleton
6 Manitoba
6 Memorial
6 Sir George Williams
6 Toronto

Finance (F)

3 6 Sherbrooke

Fisheries

1 3 British Columbia
1 3 6 Guelph

Folklore

1 3 6 Memorial

Fondements théoriques de l'éducation

3 Ottawa

Food chemistry

1 3 6 Alberta
3 6 Toronto

Food management, administration

1 3 Guelph
6 McGill

Food processing and food microbiology

1	3	6	Alberta

Food science

1	3	6	Alberta
1	3	6	British Columbia
1	3	6	Guelph
1	3	6	Manitoba
		6	McGill
		6	Saskatchewan (Sask.)
1	3	6	Toronto

Foods and nutrition

		6	Acadia
1	3	6	Alberta
	3	6	British Columbia
1	3		Guelph
	3	6	Manitoba
		6	Marianopolis[10]
		6	McGill
		6	Mount Saint Vincent
		6	St. Francis Xavier
		6	Saskatchewan (Sask.)

Forest engineering

	3		British Columbia
		6	New Brunswick

Forest hydrology

		6	Alberta

Forest management

		6	Alberta
		6	British Columbia
		6	New Brunswick
	3		Toronto

Forest technology

		7	Lakehead

Forestry

		6	Alberta
1	3	6	British Columbia
		6 7	Lakehead
	3	6	New Brunswick
1	3	6	Toronto

Français

		6	Laurentienne
1	3 4		Laval
		6	Ottawa
	3	6	Moncton
		6	Sainte-Anne
1	3 4		Sherbrooke

French

	3	6	Acadia
1	3	6	Alberta
		6	Bishop's
		6	Brandon
		6	Brescia[3]
1	3	6	British Columbia
		6	Brock
	3	6	Calgary
	3	6	Carleton
	3	6	Dalhousie
		6	Guelph
		6	Huron[3]
		6	King's (London)[8]
		6	Lakehead
		6	Laurentian
		7	Laval
		6	Lethbridge
		6	Loyola[9]
1	3	6	Manitoba
		6	Marianopolis[10]
1	3	6	McGill
	3	6	McMaster
	3	6	Memorial
		6	Mount Allison
		6	Mount Saint Vincent
	3	6	New Brunswick
		6	Notre Dame
		6	Ottawa
		6	Prince Edward Island
1	3	6	Queen's
		6	Royal Military
		9	St. Francis Xavier
		6	St. Jerome's[12]
		6	St. John's[13]
		6	Saint Mary's
		6	Sainte-Anne
	3	6	Saskatchewan (Regina)
	3	6	Saskatchewan (Sask.)
1	3	6	Simon Fraser
		6	Sir George Williams
1 2	3	6	Toronto
		6	Trent
		6	Victoria (B.C.)
		6	Waterloo
	3	6	Waterloo Lutheran
	3	6	Western Ontario
1	3	6	Windsor
	3	6	Winnipeg
		6	York

French-Canadian studies

6	Alberta
6	McGill

French studies

6	Trent

Gaelic

9	St. Francis Xavier

Génagogie

6	Québec (Trois-Rivières)

Genetics

1	3	6	Alberta
1	3		British Columbia
1	3	6	Guelph
1	3		Manitoba
1	3	6	McGill

			Génétique
1	3		Laval

			Génie
1	3	6	Laval
		6	Moncton
1	3	6 7	Montréal
		6	Québec (Chicoutimi)
		6	Québec (Trois-Rivières)
1	3	6	Sherbrooke

			Génie aérospatial
1	3		Sherbrooke

			Génie chimique
1	3	6	Laval
		6	Moncton
1	3	6	Montréal
		6	Québec (Chicoutimi)
		6	Québec (Trois-Rivières)
1	3	6	Sherbrooke

			Génie civil
1	3	6	Laval
		6	Moncton
1	3	6	Montréal
1	3	6	Sherbrooke

			Génie électrique
1	3	6	Laval
		8	Moncton
1	3	6	Montréal
		6	Québec (Chicoutimi)
		6	Québec (Trois-Rivières)
1	3	6	Sherbrooke

			Génie forestier
1	3	6	Laval

			Génie géologique
		6	Laval
1	3	6	,Montréal

			Génie industriel
		6	Moncton
1	3	6	Montréal

			Génie mécanique
1	3	6	Laval
		8	Moncton
1	3	6	Montréal
1	3	6	Sherbrooke

			Génie médical
		6	Québec (Chicoutimi)
		6	Québec (Trois-Rivières)
	3		Sherbrooke

			Génie métallurgique
		6	Laval
1	3	6	Montréal

			Génie minier
1	3	6	Laval
1	3	6	Montréal

			Génie physique
		6	Laval
1	3	6	Montréal
		6	Québec (Chicoutimi)
		6	Québec (Trois-Rivières)

			Génie rural
	3	6	Laval

			Geochemistry
	3		Laurentian
		6	McGill
1			McMaster

			Géodésie
1	3		Laval

			Géographie
		6	Laurentienne
1	3	6	Laval
		6	Moncton
1	3	6	Montréal
1	3	6	Ottawa
		6	Québec (Chicoutimi)
		6	Québec (Montréal)
		6	Québec (Rimouski)
		6	Québec (Trois-Rivières)
	3	6	Sherbrooke

			Geography
1	3	6	Alberta
		6	Bishop's
		6	Brandon
1	3	6	British Columbia
		6	Brock
1	3	6	Calgary
	3	6	Carleton
	3	6	Guelph
		6	Lakehead
		6	Laurentian
		6	Lethbridge
1	3	6	Manitoba
1	3	6	McGill
1	3	6	McMaster
	3	6	Memorial
1	3	6	Ottawa
	3	6	Queen's
		6	St. Jerome's[12]
		6	St. John's[13]
		6	Saskatchewan (Regina)
	3	6	Saskatchewan (Sask.)
1	3	6	Simon Fraser
		6	Sir George Williams
1	2 3	6	Toronto
		6	Trent
1	3	6	Victoria (B.C.)
1	3	6	Waterloo
	3	6	Waterloo Lutheran
1	3	6	Western Ontario

(Geography cont'd)

3	6			Windsor
	6			Winnipeg
3	6			York

Geological engineering

	7			Acadia
3	6			British Columbia
	6			Manitoba
1	3	6		Saskatchewan (Sask.)
	6			Toronto
	6			Windsor

Géologie

1	3	6		Laval
1	3	6		Montréal
	6			Québec (Chicoutimi)
	6			Québec (Montréal)

Geology, geological sciences

3	6			Acadia
1	3	6		Alberta
	6			Brandon
1	3	6		British Columbia
3	6			Brock
1	3	6		Calgary
1	3	6		Carleton
1	3	6		Dalhousie
	6			Lakehead
3	6			Laurentian
	6			Loyola[9]
1	3	6		Manitoba
1	3	5	6	McGill
1	3	6		McMaster
1	3	6		Memorial
	6			Mount Allison
1	3	6		New Brunswick
1	3	6		Ottawa
1	3	6		Queen's
3	6			St. Francis Xavier
	6			Saint Mary's
	6			Saskatchewan (Regina)
1	3	6		Saskatchewan (Sask.)
	6			Sir George Williams
1	3	6		Toronto
1	3	6		Western Ontario
	6			Windsor

Geophysical engineering

1 3	British Columbia

Geophysics

	6		Alberta
1	3	6	British Columbia
	6		Calgary
1	3	6	Manitoba
3	6		McGill
1	3		Memorial
	6		Saskatchewan (Regina)
	6		Saskatchewan (Sask.)
1	3		Toronto
1	3	6	Western Ontario

German, German language and literature

		6		Acadia
1	3	6		Alberta
		9		Bishop's
		9		Brandon
1	3	6		British Columbia
		6		Brock
3	6			Calgary
3	6			Carleton
3	6			Dalhousie
		6		Guelph
		6		Huron[5]
		6		King's (London)[8]
		6		Lakehead
		6		Laurentian
		6		Loyola[9]
3	6			Manitoba
1	3	6		McGill
3	6			McMaster
2	3	6		Memorial
		6		Mount Allison
		9		Mount Saint Vincent
3	6			New Brunswick
		9		Notre Dame
3	6			Ottawa
1	3	6		Queen's
		9		St. Francis Xavier
		6		Saint Mary's
		6		Saskatchewan (Regina)
3	6			Saskatchewan (Sask.)
1	3	6		Simon Fraser
		6		Sir George Williams
1	2 3	6		Toronto
		6		Trent
		6		Victoria (B.C.)
1	2 3	6		Waterloo
		6		Waterloo Lutheran
1	3	6		Western Ontario
		6		Windsor
		6		Winnipeg
		6		York

Gestion des affaires

3	Moncton

Gestion du bureau

6	Québec (Montréal)
6	Québec (Trois-Rivières)

Glaciology

3	McGill

Graphics, graphic design, graphics technology

6	Manitoba
6 7	N.S. College of Art and Design
6	Sir George Williams

Gravure

6	Québec (Montréal)

Grec, études grecques

			Institution
		9	Laurentienne
1 3		6	Laval
		6	Montréal
		6	Québec (Montréal)
		6	Québec (Trois-Rivières)
		6	Sherbrooke

Greek

		Institution
	9	Acadia
3	6	Alberta
	6	Bishop's
3	6	British Columbia
	9	Brock
	6	Calgary
3	6	Carleton
	9	Dalhousie
	6	Guelph
	6	Huron[5]
	9	King's (Halifax)[7]
	6	King's (London)[8]
	9	Lakehead
	9	Laurentian
3	6	Manitoba
	6	McGill
3	6	McMaster
	6	Memorial
	6	Mount Allison
	6	New Brunswick
	6	Ottawa
	6	Prince Edward Island
	6	Queen's
	9	St. Francis Xavier
	6	Saskatchewan (Regina)
	6	Saskatchewan (Sask.)
	9	Sir George Williams
1 2 3	6	Toronto
	6	Trent
3	6	Victoria (B.C.)
	6	Waterloo
	6	Waterloo Lutheran
3	6	Western Ontario
	6	Windsor
	9	Winnipeg
	6	York

Guidance and counselling

		Institution
3		Acadia
1 3		Alberta
	6	Brandon
3	5	British Columbia
1 3		Calgary
1 3		McGill
3	5	Memorial
3		Ontario Institute for Studies in Education[11]
1 3		Ottawa
3		St. Francis Xavier
3	5	Saskatchewan (Regina)
3	5	Saskatchewan (Sask.)

Health administration

	Institution
3	Alberta

	Institution
1 3	Toronto

Hébreu

	Institution
9	Ottawa

Hebrew

	Institution
9	Bishop's
9	British Columbia
9	Dalhousie
9	King's (Halifax)[7]
6	Manitoba
9	McGill
9	Ottawa
9	Queen's
9	Saskatchewan (Sask.)
9	Sir George Williams
9	Toronto
9	Waterloo Lutheran
9	York

Hellenistic Greek

	Institution
6	St. John's[13]
6	Toronto

Hindi, Urdu

	Institution
9	British Columbia
9	McGill
9	Simon Fraser
9	Toronto
9	Windsor

Hispanic studies

		Institution
1 3	6	British Columbia
1 2 3	6	Toronto
	6	Trent

Histoire

		Institution
	6	Laurentienne
1 3	6	Laval
3	6	Moncton
1 3	6	Montréal
1 3	6	Ottawa
	6	Québec (Chicoutimi)
	6	Québec (Montréal)
	6	Québec (Trois-Rivières)
	6	Sainte-Anne
3	6	Sherbrooke

Histoire de l'art

		Institution
	6	Laval
3	6	Montréal
	6	Québec (Montréal)

Histologie

	Institution
1 3	Laval

Histology (pure science)

		Institution
1 3		Ottawa
	6	Saskatchewan (Sask.)

Histology (veterinary medicine)

	Institution
3	Guelph

History

				University
		3	6	Acadia
1		3	6	Alberta
		3	6	Bishop's
			6	Brandon
			6	Brescia[3]
1		3	6	British Columbia
			6	Brock
		3	6	Calgary
		3	6	Carleton
1		3	6	Dalhousie
1		3	6	Guelph
			6	Huron[5]
			6	King's (London)[8]
		3	6	Lakehead
			6	Laurentian
			6	Lethbridge
			6	Loyola[9]
1		3	6	Manitoba
			6	Marianopolis[10]
1		3	6	McGill
1		3	6	McMaster
	2	3	6	Memorial
			6	Mount Allison
			6	Mount Saint Vincent
1		3	6	New Brunswick
			6	Notre Dame
1		3	6	Ottawa
			6	Prince Edward Island
1		3	6	Queen's
		3	6	Royal Military
			6	St. Francis Xavier
			6	St. Jerome's[12]
			6	St. John's[13]
		3	6	Saint Mary's
			6	Sainte-Anne
		3	6	Saskatchewan (Regina)
1		3	6	Saskatchewan (Sask.)
1		3	6	Simon Fraser
1		3	6	Sir George Williams
1	2	3	6	Toronto
		3	6	Trent
		3	6	Victoria (B.C.)
1	2	3	6	Waterloo
		3	6	Waterloo Lutheran
1		3	6	Western Ontario
		3	6	Windsor
			6	Winnpeg
1		3	6	York

History and philosophy of religion

3	6	Sir George Williams

History and philosophy of science, technology

3		Toronto
	6	York

History of canon law

1	4	St. Michael's[14]

History of Christian worship

1	4	St. Michael's[14]

History of education, philosophy of education

1	3	Alberta
	3	McGill
1	3	Ontario Institute for Studies in Education[11]

Home economics, household science

	6	Acadia
3	6	Alberta
	6	Brescia[3]
	6	British Columbia
1	3	6	Guelph
3	6	Manitoba
	6	McGill
	6	Mount Saint Vincent
	6	Ottawa
	6	Prince Edward Island
	6	St. Francis Xavier
	6	Saskatchewan (Sask.)
	6	Western Ontario
	6	Windsor

Home economics management

3		Manitoba
	6	Saskatchewan (Sask.)

Home economics teaching

	6	British Columbia
	6	McGill
3	6	Mount Saint Vincent
	6	New Brunswick
	6	Saskatchewan (Sask.)

Horticulture

1	3	6	Alberta
	6	British Columbia
1	3	6	Guelph
3	6	McGill
1	3	6	Saskatchewan (Sask.)

Hospital administration

3		Ottawa
	5	Toronto

Hospital pharmacy

6	Alberta
6	British Columbia
6	Saskatchewan (Sask.)

Hotel and food administration

6	Guelph

Housing and design (home economics)
6 Guelph
6 Saskatchewan (Sask.)

Housing and housing design (architecture)
3 British Columbia
3 McGill

Human development (home economics)
3 6 Manitoba

Humanités
6 Jean-de-Brébeuf[6]

Humanities and social sciences
6 Marianopolis[10]
6 Mount Saint Vincent
3 6 St. Paul's (Winnipeg)[16]
3 6 Saskatchewan (Regina)
6 Saskatchewan (Sask.)
6 Winnipeg
6 York

Humanities of science
6 Dalhousie
6 Sir George Williams

Human relations (psychology)
1 3 Waterloo

Human resources development
6 York

Hydrology
1 3 Guelph

Hygiene
1 3 Toronto

Hygiène
1 3 5 7 Montréal

Hygiène mentale (nursing)
3 Montréal

Icelandic
6 Manitoba

Illustration
6 Manitoba

Immunologie
1 3 Laval

Immunology (medicine)
1 3 Manitoba
1 3 6 McGill
1 3 Ottawa
1 3 6 Queen's
1 3 6 Western Ontario

Immunology (veterinary medicine)
1 3 Guelph

Indian-Eskimo studies
6 Laurentian
6 Trent
6 Waterloo

India studies
1 2 3 6 Toronto

Industrial administration (commerce)
6 British Columbia

Industrial engineering
7 Acadia
1 3 6 Alberta
3 6 Memorial
1 3 6 Nova Scotia Technical
1 3 6 Toronto
1 3 6 Windsor

Industrial health
5 Toronto

Industrial relations
6 Alberta
6 Carleton
6 Lakehead
6 McGill
6 Memorial
6 Queen's

Information culturelle
6 Québec (Montréal)

Information scolaire et professionnelle
8 Laval
6 Québec (Montréal)
6 Sherbrooke

Informatique
6 Laval
1 3 6 Montréal
6 Sherbrooke

Intercultural education
6 Alberta
6 Brandon
9 British Columbia
9 Manitoba
6 Western Ontario

		Interior design				Journalism
	6	Guelph			6	Carleton
	6	Manitoba			5 6	Western Ontario

International affairs, relations, studies

	6	British Columbia
3		Carleton
	6	Lakehead
3	6	Manitoba
	6	Royal Military
	6	Saskatchewan (Sask.)
	6	Sir George Williams
	6	Waterloo
3	6	Windsor
	6	York

Journalisme et information

	6	Laval

Judaic studies, Jewish studies

	6	Manitoba
	6	McGill
3	6	Sir George Williams
	6	Toronto

International co-operation

5		Ottawa

Kinanthropologie

3	6	Ottawa

Kinanthropology

3	6	Ottawa

International programs

3		Guelph
	6	Lakehead

Kinesiology

3	6	Simon Fraser
	6	Waterloo

Islamic studies

1 3		McGill
1 2 3	6	Toronto

Laboratory science, technology

3			Dalhousie
	6	8	Saskatchewan (Regina)
	6		Saskatchewan (Sask.)

Italian

	6	Alberta
3	6	British Columbia
	9	Brock
	9	Calgary
	9	Carleton
	6	Guelph
	6	Lakehead
	6	Laurentian
	6	Loyola[9]
	9	Manitoba
3	6	McGill
	6	McMaster
	9	Queen's
	9	St. Francis Xavier
	6	St. Jerome's[12]
	9	Sir George Williams
1 2 3	6	Toronto
	9	Victoria (B.C.)
	9	Western Ontario
	6	Windsor
	9	York

Labor relations

	8	Ottawa

Landscape architecture

3	6	Guelph
	6	Toronto

Langue crise

	9	Ottawa

Langue esquimaude

	9	Ottawa

Latin (E)

	6	Acadia
3	6	Alberta
	6	Bishop's
	9	Brandon
3	6	British Columbia
	6	Brock
	6	Calgary
3	6	Carleton
	9	Dalhousie
	6	Guelph
	6	Huron[5]
	9	King's (Halifax)[7]
	9	King's (London)[8]
	6	Lakehead
	6	Laurentian
3	6	Manitoba
3	6	McGill

Italien

	6	Laurentienne
	6	Montréal

Japanese, Japanese studies

1 3	6	British Columbia
1 2 3	6	Toronto
	9	Victoria (B.C.)
	9	York

(Latin (E) cont'd)

3	6		McMaster
	6		Memorial
	6		Mount Allison
	6		New Brunswick
		9	Notre Dame
1	3		Ottawa
	6		Prince Edward Island
	6		St. John's[13]
	6		Saint Mary's
1	4		St. Michael's[14]
	6		Saskatchewan (Regina)
3	6		Saskatchewan (Sask.)
	6		Sir George Williams
	6		Toronto
	6		Trent
3	6		Victoria (B.C.)
	6		Waterloo
	6		Waterloo Lutheran
3	6		Western Ontario
	6		Windsor
	6		Winnipeg
	6		York

Latin (F)

		6	Laurentienne
1	3	6	Laval
1	3	6	Ottawa
		6	Québec (Montréal)
		6	Québec (Trois-Rivières)
		6	Sherbrooke

Latin-American studies

6	British Columbia
6	Laurentian
9	Manitoba
6	Queen's
6	Simon Fraser
6	Toronto
3	Waterloo
6	Windsor

Law

3	6	Alberta
3	6	British Columbia
	9	Carleton
3	6	Dalhousie
3	6	Manitoba
1 3	6	McGill
	6	New Brunswick
	6	Ottawa
3	6	Queen's
3	6	Saskatchewan (Sask.)
1 3	6	Toronto
	6	Western Ontario
	6	Windsor
1 3	6	York

Lettres

		6	Jean-de-Brébeuf[6]
1	3	6	Laval
		6	Montréal

		6	Québec (Chicoutimi)
		6	Québec (Montréal)
		6	Québec (Rimouski)
		6	Québec (Trois-Rivières)
1	3	6	Sherbrooke

Library science, library service

	6	Alberta
3		British Columbia
3		Dalhousie
	7	Lakehead
3		McGill
3	6	Ottawa
1 3		Toronto
1 3		Western Ontario

Life sciences

6	Queen's

Linguistics

1 3	6	Alberta
3	6	British Columbia
	6	Calgary
	6	Carleton
	6	Guelph
1 3	6	McGill
2 3	6	Memorial
3	6	Ottawa
	6	Saskatchewan (Sask.)
1 3	6	Simon Fraser
1 3	6	Toronto
3	6	Victoria (B.C.)

Linguistics – translation

6	Ottawa

Linguistique

1 3	6	Laval
1 3	6	Montréal
3	6	Ottawa
	6	Québec (Montréal)
	6	Québec (Trois-Rivières)

Linguistique – traduction

6	Ottawa

Littérature canadienne

1 3	Montréal
3	Sherbrooke

Littérature comparée

1 3	Montréal

Logging

8	Lakehead

Machinery (engineering)

3	Guelph

Management, management sciences

1	3	5	6	
			6	Alberta
	3			British Columbia
			6	Calgary
		5		McGill
			6	Memorial
	3	5	6	Ottawa
			6	St. Francis Xavier
			6	Sir George Williams
1	3			Waterloo

Man-environment studies

	6	Waterloo

Marine biology, marine sciences

1	3	6	
1	3	6	Guelph
1	3	6	McGill
1	3	6	Memorial

Marketing (E)

	3	6	
		6	Alberta
	3	6	British Columbia
		6	Calgary
		6	Manitoba
		6	Memorial
		6	Saskatchewan (Sask.)
		6	Sir George Williams

Marketing (F)

3	6	Sherbrooke

Materials engineering, materials handling

3	Carleton
3	Guelph

Materials science

1	3	6	
1	3	6	McMaster
	3	6	Queen's
1	3	6	Toronto
1	3	6	Western Ontario

Mathematical physics

1	3	6	
1	3		Alberta
		6	Lakehead

Mathematics

1	3	6	
	3	6	Acadia
1	3	6	Alberta
		6	Bishop's
		6	Brandon
1	3	6	British Columbia
		6	Brock
1	3	6	Calgary
1	3	6	Carleton
1	3	6	Dalhousie
	3	6	Guelph
		6	King's (London)[8]
	3	6	Lakehead
		6	Laurentian
		6	Lethbridge
		6	Loyola[9]
1	3	6	Manitoba
		6	Marianopolis[10]
1	3	6	McGill
1	3	6	McMaster
	3	6	Memorial
		6	Mount Allison
		6	Mount Saint Vincent
1	3	6	New Brunswick
		6	Notre Dame
1	3	6	Ottawa
		6	Prince Edward Island
1	3	6	Queen's
	3	6	Royal Military
		6	St. Francis Xavier
		6	St. Jerome's[12]
		6	St. John's[13]
		6	Saint Mary's
1	3	6	Saskatchewan (Regina)
1	3	6	Saskatchewan (Sask.)
1	3	6	Simon Fraser
		6	Sir George Williams
1	3	6	Toronto
		6	Trent
	3	6	Victoria (B.C.)
1	3	6	Waterloo
		6	Waterloo Lutheran
1	3	6	Western Ontario
1	3	6	Windsor
		6	Winnipeg
	3	6	York

Mathematics (teaching of)

3	6	
3		Sir George Williams
	6	Waterloo

Mathématiques

1	3	4	6	
			6	Jean-de-Brébeuf[6]
1	3		6	Laval
			6	Moncton
1	3	4	6	Montréal
			6	Ottawa
			6	Québec (Chicoutimi)
	3		6	Québec (Montréal)
			6	Québec (Rimouski)
			6	Québec (Trois-Rivières)
1	3		6	Sherbrooke

Mechanical engineering

1	3	5	6	7	
				7	Acadia
1	3		6		Alberta
1	3		6		British Columbia
1	3		6		Calgary
1	3		6		Carleton
				7	Lakehead
				7	Laurentian
			6		Loyola[9]
1	3		6		Manitoba
1	3	5	6		McGill
1	3		6		McMaster
	3		6		Memorial
	3		6		New Brunswick

(Mechanical engineering cont'd)

1	3	6	Nova Scotia Technical
1	3	6	Ottawa
1	3	6	Queen's
	3	6	Royal Military
	3	6	Saskatchewan (Regina)
1	3	6	Saskatchewan (Sask.)
1	3	6	Sir George Williams
1	3	6	Toronto
1	3	6	Waterloo
1	3	6	Western Ontario
1	3	6	Windsor

Médecine

1	3	6	Laval
1	3	6	Montréal
1	3	6	Sherbrooke

Médecine dentaire

	6	Laval

Médecine et chirurgie expérimentales

1	3	Laval
1	3	Montréal

Médecine vétérinaire

3	6	Montréal

Mediaeval studies

		9	Manitoba
	6		Queen's
1	4		St. Michael's[14]
1 2 3			Toronto
	6		Waterloo

Medical biophysics

1	3	Toronto

Medical laboratory science and technology

6		Alberta
6	8	Saskatchewan (Regina)
6		Saskatchewan (Sask.)

Medical microbiology

3	Manitoba

Medical records science

6	Notre Dame

Medical science

	3	Calgary
1	3	McMaster
	6	New Brunswick
1	3	Toronto

Medical secretarial science

7	Mount Saint Vincent
7	St. Francis Xavier

Medical-surgical nursing

3	Toronto

Medicine

		6	Alberta
1	3	6	British Columbia
		6	Calgary
		6	Dalhousie
1	3	6	Manitoba
1	3	5 6	McGill
1	3	6	McMaster
1	3	6	Memorial
1	3	6	Ottawa
	3	6	Queen's
1	3	6	Saskatchewan (Sask.)
1	3	6	Toronto
1	3	6	Western Ontario

Mesure et expérimentation (éducation)

3	Ottawa

Metallurgical engineering

1	3	6	Alberta
	3	6	British Columbia
			7 Laurentian
1	3	6	McGill
	3	6	McMaster
1	3	6	Nova Scotia Technical
	3	6	Queen's

Metallurgie

1	3	Laval

Metallurgy

1	3	6	British Columbia
	3		McGill
1	3	6	McMaster
1	3	6	Toronto

Meteorology

1	3		Alberta
1	3	6	McGill

Microbial genetics

6	McGill

Microbiologie et immunologie

1	3	6	Laval
1	3		Montréal
1	3		Sherbrooke

Microbiology

1	3	6	Alberta
1	3	6	British Columbia
		6	Calgary
1	3		Dalhousie
1	3	6	Guelph
1	3	6	Manitoba
1	3	6	McGill

(Microbiology cont'd)			
1	3		New Brunswick
1	3		Ottawa
1	3	6	Saskatchewan (Regina)
1	3	6	Saskatchewan (Sask.)
1	3		Toronto

Microbiology (veterinary medicine)

1	3		Guelph
1			Saskatchewan (Sask.)

Minéralogie

1	3	Laval

Mineral and mining engineering

			7	Acadia
1	3	6		Alberta
1	3	6		British Columbia
			7	Laurentian
1	3	5	6	McGill
	3	6		Memorial
			7	New Brunswick
1	3	6		Nova Scotia Technical
1	3	6		Queen's
	3	6		Saskatchewan (Sask.)

Missiologie (théologie)

3	Ottawa
3	Saint-Paul (Ottawa)[15]

Missiology (theology)

3	Ottawa
3	Saint Paul (Ottawa)[15]

Mission studies

	3		Ottawa
1	3	7	Saint Paul (Ottawa)[15]

Molecular biology

	6	Bishop's
	6	Lethbridge
1	3	McMaster
	6	Winnipeg

Museology

3	Toronto

Music

	6		Acadia
3	6		Alberta
	6		Brandon
3	6		British Columbia
	6		Calgary
	6		Carleton
	6		Dalhousie
	6		Guelph
	6		Lethbridge
	6		Manitoba
	6		Marianopolis[10]
3	6	7	McGill

		6	McMaster
		6	Mount Allison
		6	Mount Saint Vincent
		6	Ottawa
		6	Prince Edward Island
		6	Queen's
		6	St. Francis Xavier.
		6	Saskatchewan (Regina)
		6	Saskatchewan (Sask.)
1	3	6 7	Toronto
		6	Victoria (B.C.)
		6	Waterloo Lutheran
	3	6	Western Ontario
		6	Windsor
		6	York

Music education

		6	Acadia
		6	Brandon
		6	British Columbia
		6	Dalhousie
		6	McGill
		6	Mount Allison
		6	Ottawa
		6	Saskatchewan (Regina)
	3	5 6	Saskatchewan (Sask.)
	3	6	Toronto
		6	Western Ontario

Music history and literature

3	6	Alberta
	6	Calgary
	6	McGill
	6	Queen's
	6	Saskatchewan (Sask.)
3	6	Toronto
	6	Western Ontario
	6	Windsor

Musicologie

1	3	6	Montréal
		6	Ottawa

Musicology

3	6	British Columbia
3		McGill
	6	Ottawa
1	3	Victoria (B.C.)
3		Western Ontario

Musique

1	4	6	Laval
		6	Moncton
1	4	6	Montréal
		6	Ottawa
		6	Québec (Montréal)
		6	Québec (Trois-Rivières)

Natural resource management

	3	Manitoba
	6	McGill

				Natural sciences
	6			Lakehead
	6			York

				Near Eastern studies
	6			Manitoba
1 2 3	6			Toronto
	6			Waterloo Lutheran

				Neurologie
	5			Laval

				Neurology
	3			British Columbia
1	3	5		McGill

				Neurosurgery
1	3			McGill

				North American studies
	6			Bishop's
	6			McGill

				Norwegian
		9		Saskatchewan (Sask.)

				Nursing
	6	8		Alberta
3	6	7		British Columbia
	6			Calgary
	6	7		Dalhousie
	6			Lakehead
	6			Laurentian
	6	8		Manitoba
3	6			McGill
	6			McMaster
	6			Memorial
	6			Mount Saint Vincent
	6			New Brunswick
	6	8		Ottawa
	6			Queen's
	6			St. Francis Xavier
	6	7		Saskatchewan (Sask.)
3	6	7		Toronto
3	6			Western Ontario
	6	7		Windsor

				Nursing education
	6			McGill
	6			Ottawa
3				Western Ontario

				Nursing service administration
		7		Dalhousie
		7		Saskatchewan (Sask.)
3				Western Ontario

				Nutrition (F)
3	6			Montréal

				Nutrition (agriculture)
1	3			Guelph

				Nutrition (applied human)
	3			British Columbia
1	3	6		Guelph
		6		McGill
		6		Prince Edward Island
1	3	5 6		Toronto

				Nutritional biochemistry
1	3			Victoria (B.C.)

				Obstetrics and gynaecology
	3			Toronto
	3			Western Ontario

				Obstetrique et gynécologie
		5		Laval

				Occupational therapy
		6 7		Alberta
		6		British Columbia
		6 7		Manitoba
		7		McGill
		7		Queen's
		6		Toronto
		6		Western Ontario

				Occupational therapy (teaching of)
		7		Alberta
			8	Toronto

				Ocean engineering
1	3	6		Memorial

				Oceanography
1	3			British Columbia
1	3			Dalhousie

				Opthalmic science, opthalmology
		5		Toronto
		5		Western Ontario

				Opthalmologie
		5		Laval

				Optométrie
		4		Montréal

				Optometry
		6		Waterloo

				Oral biology
1	3			Manitoba
		5		Toronto

			Oral surgery
3			Dalhousie
	5		Toronto

			Organizational behavior (commerce)
1		6	British Columbia

			Orientation (F)
1	3	6	Laval
3			Moncton
3		6	Montréal

			Orthodontics, paedodontics, periodontics
		8	Manitoba
	5		Toronto

			Orthodontie, pédodontie
3	5		Montréal

			Orthopédagogie
3	6		Montréal
	6		Sherbrooke

			Orthophonie et audiologie
3	6		Montréal

			Oto-rhino-laryngologie
	5		Laval

			Otolaryngology
3			McGill
3			Toronto
	5		Western Ontario

			Outpost nursing
		7	Dalhousie

			Pacific studies
		6	Victoria (B.C.)

			Paediatrics
3			Alberta
3			Manitoba
3			Queen's
3			Toronto
3			Western Ontario

			Painting
		6	Manitoba

			Palaeobiology
		6	McGill

			Pali
	9		Toronto

			Parasitologie
3			Montréal

		Parasitology
1	3	McGill
1	3	Toronto

		Parasitology (veterinary medicine)
1	3	Guelph

	Pastoral counselling
3	Ottawa

	Pastorale familiale
3	Laval
3	Ottawa
3	Saint-Paul (Ottawa)[15]

	Pastorale scolaire
3	Sherbrooke

	Pastoral studies
3	Ottawa
3	Saint Paul (Ottawa)[15]

		Pathological chemistry
1	3	Toronto
1	3	Western Ontario

		Pathologie
1	3	Laval
1	3	Montréal
1	3	Sherbrooke

	Pathologie (médecine vétérinaire)
3	Montréal

		Pathology (human)
	3	Alberta
1	3	British Columbia
	3	Dalhousie
	3	Manitoba
1	3	McGill
1	3	Ottawa
1	3	Queen's
1	3	Saskatchewan (Sask.)
1	3	Toronto
1	3	Western Ontario

			Pathology (veterinary medicine)
1	3	5	Guelph
1			Saskatchewan (Sask.)

	Pédiatrie
5	Laval

		Pédologie (forestière)
1	3	Laval

	Peinture
6	Québec (Montréal)

Performance (music)

			6	Acadia
	3		6	Alberta
			6	Brandon
	3		6	British Columbia
			6	Manitoba
			6	McGill
			6	Ottawa
			6	Queen's
			6	Saskatchewan (Sask.)
	3		6	Toronto
	3			Victoria (B.C.)
			6	Western Ontario

Persian

9	Toronto

Petroleum engineering

1	3	6	Alberta

Pharmaceutical chemistry

1	3		Alberta
	3	6	Manitoba
	3	6	Saskatchewan (Sask.)
1	3		Toronto

Pharmaceutics, pharmaceutical science

1	3	6	Alberta
	3	6	Manitoba
	3	6	Saskatchewan (Sask.)
1	3		Toronto

Pharmacie

1	3		6	Laval
1	3	5	6	Montréal

Pharmacognosie

1	3	Montréal

Pharmacognosy

1	3		Alberta
	3	6	Manitoba
	3	6	Saskatchewan (Sask.)
1	3		Toronto

Pharmacologie

1	3	Laval
1	3	Montréal
1	3	Sherbrooke

Pharmacology

1	3	6	Alberta
1	3		British Columbia
1	3		Dalhousie
1	3		Guelph
1	3		Manitoba
1	3		McGill
1	3		Ottawa
1	3		Queen's
1	3	6	Saskatchewan (Sask.)
1	3		Toronto
1	3		Western Ontario

Pharmacy

1	3	6	Alberta
1	3	6	British Columbia
	3	6	Dalhousie
1	3	6	Manitoba
	3	6	Saskatchewan (Sask.)
1	3	6	Toronto

Philosophie

		6	Laurentienne
1	3	6	Laval
	3	6	Moncton
1	3	6	Montréal
1	3	6	Ottawa
		6	Québec (Chicoutimi)
		6	Québec (Montréal)
	3	6	Québec (Trois-Rivières)
	3 4	6	Saint-Paul (Ottawa)[15]
	3	6	Sherbrooke
		6	Sudbury[4]

Philosophy

		6	Acadia
1	3	6	Alberta
		6	Bishop's
		6	Brandon
		6	Brescia[3]
1	3	6	British Columbia
		6	Brock
1	3	6	Calgary
	3	6	Carleton
		6	Christ the King
	3	6	Dalhousie
	3	6	Guelph
		6	Huron[5]
		6	King's (London)[8]
		6	Lakehead
		6	Laurentian
		6	Lethbridge
		6	Loyola[9]
	3	6	Manitoba
		6	Marianopolis[10]
1	3	6	McGill
	3	6	McMaster
	3	6	Memorial
		6	Mount Allison
		6	Mount Saint Vincent
	3	6	New Brunswick
		6	Notre Dame
1	3	6	Ottawa
		6	Prince Edward Island
1	3	6	Queen's
		6	St. Francis Xavier
		6	St. Jerome's[12]
		6	St. John's[13]
	3	6	Saint Mary's
1	4		St. Michael's[14]
	3 4	6	Saint Paul (Ottawa)[15]
	3	6	Saskatchewan (Regina)
	3	6	Saskatchewan (Sask.)
	3	6	Simon Fraser
	3	6	Sir George Williams
1 2	3	6	Toronto

(Philosophy cont'd)

				6	Trent
		3		6	Victoria (B.C.)
1	2	3		6	Waterloo
				6	Waterloo Lutheran
1		3		6	Western Ontario
		3		6	Windsor
				6	Winnipeg
1		3		6	York

Philosophy of education

1	3		Alberta
	3	·	McGill
		9	Sir George Williams

Phonétique

1	3	6	Laval

Photogrammétrie

1	3	6	Laval

Physiatrie

5	6	Laval

Physical education, physical and health education

		6	Acadia
1	3	6	Alberta
	3	6	British Columbia
	3	6	Calgary
	3	6	Dalhousie
		6	Guelph
		6	Lakehead
		6	Laurentian
		6	Lethbridge
		6	Manitoba
	3 5	6	McGill
		6	McMaster
		6	Memorial
		6	New Brunswick
	3	6	Ottawa
		6	Queen's
		6	St. Francis Xavier
		6	Saskatchewan (Regina)
	3	6	Saskatchewan (Sask.)
		6	Toronto
		6	Waterloo
	3	6	Western Ontario
	3	6	Windsor
		6	York

Physics

		6	Acadia
1	3	6	Alberta
		6	Bishop's
		6	Brandon
1	3	6	British Columbia
	3	6	Brock
1	3	6	Calgary
1	3	6	Carleton
1	3	6	Dalhousie
1	3	6	Guelph
	3	6	Lakehead
	3	6	Laurentian
		6	Lethbridge
		6	Loyola[9]
1	3	6	Manitoba
		6	Marianopolis[10]
1	3	6	McGill
1	3	6	McMaster
1	3	6	Memorial
		6	Mount Allison
		6	Mount Saint Vincent
1	3	6	New Brunswick
		6	Notre Dame
1	3	6	Ottawa
		6	Prince Edward Island
1	3	6	Queen's
	3	6	Royal Military
		6	St. Francis Xavier
		6	Saint Mary's
1	3	6	Saskatchewan (Regina)
1	3	6	Saskatchewan (Sask.)
1	3	6	Simon Fraser
1	3	6	Sir George Williams
1	3	6	Toronto
	3	6	Trent
1	3	6	Victoria (B.C.)
1	3	6	Waterloo
		6	Waterloo Lutheran
1	3	6	Western Ontario
1	3	6	Windsor
		6	Winnipeg
1	3	6	York

Physiological hygiene

1	3	Toronto

Physiological optics

3	Waterloo

Physiologie

1	3	Laval
1	3	Montréal
1	3	Sherbrooke

Physiologie animale

3	Montréal

Physiology

1	3	6	Alberta
1	3	6	British Columbia
1	3		Dalhousie
1	3		Manitoba
1	3	6	McGill
	3		New Brunswick
1	3		Ottawa
1	3	6	Queen's
1	3	6	Saskatchewan (Sask.)
		6	Sir George Williams
1	3	6	Toronto
1	3	6	Western Ontario

Physiology (veterinary medicine)

1	3	Guelph
1		Saskatchewan (Sask.)

Physiothérapie

6	Laval
6	Montréal

Physiotherapy

6 7		Alberta
6		British Columbia
	7	Dalhousie
6 7		Manitoba
6		McGill
	7	Queen's
	7	Saskatchewan (Sask.)
6		Toronto
6		Western Ontario

Physiotherapy (teaching of)

8	Toronto

Physique

1	3	6	Laval
	3	6	Moncton
1	3 4	6	Montréal
		6	Québec (Chicoutimi)
		6	Québec (Montréal)
		6	Québec (Rimouski)
		6	Québec (Trois-Rivières)
1	3	6	Sherbrooke

Phytotechnie

1	3	Laval

Planification régionale

3	Ottawa

Plant ecology

1	3	6	Saskatchewan (Sask.)

Plant physiology

1	Guelph

Plant science

1	3	6	Alberta
1	3	6	British Columbia
1	3	6	Guelph
1	3	6	Manitoba
		6	McGill
		7	Nova Scotia Agricultural
1	3	6	Saskatchewan (Sask.)
1	3	6	Western Ontario

Polish

9	Alberta
9	British Columbia
9	Manitoba
9	Ottawa
9	Saskatchewan (Sask.)
9	Toronto

Political philosophy

6	Sir George Williams

Politics, political science, studies

	3	6		Acadia
1	3	6		Alberta
		6		Bishop's
		6		Brandon
1	3	6		British Columbia
		6		Brock
1	3	6		Calgary
1	3	6		Carleton
1	3	5 6	8	Dalhousie
	3	6		Guelph
		6		Lakehead
		6		Laurentian
		6		Lethbridge
		6		Loyola[9]
	3	6		Manitoba
1	3	6		McGill
1	3	6		McMaster
2	3	6		Memorial
		6		Mount Allison
		6		Mount Saint Vincent
	3	6		New Brunswick
1	3	6		Ottawa
		6		Prince Edward Island
1	3	6		Queen's
	3	6		Royal Military
		6		St. Francis Xavier
		6		St. Jerome's[12]
		6		St. John's[13]
		6		Saint Mary's
	3	6		Saskatchewan (Regina)
1	3	6		Saskatchewan (Sask.)
1	3	6		Simon Fraser
		6		Sir George Williams
1 2	3	6		Toronto
		6		Trent
	3	6		Victoria (B.C.)
	3	6		Waterloo
	3	6		Waterloo Lutheran
1	3	6		Western Ontario
	3	6		Windsor
		6		Winnipeg
1	3	6		York

Polonais

9	Ottawa

Portuguese

9	British Columbia
9	Calgary
9	Carleton
9	Sir George Williams
9	Toronto
9	Victoria (B.C.)
9	Western Ontario
9	Windsor

Poultry science

1	3	6	Alberta

(Poultry science cont'd)			
1	3	6	British Columbia
1	3	6	Guelph
1	3	6	Saskatchewan (Sask.)

Power engineering

	3		Guelph

Preventive medicine

		5	Toronto
1	3		Western Ontario

Print-making

		6	Manitoba

Processing, process control (engineering)

1	3	6	Alberta
	3		Guelph

Product manufacturing, development (pharmacy)

		6	British Columbia
		6	Saskatchewan (Sask.)

Psychiatric nursing

		7	Saskatchewan (Sask.)
	3		Toronto

Psychiatrie

		5	Laval

Psychiatrie (nursing)

	3		Montréal

Psychiatry

	3		British Columbia
		5	Manitoba
	3	5	McGill
		5	Ottawa
1	3		Saskatchewan (Sask.)
		5	Toronto
		5	Western Ontario

Psychobiology

		6	Lethbridge

Psycho-éducation

	3	6	Montréal
	3	6	Sherbrooke

Psychologie

		6	Laurentienne
1	3	6	Laval
	3	6	Moncton
1	3	6	Montréal
1	3	6	Ottawa
		6	Québec (Chicoutimi)
		6	Québec (Montréal)
		6	Québec (Trois-Rivières)
		6	Sherbrooke

Psychologie clinique, psychologie clinique de l'enfant

1	Ottawa

Psychologie scolaire, psychologie éducationnelle

	3	Moncton
1		Ottawa

Psychology

	3		6	Acadia
1	3		6	Alberta
			6	Bishop's
			6	Brandon
1	3		6	British Columbia
			6	Brock
1	3		6	Calgary
1	3		6	Carleton
1	3	5	6	Dalhousie
	3		6	Guelph
			6	Huron[5]
			6	King's (London)[8]
	3		6	Lakehead
			6	Laurentian
			6	Lethbridge
			6	Loyola[9]
1	3		6	Manitoba
			6	Marianopolis[10]
1	3		6	McGill
1	3		6	McMaster
	3		6	Memorial
			6	Mount Allison
			6	Mount Saint Vincent
	3		6	New Brunswick
			6	Notre Dame
1	3		6	Ottawa
			6	Prince Edward Island
1	3		6	Queen's
			6	St. Francis Xavier
			6	St. Jerome's[12]
			6	St. John's[13]
			6	Saint Mary's
1	3		6	Saskatchewan (Regina)
1	3		6	Saskatchewan (Sask.)
1	3		6	Simon Fraser
	3		6	Sir George Williams
1	3		6	Toronto
			6	Trent
1	3		6	Victoria (B.C.)
1	3		6	Waterloo
	3		6	Waterloo Lutheran
1	3		6	Western Ontario
1	3		6	Windsor
			6	Winnipeg
1	3		6	York

Psycho-mathématiques

1	3	Sherbrooke

Psycho-pédagogie

1	3	Ottawa

Psychopedagogy

					Institution
1	3				Ottawa

Public administration

				Institution
3	5 6	8		Carleton
3	5	8		Dalhousie
	6			McGill
	6 7			Ottawa
3				Queen's
3	5			Toronto
		7		Windsor
3				York

Public health

		Institution
5	8	Toronto

Public health nursing

		Institution
7		Dalhousie
	8	Manitoba
6		Ottawa
7		Saskatchewan (Sask.)
7		Toronto
6		Western Ontario
7		Windsor

Quantitative analysis

	Institution
6	Saskatchewan (Sask.)

Quantitative methods, operations research

	Institution
6	Carleton
6	Manitoba
6	Memorial
6	Ottawa
6	Sir George Williams

Radioactive tracer work (pharmacy)

		Institution
1	3	Alberta

Radiologie, radiothérapie

	Institution
5	Laval

Radiology

		Institution
3		Alberta
3	5	McGill
	5	Queen's
	5	Toronto
	5	Western Ontario

Réadaptation (F)

		Institution
3	6	Montréal

Recherche culturelle

	Institution
6	Québec (Montréal)

Recherche opérationnelle (administration)

	Institution
6	Ottawa
6	Québec (Trois-Rivières)

Recreation

	Institution
6	Waterloo

Recreation administration

	Institution
6	Alberta

Recreation education

	Institution
6	British Columbia

Récréologie

	Institution
6	Ottawa
6	Québec (Trois-Rivières)

Recreology

	Institution
6	Ottawa

Regional planning

			Institution
	3		British Columbia
	3		Ottawa
1	3		Waterloo

Rehabilitation medicine

		Institution
3	6	Alberta
	6	British Columbia
	6 7	Manitoba
3		Saskatchewan (Sask.)
	6	Toronto
	6	Western Ontario

Relations de travail

	Institution
8	Ottawa

Relations humaines

	Institution
6	Québec (Montréal)

Relations industrielles

			Institution
1	3	6	Laval
1	3	6	Montréal

Religion, religious studies

			Institution
		6	Acadia
		6	Alberta
		6	Bishop's
		6	Brandon
	3	6	British Columbia
		6	Carleton
		6	Laurentian
		6	Lethbridge
		6	Manitoba
1	3	6	McGill
1	3	6	McMaster
		6	Memorial
1	3	6	Ottawa
		6	Notre Dame
		6	Prince Edward Island
		6	Queen's
		6	St. Jerome's[12]
		6	St. John's[13]
		6	Saint Mary's
	3	6	Sir George Williams
		6	Toronto

(Religion, religious studies cont'd)

	6	Victoria (Toronto)[19]
	6	Waterloo
3	6	Waterloo Lutheran
	6	Winnipeg

Resource management (forestry)

5	Toronto

Resources, resources development

3		Calgary
3	6	Guelph
	6	McGill
1	3	Waterloo

Restorative dentistry and prosthodontics

5	McGill

Retailing (business)

6	Sir George Williams

Roman studies

3	McMaster
6	Ottawa

Rural sociology

1	3	6 Alberta

Russe, études russes

	6	Laurentienne
3	6	Montréal
	9	Ottawa

Russian

3	6	Alberta
	6	British Columbia
	6	Brock
	6	Calgary
	6	Carleton
	9	Dalhousie
	9	Guelph
	6	Huron[5]
	6	King's (London)[8]
	6	Lakehead
	6	Laurentian
	6	Loyola[9]
	6	Manitoba
1	3	6 McGill
	3	6 McMaster
	9	Memorial
	9	New Brunswick
	9	Ottawa
	6	Queen's
	9	St. Francis Xavier
	6	Saskatchewan (Regina)
	6	Saskatchewan (Sask.)
1	3	6 Simon Fraser
	6	Sir George Williams
1 2 3	6	Toronto

6	Victoria (B.C.)
3 6	Waterloo
6	Waterloo Lutheran
6	Western Ontario
6	Windsor
6	York

Sanskrit

9	British Columbia
9	Saskatchewan (Sask.)
9	Toronto
9	Windsor

School music

6	Calgary
6	McGill
6	St. Francis Xavier
6	Windsor

Science (E) (general program)

6	Acadia
6	Alberta
6	Bishop's
6	Brandon
6	British Columbia
6	Brock
6	Calgary
6	Carleton
6	Dalhousie
6	Guelph
6	King's (Halifax)[7]
6	Lakehead
6	Laurentian
6	Lethbridge
6	Loyola[9]
6	Manitoba
6	McGill
6	McMaster
6	Memorial
6	Mount Allison
6	Mount Saint Vincent
6	New Brunswick
6	Notre-Dame
6	Ottawa
6	Prince Edward Island
6	Queen's
6	Royal Military
6	St. Francis Xavier
6	St. John's[13]
6	Saint Mary's
6	St. Michael's[14]
6	St. Paul's (Winnipeg)[15]
6	St. Thomas More[18]
6	Saskatchewan (Regina)
6	Saskatchewan (Sask.)
6	Sir George Williams
6	Toronto
6	Trent
6	Trinity[19]
6	Victoria (B.C.)
6	Victoria (Toronto)[19]
6	Waterloo

(Science (E) general program cont'd)

		6		Waterloo Lutheran
		6		Windsor
		6		Winnipeg
		6		York

Sciences (F) (cours général)

6	Jean-de-Brébeuf[6]
6	Laurentienne
6	Laval
6	Moncton
6	Montréal
6	Ottawa
6	Québec (Chicoutimi)
6	Québec (Montréal)
6	Québec (Rimouski)
6	Québec (Trois-Rivières)
6	Sherbrooke

Sciences politique

		6	Laurentienne
1	3	6	Laval
		6	Moncton
1	3	6	Montréal
1	3	6	Ottawa
	3	6	Québec (Montréal)

Sciences agronomiques

6	Laval

Sciences cliniques

1	3	Montréal
1	3	Sherbrooke

Sciences de la gestion

3	5 6	Ottawa

Sciences de la santé

6	Laval
6	Québec (Trois-Rivières)

Sciences de la terre

6	Québec (Montréal)

Sciences de l'eau

3	Québec (INRS)

Sciences domestiques

6	Moncton
6	Ottawa

Sciences du bois

1 3	Laval

Sciences forestières

1	3 6	Laval

Sciences humaines de la religion

3 6	Sherbrooke

Sciences infirmières, nursing

	6	Laval
	6	Moncton
3	6 7	Montréal
	6	Québec (Trois-Rivières)

Sciences missionnaires

	3		Ottawa
1	3	7	Saint-Paul (Ottawa)[15]

Sciences religieuses

	6	Laurentienne
3 4		Laval
	6	Moncton
1	3 4	Montréal
1	3 6	Ottawa
	6	Québec (Montréal)
3	6	Sherbrooke

Sciences secrétarielles

6	Moncton

Scottish studies

1 3	Guelph

Sculpture (E)

6	Manitoba

Sculpture (F)

6	Québec (Montréal)

Secondary school education

1	3 6	Alberta
	6	Brandon
1	3 6	British Columbia
	6	Calgary
	6	Dalhousie
	6	Lakehead
	6	Lethbridge
	6 8	Manitoba
	6 7	Memorial
	6	Mount Allison
	6 7	Mount Saint Vincent
	6	Queen's
	6	St. Francis Xavier
	6	Saskatchewan (Regina)
	6	Saskatchewan (Sask.)
	6	Simon Fraser
	6	Toronto
	5 6	Victoria (B.C.)
	6	Western Ontario

Secretarial administration

6	Acadia

Secretarial science, secretarial arts

6 7	Acadia
8	Mount Allison
7	Mount Saint Vincent

(Secretarial science, secretarial arts cont'd)

6 7			Notre Dame
	6		St. Francis Xavier
	6		Western Ontario

Serbo-Croatian

9	Alberta
9	British Columbia
9	Toronto
9	Victoria (B.C.)

Service social, travail social

	3	6	Laval
		6	Moncton
1	3	6	Montréal
		6	Québec (Montréal)
	3 5	6	Sherbrooke

Silvics, silviculture

6	British Columbia
6	New Brunswick
3	Toronto

Slavonics, Slavic studies

	3	6	Alberta
1	3	6	British Columbia
	3		Calgary
	3	6	Manitoba
1	3	6	Ottawa
	3	6	Saskatchewan (Sask.)
1 2	3	6	Toronto

Social action, development, theory

6	Saskatchewan (Regina)
6	Trent
6	Windsor

Social communications

6	Ottawa
6 7	Saint Paul (Ottawa)[15]

Social leadership, development

7	St. Francis Xavier

Social, political and economic thought

6	York

Social work, social welfare

3		British Columbia
3	6	Calgary
3		Carleton
3		Dalhousie
	6	King's (London)[8]
	6	Laurentian
3	6	Manitoba
3 5	6	McGill

		6	McMaster
		6	Memorial
		6	Sir George Williams
1	3 5		Toronto
	3		Waterloo Lutheran
		6	Western Ontario
	3	6	Windsor

Sociologie

		6	Laurentienne
1	3	6	Laval
	3	6	Moncton
1	3	6	Montréal
	3	6	Ottawa
		6	Québec (Montréal)
		6	Sainte-Anne

Sociology

		6	Acadia
1	3	6	Alberta
		6	Bishop's
		6	Brandon
1	3	6	British Columbia
		6	Brock
	3	6	Calgary
1	3	6	Carleton
	3	6	Dalhousie
	3	6	Guelph
		6	King's (London)[8]
		6	Lakehead
		6	Laurentian
		6	Lethbridge
		6	Loyola[9]
	3	6	Manitoba
		6	Marianopolis[10]
1	3	6	McGill
1	3	6	McMaster
2	3	6	Memorial
		6	Mount Saint Vincent
	3	6	New Brunswick
		6	Notre Dame
	3	6	Ottawa
		6	Prince Edward Island
		6	Queen's
		6	St. Francis Xavier
		6	Saint Jerome's[12]
		6	St. John's[13]
		6	Saint Mary's
		6	Sainte-Anne
		6	Saskatchewan (Regina)
1	3	6	Saskatchewan (Sask.)
1	3	6	Simon Fraser
		6	Sir George Williams
1	3	6	Toronto
		6	Trent
	3	6	Victoria (B.C.)
1	3	6	Waterloo
		6	Waterloo Lutheran
	3	6	Western Ontario
	3	6	Windsor
		6	Winnipeg
1	3	6	York

Soil science

1	3	6	Alberta
1	3	6	British Columbia
1	3	6	Guelph
1	3	6	Manitoba
1	3	5	McGill
1	3	6	Saskatchewan (Sask.)

Sols

1	3		Laval

Soviet studies, Russian studies, East European studies

	3	6	Alberta
	3	6	Carleton
		6	Manitoba
		6	Queen's
		6	St. John's[13]
		6	Sir George Williams
1	3	5	Toronto

Space science (experimental)

1	3		York

Spanish

		6	Acadia
1	3	6	Alberta
		9	Bishop's
1	3	6	British Columbia
		6	Brock
		6	Calgary
	3	6	Carleton
		6	Dalhousie
		6	Guelph
		6	Lakehead
		6	Laurentian
		6	Loyola[9]
		6	Manitoba
		6	Marianopolis[10]
1	3	6	McGill
		6	McMaster
		9	Memorial
		9	Mount Allison
		9	Mount Saint Vincent
		6	New Brunswick
		6	Ottawa
	3	6	Queen's
		9	St. Francis Xavier
		9	Saint Mary's
		6	Saskatchewan (Sask.)
1	3	6	Simon Fraser
		6	Sir George Williams
1 2	3	6	Toronto
		6	Trent
		6	Victoria (B.C.)
		6	Waterloo
	3	6	Waterloo Lutheran
	3	6	Western Ontario
	3	6	Windsor
		6	York

Spanish-American studies

6	Alberta

Special education

	3		Acadia
		6	Brandon
		5	British Columbia
		6	Lethbridge
	3		McGill
1	3		Ontario Institute for Studies in Education[11]
	3	5 6	Saskatchewan (Sask.)

Speech pathology and audiology

		6	Alberta
	3		British Columbia
1	3		McGill
		5	Toronto
		6	Western Ontario

Statistics

1	3	6	Alberta
		6	Calgary
1	3		Carleton
		6	Guelph
	3	6	Manitoba
	3		McMaster
	3		Memorial
		6	New Brunswick
		6	Sir George Williams
1	3	6	Toronto
1 2	3	6	Waterloo
1	3	6	Western Ontario
		6	Winnipeg

Structures (architecture, engineering)

	3		British Columbia
	3		Guelph
1	3	6	Memorial
1			Sir George Williams

Studio art

	3	6	Saskatchewan (Sask.)
		6	Sir George Williams
		6	Toronto
		6	York

Surgery

1	3	Alberta
	3	Manitoba
1	3	McGill
	3	Queen's
1	3	Toronto
	3	Western Ontario

Surgery (veterinary medicine)

3	Guelph

Surveying engineering

1	3	4	6	7	Institution
		5			British Columbia
	3		6	7	New Brunswick

Sylviculture (F)

1	3	4	6	7	Institution
1	3				Laval

Syriac, Aramaic

1	3	4	6	7	Institution
		9			Dalhousie
		9			King's (Halifax)[7]
		9			Manitoba
		9			Toronto

Systems design

1	3	4	6	7	Institution
1	3		6		Waterloo

Taiga studies

1	3	4	6	7	Institution
			6		Lakehead

Teaching and supervision in nursing

1	3	4	6	7	Institution
			8		Manitoba
	3				McGill

Technologie de l'enseignement

1	3	4	6	7	Institution
			6		Laval

Technologie médicale

1	3	4	6	7	Institution
				7	Montréal

Testing and measurement, experimentation (education)

1	3	4	6	7	Institution
1	3				Alberta
	3				Mount Saint Vincent
1	3				Ontario Institute for Studies in Education[11]
	3				Ottawa
		5			Saskatchewan (Sask.)

Textiles and design

1	3	4	6	7	Institution
			6		St. Francis Xavier

Théâtre

1	3	4	6	7	Institution
			6	7	Ottawa

Theatre, theatre arts

1	3	4	6	7	Institution
	3		6		British Columbia
			6		Dalhousie
			6		Lakehead
			6		Loyola[9]
			6	7	Ottawa
			6		Sir George Williams
	3		6		Victoria (B.C.)
			6		Winnipeg
			6		York

Théologie

1	3	4	6	7	Institution
1	3		6		Laval
1		4	6		Montréal
1	3		6		Ottawa
			6		Québec (Chicoutimi)
			6		Québec (Rimouski)
	3		6		Québec (Trois-Rivières)
1	3	4	6	7	Saint-Paul (Ottawa)[15]
	3		6		Sherbrooke

Theology, theological studies

1	3	4	6	7	Institution
	3				Acadia
			6		Alberta
	3	4	6		Bishop's
			6		Huron[5]
			6		Loyola[9]
1	3		6		McGill
			8		McMaster
			6		Mount Allison
			6		Mount Saint Vincent
1	3		6		Ottawa
			6		Queen's
			6		St. Francis Xavier
	3	4	6		St. John's[13]
1		4	6		St. Michael's[14]
1	3	4	6	7	Saint Paul (Ottawa)[15]
	3		6		Trinity[19]
1	3	4			Victoria (Toronto)[19]
	3				Waterloo Lutheran
	3		6		Windsor
	3				Winnipeg

Theory and composition (music)

1	3	4	6	7	Institution
	3		6		Alberta
			6		Calgary
	3		6		McGill
			6		Queen's
			6		Saskatchewan (Sask.)
	3		6		Toronto
			6		Western Ontario
			6		Windsor

Therapeutics

1	3	4	6	7	Institution
	3				Manitoba
	3		6		McGill

Tibetan

1	3	4	6	7	Institution
		9			Saskatchewan (Sask.)

Traduction

1	3	4	6	7	Institution
			6		Laurentienne
1	3		6		Laval
	3		6		Montréal
	3		6		Ottawa

Translation and interpretation

1	3	4	6	7	Institution
			6		Laurentian
				7	McGill
1	3		6		Ottawa

				Transportation and utilities, transportation planning				Visual arts
		6		British Columbia	6 7			Ottawa
3				Calgary	6			Saskatchewan (Regina)
					6			Sir George Williams

			Turkish				Vivres
	9		Toronto	1	3	6	Laval

		Ukrainian		War studies
6		Alberta	9	Acadia
6		Manitoba	3	Royal Military
	8	McMaster		
9		Ottawa		Water resources engineering
9		Saskatchewan (Regina)	6	Guelph
6		Saskatchewan (Sask.)		
9		Toronto		West Indian studies
9		Waterloo	6	Acadia
9		Western Ontario		

		Ukrainien				Wildlife biology
	9	Ottawa		5		Brandon
			1	3	6	Guelph
		Urban and regional planning, studies		3		Laurentian
	6	Lethbridge	1	3	6	McGill

			Urban and regional planning, studies			Wildlife management
	6		Lethbridge		3	British Columbia
	6		Queen's	1	3	Guelph
	6		St. Jerome's[12]			
	6		Saskatchewan (Sask.)			Wildlife resources
3	5		Toronto	6	McGill
	6		Waterloo		

	Urban forestry			Yiddish
3	Toronto	9		Manitoba
		6		McGill

	Urbanisme				Zoologie
3	Montréal	1	3		Montréal

	Urban planning
3	McGill

				Zoology, zoological sciences
	Urban studies	1	3	6	Alberta

	Urban studies				Zoology, zoological sciences
6	Brock	1	3	6	Alberta
6	Sir George Williams			6	Brandon
6	Winnipeg	1	3	6	British Columbia
6	York			6	Calgary
		1	3	6	Guelph
	Urologie	1	3	6	Manitoba
5	Laval	1	3	6	McGill
			3		New Brunswick
	Urology			6	Notre Dame
5	McGill	1	3	6	Saskatchewan (Regina)
		1	3	6	Toronto
	Vernacular literature	1	3	6	Western Ontario

		Vernacular literature			Zootechnie
1	4	St. Michael's[14]	1	3	Laval

			Veterinary medicine
1	3	5 6	Guelph
1	3	5 6	Saskatchewan (Sask.)

	Veterinary public health
5	Toronto

Footnotes	Renvois

1. Assumption University is federated with the University of Windsor. It grants degrees in theology but holds in abeyance its power to grant degrees in arts and science. Graduates of its programs in arts and science receive the degree of the University of Windsor.

2. Bathurst, Saint-Joseph, and Saint-Louis Colleges are affiliated with the University of Moncton, and hold in abeyance their right to confer degrees. Graduates receive the degree of the University of Moncton.

3. Brescia College is associated with The University of Western Ontario. It offers arts and social science programs in co-operation with the university. All Brescia graduates receive the BA degree of the university.

4. Huntington, Sudbury, and Thorneloe Universities are federated with Laurentian University of Sudbury and offer undergraduate programs in religious studies. They hold their right to confer degrees in abeyance.

5. Huron College is affiliated with The University of Western Ontario. The bachelor of arts degree awarded to students of the college is that of The University of Western Ontario. Huron grants its own degrees in theology.

6. Jean-de-Brébeuf College is affiliated with the University of Montreal. It offers instruction in arts subjects and its students receive the degree of the University of Montreal.

7. The University of King's College is associated with Dalhousie University. It holds in abeyance its right to confer degrees in arts and science; these programs are offered through Dalhousie and graduates receive the degree of Dalhousie. King's confers its own degrees in divinity.

8. King's College is affiliated with The University of Western Ontario. All of its graduates receive the degree of the university.

9. Loyola College is affiliated with the University of Montreal. All of its students receive the degree of the university.

1. L'Université Assumption est fédérée à l'Université de Windsor. Elle confère des grades en théologie, mais n'exerce pas son pouvoir de conférer des grades dans les arts et les sciences. Les diplômés de ses programmes d'études en arts et en sciences reçoivent le grade de l'Université de Windsor.

2. Le Collège de Bathurst ainsi que les Collèges Saint-Joseph et Saint-Louis sont affiliés à l'Université de Moncton et n'exercent pas leur droit de conférer des grades. Les diplômés reçoivent leur grade de l'Université de Moncton.

3. Le Collège Brescia est associé à l'Université Western Ontario. Il offre des programmes d'études dans les arts et en sciences sociales, en collaboration avec l'université. Tous les diplômés du Collège Brescia reçoivent le baccalauréat ès arts de l'Université Western Ontario.

4. L'Université Huntington, l'Université de Sudbury et l'Université Thorneloe sont fédérées à l'Université Laurentienne de Sudbury et offrent des programmes d'études du niveau pré-grade en sciences religieuses. Elles n'exercent pas leur droit de conférer des grades; leurs diplômés reçoivent leurs grades de l'Université Laurentienne.

5. Le Collège Huron est affilié à l'Université Western Ontario. Le baccalauréat ès arts conféré aux étudiants du collège est celui de l'Université Western Ontario. Le Collège Huron accorde ses propres grades en théologie.

6. Le Collège Jean-de-Brébeuf est affilié à l'Université de Montréal. Il dispense des cours dans les arts et ses étudiants reçoivent le diplôme conféré par l'Université de Montréal.

7. L'Université du Collège King's est associée à l'Université de Dalhousie. Elle n'exerce pas son droit de conférer des grades dans les arts et les sciences; les diplômés reçoivent leurs grades de l'Université de Dalhousie. L'Université du Collège King's confère ses propres grades en sciences religieuses.

10. Marianopolis College is affiliated with the University of Montreal. Its students receive the degree of the University of Montreal.

11. The Ontario Institute for Studies in Education is affiliated with the University of Toronto. Degrees in OISE's specialization, education, are conferred on graduates of OISE programs by the University of Toronto.

12. The University of St. Jerome's College is federated with the University of Waterloo. Graduates of its program in arts, mathematics, and environmental studies receive the degree of the University of Waterloo. St. Jerome's confers its own degrees in theology.

13. St. John's College is affiliated with The University of Manitoba. It confers its own degrees in theology, but its students in arts and science receive the degree of the university.

14. St. Michael's College is federated with the University of Toronto. It grants degrees in mediaeval studies, through the Pontifical Institute of Mediaeval Studies, and theology, but holds in abeyance its right to grant degrees in arts and science. Graduates of its programs in arts, science, and commerce receive the degree of the University of Toronto.

15. Saint Paul University is federated with the University of Ottawa. It grants degrees in theology, philosophy, and canon law; its students also receive the degrees of the University of Ottawa.

16. St. Paul's College is affiliated with The University of Manitoba. Its students in arts and science programs receive the degree of the university.

17. St. Thomas University is federated with the University of New Brunswick. It grants bachelor degrees in arts and education but holds in abeyance its powers to grant degrees in other fields.

18. St. Thomas More College is affiliated with the University of Saskatchewan, Saskatoon campus. Its students receive the degree of the university.

19. The University of Trinity College and Victoria University are federated with the University of Toronto. Both grant degrees in theology but hold in abeyance their right to confer degrees in arts and science.

8. Le Collège King's est affilié à l'Université Western Ontario. Tous ses diplômés reçoivent leurs grades de l'Université Western Ontario.

9. Le Collège Loyola est affilié à l'Université de Montréal. Tous ses étudiants reçoivent leurs grades de cette université.

10. Le Collège Marianopolis est affilié à l'Université de Montréal. Tous ses étudiants reçoivent leurs grades de l'Université de Montréal.

11. L'Ontario Institute for Studies in Education est affilié à l'Université de Toronto. Les diplômés d'études spécialisées en éducation de l'OISE sont accordés par l'Université de Toronto.

12. L'Université du Collège St. Jerome's est fédérée à l'Université de Waterloo. Les diplômés de ses programmes d'études dans les arts, les mathématiques et les études de l'environnement reçoivent leurs diplômes de l'Université de Waterloo. L'Université du Collège St. Jerome's confère ses propres grades en théologie.

13. Le Collège St. John's est affilié à l'Université du Manitoba. Il confère ses propres grades en théologie, mais ses étudiants dans les arts et les sciences reçoivent les diplômes de l'université.

14. L'Université du Collège St. Michael's est fédérée à l'Université de Toronto. Elle confère des grades dans les études médiévales par l'intermédiaire du Pontifical Institute of Mediaeval Studies et en théologie, mais n'exerce pas son droit de conférer des grades dans les arts et les sciences. Les diplômés de ses programmes d'études dans les arts, les sciences et le commerce reçoivent leurs grades de l'Université de Toronto.

15. L'Université Saint-Paul est fédérée à l'Université d'Ottawa. Elle confère des grades en théologie, en philosophie et en droit canonique; ses étudiants reçoivent aussi des grades de l'Université d'Ottawa.

16. Le Collège St. Paul's est affilié à l'Université du Manitoba. Ses étudiants dans les arts et les sciences reçoivent leurs grades de cette université.

17. L'Université St. Thomas est fédérée à l'Université du Nouveau-Brunswick. Elle décerne les baccalauréats ès arts et en pédagogie, mais n'exerce pas son pouvoir

Their programs in arts and science are offered in conjunction with the University of Toronto and graduates receive the University of Toronto degree.

de conférer des grades dans d'autres domaines.

18. Le Collège St. Thomas More est affilié à l'Université de la Saskatchewan, campus Saskatoon. Ses étudiants reçoivent leurs grades de cette université.

19. L'Université du Collège Trinity et l'Université Victoria sont fédérées à l'Université de Toronto. Elles confèrent toutes les deux des grades en théologie, mais n'exercent pas leur droit de conférer des grades dans les arts et les sciences. Leurs programmes d'études dans les arts et les sciences sont offerts conjointement avec l'Université de Toronto et leurs diplômés reçoivent leurs grades de l'Université de Toronto.

Index

Ce volume doit être rendu à la dernière
date indiquée ci-dessous.